COMPUTER SCIENCE: A FIRST COURSE

COMPUTER SCIENCE:

A First Course

ALEXANDRA I. FORSYTHE, M.A.

Department of Mathematics,
Gunn High School,
Palo Alto

THOMAS A. KEENAN, Ph.D.

Director, Educational Information Network,
EDUCOM

ELLIOTT I. ORGANICK, Ph.D.

Professor and Chairman, Department of Computer Science,
University of Houston

WARREN STENBERG, Ph.D.

Associate Professor of Mathematics,
University of Minnesota

JOHN WILEY & SONS

New York · London · Sydney · Toronto

Reprinted January 1977
Reprinted October 1977
Reprinted June 1978.

Marketed and distributed to secondary
schools by Benziger, Inc.

11 12 13 14 15 16 17 18 19 20

Library of Congress Catalog Card Number 74-76053
ISBN 0 471 26678 7
Reproduced and printed by photolithography and bound
in Great Britain at The Pitman Press, Bath

PREFACE

Computer science is an entirely new course subject, although its concept has been developing for many years. Our purpose in this book, *Computer Science: A Primer,* is to help students understand today's world (and the world of tomorrow) where information of all kinds is the prime commodity. The processing of this information in business, science, government, and industry is rapidly becoming one of the nation's major endeavors. Computers are an indispensable tool in information processing. Students in this course will learn not only what computers are but what computers can and cannot do—they will learn to understand and appreciate the step-by-step methodical chain that begins with a problem, processes it through a computer, and ends with a satisfactory solution.

This book is the outgrowth of a School Mathematics Study Group (SMSG) program, begun in 1964, of which we were a part. This effort resulted in 1966 in a widely used experimental SMSG text called *Algorithms, Computation and Mathematics* which was directed to twelfth-grade mathematics students. From the beginning, we found that this material was equally instructive for college-level audiences. *Computer Science: A Primer* is based on the SMSG text and on our experience in teaching this text at high-school and college levels. Although the present volume draws significantly from the SMSG material and retains its spirit, we believe that this book and its supplementary texts comprise a major revision of the SMSG material with significant modifications in content. In short, we think that this work and its supplements are a distinct improvement worthy of independent use.

A recent report of the Curriculum Committee on Computer Science of the Association for Computing Machinery* has offered recommendations for a college-level course, entitled, "Introduction to Computing."

* "Curriculum 68, Recommendations for Academic Programs in Computer Science," *Communications of the ACM, Vol 11,* No. 3, March 1968, pp. 151–197.

We believe that this book is compatible with those recommendations and that it will be useful as a text for such a course.

An even more complete version of this book is also available; it is entitled *Computer Science: A First Course.* This version includes Part III, "Nonnumerical Applications," which is designed to help the reader get the broadest possible view of the computer science field in an introductory experience. The *First Course* version may be found more suitable for courses that extend over more than one semester or for courses that meet for three or more hours per week.

As companion pieces to this volume and to the *First Course* version, several programming language supplements and a teacher's commentary are available. The programming language texts are especially useful because they are designed to dovetail, section for section, with the principal chapters of the basic text. The study of a computer programming language, such as FORTRAN, BASIC, or PL/1, from one of these supplements will help the student to convert the abstract algorithmic solutions of the problems from the basic text into actual solutions on the computer that is available to him.

The present volume centers around the study of comput*ing* rather than comput*ers*. Whereas many computer textbooks place significant emphasis on the design of complex networks of circuits and electronics that make up a computer, *Computer Science: A Primer* deals with the organization of problems so that computers can work them. Computing hinges primarily on the study of algorithms: not only learning to understand them but learning to construct and improve them.

Much thought has been given to the selection and ordering of the problems and exercises. The exercises are to be considered in the sense of five-finger piano exercises that test or strengthen some specific "local" learning. On the other hand, the problems require that the student *organize* local learning in order to reach a satisfactory solution. The solving of problems helps to synthesize knowledge into a more unified whole. The solution of at least some problems and exercises is considered vital to the progress of any student who uses this text.

The subject matter of this book constitutes a challenging first course in computer science for students with good high school-level preparation in mathematics.

Alexandra I. Forsythe
Thomas A. Keenan
Elliott I. Organick
Warren Stenberg

ORGANIZATION OF THE BOOK

For organizational purposes, the eight chapters of this book are divided into two parts. The first five chapters, which comprise Part I, form a basic introductory unit. Three fundamental ideas of computing are presented in the first chapter: the algorithm, its expression as a flow chart, and a conceptual model of a computer. In addition, the reader is introduced to a hypothetical but realistic digital computer capable of executing algorithms. By the end of this chapter, all of the fundamentals of flow-chart language have been introduced with appropriate discussions of assignment, branching, and looping. The next two chapters develop a more thorough explanation of the fundamentals and add some auxiliary concepts for *computation* and for *data organization* such as arithmetic expressions, compound conditions, multiple branching, vectors, and arrays. Chapter 4 integrates and refines the student's understanding of all these concepts by means of illustrative examples. An efficient shorthand for loop control, which simplifies the construction of many algorithms, is presented. Chapter 5, which does not depend on the specifics of the earlier chapters, alerts the student to pitfalls inherent in the use of approximations.

Part II is primarily concerned with numerical applications. In Chapter 6 the student is introduced to the *procedure*, the (isolated) program building-block unit from which complex systems can be formed. Procedures are explained in terms of a conceptual model that is easy to understand and to remember. Chapters 7 and 8 develop mathematical applications of computing that are selected from those called numerical methods. The solution of an equation by bisection is studied in Chapter 7, along with methods for finding the maximum or minimum of a function and for computing the area under a curve. The Gauss elimination method for solving a system of linear equations is given in Chapter 8, followed by an introductory treatment of averaging and linear regression. Part II is designed for students who have *not* studied calculus. However, students with calculus training may find that their understanding of mathematics and statistics has been strengthened after studying this material.

Part III is devoted to nonnumerical applications of computing (sometimes called symbol manipulation), representative of the newer areas of computer science research. Chapter 9 introduces the reader to an interesting representation of important classes of information: tree structures. Only the first four chapters of the book are prerequisite to this material. Certain decision processes (such as two-person games) and certain types of data (such as strings that represent arithmetic expressions) inherently possess or are best exhibited as tree structures. Tree-searching algorithms are introduced. Chapter 10 considers the subject of compiling, the process of translating from the familiar mathematical notation exhibited in various programming languages to forms that computers can execute more easily. Chapter 11 returns to the topic of trees. A level-by-level tree search method is applied to the problem of finding the best route or path on a map. Several new concepts for storing tree-structured data and for the pruning of such structures are introduced. Algorithms are developed that analyze the outcome of games. Chapter 12, on text editing and list processing, gives the student some insight into the kinds of problems involved in representing and operating on character "strings." For such data, an effective storage model is designed and algorithms are built up to transform strings in various ways. This chapter provides an excellent background for a student who will use one of the string-processing programming languages, such as SNOBOL. Chapter 13 takes another look at compiling, this time as an application of the string-operation concepts developed in Chapter 12. Combining this material with the material in Chapter 10, the student can follow the principal steps of compiling from the input (consisting of statements like those in a FORTRAN program) to the output (consisting of the equivalent machine language code).

The SAMOS Appendix amounts to an elementary programmer's reference manual for the hypothetical digital computer called SAMOS that was discussed briefly in Chapter 1. This appendix is suggested for collateral reading at various times in the course. SAMOS has been simulated on several actual computers,* making it possible for students to gain an easy initial exposure to machine-language programming through laboratory practice.

* Simulated on the IBM 1401 and 7090 computers and on the CDC 6400. (The simulator program written in FORTRAN was developed by and has been made available from the Florida State University Computer Center, E. P. Miles, Director.)

ACKNOWLEDGMENTS

Much of the credit for this book belongs to our many colleagues who participated in the organizational, planning, and computer text-writing sessions of the SMSG project and to the excellent supporting staff of SMSG at Stanford University. Below is a copy of the title page (and copyright) from the student text, which gives the names of the project's many contributors. To each of our colleagues on this list and to others who have offered contributions to this project, we express our sincere appreciation and the hope that our new book confirms the value of the initiating work.

ALGORITHMS,
COMPUTATION
AND
MATHEMATICS

Student Text

Revised Edition

The following is a list of all those who participated in the preparation of this volume:

Sylvia Charp, Dobbins Technical High School, Philadelphia, Pennsylvania
Alexandra Forsythe, Gunn High School, Palo Alto, California
Bernard A. Galler, University of Michigan, Ann Arbor, Michigan
John G. Herriot, Stanford University, California
Walter Hoffmann, Wayne State University, Detroit, Michigan
Thomas E. Hull, University of Toronto, Toronto, Ontario, Canada
Thomas A. Keenan, University of Rochester, Rochester, New York
Robert E. Monroe, Wayne State University, Detroit, Michigan
Silvio O. Navarro, University of Kentucky, Lexington, Kentucky
Elliott I. Organick, University of Houston, Houston, Texas
Jesse Peckenham, Oakland Unified School District, Oakland, California
George A. Robinson, Argonne National Laboratory, Argonne, Illinois
Phillip M. Sherman, Bell Telephone Laboratories, Murray Hill, New Jersey
Robert E. Smith, Control Data Corporation, St. Paul, Minnesota
Warren Stenberg, University of Minnesota, Minneapolis, Minnesota
Harley Tillitt, U.S. Naval Ordnance Test Station, China Lake, California
Lyneve Waldrop, Newton South High School, Newton, Massachusetts

The following were the principal consultants:
George E. Forsythe, Stanford University, California
Bernard A. Galler, University of Michigan, Ann Arbor, Michigan
Wallace Givens, Argonne National Laboratory, Argonne, Illinois

Like many texts that originate as a committee effort, the early drafts were revised a number of times. Two parts of the present work have passed the scrutiny of these repeated revisions without losing the character or content contributed by their originators. Chapter 5, "Approximations," still bears the distinctive imprint of Professor Walter Hoffman of Wayne State University who wrote the first draft. The SAMOS Appendix, which appears here in much the same form as in its first draft, is the work of the late Silvio O. Navarro, Professor of Computer Science at the University of Kentucky, who is fondly remembered by his friends and colleagues.

We also acknowledge the support of individuals who either recommended that the writing project be initiated or who played a part in organizing it. Among these were:

Dr. Arthur C. Downing, Control Data Corp.
W. Eugene Ferguson, Newton Mass. School System
Professor Robert Gregory, The University of Texas
George Heller, International Business Machines Corp.
Professor R. J. Walker, Cornell University

Four men were the "prime movers" of the SMSG project: Professor Edward G. Begle, SMSG's Director convinced the SMSG Executive Board and the National Science Foundation that the computer text project was a worthy undertaking and deserved the financial support of NSF. Professor George E. Forsythe of Stanford University, Professor Bernard A. Galler of the University of Michigan, and Dr. Wallace Givens of Argonne National Laboratories not only helped Professor Begle in his initiating efforts but provided the project with critical technical and organizational guidance during its initial stages.

Finally, we thank the National Science Foundation for its continued support of SMSG projects in the computer science area and Stanford University for giving us approval to incorporate the cited SMSG material in our text. SMSG, by giving this approval, does not endorse the current work in any way.

A.I.F.
T.A.K.
E.I.O.
W.S.

USING THE COMPUTER

For optimal learning, each beginner needs contact with a computer, primarily to verify and troubleshoot the algorithms that he constructs. What is meant by "contact" with a computer varies. One excellent form of contact is gained these days through the use of typewriter-like or keyboard/TV consoles that are connected to time-shared computer systems. Another form of desirable contact can be obtained by submitting programs and data that are prepared on punch cards and run on computers controlled by batch monitor operating systems. In any case, the computer contact should be held to the minimum that is necessary for adequate check-out of programs. Hands-on-the-computer experience is *not* a goal of this course.

At least as important as one's physical proximity to the computer should be the *programming language* that it requires and the special program that implements this language on the computer. Since the number of people using it is *not* necessarily a measure of how good a programming language is, the choice of a language, a computer, and a software system requires very careful professional study. ("Software" refers to the service programs used to operate and exploit the computer for the user's benefit.)

The software program that carries a language into effect on a computer is called a *compiler.* Compilers vary a great deal in the *rate* at which they cause programs to be translated or interpreted by the computer. A fast compiler is wanted. Compilers also vary widely in their handling of programming and language errors. For teaching purposes, the best compiler is one that detects, clearly identifies, and either reports or corrects these errors at the time the program is being *compiled.*

Some types of programming errors (such as dividing by zero) can only be detected and reported during the execution of the target (compiled) program. The quality of this detection is dependent on still another piece of software called the *executive system.* Furthermore, whether this executive system detects such problems as equipment malfunction during input or output and misuse of library subroutines will be very important to you, as the user.

The ability to run large numbers of small programming exercises in a reasonable amount of time and with satisfactory results is, as one can see, highly dependent on the software system. It is a disappointing but true fact that any particular programming language, such as FORTRAN, can still vary considerably in its implementation on different computers. It is even possible that the FORTRAN used on two copies of the same machine may differ materially in its ability to provide the desired service.

Many high schools and a great many colleges (also almost all of the large business or governmental institutions) already have computers that use a batch monitor type of operating system. For those who have no such facility of their own (and, sometimes, even for those who do), an arrangement with a nearby university or other institution for the use of their computer laboratory is urged. A computer 100 miles away and well equipped with software adapted to educational use may be better for the purpose than a small computer in the next room. A smooth educational software system on a machine, even if it is remote, allows students to focus on the construction of algorithms in a programming language. With this knowledge comes more rapid insight into the uses of computers in science and industry. Arrangements for remote use of time-shared computer systems (especially if one is favored with good-quality telephone service) via rented teletype or other keyboard consoles can be very effective.

USING A PROGRAMMING LANGUAGE

To increase the applicability of this book, the specific syntactic details of computer language have been separated from the main flow-chart text into a *language supplement.* The flow-chart language used in the main textbook deals only with concepts of central interest to *all* programming languages. Although embodying a set of general syntactic concepts, flow-chart language contains few such details. Having learned one basic programming language, it is easy to learn another. After the flow-chart language in this book has been studied, PL/1, BASIC, FORTRAN, COBOL, ALGOL, or any similar algebraic procedural language can be learned with ease as a second language. This organization enables a school to choose a programming language from among any of those just mentioned (or their equivalent) and still emphasize the fundamental concepts behind most computer usage. The great reward to the student from this separation of main concepts from syntactic details is the universal applicability of flow-chart language, which he learns first.

Those who read Chapter 12 (on strings) will find themselves well prepared for the string-oriented procedural languages like SNOBOL, and for special string-manipulating features of some of the other languages. For anyone studying Part III of this text in depth, a second programming language like SNOBOL is recommended in addition to (and complementary to) others such as PL/1, BASIC, or FORTRAN.

A brief comment on how the language supplements are organized will be helpful. We recommend that Chapter 1 of the language supplement should be studied only after completing the reading of Section 1-4 of Chapter 1 in the main textbook. The reason for this is to introduce the student to elements of the flow-chart language *before* he meets the programming language equivalent. In this way, a language like FORTRAN, BASIC, or PL/1 is already a *second* language.

After reading Chapter 1 of the supplement, small computer programs can be written as laboratory exercises. The instructor can be expected to supply *particularized information* to close the gap between the language supplement and *your* computer facility. Often, this type of special information is also available from local computer personnel. General-reference manuals are detailed technical publications that are seldom appropriate as an introduction and hardly ever specific to a facility. For instance, some computer facilities require that problems be submitted on special coding sheets. At other facilities, it may be necessary to keypunch cards or paper tape. If cards are used, there are nearly always particular details that differ among facilities regarding the preparation of card decks, including, for example, identification cards or job control cards. If typewriter-like terminals are used, each has its own method of operation and such details can only be supplied locally.

Each chapter of the supplement adds more language capability. Beginning with Chapter 2, any corresponding chapter can be read, section by section, along with the main textbook.

Some final remarks are in order concerning the handling of *input-output details.* To write a program in some languages, especially FORTRAN, one must learn certain data format details, but there is a risk of spending too much time learning these particulars at the expense of developing problem-solving experience. To avoid this, the FORTRAN supplement offers format details piecemeal, as needed, beginning with Chapter 1. The complete subject of format can be quite complex and, here again, one can profit from experienced assistance. Consult highly technical reference manuals only as a last resort.

Format in a language like PL/1 (or SNOBOL) need not be studied initially (or at all) because a set of "simplified" input-output statements is available. Thus the need to learn format codes and associated details is lessened and may be avoided entirely. Some FORTRAN implementations have available a very simple, easily learned I/O scheme involving a minimum of format control or none whatsoever.

CONTENTS

PART III NONNUMERICAL APPLICATIONS

COMPUTER SCIENCE: A FIRST COURSE

PART I

BASIC CONCEPTS

CHAPTER 1

ALGORITHMS AND COMPUTERS

1-1 ALGORITHMS AND FLOW CHARTS

What is an algorithm? An *algorithm* is a list of instructions for carrying out some process step by step. A recipe in a cookbook is an excellent example of an algorithm. The preparation of a complicated dish is broken down into simple steps that every person experienced in cooking can understand. Another good example of an algorithm is the choreography for a classical ballet. An intricate dance is broken down into a succession of basic steps and positions of ballet. The number of these basic steps and positions is very small but, by putting them together in different ways, an endless variety of dances can be devised.

In the same way, algorithms executed by a computer can combine millions of elementary steps, such as additions and subtractions, into a complicated mathematical calculation. Also by means of algorithms, a computer can control a manufacturing process or coordinate the reservations of an airline as they are received from ticket offices all over the country. Algorithms for such large-scale processes are, of course, very complex, but they are built up from pieces, as in the example we will now consider.

If we *can* devise an algorithm for a process, we can usually do so in many different ways. Here is one algorithm for the everyday process of changing a flat tire.

1. Jack up the car
2. Unscrew the lugs
3. Remove the wheel
4. Put on the spare
5. Screw on the lugs
6. Jack the car down

We could add many more details to this algorithm. We could include the steps of getting the materials out of the trunk, positioning the jack, removing the hubcaps, and loosening the lugs before jacking up the car, for example. For algorithms describing mechanical processes, it is generally best to decide how much detail to include. Still, the steps we have listed will be adequate to convey the idea of an algorithm. When we get to mathematical algorithms, we will have to be much more precise.

A *flow chart* is a diagram for representing an algorithm. In Figure 1-1 we see a flow chart for the flat-tire algorithm.

The START and STOP

in the flow chart remind us of the buttons used to start and stop a piece

of machinery. Each instruction in the flow chart is enclosed in a frame or "box." As we will soon see, the shape of the frame indicates the kind

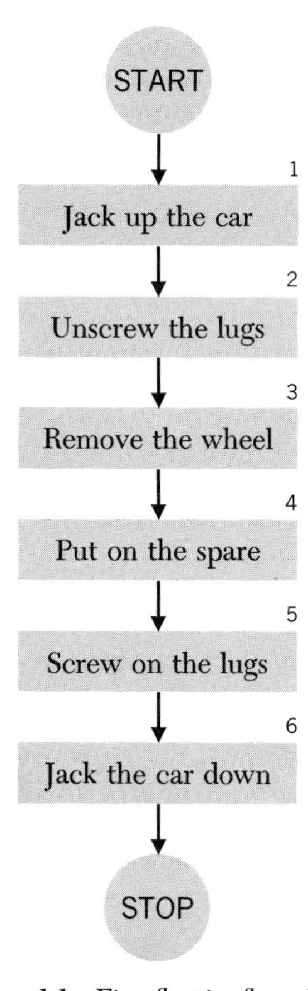

Figure 1-1 First flat-tire flow chart.

of instruction written inside. A rectangular frame indicates a command to take some action.

To carry out the task described by the flow chart, we begin at the start button and follow the arrows from box to box, executing the instructions as we come to them.

After drawing a flow chart, we always look to see whether we can improve it. For instance, in the flat-tire flow chart we neglected to check whether the spare was flat. If the spare *is* flat, we will not change the tire but will call a garage instead. This calls for a decision between two courses of action. For this purpose we introduce a new shape of frame into our flow chart.

Inside the frame we will write an assertion instead of a command.

The spare is flat

This is called a *decision box* and will have two exits, labeled T (for true) and F (for false). After checking the truth or falsity of the assertion, we choose the appropriate exit and proceed to the indicated activity.

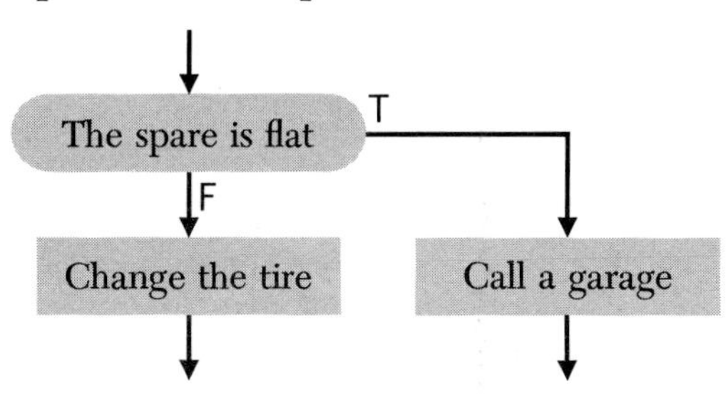

Inserting this flow-chart fragment into Figure 1-1, we obtain the flow chart in Figure 1-2.

There is another instructive improvement possible. The instruction in box 2 of our flow chart actually stands for a number of repetitions of the same task. To show the additional detail we could replace box 2 by

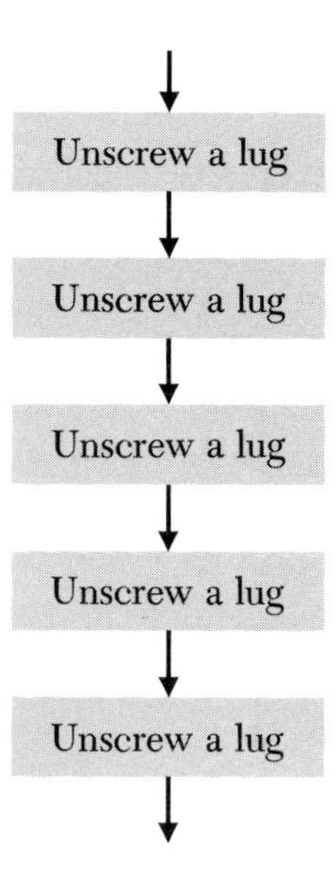

The awkwardness of this repeated instruction can be eliminated by introducing a *loop*.

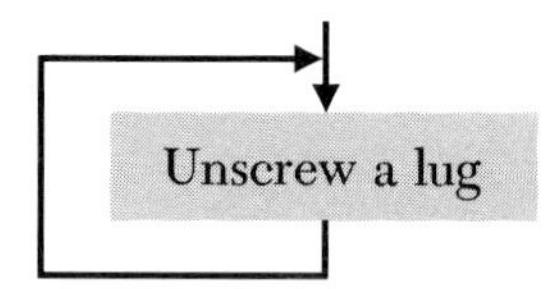

As we leave the box, we find that the arrow leads us right back to repeat the task again. However, we are caught in an endless loop, since we have provided no way to get out and go on with the next task. To rectify this situation, we again require a decision box, as follows:

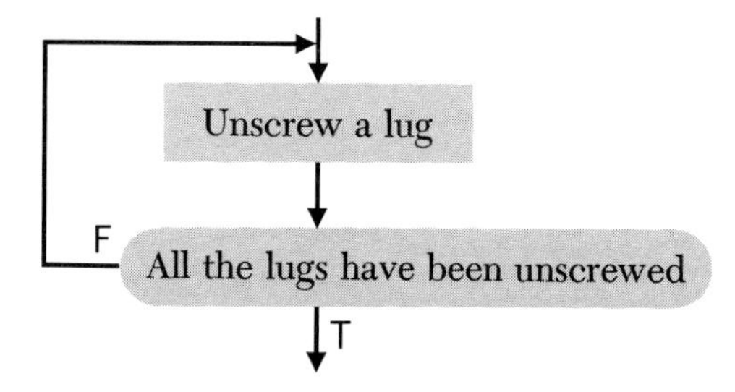

Replacing box 2 of our flow chart with this mechanism and making a similar replacement for box 5, we get the final result shown in Figure 1-3.

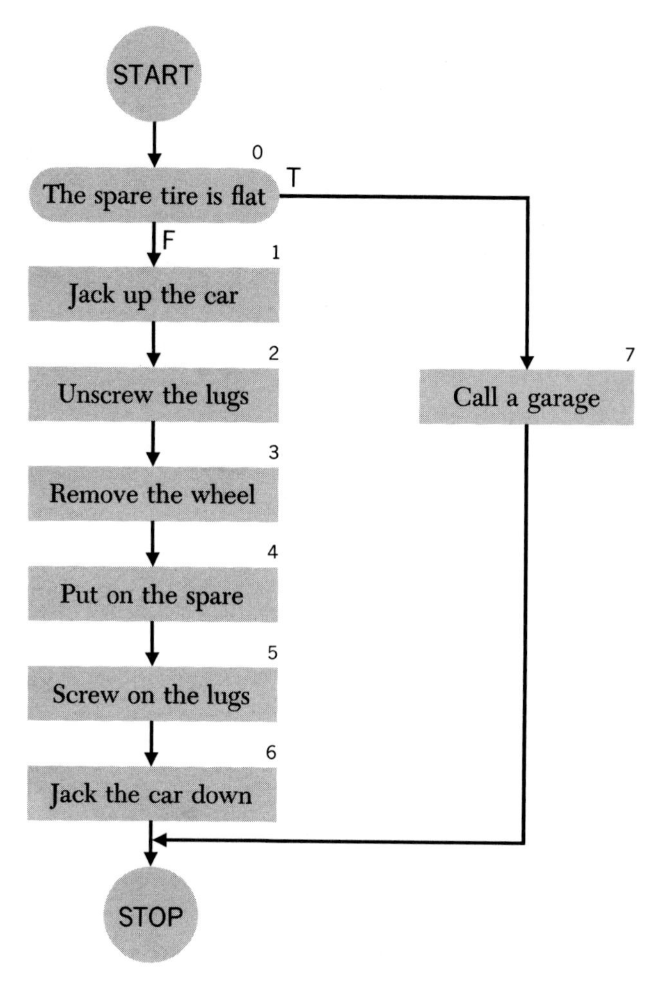

Figure 1-2 Second flat-tire flow chart.

Now that you have followed the development of the flat-tire flow chart, try to devise one of your own. In the algorithm of the following exercise, you will probably discover some decisions and loops. There are many different ways of flowcharting this algorithm, so probably many different-looking flow charts will be submitted.

EXERCISE 1-1

Prepare a flow chart representing the recipe found on page 9.

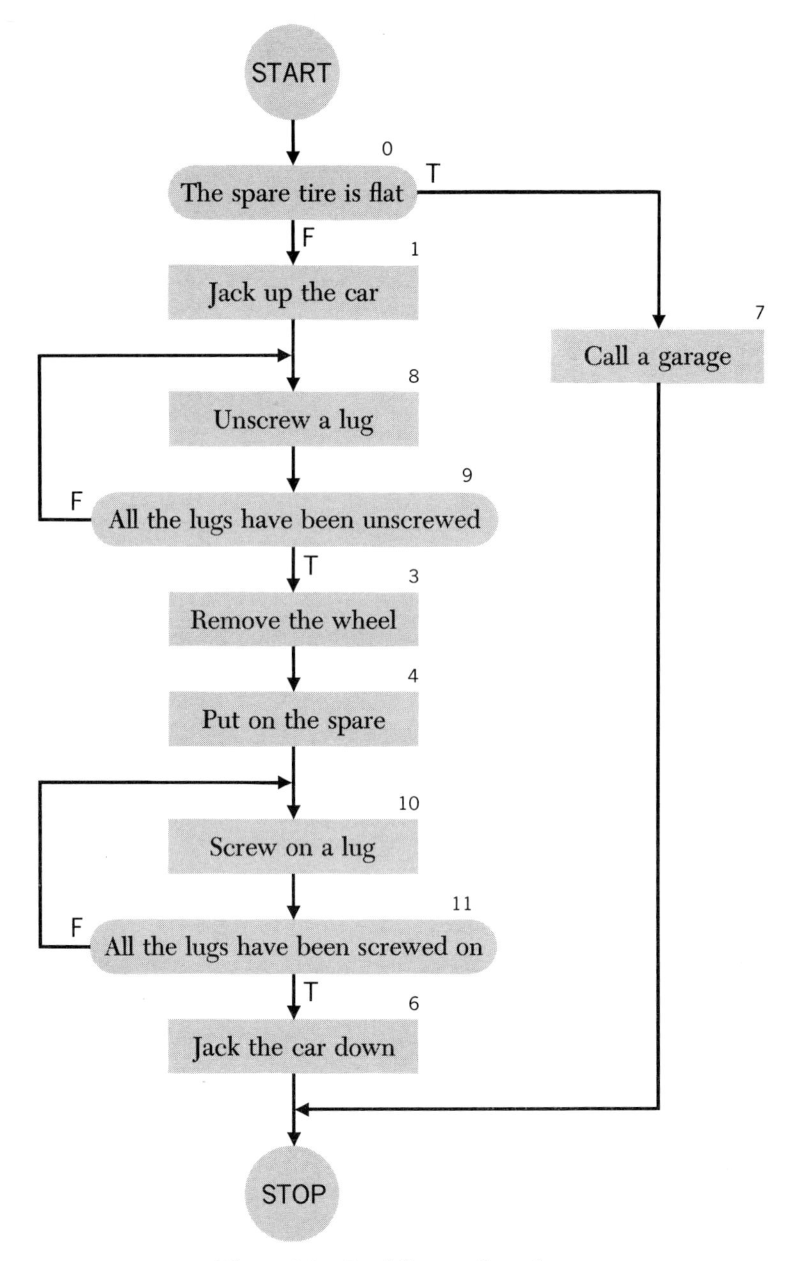

Figure 1-3 Final flat-tire flow chart.

Mrs. Good's Rocky Road

Ingredients:

1 cup chopped walnuts
$\frac{1}{4}$ lb block baker's chocolate
$\frac{1}{2}$ lb marshmallows cut in halves
3 cups sugar
$\frac{1}{2}$ cup evaporated milk
$\frac{1}{2}$ cup corn syrup
1 tsp vanilla
$\frac{1}{4}$ lb butter
$\frac{1}{2}$ tsp salt

Place milk, corn syrup, sugar, chocolate, and salt in a four-quart pan, and cook over a high flame, stirring constantly until the mixture boils. Reduce to medium flame and continue boiling and stirring until a drop of syrup forms a soft ball in a glass of cold water. Remove from the flame and allow to cool for 10 minutes. Beat in butter and vanilla until thoroughly blended. Stir in walnuts. Distribute marshmallow halves over the bottom of a 10-inch square, buttered baking pan. Pour syrup over the marshmallows. Allow to cool for 10 minutes. Cut in squares and serve.

1-2 A NUMERICAL ALGORITHM

Now we are ready to look at an algorithm for a mathematical calculation. As a first example, we will consider the problem of finding terms of the Fibonacci sequence:

$$0, 1, 1, 2, 3, 5, 8, 13, 21, 34, 55, \ldots$$

In this sequence, or list of numbers, the first two terms given are 0 and 1. After that, the terms are constructed according to the rule that each number in the list is the sum of the two preceding ones. Check that this is the case. Thus, the next term after the last one listed above is

$$34 + 55 = 89$$

Clearly, we can keep on generating the terms of the sequence, one after another, for as long as we like. But in order to write an algorithm for the process (so that a computer could execute it, for example), we have to be much more explicit in our instructions. Let's subject the process to closer scrutiny.

TABLE 1-1

Next Latest Term	Latest Term	Sum
0	1	0 + 1 = 1
1	1	1 + 1 = 2
1	2	1 + 2 = 3
2	3	2 + 3 = 5
3	5	3 + 5 = 8
5	8	5 + 8 = 13
8	13	8 + 13 = 21

Table 1-1 shows the computation of the terms of the Fibonacci sequence.

We can see that in each step the latest term gets "demoted" to the role of next-latest term and the sum becomes the new latest term.

Let's construct a flow chart for finding the first term to exceed 1000 in the Fibonacci sequence (Figure 1-4).

After going through the loop of flow-chart boxes numbered 2 to 5 enough times (it happens to be 15 times), we eventually emerge from box 3 at the T exit and proceed to box 6. This box is seen to have a different shape because it calls for a different kind of activity—that of writing down our answer. The shape is chosen so as to suggest a page torn off a line printer, one of the most common computer output devices.

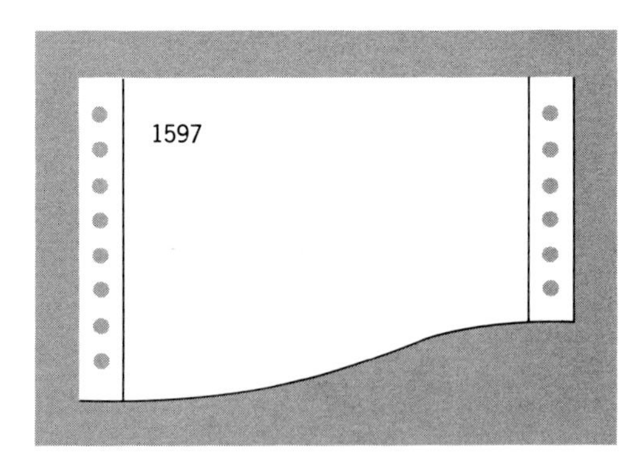

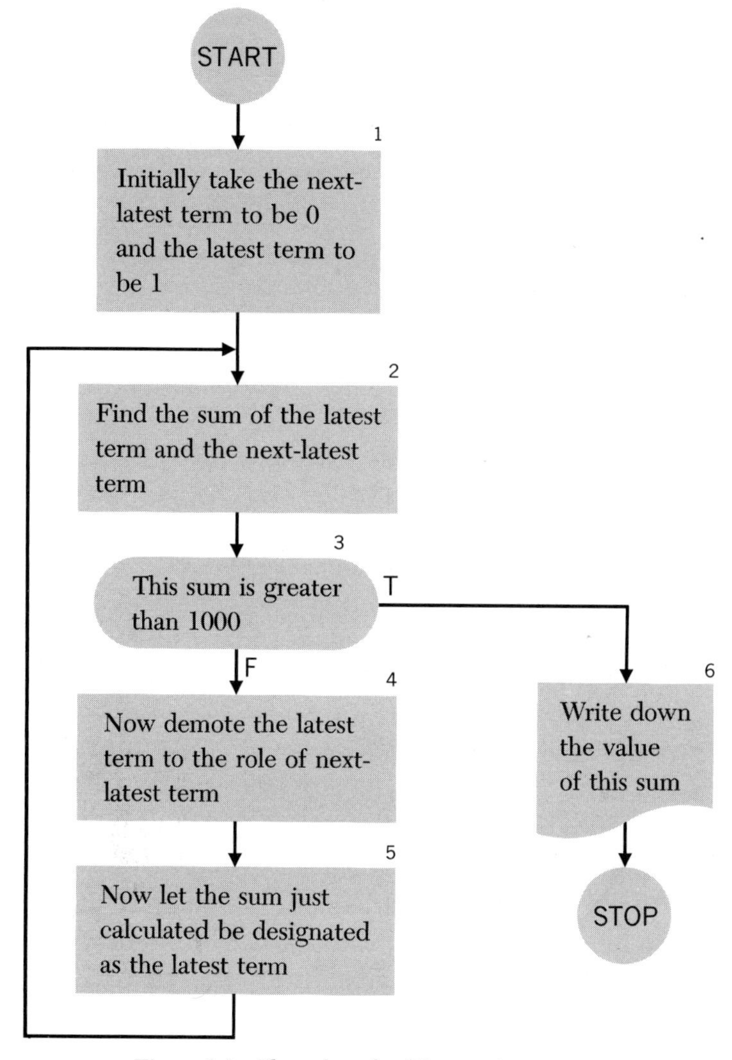

Figure 1-4 Flow chart for Fibonacci sequence.

1-3 A MODEL OF A COMPUTER

The algorithm considered in the preceding section can be presented in much simpler notation which is, at the same time, more nearly ready to be given to a computer as a set of instructions. To do this we need to introduce a conceptual model of how a computer works. This model is extraordinarily simple—childishly so, in fact. It is amazing but true that such a simple view of how a computer works is completely adequate for this entire course. We will present a more realistic picture of a computer in later sections of this chapter—but only to satisfy your curiosity, not because we have any real need of it.

Variables. In computing work, a *variable* is a letter or a string of letters used to stand for a number. In the formula

$$A = L \times W$$

the letters A, L, and W are variables. In the formula

$$DIST = RATE \times TIME$$

DIST, RATE, and TIME are variables.

At any particular time, a variable will stand for one particular number, called the *value* of the variable, which may change from time to time during a computing process. The value of a variable may change millions of times during the execution of a single algorithm.

In our conceptual model of a computer we will associate with each variable a *window box*. The associated variable is engraved on the top of each box, and inside is a strip of paper with the *present value* (or *current value*) of the variable written on it. The variable is a name for the number that currently appears inside.

Each box has a lid that may be opened when we wish to assign a new value to the variable. Each box has a window in the side so that we may read the value of a variable with no danger of altering the value. These window boxes constitute the *memory* of our computer. In Figure 1-5 we see the course of executing the Fibonacci sequence algorithm of the preceding section. Here NEXT stands for "next-latest term" and LATEST stands for "latest term."

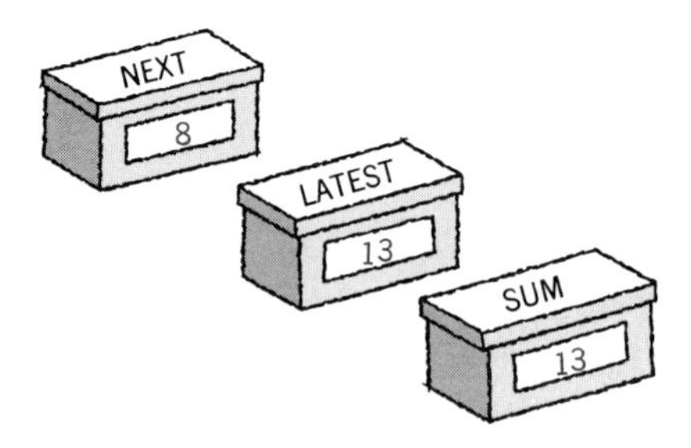

Figure 1-5 Memory.

The Model and How it Works

We visualize a computer as a room with a number of window boxes in it and a staff of three workers—the *master computer* and two assistants, the *assigner* and the *reader*. The master computer has a flow chart on his desk from which he gets his instructions, according to which he delegates certain tasks to his assistants (Figure 1-6). (In a real computer the tasks of these workers are performed by electronic circuits.)

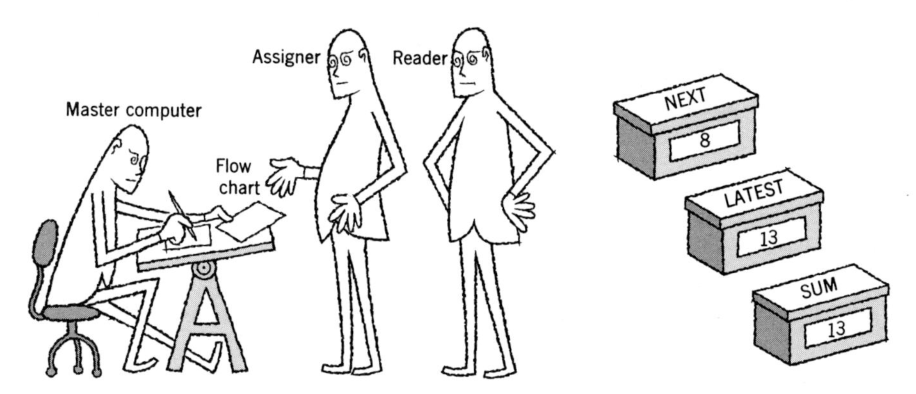

Figure 1-6 The master computer and his two assistants.

To see how this team operates, let us suppose that the computer is in the midst of executing the Fibonacci sequence algorithm of Figure 1-4. One of the instructions in this algorithm was:

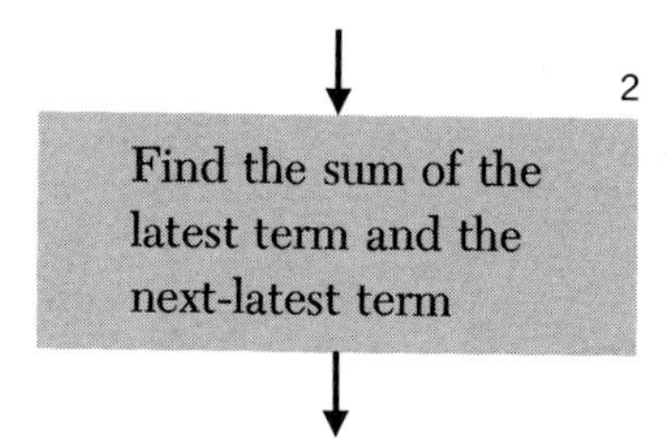

In a simplified flow-chart notation this instruction will take the form:

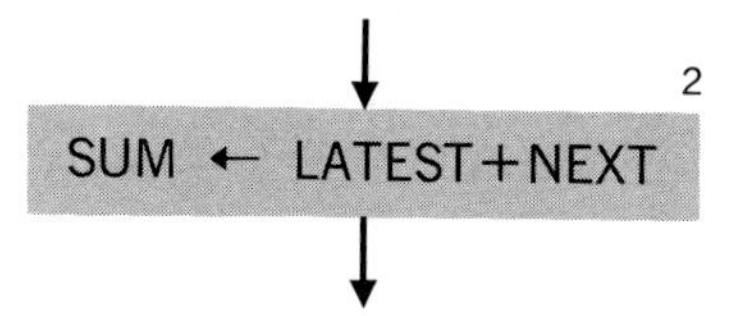

Inside this flow-chart box we find an *assignment statement*. Reading this statement aloud, we would say, "Assign to SUM the value of

LATEST + NEXT," or more simply, "Assign LATEST + NEXT to SUM." The left-pointing arrow is called the *assignment operator* and is to be thought of as an order or a command. Rectangular boxes in our flow-chart language will always contain assignment steps and will therefore be called *assignment boxes*.

Let's see what takes place when the master computer comes to this statement in the flow chart. We shall assume that the variables LATEST and NEXT (but not SUM) have the values seen in Figure 1-5.

The computation called for in the assignment statement occurs on the right-hand side of the arrow, so the master computer looks there first.

He sees that he must know the values of the variables LATEST and NEXT, so he sends the reader out to fetch these values from memory.

The reader then goes to the memory and finds the window boxes labeled LATEST and NEXT. He reads the values of these variables through the windows (Figure 1-7), jots the values down, and takes them back to the master computer (Figure 1-8).

The master computer computes the value of LATEST + NEXT using the values of these variables brought to him by the reader:

$$8 + 13 = 21$$

What does he do with this value?

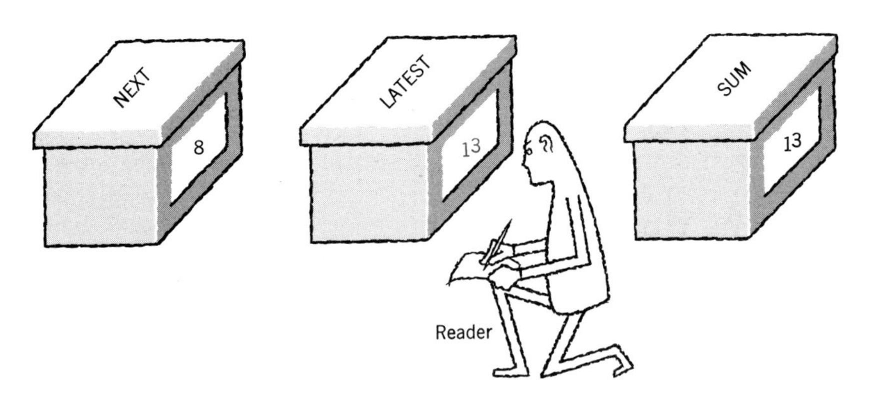

Figure 1-7 The reader copying a value in memory.

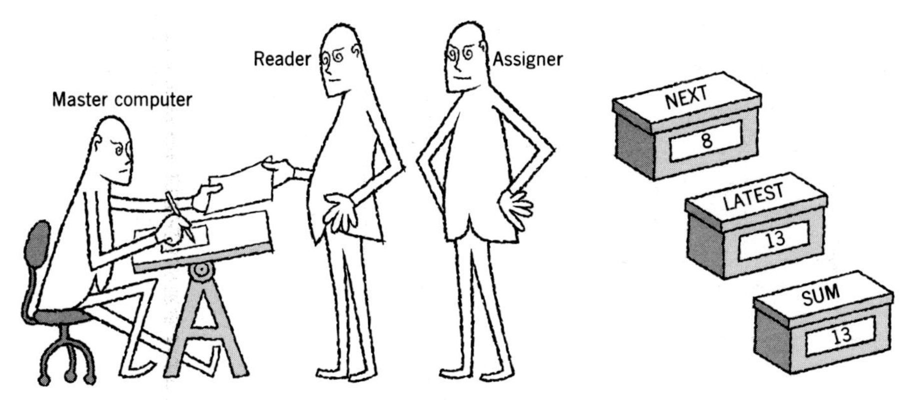

Figure 1-8 The master computer receives the copy.

The master computer now looks at the left-hand side of the arrow in his instruction.

(SUM) ← LATEST+NEXT

He sees that he must assign the computed value of LATEST+NEXT, namely, 21, so he writes "21" on a slip of paper, calls the assigner, and instructs him to assign this value to the variable SUM.

The assigner goes to the memory, finds the window box labeled SUM, and dumps out its contents (Figure 1-9). Then he puts the slip of paper with the new value in the box, closes the lid, and returns to the master computer for a new task.

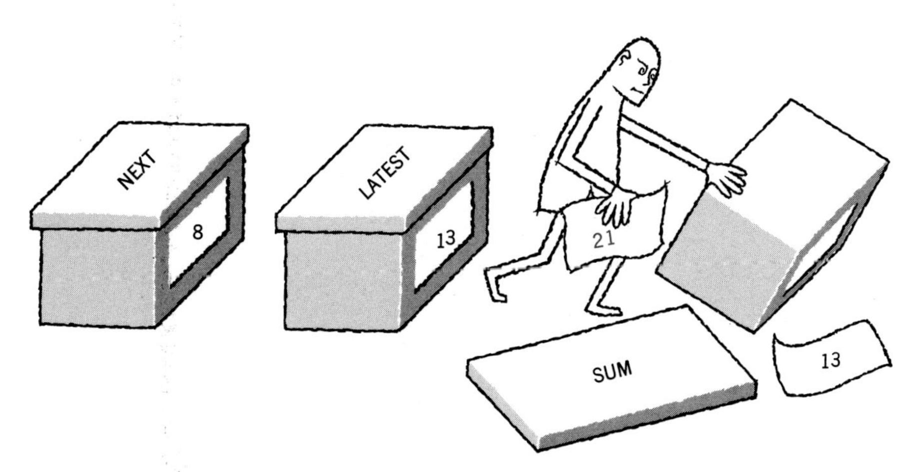

Figure 1-9 The assigner emptying a window box and refilling it.

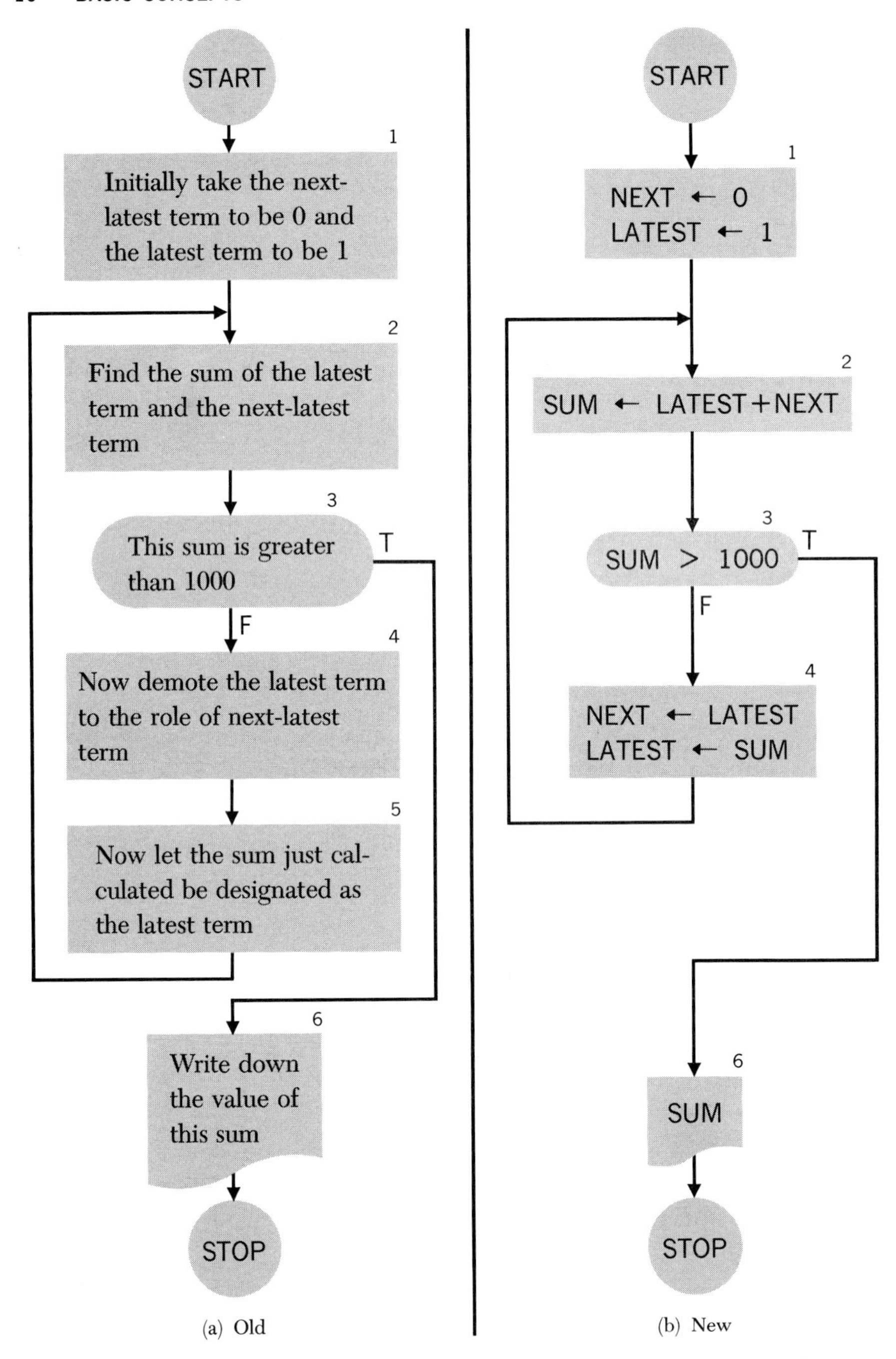

Figure 1-10 Translation of Fibonacci sequence flow chart into formal flow-chart language.

In other words, we see that assignment is the process of giving a value to a variable. We say that assignment is *destructive* because it destroys the former value of the variable. Reading is *nondestructive* because the process in no way alters the values of any of the variables in the memory.

Now we present (in Figure 1-10) the entire flow chart of Figure 1-4 in simplified flow-chart language. The old and new flow charts are placed side by side for easy comparison.

The translation requires very little explanation. It should be obvious that the statement in box 1 on the left is equivalent to the two statements in box 1 on the right. The new version of box 2 has been discussed in detail; box 3 is obvious.

We see that the two statements in boxes 4 and 5 of the old flow chart are compressed into one box, box 4 of the new flow chart. This is permissible whenever we have a number of assignment statements with no other steps in between. However, it is very important to understand that these assignment statements must be executed in order from top to bottom, not in the opposite order and not simultaneously. In fact, we should always think of a computer as doing just one thing at a time; the order in which things are done is generally extremely important.

You can see that the statements in box 4 involve no computation but merely changing the values in certain window boxes. This sort of activity will occur very frequently in future flow charts.

In box 6 of the flow chart we see written only the variable SUM. The shape of the box (called an *output box*) tells us that the value of the variable SUM is to be written down. If, in some other algorithm, we wished to write down the values of several variables, we would list these variables in an output box separated by commas, for example:

A, B, C, DIST

Tracing the Flow Chart

To understand better what our flow chart in Figure 1-10*b* does, let us trace through it, executing the steps as the master computer and his assistants would do them (see Table 1-2).

In this trace, for ease of reading, the values of the variables are reproduced only when assignments are made to them. In between such steps, the values of the variables do not change and therefore have the last pre-

TABLE 1-2 Tracing of the Flow Chart of Figure 1-10*b*

Step Number	Flow Chart Box Number	Values of Variables			Test	True or False
		NEXT	LATEST	SUM		
1	1	0	1			
2	2			1		
3	3				$1 > 1000$	F
4	4	1	1			
5	2			2		
6	3				$2 > 1000$	F
7	4	1	2			
8	2			3		
9	3				$3 > 1000$	F
10	4	2	3			
11	2			5		
12	3				$5 > 1000$	F
13	4	3	5			
14	2			8		
15	3				$8 > 1000$	F
16	4	5	8			
17	2			13		
18	3				$13 > 1000$	F
19	4	8	13			
20	2			21		
21	3				$21 > 1000$	F
22	4	13	21			
23	2			34		
24	3				$34 > 1000$	F
25	4	21	34			
26	2			55		
27	3				$55 > 1000$	F
28	4	34	55			
29	2			89		
30	3				$89 > 1000$	F
31	4	55	89			
32	2			144		
33	3				$144 > 1000$	F
34	4	89	144			
35	2			233		
36	3				$233 > 1000$	F

Table 1-2 Cont.

Step Number	Flow Chart Box Number	Values of Variables			Test	True or False
		NEXT	LATEST	SUM		
37	4	144	233			
38	2			377		
39	3				377 > 1000	F
40	4	233	377			
41	2			610		
42	3				610 > 1000	F
43	4	377	610			
44	2			987		
45	3				987 > 1000	F
46	4	610	987			
47	2			1597		
48	3				1597 > 1000	T
49	6				1597	

viously recorded values. For example, in step 33, where we are performing a test, the values of the variables are

$$\text{NEXT} = 55, \qquad \text{LATEST} = 89, \qquad \text{SUM} = 144$$

In step 34 the values are

$$\text{NEXT} = 89, \qquad \text{LATEST} = 144, \qquad \text{SUM} = 144$$

You can see that in step 48 in the execution of our algorithm we finally leave box 3 by the true exit and pass on to box 6 where we output the answer, 1597, and stop.

The utter simplicity of our conceptual model avoids and conceals certain pitfalls. There is a danger of thinking of assignment as being the same as equality or substitution. (We will have more to say about this later on.) This and other sources of confusion (such as the effect of a certain sequence of flow-chart statements) can be cleared up by thinking in terms of our model, which will always give the right answers.

In fact, the best way to get the ideas into your mind would be to make some window boxes and, with two other students, take the roles of master computer, assigner, and reader, and work through a couple of algorithms as described in this section.

EXERCISES 1-3

1. What would be the effect of changing the order of the two assignment statements in box 4 of Figure 1-10*b* so as to appear as seen below?

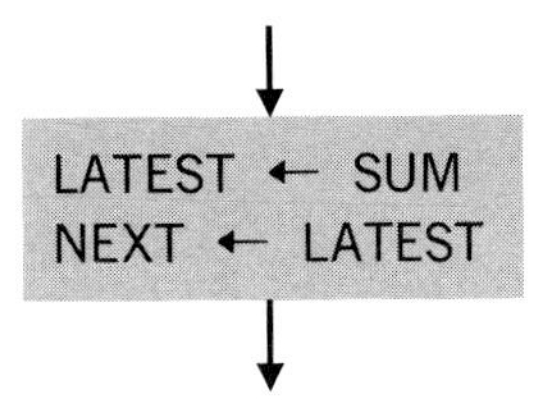

Trace through the flow chart with this modification until you find the answer.

2. (a) To compare the effects of the assignment statements

A ← B and B ← A

find the missing numbers in the table below.

Values Before Execution of Assignment		Assignment To Be Executed	Values After Execution of Assignment	
A	B		A	B
7	13	A ← B	?	?
7	13	B ← A	?	?

(b) In which of the two cases is it true that A=B after assignment?

(c) Are the effects of the two assignment statements the same or different?

1-4 INPUT/OUTPUT

Imagine that you are a bookkeeper in a large factory. You have records of the hourly rate of pay and the number of hours worked for each employee and you have to calculate the week's wages. Of course, this can be done by hand, but assume there are nearly a thousand workers in the plant, so that the job will be quite tedious. Naturally you prefer to have the computer do this task for you, so you will have to devise a flow chart to give the instructions to the computer.

How will you get the hourly rates and the hours worked into the flow chart? Will you write them all in separately? If so, it will take a long time. The characteristic situation is this. We have a stack of punch cards, one for each worker. According to a certain code of hole-patterns, each card is punched with the name of the worker, his hourly rate of pay, the number of hours worked, and perhaps some other things as well. Figure 1-11 is a sample of what such a card might look like.

Now we will introduce a new shape of frame—the *input box*—into our flow-chart language. The input box has this shape

to suggest a punch card. Inside the box will appear a single variable or a list of variables separated by commas.

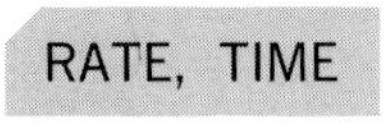

RATE, TIME

When the above box is seen in a flow chart, it is interpreted as an instruction to the master computer to do these three things.

1. Read two numbers from the top card in a stack of punch cards.
2. Assign these numbers respectively to the variables RATE and TIME.
3. Remove this card from the stack.

We see that an input box is a command to make assignments, but this command is essentially different from that in an assignment box. In an assignment box the values to be assigned are to be found in the computer's memory or are computed from values already in the computer's memory, whereas with an input box the values to be assigned are ob-

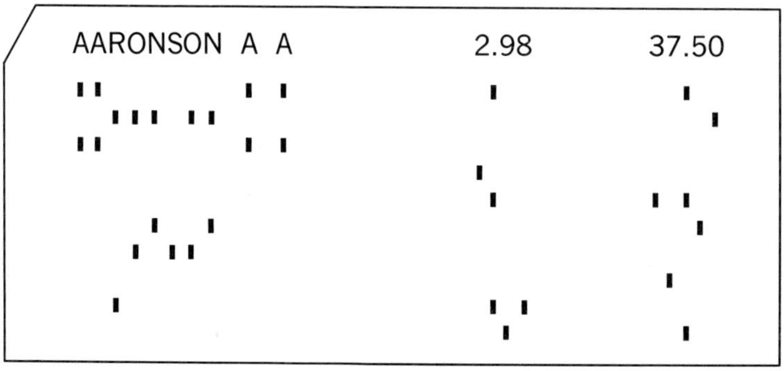

AARONSON A A 2.98 37.50

Figure 1-11 Payroll data on a punch card.

tained from outside the memory. No calculation may be called for in an input box.

In a real computer (not our conceptual one), the distinction between these two kinds of assignments shows up more sharply. The assignments called for in an input box usually involve some mechanical motion such as removing a card from a stack. However, assignments called for in an assignment box are made by electronic pulses that move at nearly the speed of light and are hence much faster than input assignments.

Now, let's see how the input box is used in our hourly rate and payroll problem. Should we input the data from all the cards before we start our calculations? If so, we would need a tremendous number of window boxes in which to store all this data. Instead, we will calculate the wages after each card is read. A description of our process is as follows.

1. Read the RATE and TIME from the top card in the stack and remove the card.
2. Multiply the RATE by the time to get the WAGE.
3. Output the values of RATE, TIME, and WAGE.
4. Return to step 1.

This is realized in the flow chart given in Figure 1-12.

Each step in the above list appears in a similarly numbered box in our

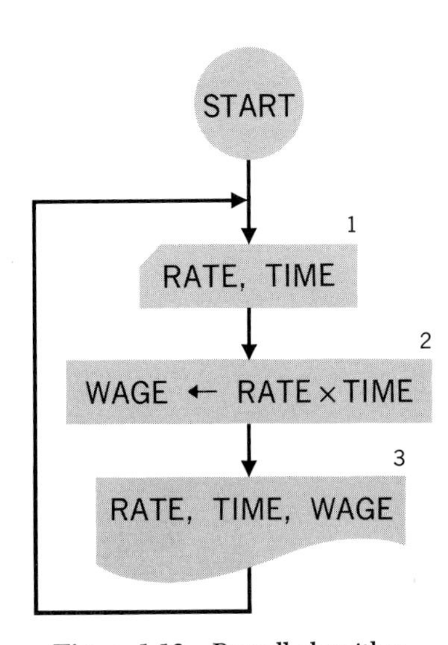

Figure 1-12 Payroll algorithm.

flow chart except for the fourth step. That is represented by the arrow returning from box 3 to box 1.

You may wonder why the flow chart does not have a stop button. We assume, as one of the functions of the input box, the duty of stopping the computation if the reading of another card is called for and the stack is empty.

EXERCISE 1-4

Modify the flow chart of Figure 1-12 to provide for an overtime feature. All hours in excess of 40 are to be paid at time and a half. You will have to place a test somewhere in the flow chart to determine whether the worker actually put in any overtime. The formula by which his wages are computed will depend on the outcome of this test.

1-5 COMPUTER MEMORY

Now we are ready to look at how our conceptual model of a computer can be realized in an actual machine. In this section and the next we will discuss a prototype machine that we will call SAMOS. SAMOS is a very simple machine, that is, it is stripped down to the bare essentials. Some features of its operation are described in considerable detail while others are glossed over. The programming of SAMOS is described briefly in Section 1-6 and in more detail in the Appendix.

In order to study this book it is only necessary that you should have a general idea of how an actual computer works. We suggest that you read over the material in this section and the one that follows quite rapidly without attempting to master it. Just retain what sticks in your mind. Of course, if you wish to study it in detail you may do so, and any time you want to learn more about machine language programming, you may read the Appendix. In short, to understand most of this book you need a good grasp of the conceptual model of the computer. Familiarity with actual computers is of secondary importance.

Cores

We will start with the memory. How are all those window boxes realized in actual practice? The memory of the SAMOS computer is contained in a rectangular box. Inside the box there is an arrangement of

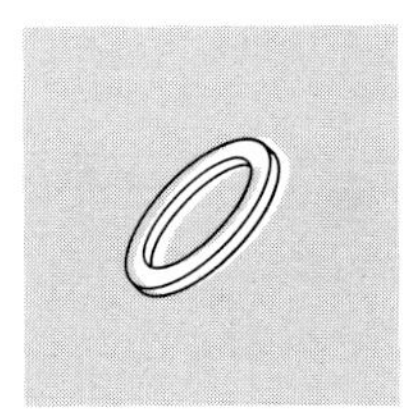

Figure 1-13 A magnetic core.

tiny magnetic doughnuts as small as 1/20 of an inch in diameter. These doughnuts are called *cores* (Figure 1-13).

Our box is divided in 61 horizontal layers or trays called *core planes* (Figure 1-14).

On each of these layers, wires are strung in two directions like the lines on a sheet of graph paper (Figure 1-15). There are a hundred wires in each direction. At each point where two wires cross, the wires are threaded through a core like the thread passing through the eye of a needle (Figure 1-16).

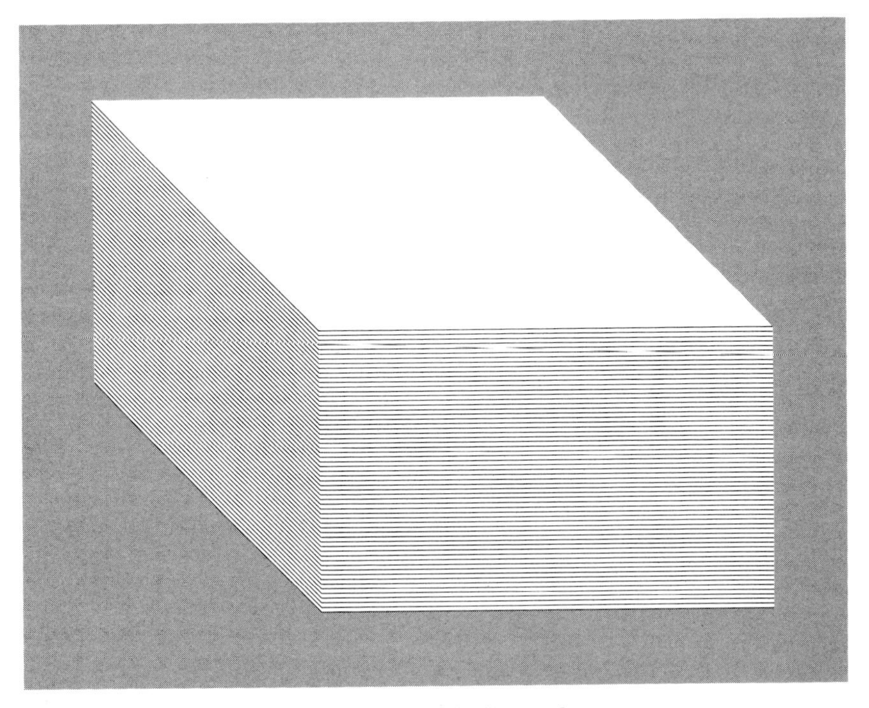

Figure 1-14 A stack of core planes.

Figure 1-15 Wire grid of a core plane.

Figure 1-17 is a picture of a core plane from an actual computer. Since there are 100×100 crossings in each layer, we see that there are 10,000 cores in each core plane and hence $61 \times 10{,}000 = 610{,}000$ cores in the entire SAMOS memory.

These cores are capable of being magnetized in either the clockwise or the counterclockwise sense (Figure 1-18).

Because of this, the core can store information. We could think of clockwise magnetization as meaning "yes" and counterclockwise as meaning "no". We will instead think of clockwise as standing for "0" and counterclockwise for "1". In any event, the information contained in the direction of magnetization of a core is the smallest unit of infor-

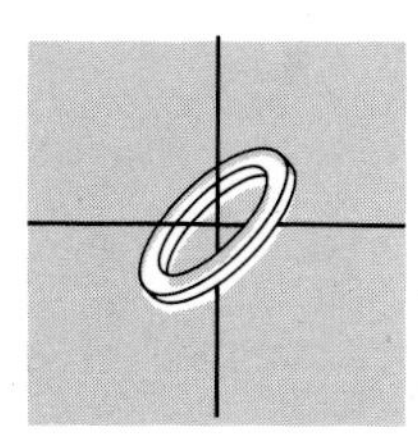

Figure 1-16 Where two wires cross.

Figure 1-17 An actual core plane (Courtesy of IBM).

mation and is called a *bit* of information. We see that one core can store one binary digit 0 or 1, but a collection of cores can store a very large number of bits. This we will discuss a little later on, after a digression to see how the cores get their magnetism.

First, you must know that a pulse of electric current moving along a wire generates a magnetic field running around the wire, as shown in Figure 1-19. This field can be detected by a pocket compass. The

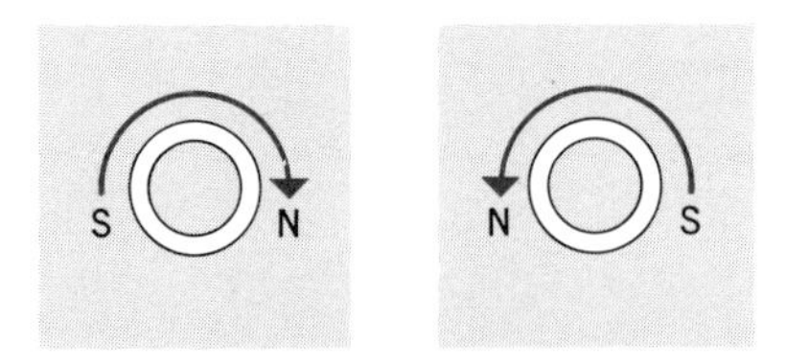

Figure 1-18 Magnetization of cores.

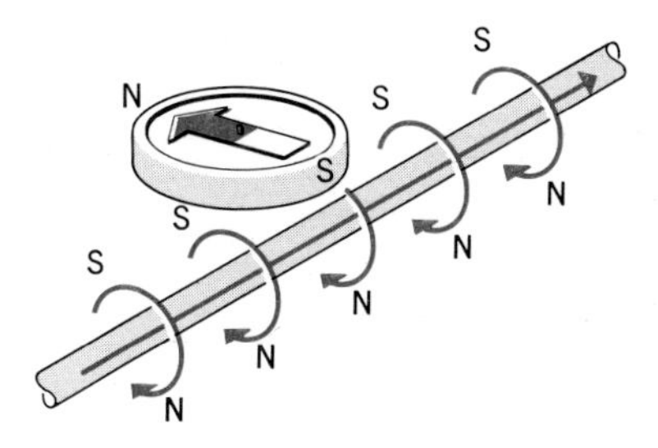

Figure 1-19 Generating a magnetic field that results from passage of a pulse of electric current.

strength of the magnetic field is strongest near the wire and dies away as we move further from the wire.

If the direction of the current is reversed, the direction of the magnetic field is also reversed (Figure 1-20).

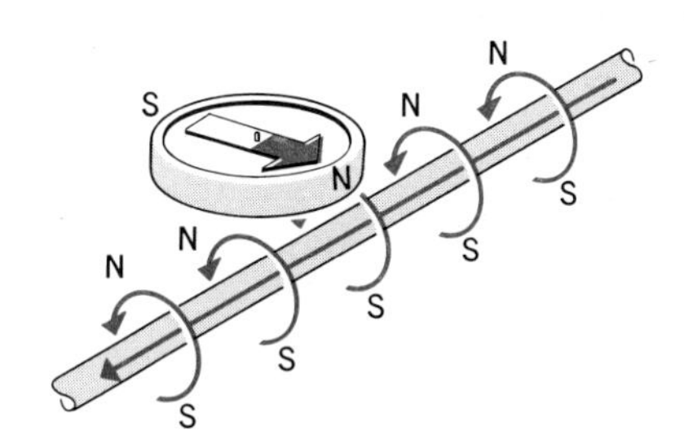

Figure 1-20 Reversing the direction of the magnetic field.

Thus, when a pulse of current passes through a core, the core will become magnetized in one direction or the other, depending on the direction of the current (Figure 1-21).

But how can we manage to magnetize just one core instead of the

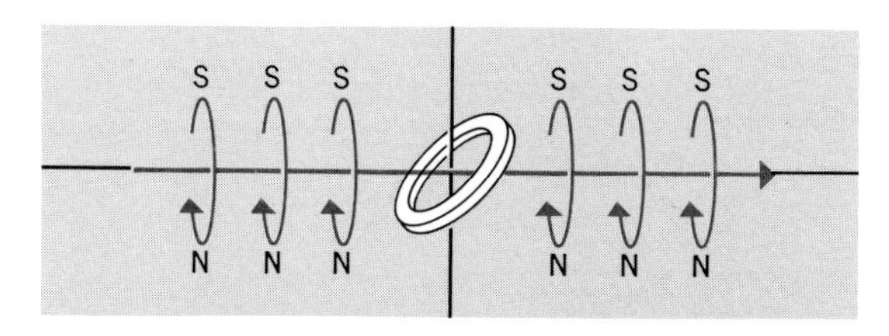

Figure 1-21 A core in a magnetic field.

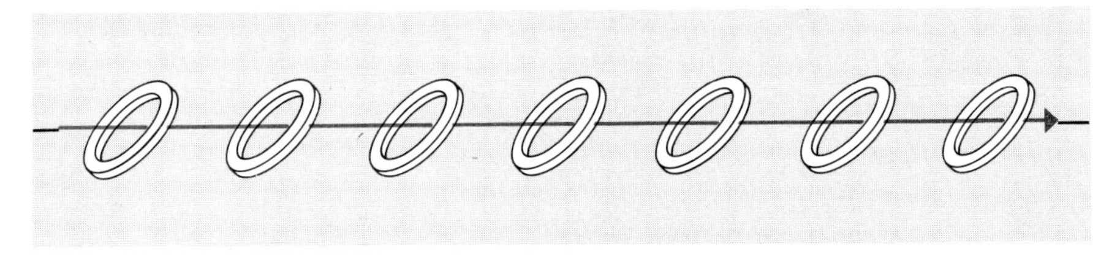

Figure 1-22 A row of cores in a magnetic field.

whole string of cores (Figure 1-22) through which the pulse passes? The answer lies in the magnetic properties of the material of which the core is made. With this material, if the pulse is too weak, then the direction of the magnetization of the core is not permanently altered. After the pulse of current has passed by, the core merely *returns* to its former magnetic condition, whatever that was.

On the other hand, if the current is strong enough, the core remains permanently magnetized in the sense established by the direction of the current, regardless of the former magnetic condition of the core. The

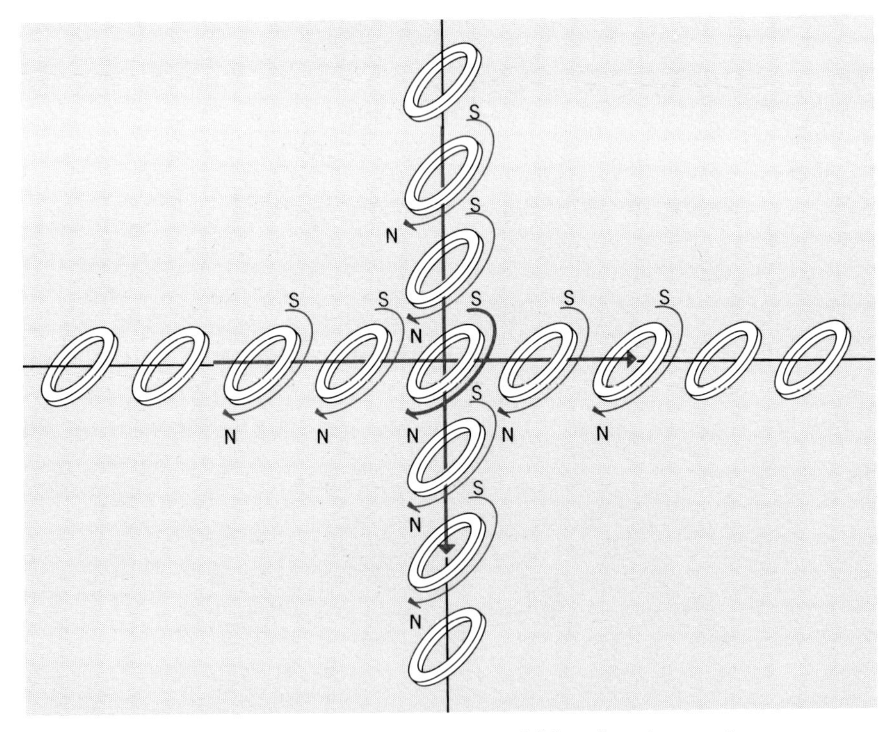

Figure 1-23 Doubling the magnetic field at the wire crossing.

situation is analogous to trying to throw a ball from the ground to the flat roof of a building. If you have enough power in your throw, the ball will land on the roof; otherwise it will bounce against the wall and fall back to the ground.

The strength of the pulses is carefully regulated so that one pulse is not sufficient to permanently magnetize a core but two pulses acting simultaneously will exceed the threshold strength and result in permanent magnetism. Thus, pulses passing along both wires (Figure 1-23) will permanently magnetize just the one core that is located where the wires cross.

The Store of the SAMOS Computer

Let's leave the individual core planes and consider the entire memory or *store* of the computer, composed of the 61 core planes (Figure 1-24). Each vertical column of 61 cores constitutes a *computer word.* Thus, the

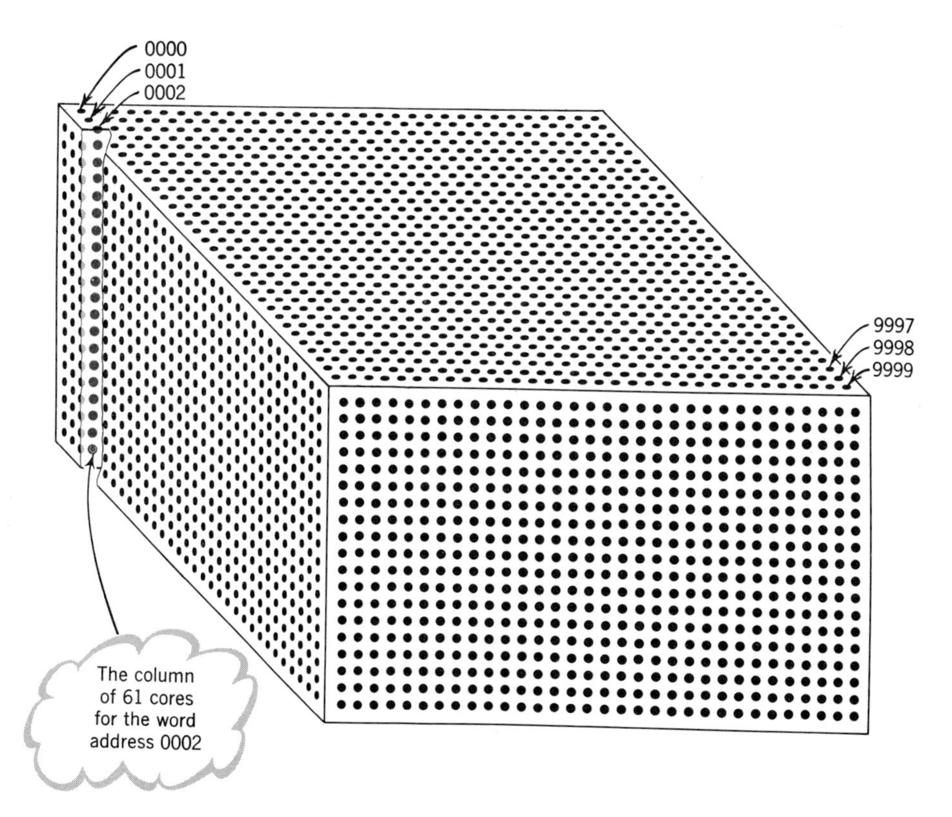

Figure 1-24 Cores of one computer word.

memory of the computer is composed of 10,000 words. These words have addresses that are four-digit numbers from 0000 to 9999 and, like house numbers, are used to identify them. Each of the 10,000 dots on the top of the box is the top of a vertical column of 61 cores (or a word). The manner of assigning the addresses is indicated in the figure.

Each of these words corresponds to a window box in our conceptual model. Each variable in the flow chart will have a certain address. The word with that address will have in it a certain pattern of "bits" (directions of magnetization of its cores) representing the value of that variable. "Assigning a value to a variable" is effected by putting a certain pattern of bits into a word.

In more detail, when we said "the master computer tells the assigner to assign the value 1597 to the variable SUM," what actually takes place is this. The variable SUM is represented inside the machine by means of its address; suppose it is 0103. Now all the $61 \times 2 = 122$ wires passing through cores in the word addressed 0103 are energized with pulses of current in the proper directions so as to achieve the pattern of bits representing the number 1597 (Figure 1-25).

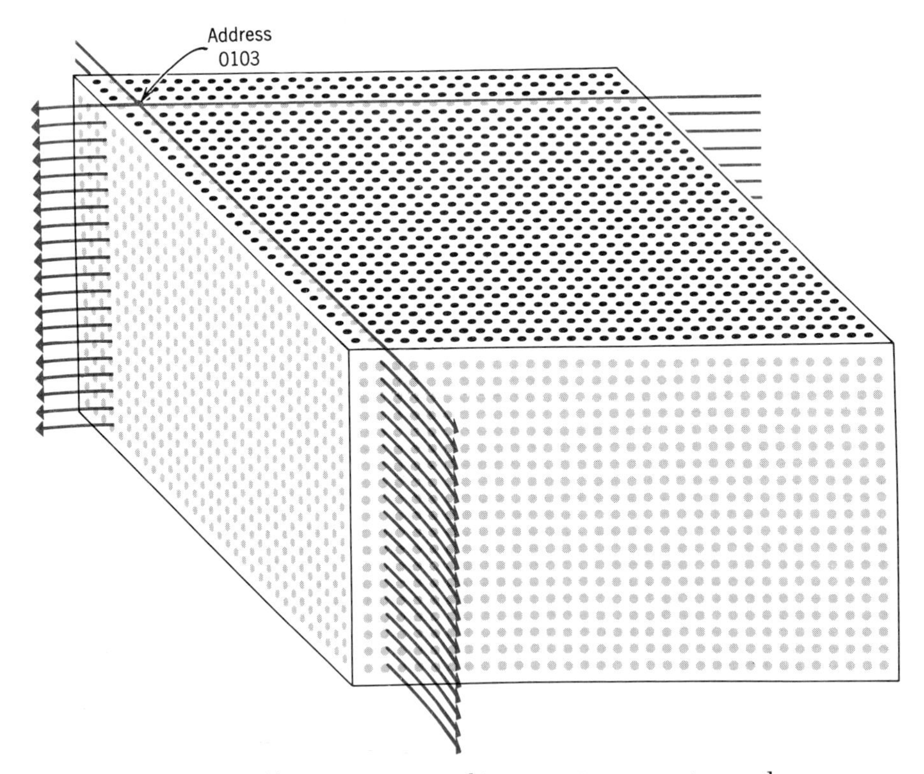

Figure 1-25 Assigning a new bit pattern to a computer word.

In a modern computer this assignment process can be performed in 3/10 of a microsecond; that is, 3/10,000,000 of a second.

Characters

One obvious way of representing the number 1597 would be in the binary system as

$$1\ 1\ 0\ 0\ 0\ 1\ 1\ 1\ 1\ 0\ 1$$

preceded by a string of zeros to fill all the bit positions of the word of memory. While numbers are coded in binary form in many computers, it is certainly not the only choice. In a machine like SAMOS, for instance, computation is to be carried out in the decimal system, which implies that bit patterns stored in a word of memory must be coded to represent decimal rather than binary numbers. Moreover, we would like to store letters as well as decimal digits. For this reason, we subdivide our 61-bit words into 11 *characters* as shown below.

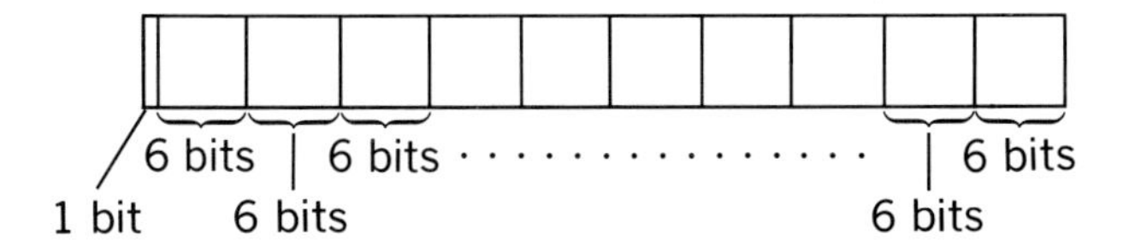

The first character (one bit only) is reserved for holding a sign, + or −. Here 0 stands for + and 1 for −. Each of the other characters consists of six bits. These characters can be used to store numbers or letters, according to the codes shown in Figure 1-26.

Character	Code	Character	Code	Character	Code	Character	Code
0	00 0000						
1	00 0001	A	01 0001	J	10 0001		
2	00 0010	B	01 0010	K	10 0010	S	11 0010
3	00 0011	C	01 0011	L	10 0011	T	11 0011
4	00 0100	D	01 0100	M	10 0100	U	11 0100
5	00 0101	E	01 0101	N	10 0101	V	11 0101
6	00 0110	F	01 0110	Ø	10 0110	W	11 0110
7	00 0111	G	01 0111	P	10 0111	X	11 0111
8	00 1000	H	01 1000	Q	10 1000	Y	11 1000
9	00 1001	I	01 1001	R	10 1001	Z	11 1001

Figure 1-26 Character codes.

Bits		Bits	
0	+	1	−
0 1 0 0 1 0	B	0 0 0 0 0 0	0
1 1 0 1 0 0	U	0 0 0 0 0 0	0
1 1 1 0 0 0	Y	0 0 0 0 1 1	3
1 1 0 0 0 0	□	0 0 1 0 0 1	9
0 0 0 1 1 0	6	0 0 0 1 1 1	7
1 1 0 0 0 0	□	0 0 0 1 0 1	5
0 1 0 1 0 1	E	0 0 0 0 0 0	0
0 1 0 1 1 1	G	0 0 0 0 0 1	1
0 1 0 1 1 1	G	0 0 0 0 1 0	2
1 1 0 0 1 0	S	0 0 1 0 0 0	8

Figure 1-27 Detailed bit patterns for two computer words.

For each group of six bits, 2^6 or 64 distinct combinations of zeros and ones are possible. In Figure 1-26 we have used up only 36 of the 64 combinations available with a 6-bit code. This leaves 28 additional combinations for other special symbols such as +, ≥, etc. We introduce one of these right now, namely, the blank space, □, which is coded as

1 1 0 0 0 0

With this code you can see that the 61-bit computer words displayed vertically in Figure 1-27 turn out to be

+	B	U	Y		6		E	G	G	S

and

−	0	0	3	9	7	5	0	1	2	8

From now on we will represent our computer words as strings of 11 characters instead of strings of 61 bits.

Here is a final remark about the coding of characters. In a number of modern computers eight, rather than six, bits are grouped for representing character codes, making it convenient to distinguish among a considerably larger set of characters than is the case in SAMOS. This distinction will, however, have no effect on the principles of character representation and manipulation that will be taken up in ensuing chapters.

1-6 ARITHMETIC AND CONTROL UNITS OF SAMOS

Now that we have seen how the SAMOS memory is structured, we will consider how the memory is used in executing an algorithm.

Our computer has several other components besides the memory. These are shown in Figure 1-28.

The solid lines indicate the directions in which values or instructions may be transferred. The dashed lines indicate the exercise of control.

The control unit and the arithmetic unit perform the duties of the "master computer" and his two helpers.

An important part of the arithmetic unit is the accumulator. This is a special computer word in which the result of each arithmetic operation is placed.

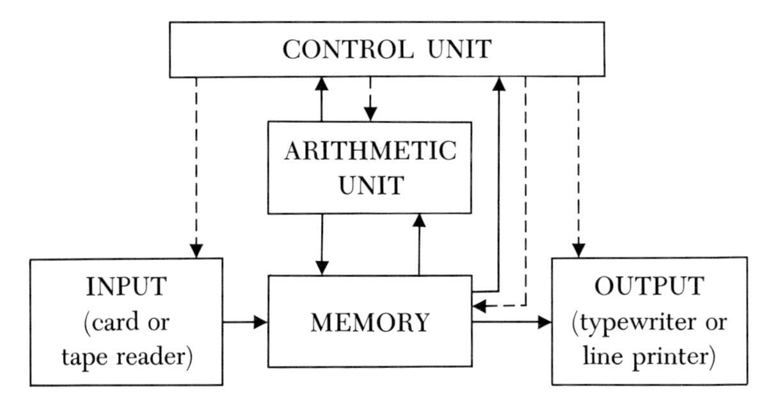

Figure 1-28 Schematic diagram of SAMOS.

Furthermore, a simple assignment like

→ LATEST ← SUM →

will be carried out by first obtaining a copy of the value of SUM, placing it in the accumulator, and then copying the value in the accumulator into the computer word belonging to the variable LATEST. The value of SUM is unchanged in this process. Notice that values to be input or output do not pass through the accumulator but go directly in and out of memory.

Each computer operation is activated as a result of the control unit receiving and interpreting an *order*. The orders are in the form of coded instructions that are stored in the computer's memory. We will learn something about that presently.

1-7 MACHINE LANGUAGE

Getting an algorithm into a form in which a machine can execute it involves several translations that may be depicted as follows:

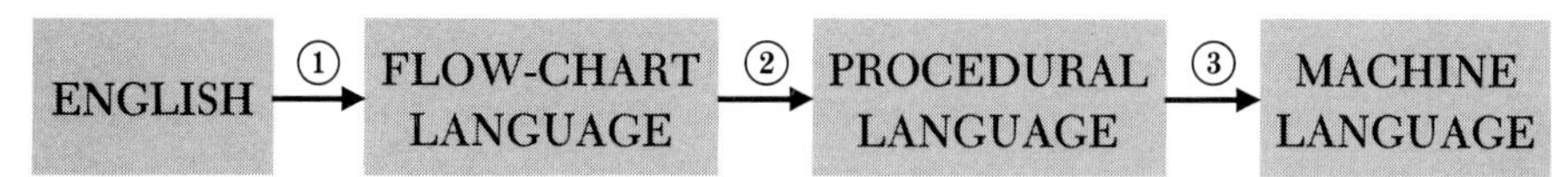

You have already had a little experience with the first translation step. The second translation step is the process of converting a flow chart into a procedural language such as FORTRAN, ALGOL, MAD, or PL/I.

You will learn how to do this in your language manual. Suffice it to say that this step is quite mechanical and can be performed by a person who has no idea what the algorithm is all about. The third translation process is completely mechanical and is done by the computer itself. This process is called *compiling.*

We don't need to know how compiling is done, but we do need to know the reason for doing it. Each make and style of computer has its own language—that is, its own set of instructions that it can understand. Use of a procedural language allows us to avoid a tower of Babel in which a programmer would have to learn a new language for each machine with which he wished to communicate. These procedural languages constitute a kind of "Esperanto," which enables a programmer to communicate with many different machines in the same language. Moreover, a procedural language is, generally speaking, far easier to learn to use than machine language. The programmer merely prepares, say, a FORTRAN program on punched cards and feeds it into the computer, which "compiles" a sequence of machine language instructions. This sequence, called a *machine language program,* is then placed in the computer's memory.

Sequencing of Computer Instructions

In our SAMOS computer these instructions will be placed in order in consecutively addressed locations in memory starting with 0000. After the computer has executed an instruction, the control unit will always obtain the next instruction from the next address, except when there is a branching instruction providing a different address for the next instruction.

To see how this works, consider the instruction taken from the Fibonacci sequence flow chart (Figure 1-10*b*), shown here in Figure 1-29.

$$\text{SUM} \leftarrow \text{LATEST} + \text{NEXT}$$

Figure 1-29 A flow-chart box.

The procedural language equivalent will not look much different. Thus, in FORTRAN this instruction would appear as

```
SUM = LATEST + NEXT
```

and in ALGOL as

```
SUM := LATEST + NEXT;
```

+	L D A	0 0 0	0 1 0 1
+	A D D	0 0 0	0 1 0 0
+	S T Ø	0 0 0	0 1 0 2

Figure 1-30 SAMOS instructions for Figure 1-29.

In the SAMOS machine language, these variables cannot be referred to by *name* but only by the *addresses* in memory associated with the variables. Suppose that NEXT, LATEST, and SUM have been given, respectively, locations 0100, 0101, and 0102. Then in the SAMOS language, the flow-chart instruction would take the form of a sequence of three machine instructions as shown in Figure 1-30.

These instructions have the form of 11-character words, but the first character is not used here and neither are the fifth, sixth, and seventh. The letters at the left of the instructions indicate the *operation* being performed, and the four-digit numerals at the right are *addresses*.

The letters LDA stand for "LoaD the Accumulator." The whole instruction means, "Copy the contents of the memory word addressed 0101 into the accumulator without altering the contents of address 0101." Clearly, this is the function of the reader in our conceptual model. We will not go into the details of the electronics involved in carrying out this instruction. It is sufficient to know that when the pattern of bits in the instruction

+	L D A	0 0 0	0 1 0 1

is brought to the control unit, certain switches are set by the control unit that allow a pulse current to pass through the cores of the word 0101. The magnetized cores effect an alteration of the current which, in turn, permits a copy to be made.

The second instruction in Figure 1-30 means, "ADD the value in the word addressed 0100 to the value already in the accumulator and place the result in the accumulator." The third instruction means, "Copy (or STØre) the number in the accumulator *into* the word addressed 0102." Executing a STØ instruction is analogous to the work of the assigner in our conceptual model. Times vary from machine to machine, but in modern computers, the time required for carrying out such instructions will usually be on the order of a millionth of a second.

A Complete SAMOS Program

We are almost ready to see how the entire flow chart for the Fibonacci sequence algorithm (repeated here in Figure 1-31) will emerge in SAMOS language. First, however, we note again that in the SAMOS language we can never refer to a number directly but only to a memory address in which this number may be found. This even applies to constants. Thus, part of the compiling process will involve providing memory addresses for the constants (as well as for the variables) appearing in the program. We assume that the addresses 0103, 0104, and 0105 have been set aside for the constants 0, 1, and 1000 appearing in the flow chart and that the proper values have already been put in the words with these

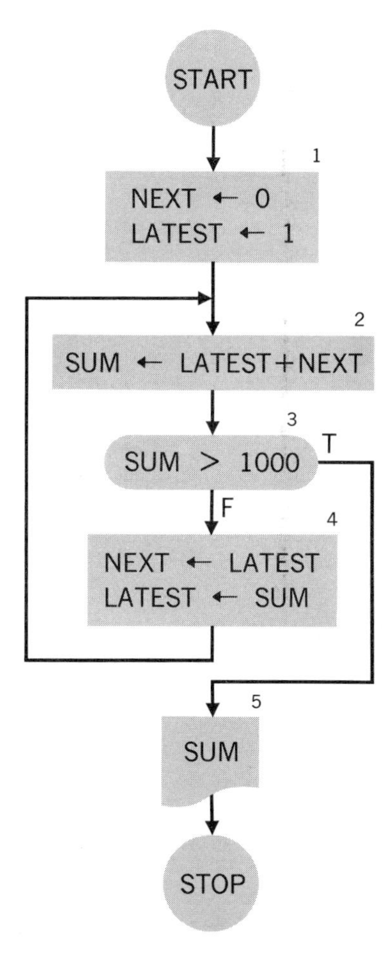

Figure 1-31 Fibonacci sequence algorithm.

addresses. We will also assume that the memory locations 0100, 0101, and 0102 have been allocated for the variables NEXT, LATEST, and SUM, but that no values have been placed in these words. The state of the memory at the beginning of the execution of the SAMOS program for the Fibonacci algorithm is shown in Figure 1-32. You will notice several new SAMOS operations not previously seen. These are explained in the following discussion.

MEMORY LOCATION (Address)	±	OPERATION						ADDRESS				FLOW-CHART EQUIVALENT
	1	2	3	4	5	6	7	8	9	10	11	← Character number
0 0 0 0		L	D	A				0	1	0	3	1a NEXT←0
0 0 0 1		S	T	Ø				0	1	0	0	
0 0 0 2		L	D	A				0	1	0	4	1b LATEST←1
0 0 0 3		S	T	Ø				0	1	0	1	
0 0 0 4		L	D	A				0	1	0	1	2 SUM←LATEST+NEXT
0 0 0 5		A	D	D				0	1	0	0	
0 0 0 6		S	T	Ø				0	1	0	2	
0 0 0 7		L	D	A				0	1	0	5	3 SUM>1000 T→ ↓F
0 0 0 8		S	U	B				0	1	0	2	
0 0 0 9		B	M	I				0	0	1	5	
0 0 1 0		L	D	A				0	1	0	1	4a NEXT←LATEST
0 0 1 1		S	T	Ø				0	1	0	0	
0 0 1 2		L	D	A				0	1	0	2	4b LATEST←SUM
0 0 1 3		S	T	Ø				0	1	0	1	
0 0 1 4		B	R	U				0	0	0	4	Arrow from flow chart box 4 to box 2
0 0 1 5		W	W	D				0	1	0	2	5 SUM
0 0 1 6		H	L	T								STOP
0 1 0 0												The variable NEXT
0 1 0 1												The variable LATEST
0 1 0 2												The variable SUM
0 1 0 3	+	0	0	0	0	0	0	0	0	0	0	The constant 0
0 1 0 4	+	0	0	0	0	0	0	0	0	0	1	The constant 1
0 1 0 5	+	0	0	0	0	0	0	1	0	0	0	The constant 1000

Figure 1-32 SAMOS program for Fibonacci sequence algorithm.

Discussion

The instructions in memory addresses 0004, 0005, and 0006 have already been discussed. Before looking at the other instructions, look first at memory locations 0100 through 0105 to see where the variables and constants are located.

From previous discussions you see that the instruction found at 0000 will, when executed, copy the value in 0103 (that is, the number 0) into the accumulator. Next, the instruction in 0001 copies (stores away) the value in the accumulator into the word with address 0100. Together these steps are equivalent to assigning 0 to the variable NEXT. Similarly, the instructions in addresses 0002 and 0003 are equivalent to assigning the value 1 to the variable LATEST.

Remember that the control unit executes the instructions in order until it comes to a branching instruction. The first of these branching instructions is found in address 0009, reading

	B	M	I				0	0	1	5

The code BMI stands for "Branch on a MInus." The whole instruction means, " If the number in the accumulator is negative, go to address 0015 for the next instruction; otherwise, go on as usual to the next numbered address (0010)." We will see shortly that the number in the accumulator at this time is just

$$1000 - \text{SUM}$$

so that the number in the accumulator will be negative only in the case that

$$\text{SUM} > 1000$$

In this case, the branching instruction sends us to address 0015 where we see the instruction

	W	W	D				0	1	0	2

which means, "Write the WorD in address 0102." This amounts to printing out the value of SUM.

Now why is it that when the instruction in address 0009 is reached, the number in the accumulator is

$$1000 - \text{SUM}$$

Well, on looking at the instruction in address 0007, we see that it instructs us to load the accumulator with the contents of 0105, that is, to put the number 1000 in the accumulator. The next instruction, the one in 0008, tells us to "subtract the contents of 0102 from the accumulator and put the result in the accumulator." Since the contents of 0102 are just the value of SUM, this amounts to the placing of

$$1000 - \text{SUM}$$

in the accumulator.

You should be able to verify for yourself that the instructions in addresses 0010 through 0013 accomplish the assignments indicated in the right-hand column.

The instruction in memory address 0014 needs to be described.

	B	R	U				0	0	0	4

BRU stands for "BRanch Unconditionally." The meaning of the entire instruction is, "Go back to memory address 0004 for the next instruction and continue in order from there." You can see that this corresponds to the arrow from flow-chart box 4 leading back to flow-chart box 2, where we again repeat the assignment

$$\text{SUM} \leftarrow \text{LATEST} + \text{NEXT}$$

The instruction in 0016, of course, stands for HaLT and amounts to stopping the computing process.

You can best understand all this by tracing through the SAMOS program by hand, keeping a record of the following details.

1. Which instruction is being executed.
2. The valuc in the accumulator.
3. The values in the memory locations 0100, 0101, and 0102 (the values of NEXT, LATEST, and SUM).

Notice that the contents of the instructions in addresses 0000–0016 are never altered nor are the contents of the locations 0103–0105 (the constants 0, 1, and 1000).

EXERCISE 1-7

Construct a list of SAMOS instructions for the flow chart in Figure 1-12. You will need two additional types of instructions. The first is

	OPERATION						ADDRESS			
1	2	3	4	5	6	7	8	9	10	11
	R	W	D				1	0	0	5

which is an instruction to read a number from a card into the computer word addressed 1005.

The second is

	M	P	Y				1	0	2	3

which is an instruction to multiply the number in the accumulator by the number in address 1023 and put the result in the accumulator. (Of course, in the address part of these instructions we may put any address we wish.)

1-8 FLOATING-POINT REPRESENTATION

Only a few of the ideas we have learned about SAMOS need to be remembered. Among these is the sequential nature in which the computer works, that is, the step-by-step way in which the computer performs its tasks. The order in which the tasks are performed is just as important as what it does.

Another property of computers that we must understand is the *finite word length.* We have seen that SAMOS words consist of ten characters and a sign, so that the largest number representable in this coding system is

$$+9{,}999{,}999{,}999$$

a rather large number but still finite.

You should be aware that there are other ways of coding numbers that allow us to work with numbers other than integers. One of the most common of these is *floating-point* form, which is related to the so-called "scientific notation."

To see how this works, recall that any decimal numeral such as

$$-382.519$$

can be expressed as

$$-.382519 \times 10^3$$

in which there is a decimal point (right after the sign, if any) followed by a nonzero digit multiplied by a suitable power of 10. We can code

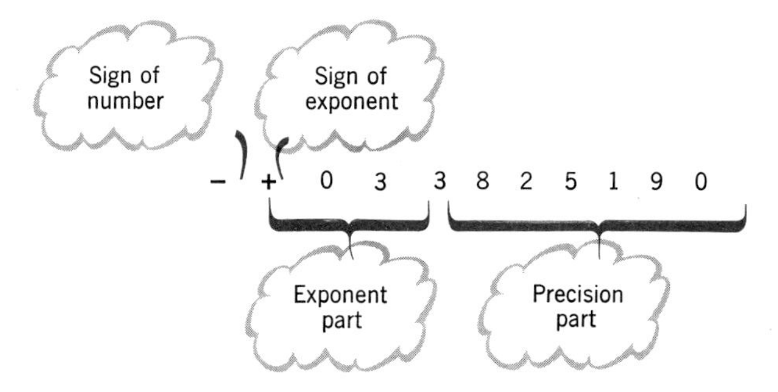

Figure 1-33 Anatomy of a SAMOS floating-point number.

numbers in this way in SAMOS by reserving three characters for the exponent. The result is shown in Figure 1-33.

Some examples of how numbers are coded in this system are given in Figure 1-34. In this figure, we see that the eight-digit representation of π in the top of the left-hand column has to be chopped down to seven digits of precision because of space requirements. The same holds true for 1/3 and 11/7 at the bottom of the table. Thus, we see that in a computer even such a simple fraction as 1/3 cannot be represented exactly, but only to a close approximation. This characteristic of "finite word length" presents important problems in computer work that will be discussed in various places in this text and in your companion language manual.

In this coding system we can represent large numbers, but we pay a

Number	Floating-Point Form	SAMOS Coding of Floating-Point Form										
3.1415926	$.31415926 \times 10^{1}$	+	+	0	1	3	1	4	1	5	9	2
−273.14	$-.27314 \times 10^{3}$	−	+	0	3	2	7	3	1	4	0	0
.0008761	$.8761 \times 10^{-3}$	+	−	0	3	8	7	6	1	0	0	0
.73	$.73 \times 10^{0}$	+	+	0	0	7	3	0	0	0	0	0
4	$.4 \times 10^{1}$	+	+	0	1	4	0	0	0	0	0	0
1/3	$.333333333 \times 10^{0}$	+	+	0	0	3	3	3	3	3	3	3
11/7	$.157142857 \times 10^{1}$	+	+	0	1	1	5	7	1	4	2	8

Figure 1-34 Floating-point coding of numbers.

price in giving up three places of precision. The largest number representable in floating-point form is

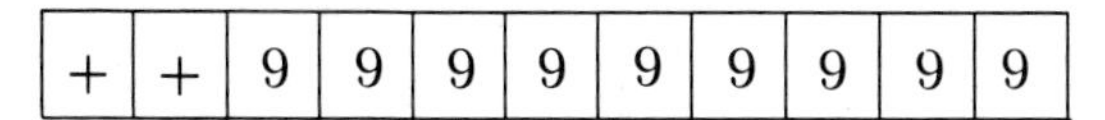

which represents the number

999,999,900,000,000,000,000,000,000,
000,000,000,000,000,000,000,000,000,
000,000,000,000,000,000,000,000,000,
000,000,000,000,000,000

Similarly, there is a smallest positive number that can be represented:

+	−	9	9	1	0	0	0	0	0	0

or

.000 000 000 000 000 000 000 000 000
000 000 000 000 000 000 000 000 000
000 000 000 000 000 000 000 000 000
000 000 000 000 000 000 1

which is very small, indeed.

CHAPTER 2

THE FLOW-CHART LANGUAGE

2-1 RULES OF "BASIC FLOW CHART"

In Chapter 1 we described a flow chart as a diagram for representing an algorithm. We may also view flow charts as constituting a language for expressing algorithms. As things stand now, our algorithms must still be translated into a procedural language before a computer can understand them. But the day may not be far off when algorithms written in the flow-chart language can be communicated directly to a machine.

Fortunately, the vocabulary and structure of the flow-chart language are much simpler than in Latin or French. Indeed, these rules can be learned in half an hour or less. What is more difficult is learning to use the language as an effective tool for expressing ideas. That will come only with practice.

Additional structures will be added to the language in Chapters 4 and 6 that will streamline and simplify the language. However, the components introduced in Chapter 1 already constitute a "basic flow chart" language in which any algorithm may be expressed, albeit somewhat inelegantly. It is the purpose of this section to discuss these components in a little more detail.

The flow-chart components presented in Chapter 1 were:

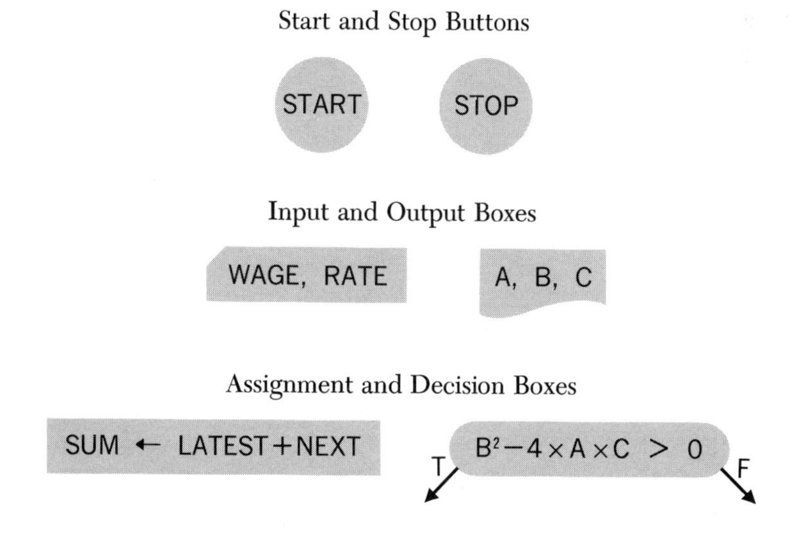

Let's start with the discussion of the assignment box.

The Assignment Box

The assignment instruction appearing inside an assignment box will always have the form

variable ← expression

The expression appearing on the right-hand side of the arrow may be a simple constant or a single variable, as in

K ← 35.29 or A ← B

Or the expression may be more complicated, as in

$D \leftarrow B^2 - 4 \times A \times C$

We cannot "assign" values to expressions. Thus, such an assignment instruction as

$B^2 - 4 \times A \times C \leftarrow 5$

would be invalid. (Since only variables have window boxes, the assigner would have no place to put the value 5.)

Similarly, we cannot assign values to constants. Thus, each of the assignment instructions

2 ← 3 and 2 ← 2

would be invalid.

Carrying out an assignment instruction involves a number of steps.

1. The current values of any variables appearing on the right-hand side of the arrow must be fetched from memory (the work of the "reader").
2. If the expression on the right-hand side of the arrow is more complicated than a simple constant or a single variable, then this expression must next be evaluated (the work of the "master computer").
3. The value of this expression must now be assigned to the variable on the left-hand side of the arrow (the work of the "assigner").

We must always keep in mind that assignment is destructive; that is, each time a new value is assigned to a variable, the former value of that variable is destroyed and no longer recoverable from the computer's memory.

It is important that we think of assignment as "the act of giving a value to a variable" and not as meaning "equals." To see why this is true, we consider the following assignment instruction, which is one of the most commonplace types of assignment instruction in all computer work:

N ← (N) +1

Surely this cannot be interpreted as meaning N = N + 1, which is nonsense. To see what this does mean, think in terms of our conceptual model. First, the master computer looks on the right-hand side of the arrow and sees the variable N:

N ← (N) +1

He sends the reader to fetch the value of this variable and adds 1 to it. Only now does he look at the left side of the arrow and finds that N appears here as well. So he sends the assigner to assign the computed value as the new value of N. Thus, for example, if the value of N was 7 before the execution of the instruction, then the value of N will be 8 after the execution.

Another thing to remember: the instructions

A ← B and B ← A

have quite different effects, even though they both result in

A = B

being true.

Variables and Expressions

As was mentioned in Chapter 1, in computing work as in mathematics we have considerable leeway in the symbols that may be used as variables. The following is a complete list of symbols that may be used as variables. These are single letters such as

A, B, K, N, Ø, X, Z

or descriptive combinations of letters such as

DIST, AREA, LENGTH, UGH

or strings of letters and digits *commencing with a letter* such as

A3, ANY6, Y365, R5C6

There are two principal reasons for enlarging our list of variables to include these strings. First, the list of symbols available to computers is usually limited to uppercase Roman letters. There are no Greek letters and usually no lowercase letters. We just do not have enough letters available for use as variables. Second, using a descriptive combination of letters as a variable is often very helpful in reminding us how the variable is being used.

We have a special attitude toward such unbroken strings of letters and digits starting with a letter. We regard them as being connected together to form a brand new symbol, somewhat like handwriting. We think of symbols above as being written as follows:

DIST *dist*
R5C6 *R5C6*

The above attitude applies only to strings of letters and/or digits commencing with a letter. Any such string of characters will be regarded as a variable unless there has been a specific statement to the contrary. From this point of view, an expression like XN is *not* considered to contain either of the variables X or N but rather to be a brand new symbol. In other words, we insist no variable should be considered to be part of another variable.

Following the conceptual model of a computer introduced in Section 1-3, we think of each variable as having a window box associated with it, with the value of the variable inside the window box (Figure 2-1). At any time *the variable is considered to be a name for the number that appears in its window box.*

Expressions (or arithmetic expressions) are written just as in the usual mathematical notation with one exception. We cannot write

AB

to denote the product of A and B, since the symbol AB would denote

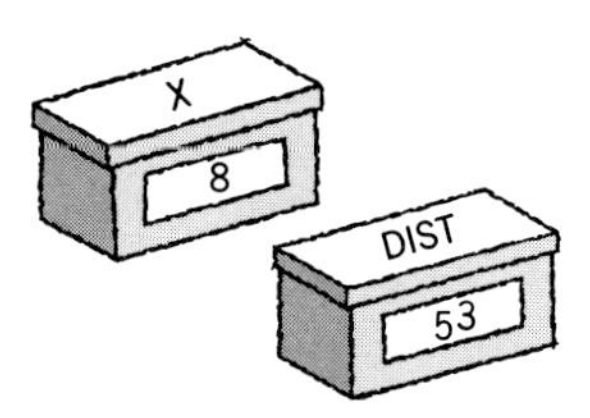

Figure 2-1

a single variable. *The multiplication operator must therefore always appear explicitly* so that the product of A and B must be written as

$$A \times B$$

Similarly, we write

$$3 \times Y$$

instead of 3Y.

The familiar expression

$$B^2 - 4AC$$

will be written as

$$B^2 - 4 \times A \times C$$

In the text we will always use $\times$ instead of $\cdot$ to denote multiplication and / instead of $\div$ to denote division, so that $A \div B$ will always appear as A/B. It is not mandatory that the student use these notations.

We will have more to say about arithmetic expressions in a later section.

The Decision Box

The contents of a decision box have the form of an assertion that a certain relation holds between the current values of two expressions as in Figure 2-2. The complete list of relations that may appear in place of $>$ in Figure 2-2 is

$$=, \neq, >, <, \geq, \leq.$$

(Some beginners are reminded here that the symbols $\geq$ and $\leq$ mean "greater than or equal to" and "less than or equal to," respectively.) Either or both of the expressions may have the form of a constant or a single

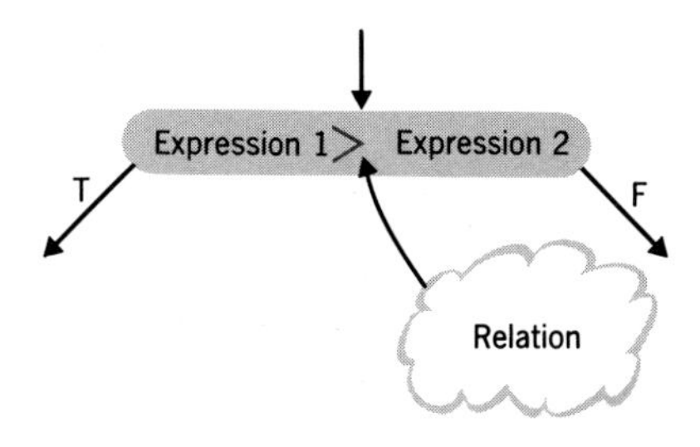

Figure 2-2

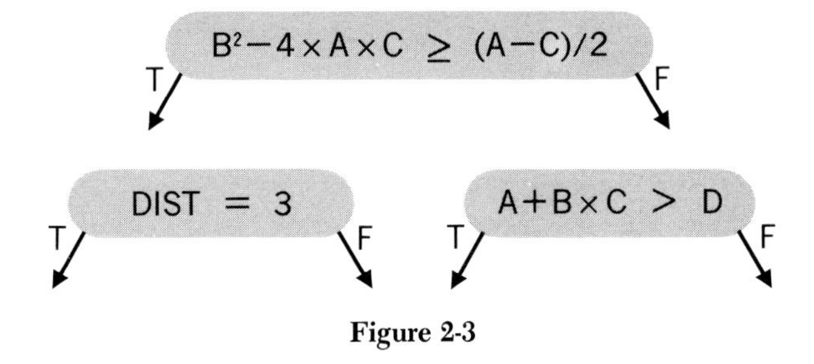

Figure 2-3

variable but, of course, more complicated expressions are also permitted. Examples of valid decision boxes are shown in Figure 2-3.

The steps in the execution of a decision box can be described as follows.

1. Read (or look up) the values of the variables appearing in the box.
2. Evaluate (if necessary) the expressions on either side of the relation using the values of the variables found in step 1.
3. Test the truth or falsity of the assertion appearing in the decision box.
4. Choose the appropriate exit path from the box depending on the result of the test in step 3.

We can see that reading from memory and evaluation are involved in the execution of a decision box, but assignment to memory is not.

Input and Output Boxes

The contents of input and output boxes take the form of a list of variables separated by commas:

N, A, B, C   N, SUM, AVG

Evaluation of arithmetic expressions is never called for in input or output boxes.

The *input box* is an instruction to read the values off the top card in a stack, assign these values to the indicated variables, and remove the card from the stack. (The values may be obtained from some input device other than punched cards, such as magnetic tapes, but we still use the same characteristic shape to denote input.)

We see that *execution of an input box involves the work of the assigner* but not the reader. (Remember that the reader reads values only from window boxes.) The assignment instruction found in an input box differs from the instruction found in an assignment box in that the values to be assigned come from outside the computer. We see that input is "destructive" of the former values of the input variables.

The *output box* is an instruction to read the values of the listed variables and print them out in the order listed by means of a line printer, typewriter, or other output device. *The work of the reader is involved* but not that of the assigner. Thus, output is nondestructive, as no variables have their values changed in the process.

PROBLEM 2-1

Two assignment instructions appear in a single assignment box, as shown below. Give a general criterion under which these instructions may be interchanged without altering the resulting values of any variables.

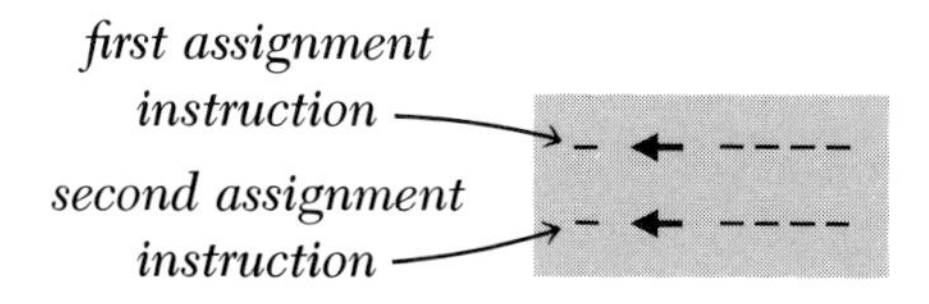

Hint. Consider the following five cases before you give your answer.

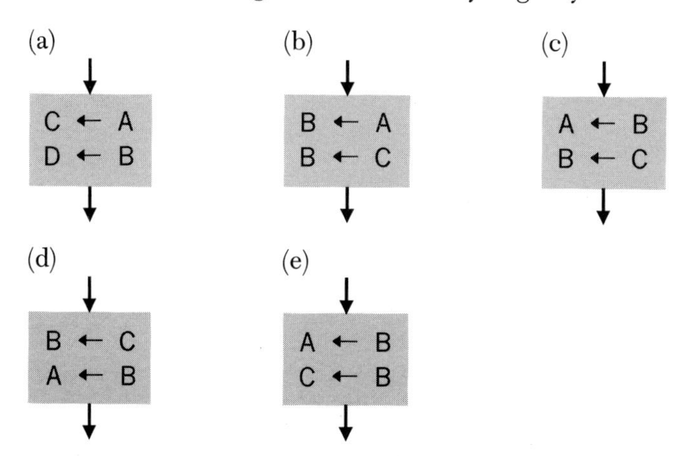

2-2 AN ILLUSTRATIVE EXAMPLE

Each year a nationwide "advanced placement" examination in mathematics is given to high school students wishing to receive college credit for college level math courses taken in high school. After the exam is graded, the grades are subjected to a lot of statistical analysis, such as computing the average grade. Since there are ten to twenty thousand students taking the exam, you can imagine that no one is very anxious to do this work by hand. Let's see how to write an algorithm to get a computer to do the job.

Suppose that the grades are punched on cards so that we will need an instruction to read grades into the computer's memory:

GRADE

In order to average a list of numbers, first find the sum of all the entries in the list and then divide this sum by the number of entries. Thus, we will need a variable N, which keeps a count of the number of grades read from the cards, and a variable SUM, which keeps a running total of these grades as they are received.

Each time we input a grade we will increase or *increment* the value of N by 1:

N ← N+1

(We have already seen the effect of this instruction in the preceding section.) We will also want to increase the cumulative sum by the amount of the grade just read from the card. The flow-chart box

SUM←SUM+GRADE

clearly produces a new value of SUM by adding the latest grade to the former sum—just what we want. We repeat these operations over and over, thus obtaining a loop as shown in Figure 2-4.

Let's see what happens to N the first time through this loop. The master computer first reads the value of N on the right side of the arrow—but N has not yet been given a value! This brings out an important point in computer algorithms. The first occurrence of a variable in a flow chart must be an *assignment,* either via an assignment box or via an input box. Accordingly, if a variable is to be assigned a new value, calculated in terms

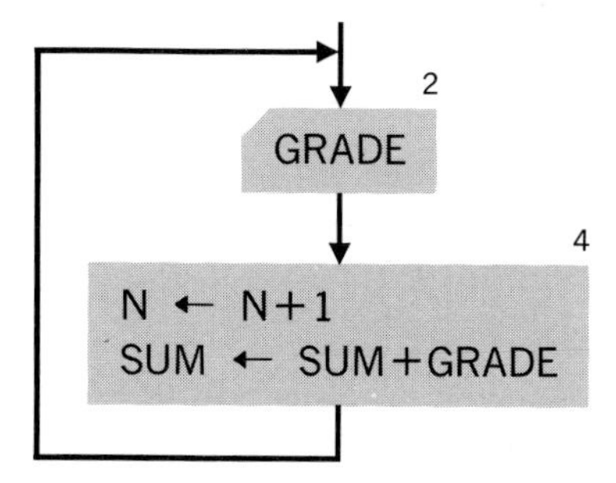

Figure 2-4 First attempt.

of the former value of the same variable, then this variable must previously have been given a "starting value" or "initial value." In the example above, this observation applies to SUM as well as to N. For both these variables the correct value, before any cards are read, is zero. Thus we have the improvement shown in Figure 2-5.

Remember that after this loop has been traversed for each data card, we want to compute the average grade:

AVG ← SUM/N

How can we get to this instruction? You might suggest that we do this

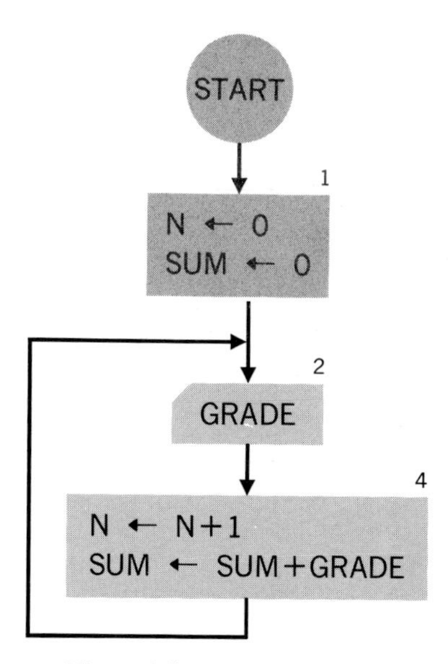

Figure 2-5 Second attempt.

when we run out of cards. Unfortunately, when a computer is instructed to read another card and finds none left, the control of the machine is usually taken away from the present user and turned over to the next person waiting to run a program. The moral of this story is that unless we are content to lose control of the machine when the cards are exhausted, we must provide an exit from our loop.

How can we do it in this case? We could, of course, count the number of cards and find that there are, say, 17,368 and handle the problem as shown in Figure 2-6*a* or we could resort to the common trick (explained below) shown in 2-6*b* and avoid counting the cards by hand.

The trick in Figure 2-6*b* is very commonly used; it works like this. We know that the maximum possible grade in the examination is 150. So we prepare a special card with a ridiculous value for the grade, say 999, and put this card at the end of our stack. Now all the legitimate grades will pass straight through the test in box 3, but when the phony card is reached, the test in box 3 will fail and the average will be computed. Since the test (box 3) was placed before box 4 rather than after, this "grade" will not be included in the count, nor will it be added into our SUM.

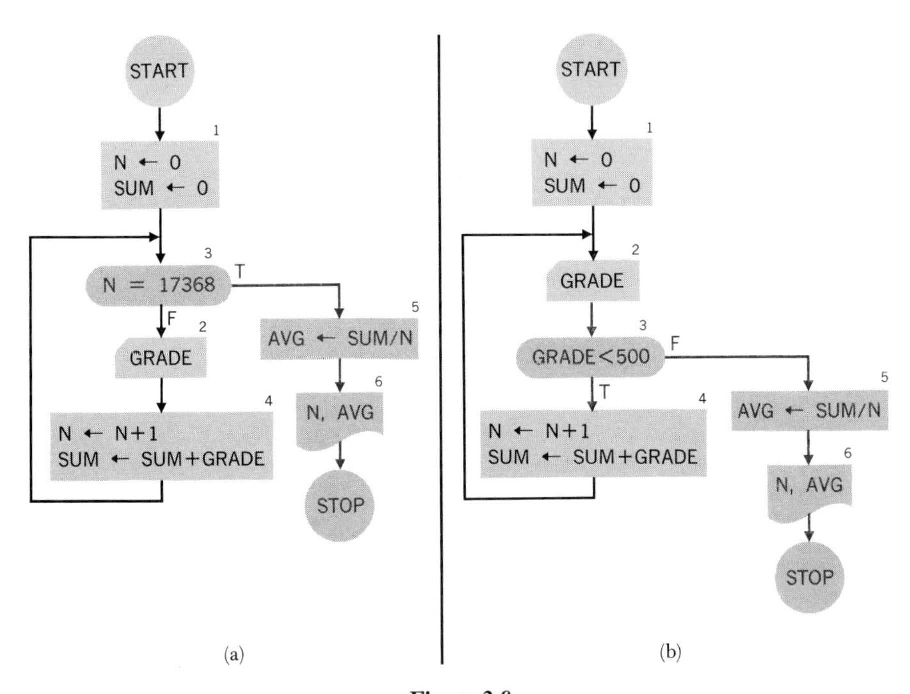

Figure 2-6

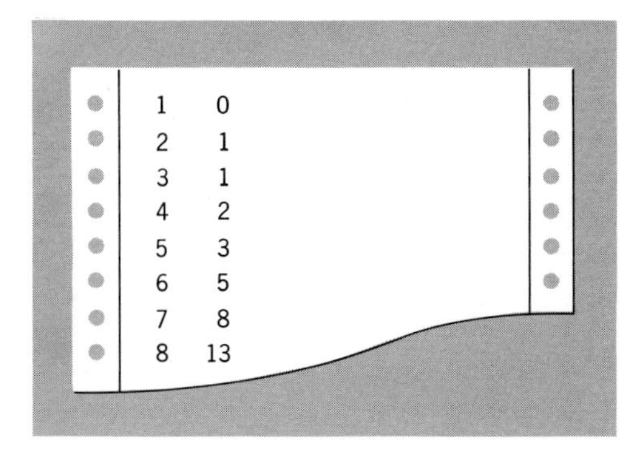

Figure 2-7

EXERCISES 2-2

1. Modify the Fibonacci sequence flow chart (Figure 1-10*b*) so as to print out all terms of the Fibonacci sequence that are less than 10 million. Also include the feature of having the lines of output consecutively numbered to look like Figure 2-7.

2. A teacher assigned his students the problem of constructing a flow chart as follows. The input consists of the lengths and widths of several rectangles. The purpose is to produce a list with consecutively numbered lines giving the length, L, the width, W, and the area, A, of only those rectangles with perimeter greater than 12. The flow charts shown in Figure 2-8 were submitted by students as solutions of the problem.

(a) Tell which of the solutions are correct and which incorrect. (For our purposes a correct solution is one that produces the required output. It may not be the most efficient solution, however.)

(b) For those that are incorrect, in what way will the answers produced be wrong?

(c) Study those that are correct for efficiency, and construct a flow chart using the most efficient features of each. (Of two programs, the one requiring the smaller number of calculations is the more efficient.)

3. According to U.S. Postal regulations, no box may be mailed if its length plus its girth exceeds 72 inches. (The girth is the length of the shortest string that will go all the way around the box.) A manufacturer has a large number of boxes that he wishes to mail. For each box he has a punch card with an I.D. number for the box and the three dimensions (the longest first) punched on it. Construct a flow chart for reading these cards and printing out the I.D. number and the length plus girth of each box failing to meet postal regulations.

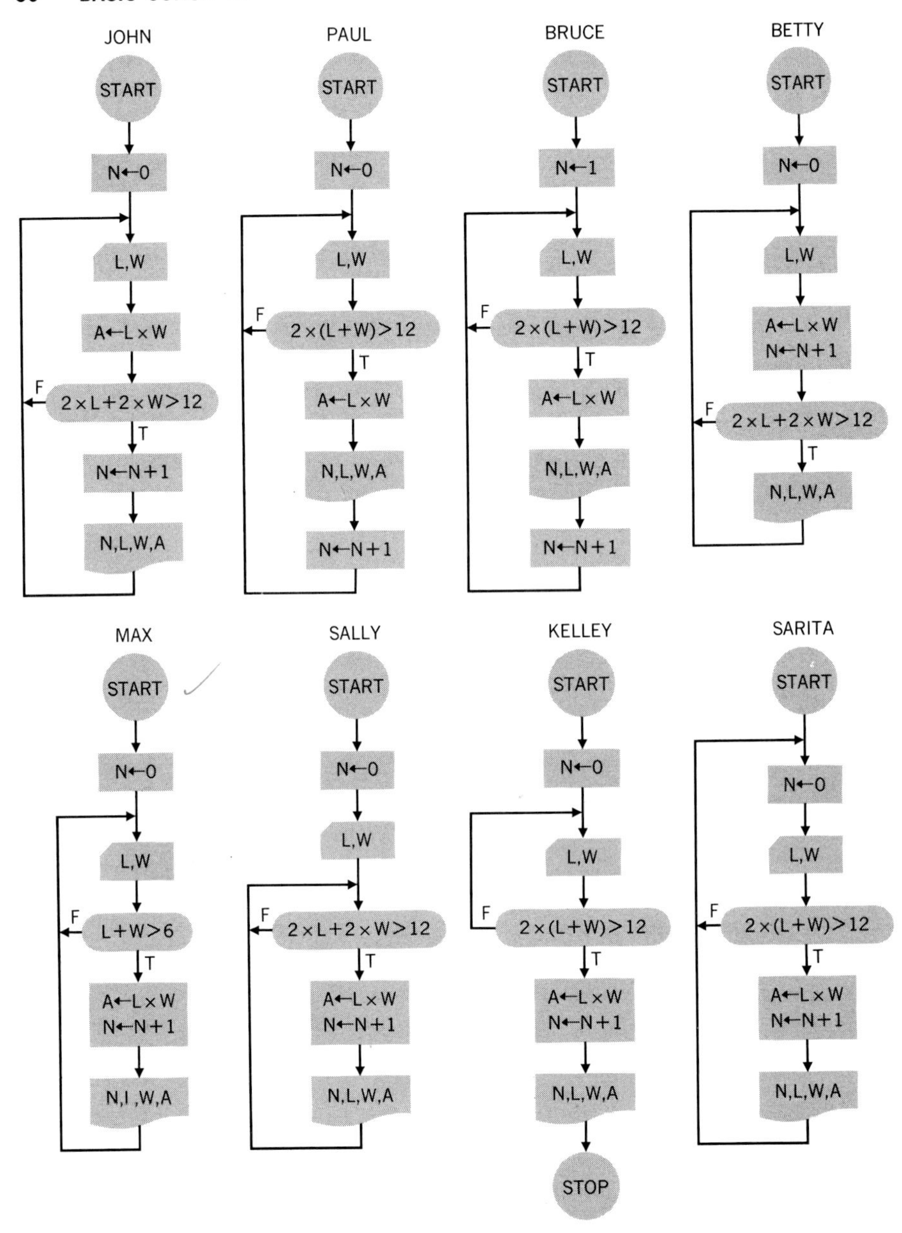

Figure 2-8

Pails of Water Problems

1. Suppose you are at a river with two pails, a five-quart pail and a nine-quart pail (no single quart markings on the sides). You can measure out four quarts by filling the five-quart pail from the nine-quart pail and emptying the five-quart pail back into the river.

(a) Your task is to make a flow chart that will output all numbers of quarts that can be measured by such back-and-forth pouring. You will need only one variable, T, which keeps a record of the total amount of water in the two pails. The value of T is altered each time water is dipped out of the river or poured back, but not when water is transferred from pail to pail. When T is less than 5, you will fill the nine-quart pail, thus increasing T by 9, while if T is greater than or equal to 5, you will empty the five-quart pail, thus decreasing T by 5. Output each value of T obtained. Don't forget to initialize T with the value 0. Stop when the value of T returns to 0. The flow-chart structure is indicated in Figure 2-9. All you have to do is fill in the boxes.

(b) Make a partial trace of your completed flow chart, just listing the values of T in the order in which they are output. What value of T is missing in this output? How can the flowchart be modified to eliminate this flaw?

2. Modify the flow chart of Problem 1 to output with each value of T, the number of fillings of the nine-quart pail and emptyings of the five-quart

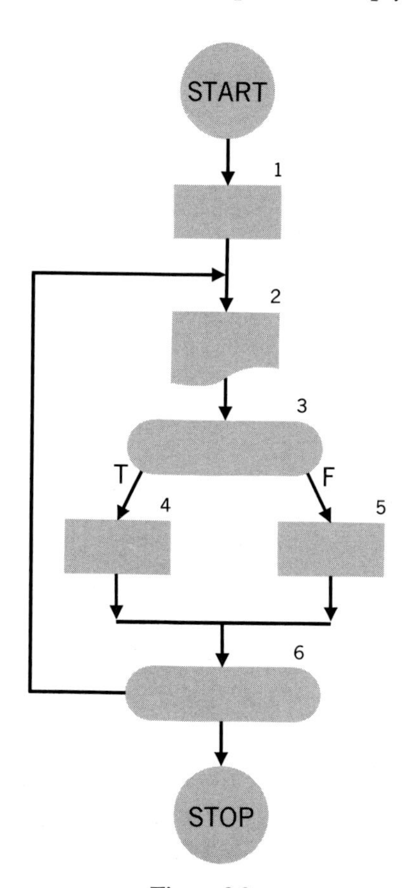

Figure 2-9

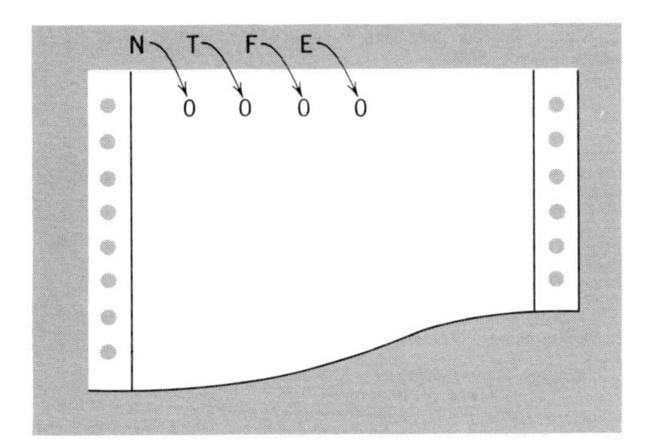

Figure 2-10

pail required to get this value of T. You will need to introduce two new variables F and E. Be sure to initialize them.

3. Modify the flow chart of Problem 2 so that it will work with any whole number of quart capacities (A and B) for the two pails. Fill the A quart pail and empty the B quart pail. Be sure to provide for the input of A and B. Also introduce a variable N that numbers the lines of output starting with 0 so that the first line of output will have the form that is shown in Figure 2-10.

4. Trace the flow chart of Problem 3 (just giving the lines of output) for the following pairs of input values of A and B.

(a) A = 7, B = 10 (c) A = 54, B = 36

(b) A = 10, B = 7

5. In connection with Problem 4, explain why the following relations always hold.

(a) N = F+E (b) T = F×A−E×B

2-3 ARITHMETIC EXPRESSIONS

As seen in earlier sections, the basic calculations done by a computer consist of the evaluation of arithmetic expressions found in assignment boxes and decision boxes. As an example of such an arithmetic expression, consider

$$\frac{-b + \sqrt{b^2 - 4ac}}{2a}$$

which is familiar from the quadratic formula. This ordinary mathematical notation might be acceptable in our informal flow-chart language, but it is not at all satisfactory for a procedural language such as FORTRAN or

ALGOL. In such procedural languages the expressions must be written in such a form that they can be punched on a card and read by a machine. To make this expression machine readable, several alterations are necessary, as discussed below. The various programming languages will handle these problems differently. The solutions we propose are merely possibilities.

1. We have already observed that our conventions regarding variables render it impossible to continue the practice of using juxtaposition to represent multiplication. Thus, "4ac" would have to be written as "4 × a × c" and "2a" as "2 × a". Some languages use symbols other than × for the multiplication operator. The important idea here is that the multiplication operator must appear explicitly.

2. The introduction of special symbols to represent particular functions complicates the process of machine reading. Thus, we could introduce some such suggestive letters as SQRT to replace $\sqrt{}$ and write

$$\text{SQRT}(\text{B}^2 - 4 \times \text{A} \times \text{C}) \qquad \text{for} \qquad \sqrt{\text{B}^2 - 4 \times \text{A} \times \text{C}}$$

Similarly, instead of $|\text{R}|$ we could write ABS(R), especially in a language whose alphabet does not contain the vertical bar.

How would the computer know that SQRT and ABS denote functions and not variables? The reason is that they are followed by left parentheses. We must therefore always be careful to enclose function arguments in parentheses and write, for example, SIN(X) instead of SIN X.

3. Many procedural languages do not have lowercase letters in their character sets. For these, the variables a, b, and c would have to be replaced by some other variables, most likely A, B and C. (If A, B, and C are already used in your program, then you might, for example, use LCA, LCB, and LCC standing for "lowercase A," etc.)

4. In order to be read by a computer, an arithmetic expression must be written as a linear string of symbols. Off-the-line notations, such as B^2, are unacceptable. Thus, we will have to introduce an operator, such as ↑, to represent exponentiation and write B↑2 instead of B^2.

Also, the division by 2a was represented above by an off-the-line notation. We will have to give up this commonly used "fraction" notation and use the slash "/" as the division operator.

With all these changes made, our quadratic formula expression would have the form

(−B+SQRT(B↑2−4×A×C))/(2×A)

Although the changes were slight, the aggregate of all the changes produces an expression that looks quite foreign to us. It is hard to recognize it at first glance as the quadratic formula. Because these expressions look unfamiliar, we must be especially careful to avoid mistakes.

Notice that when we shifted from fraction notation to slash notation for division, two additional pairs of parentheses had to be included, one pair embracing the numerator of our fraction and one pair embracing the denominator. Were either pair of parentheses omitted, our expression would not be evaluated correctly. For example, if the parentheses around 2 × A were omitted, then the resulting expression would have the meaning of

$$\frac{-B+\sqrt{B^2-4AC}}{2} \times A$$

Good advice concerning parentheses is, "If in doubt whether parentheses are necessary, put them in."

The question as to whether parentheses are necessary or not can be answered by consulting the precedence rules for performing operations in the absence of parentheses. These rules conform with the usual mathematical conventions in this regard (where such conventions exist). For example, as you well know, in evaluating the expression

$$A + B \times C$$

with the values of the variables being $A = 5$, $B = 3$, $C = 2$, multiplication takes precedence over addition and we first multiply B times C and add A to the result. Thus,

$$A + B \times C = A + 3 \times 2 = A + 6 = 5 + 6 = 11$$

If we want A and B to be added first, then we must include the parentheses, thus,

$$(A + B) \times C$$

In evaluating this expression, we obtain

$$(A + B) \times C = (5 + 3) \times C = 8 \times C = 8 \times 2 = 16$$

The complete table of precedence levels for arithmetic operations is found in Table 2-1.

TABLE 2-1 Precedence Levels for Evaluating Parenthesis-Free Expressions

Level		Operation Name	Operator Symbol
High ↑	First	Exponentiation	↑
	Second	Multiplication Division Taking the negative	× / − (unary)
↓ Low	Third	Addition Subtraction	+ − (binary)

The Minus Sign

Before showing how the table works, we must explain the two occurrences of the minus sign. There are actually three ways in which the minus sign is used in mathematics.

1. To indicate the *binary* operation of subtraction as in

$$X - 5$$

2. To indicate the *unary* operation of taking the negative as in

$$-X$$

3. As part of the name of a negative number as in

$$-5$$

In the expression

$$X - (-(-5))$$

Binary *Unary* *Number naming*

the minus is seen in all three roles, as indicated. The three uses of minus are all handled differently by the computer. Why doesn't this lead to confusion? Only because the role of the minus can always be determined from the way it occurs in the expression. A minus is binary unless it occurs at the beginning of the expression or immediately after a left parenthesis. If the minus occurs in one of these positions, then it is *number naming* if the next symbol is a digit or a decimal point, and unary otherwise.

The Evaluation Process Using the Precedence Table

The main purpose of this illustration is to show how evaluation of arithmetic expressions can be made into a mechanical process performable by a machine.

To see how a computer could use the precedence table in evaluating expressions, cast yourself in the role of the master computer. First you scan the expression *from left to right* for operators of the first level. When you find an operator of this level, perform the operation it indicates and resume scanning at the point where you left off. When all operations of the first level have been performed, repeat the left-to-right scan for operators of the second level, etc. (Actual computers are usually equipped with compilers which obtain equivalent results without all this repeated scanning.)

Here is an example to show how all this works out.

Example. The expression is

$$-A \times L - G \times O \uparrow R / I + T / H \times M$$

Here we tabulate the values of the variables:

A	L	G	O	R	I	T	H	M
5	6	8	2	3	4	6	2	7

Table 2-2 shows the step-by-step evaluation process. Little triangular marks (▲) are used to indicate the operator to be dealt with next.

This scanning procedure is the heart of the evaluation process. We finish the description of evaluation by telling what to do with expressions containing parentheses. A *subexpression* is the part of an expression included between a pair of parentheses. For example, in

$$(A \times C - D) \times E$$

we see that

$$A \times C - D$$

is a subexpression. General rules are given in Table 2-3.

(*Note.* Parentheses surrounding a constant should be deleted if possible. Undeletable parentheses surrounding a negative constant but not preceded by a function name should be ignored. That is, the negative constant together with its surrounding parentheses are to be treated as a numerical constant.)

TABLE 2-2 Display of Step-by-Step Evaluation

Step Number	Action	Appearance of Expression After Each Step	Remarks
	Initial Expression	−A×L−G×O↑R/I+T/H×M ▲	
1	Compute O↑R	−A×L−G×8/I+T/H×M ▲	No more level 1
2	Compute −A	−5×L−G×8/I+T/H×M ▲	Leading minus is *number-naming*
3	Compute −5×L	−30−G×8/I+T/H×M ▲	
4	Compute G×8	−30−64/I+T/H×M ▲	
5	Compute 64/I	−30−16+T/H×M ▲	
6	Compute T/H	−30−16+3×M ▲	
7	Compute 3×M	−30−16+21 ▲	No more level 2
8	Compute −30−16	−46+21 ▲	
9	Compute −46+21	−25	

TABLE 2-3 Rules for Evaluating Arithmetic Expressions with Parentheses

1. Scan the expression from left to right for first right parenthesis ")".
2. Evaluate the subexpression ending with this right parenthesis according to the rule for parenthesis-free expressions (Table 2-1).
3. If this subexpression is a constant, see whether it is preceded by a function name, and if so, compute the indicated functional value.
4. Return to step 1.

A Deviation From Mathematical Convention

There is only one place where our rules for the order of evaluation are not in conformity with usual mathematical conventions. Consider an expression of the form

$$A^{B^C} \qquad \text{or (in our notation)} \qquad A\uparrow B\uparrow C$$

What is the value, for example, of

$$2^{3^3}$$

It can be either 512 or 134,217,728, depending on how parentheses are inserted. The rule we have given would evaluate

A↑B↑C   in the order   (A↑B)↑C

In mathematics, however, the convention is that

A↑B↑C   means   A↑(B↑C)

Or, in more usual notation,

$$A^{B^C} \qquad \text{means} \qquad A^{\left(B^C\right)}$$

Be sure you are aware of this discrepancy. You can always force your intent by use of parentheses.

Reading Expressions into Computer Memory

Once an arithmetic expression like

$$\frac{-b + \sqrt{b^2 - 4ac}}{2a}$$

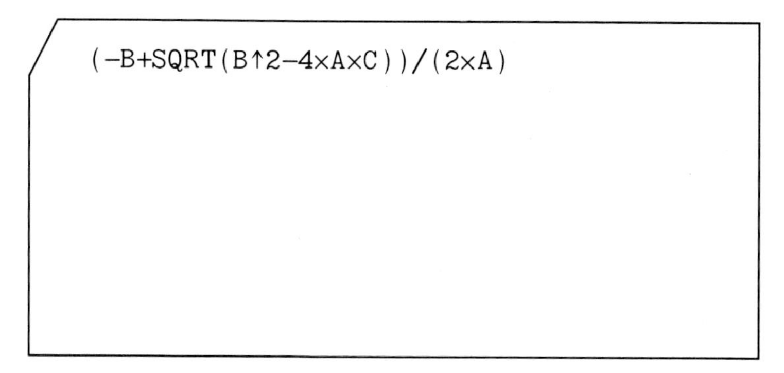

Figure 2-11 Punch card with arithmetic expression.

has been properly represented as a string of characters, such as

$$(-\mathrm{B}+\mathrm{SQRT}(\mathrm{B}\uparrow 2-4\times \mathrm{A}\times \mathrm{C}))/(2\times \mathrm{A})$$

it can be punched on a card as suggested in Figure 2-11[1] and stored in the computer's memory ready to be broken down into a list of machine-language instructions.

A string of symbols such as the one shown above is much too long to be stored in a single word of memory. Instead, it will be stored in consecutively addressed words of memory, perhaps at one character to a word, perhaps at several characters to a word, as shown in Figure 2-12.

When we speak of the computer scanning an expression, we will mean that the expression, originally punched on a card or transmitted by some other input medium, is examined one character at a time from the locations in memory where it is stored. The scan proceeds character by character, word by word, until the last character has been examined.

EXERCISES 2-3

If you are a student in a computer course, this is a good place to stop and experiment a little with the computer and with the computer programming language you may be learning in the laboratory phase of this course. One set of rudimentary experiments could concern the evaluation of expressions like

[1] In actual fact, most available key punches do not have keys for the ↑ and × characters. Generally, a "transliteration" is used. For example, the ↑ character is commonly represented by ** (double asterisk obtained using two key strokes) and the × symbol by * (single asterisk).

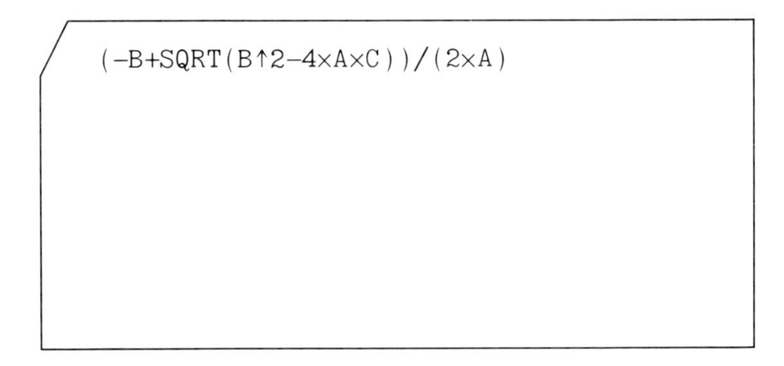

addresses

0101	0102	0103	0104	0105
(	−	B	+	S
0106	**0107**	**0108**	**0109**	**0110**
Q	R	T	(	B
0111	**0112**	**0113**	**0114**	**0115**
↑	2	−	4	×
0116	**0117**	**0118**	**0119**	**0120**
A	×	C	)	)
0121	**0122**	**0123**	**0124**	**0125**
/	(	2	×	A
0126	**0127**	**0128**	**0129**	**0130**
)				

(a) Characters stored one per word of memory.

0055	0056	0057
(−B	+SQ	RT(
0058	**0059**	**0060**
B↑2	−4×	A×C
0061	**0062**	**0063**
))/	(2×	A)□

(b) Characters stored three per word of memory.

0023
(−B+SQRT(B
0024
↑2−4×A×C))
0025
/(2×A)□□□□

(c) Characters stored ten per word of memory (as possible in SAMOS).

Figure 2-12 An expression in memory.

$$-A \times L - G \times O + R / I + T / H \times M$$

or

$$(-B + SQRT(B \uparrow 2 - 4 \times A \times C)) / (2 \times A)$$

For example, you might use a simple type of computer program characterized by the flow chart in Figure 2-13. The purpose of the experiment would be to determine how close are the printed values for R1 and R2 when box 4 is executed. You might experiment further by changing the order in which operations of equal precedence are carried out in the assignment steps of box 3.

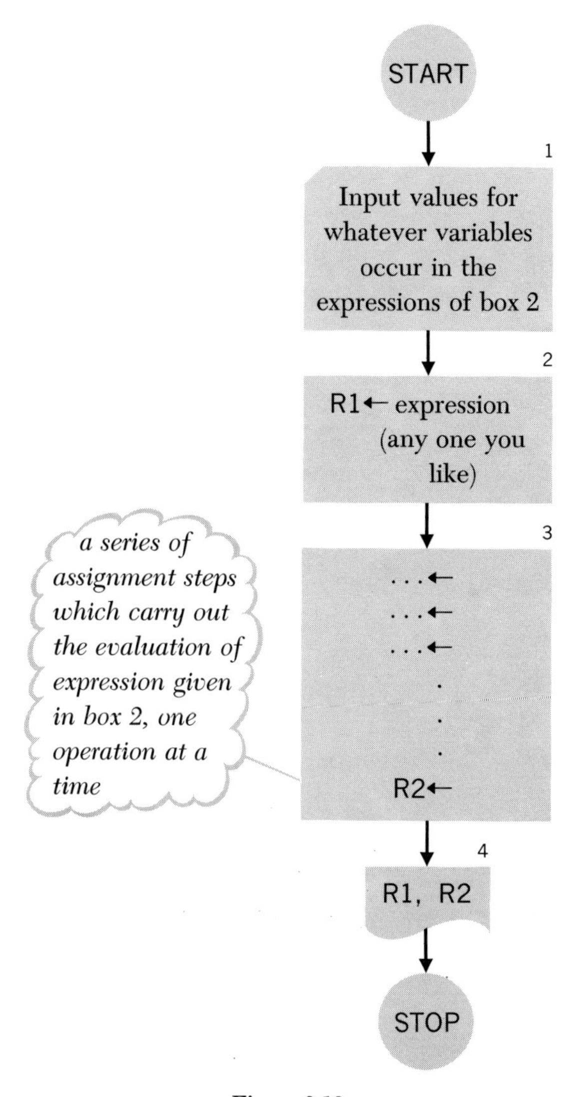

Figure 2-13

2-4 ROUNDING

You have learned several different ways of representing numbers. For example, if asked to express the quotient of 125 and 8, you could write the answer in any of these forms:

$\frac{125}{8}$	$15\frac{5}{8}$	15.625	$.15625 \times 10^2$
Fraction	Mixed number	Decimal	Floating-point

All these answers are equally correct; which form you choose depends on the use to which you intend to put your answer. Generally speaking, however, only the floating-point form is conveniently represented in a computer like SAMOS. But for our discussion here, we will suppose the decimal form, which can be regarded as a variant of the floating point, is the way such numbers are represented in SAMOS. We will not make any distinction here between decimal form and computer notation.

If we replace the problem discussed above by that of finding the quotient of 125 and 7, we would have

$\frac{125}{7}$	$17\frac{6}{7}$	17.8571428
Fraction	Mixed number	Decimal

Here, the first two forms are exact representations of the quotient, but the decimal form (the one used by the computer) is only approximate. The reason for this is that our process of grinding out successive digits in the quotient cannot be allowed to go on forever and must eventually terminate.

$$
\begin{array}{r}
1\;7.\;8\;5\;7\;1\;4\;2\;8\;5\;7\;1 \\
7\,\overline{)\;1\;2^5 5.^6 0^4 0^5 0^1 0^3 0^2 0^6 0^4 0^5 0^1 0}
\end{array}
$$

The same holds true for the computer. The number of digits a computer will carry in the solution to such a division problem depends on its "word length." In our SAMOS computer with its eleven-character word length, the solution to this division problem would be stored as

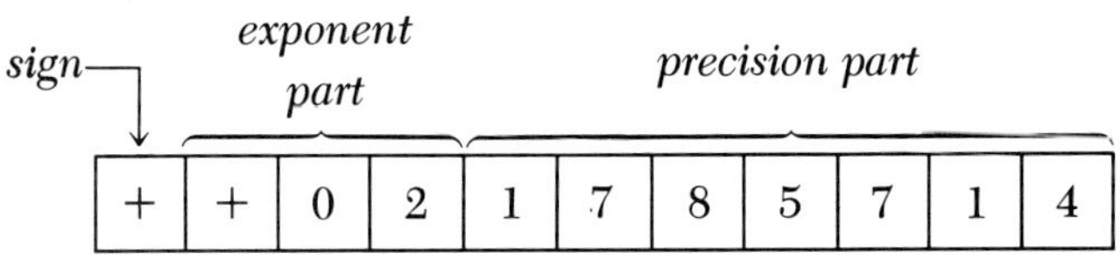

sign	*exponent part*			*precision part*						
+	+	0	2	1	7	8	5	7	1	4

which, you may recall from Chapter 1, means

$$.1785714 \times 10^2$$

which is equal to

$$17.85714$$

We see, then, that in SAMOS (as in all computers) numbers calculated are *rounded* to a certain number of digits of precision. You may feel that 17.85714 is close enough to 125/7 "for all practical purposes," but there are some dangers inherent in this attitude, as will be seen in Chapter 5. In that chapter it will also be seen that rounding may occur in connection with all arithmetic operations, not only with division.

What You Used to Know About Rounding

We are all inclined to think of rounding as a sort of anomaly—something to apologize for—certainly not a mathematical process. And yet there is a large class of problems in which rounding is absolutely necessary in order to get the correct answers! For an example of such a problem, let's pass backward in time to the fourth grade level.

> *Problem.* A playground director found a sack containing 125 marbles in his desk and decided to distribute them equally among the eight boys on the playground. How many marbles did each boy get?

In order to solve this problem, you would first divide 125 by 8, obtaining

$$15\tfrac{5}{8} \qquad \text{or} \qquad 15.625$$

You know that this is not yet the right answer, since the playground director will not smash up any marbles into eighths in order to distribute them in this way. (If he is wise, he will also make it a point to give all the boys the same number of marbles.) What he will do is to "round-off" the number $15\frac{5}{8}$ obtained by division and give each boy 15 marbles. The 5 leftover marbles he will quietly return to his desk.

Back at the fourth-grade level, we had no difficulty in finding the answer 15, since the method of "integer division" we used in those days gave this answer directly. Our work looked like this:

$$\begin{array}{r|l} & 15 \\ \hline 8 & 125 \\ & \underline{8} \\ & 45 \\ & \underline{40} \\ & 5 \end{array}$$

We then said that "each boy gets 15 marbles with 5 left over."

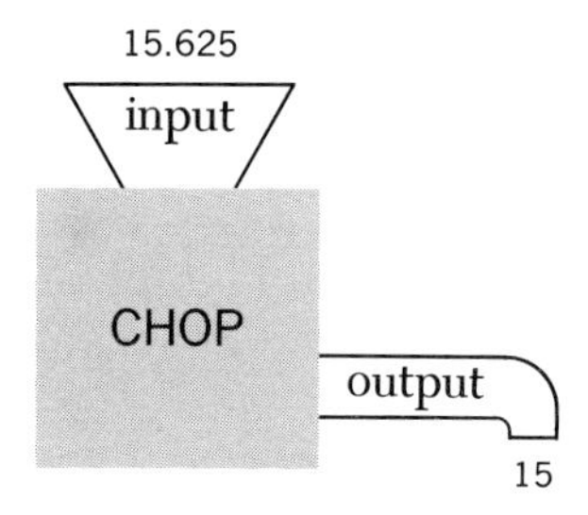

Figure 2-14

From the fourth-grade viewpoint, this "integer division" process for dividing N by D consisted of finding integers Q and R so that

$$N = D \times Q + R \qquad \text{with} \qquad R < D$$

This is the *division algorithm* of elementary school arithmetic. The method of finding Q and R is one of repeated subtraction and is easily flowcharted.

The process by which the playground director got the answer 15 from the quotient 15.625 can be viewed as being performed by a mathematical function, CHOP (Figure 2-14). We may think of CHOP as a machine that accepts real numbers as input and outputs whole numbers.

In functional notation, the fact represented in this picture may be expressed as

$$\text{CHOP}(15.625) = 15$$

(If you are unfamiliar with this notation or the concept of a function, look ahead to Section 6-2 where these ideas are discussed in detail.)

To understand the behavior of CHOP, we note that every real number is composed of a whole number part and a fractional part. When a number is put into the input hopper of the function, CHOP, the fractional part is lopped off and the whole number part is returned as the output value. Thus,

$$\text{CHOP}(-17.68) = -17 \qquad \text{CHOP}(\pi) = 3$$
$$\text{CHOP}(7\tfrac{3}{4}) = 7 \qquad \text{CHOP}(-\tfrac{14}{3}) = -4$$
$$\text{CHOP}(29) = 29 \qquad \text{CHOP}(-537) = -537, \text{ etc.}$$

There are several reasonable integer rounding processes, and the CHOP function carries out one of them.

Now we can see that Q and R in the division algorithm can be expressed in the form

$$Q = \text{CHOP}\left(\frac{N}{D}\right) \qquad R = N - D \times \text{CHOP}\left(\frac{N}{D}\right)$$

Frequently, in our flowcharting, we will wish to make such tests as

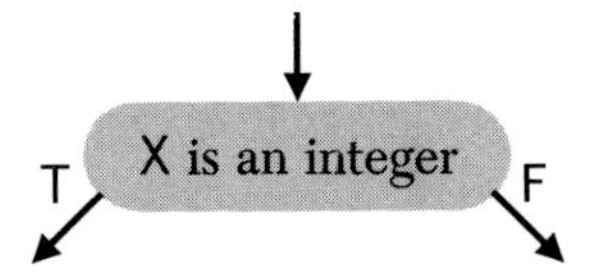

The CHOP function enables us to rewrite this test as

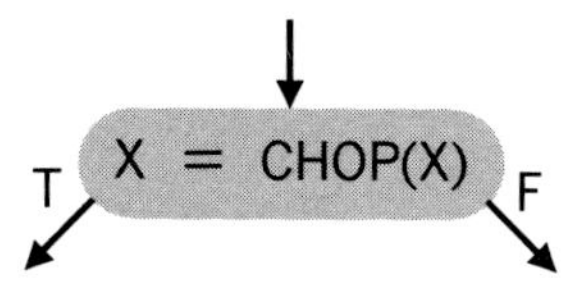

The statement in this box is true only in the case that X has an integer value.

This same CHOP function can be used in rounding to a certain number of decimal places. For example, if we wish to round

$$23.84627$$

to two decimal places to get

$$23.84$$

this can be accomplished according to the following recipe.

1. Multiply the number to be rounded by 100:

$$100 \times 23.84627 = 2384.627$$

2. Apply the function CHOP to the result:

$$\text{CHOP}(2384.627) = 2384$$

3. Divide this result by 100:

$$\frac{2384}{100} = 23.84$$

This is called "rounding by chopping to two decimal places" and is described by the expression

$$\text{CHOP}(100 \times X)/100$$

Similarly, chopping X to three decimal places is accomplished by

$$\text{CHOP}(1000 \times X)/1000$$

Fifth Grade Rounding

In the fifth grade, in your work on measurement, you were often asked to round your measurements to "the nearest whole number of inches." Thus, a measurement of $15\frac{5}{8}$ would be rounded to 16 rather than 15 inches.

We can think of another integer rounding function called ROUND, which does this job for us. The effect of ROUND can be defined in terms of CHOP. That is (for positive values of X),

ROUND(X)=CHOP(X+.5)

For example:

ROUND(15.625) = CHOP(15.625+.5) = CHOP(16.125) = 16

If the value of X is negative, then we must subtract .5 before applying CHOP. The flow chart in Figure 2-15 covers both uses. The output value of Y is ROUND(X).

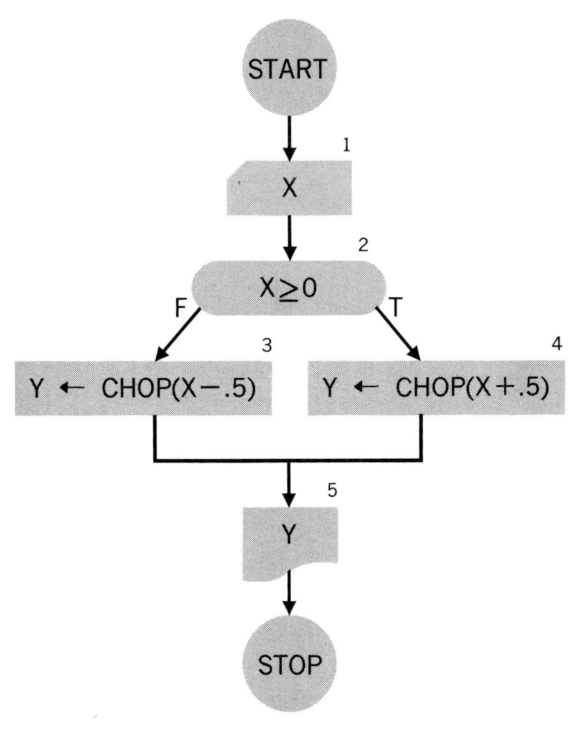

Figure 2-15

We may also ROUND to a given number of decimal places as we did with CHOP. The formula for ROUNDing X to the nearest thousandth is

$$\text{ROUND}(1000 \times X)/1000$$

Thus, 17.68479 rounded to three decimal places is

$$\text{ROUND}(1000 \times 17.68479)/1000 = \text{ROUND}(17684.79)/1000 = 17685/1000 = 17.685$$

A Final Warning

We must remember that all computer calculations are rounded by chopping or by some other method to produce results that will fit into a computer word. From a mathematical viewpoint, it is convenient to consider that the computer makes the exact calculation followed by the application of some rounding function.

In our flow-chart language we will normally not take the effect of rounding into account but will act as though all calculations were exact. But before translating our flow charts into programming languages, we will often find it expedient to replace condition boxes like

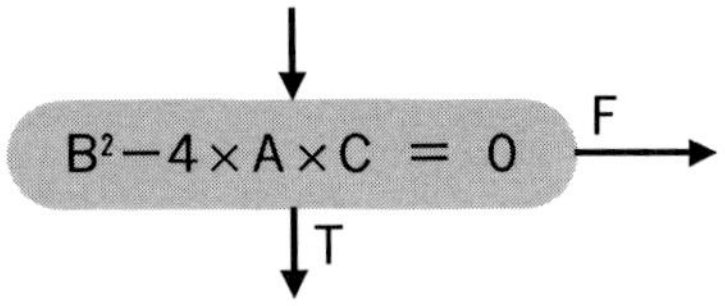

$$B^2 - 4 \times A \times C = 0$$

F →
T ↓

by approximate forms such as

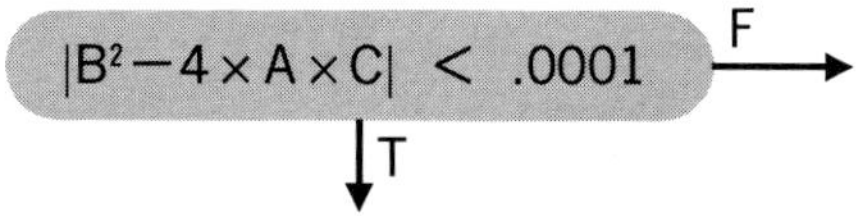

$$|B^2 - 4 \times A \times C| < .0001$$

F →
T ↓

EXERCISES 2-4

1. A camp director wishes to divide the boys into baseball teams. Give a formula involving one of the rounding functions, CHOP or ROUND, giving the number of teams as a function of NBOY (the number of boys). No boy is to be on more than one team, and each team is to have nine players.

2. It costs 10¢ an ounce to send an airmail letter. Draw flow-chart steps to represent evaluating the cost of sending an airmail letter as a function of the (real) variable WT. Use either CHOP or ROUND.

3. A and B are four-digit positive integers. You are given the flow chart in Figure 2-16.

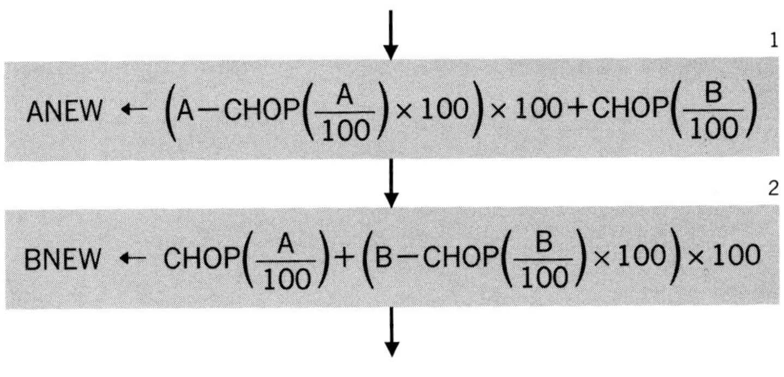

Figure 2-16

(a) If the value of A is 1468 and the value of B is 2357, then what is the value of ANEW after executing box 1?

(b) For the same values of A and B, what is the value of BNEW after executing box 2?

4. Draw a flow chart that describes the following process. A series of data values are input, one value at a time. The computer prints a two-digit number that consists of the lowest-order two digits of each input value. A series of positive integers is available as data, one data value per input record (i.e., one value per data card).

5. Draw a flow chart that describes the following process. Values are read two at a time. A new number consisting of the high-order two digits of the first number and the low-order two digits of the second number is formed and printed. The process is repeated for the next pair of numbers, etc. A series of four-digit positive integers is available as data.

6. Study the sequence of flow-chart boxes in Figure 2-17.

These boxes are intended to represent a series of computations involving only integers (i.e., no reals). Assume that prior to executing box 1, the value of T is that of an eight-digit positive integer.

(a) What is the maximum value of R1 after executing box 1?

(b) What is the maximum value of S after executing box 3?

(c) Someone observes that the effect of executing boxes 1 through 3 is that of an "extraction" process, i.e., that the value assigned to S is an "extract" of T. Explain what specific extraction process is performed.

7. Determine the values of ROUND(x) when x is an odd multiple of 1/2.

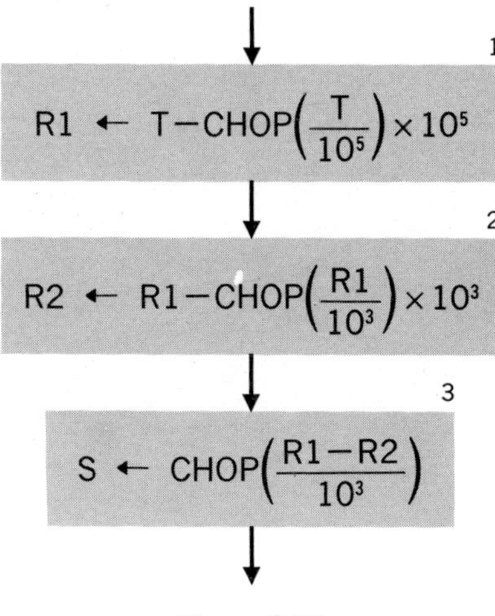

Figure 2-17

8. A game wheel shown in Figure 2-18 is divided into five equal sectors numbered consecutively from 1 in a clockwise manner as shown. There is a spinner that rotates on a shaft mounted at the center of the wheel.

Let S be the sector pointed to by the spinner at rest. We now flick the spinner with our fingers in a clockwise direction. It spins through m sectors and comes to rest inside a sector, i.e., not on a line.

(a) Write a formula involving one of the rounding functions that gives you the new sector number NEWS in terms of the original rest position S and the spin span M.
(b) Generalize the formula developed in part *a* of this problem to the case of a game wheel having k sectors numbered consecutively from 1.
(c) Draw the flow chart steps needed in arriving at NEWS computed in *a* that would be applicable for spins in either the clockwise or the counterclockwise directions.

Figure 2-18

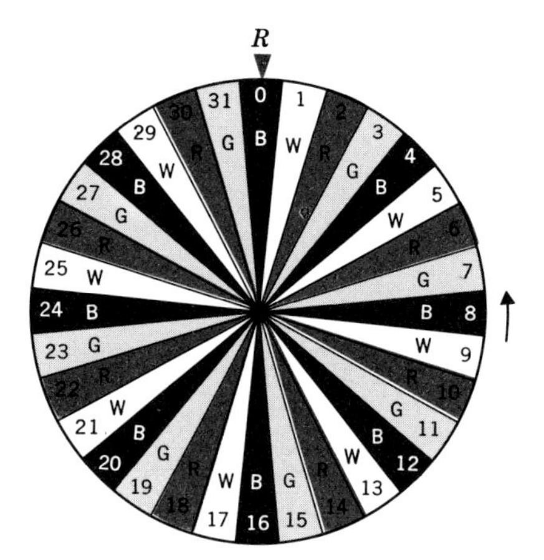

Figure 2-19

9. The carnival wheel shown in Figure 2-19 has 32 painted sectors numbered clockwise, s = 0, 1, 2, . . . , 31. The sectors are divided into 8 groups, 4 sectors per group. In each group, the sectors are painted black, white, rust, and gray (B, W, R, and G) going clockwise.

When the wheel is spun (always counterclockwise) and comes to rest, the color of the sector opposite the fixed pointer, R, tells how the game comes out.

Suppose the rule is

Player loses 30 points for black
Player loses 10 points for white
Player wins 10 points for rust
Player wins 30 points for gray

Also suppose that, before any one spin, the wheel is considered to be at rest with sector number s opposite the ratchet R. We now imagine that the wheel is spun a distance of m sector positions. How many points p will be won or lost for each data pair s and m? How can we develop a simple algorithm that simulates repeated plays at the wheel?

Hint. Your flow chart should show a loop beginning with a step for the input of s and m, one or more assignment boxes to compute p, an output statement to print p, and a return to the input step. One way to compute p is first to compute the *new* sector number s *after* the spin, in terms of the given (or old) s and m. Then we can compute the position k (= 0, 1, 2, or 3) within the group—corresponding to black, white, rust, or gray, respectively. (Actually, it is simpler to compute k directly from m and the old s without first computing the new s.) To simulate repeated spins, return to the input step after printing p.

2-5 ALPHANUMERIC DATA

In Section 2-3 we learned that computers are able to read and store alphabetic letters and special characters in the words of memory. Coupling this fact with the six-bit character code we learned about in Section 1-5, it becomes clear that characters like 1, 4, 7, or T, X, N, or like *, /, or) can each be stored (one or more per word of memory) as a particular combination of six bits.

In the SAMOS type of computer, bit patterns that represent decimal integers are necessarily identical with bit patterns for strings that consist of the same digits. Thus, the integer 14 and the string "14" would both be coded as 000001000100. This coincidence does not hold, however, in a typical *binary* type computer. Such computers may very well use character codes that are the same as for SAMOS, but integers are coded in the binary system. Thus, the integer 14, if represented with 12 bits, would now appear as 000000001110. Using such a computer, if we mistakenly interpreted the bit coding for "14" (namely, 000001000100) as that of an integer, we would get 68. A useful conclusion can be drawn. Although both characters and numerical values may be coded for storage in any word of memory, we should avoid assuming that any special relation exists between the bit patterns for numerical values and the bit patterns for strings of characters.

How do these facts relate to our flow-chart language? Well, for one thing, we can see that a window box stores characters as well as numbers (Figure 2-20). In other words, a variable X can have a value that is not numerical at all but *alphanumerical*. By alphanumerical, we shall mean

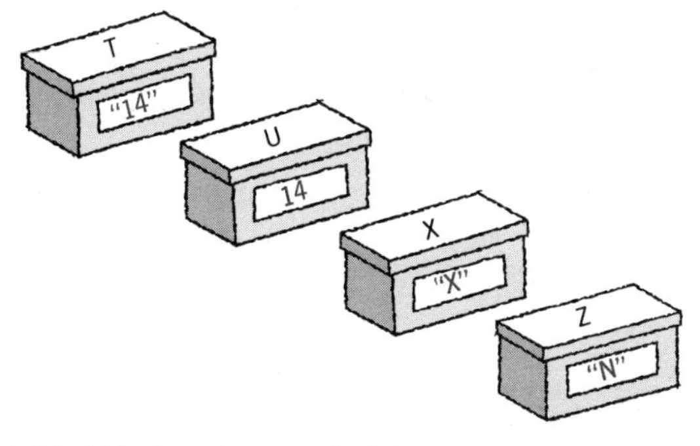

Figure 2-20 Window boxes with alphanumeric and numeric values.

a value consisting of some collection of letters, digits, and special characters such as those discussed in connection with Figure 1-26.

Exactly how many characters can be stored in one window box depends on the size of the box, that is, the memory word size. Since we are not dealing with any one computer here, we will not be too specific. Let us just say that a window box can store a string of "several" characters. We will leave it to your language manual or your laboratory instructor to be more specific on this point.

If a variable can have an alphanumeric value, it must be able to acquire this value the same way it can acquire a numerical value, namely, as a result of input or as a result of an assignment step. Having once acquired an alpanumeric value, it must also be possible to output it by an output step.

It appears that our input, output, and assignment boxes allow us to describe computer procedures for doing things with alphanumerical data as well as numerical data! To illustrate this point, Figure 2-21*a* shows a very simple flow chart with input data consisting of names, one per card, and with a list of name pairs as the printed results.

What will we find in the window box with the letter A on its cover before and after box 4 is executed for the first time? To answer this, we will step through the process from the beginning.

When box 1 is executed, the four letters, "MUTT", are read from the card and assigned to the variable A. Next, box 2 is executed causing "JEFF" to be assigned to the variable B. At box 3, values of A and B are printed. When we arrive at box 4, we see that A still has the value "MUTT". But after box 4 is executed, the current value of B (which is "JEFF") will have been assigned to A. To answer our original question, A has the value "MUTT" before the first execution of box 4 and the value "JEFF" after. If you're wondering about the third card in the stack, it got there by mistake, but we deliberately left it in to illustrate how the algorithm takes it in stride.

We have been using quotation marks when we refer to alphanumerical values like "MUTT" in a flow chart or in a sentence. The quotation marks would probably not actually appear on the data cards (see Figure 2-21*b*). They certainly will not appear around printed alphanumerical values (see Figure 2-21*c*).

In exactly the same way as with numerical constants, we can have alphanumerical constants and can assign the value of such a constant to a variable. The parallel is illustrated in Figure 2-22.

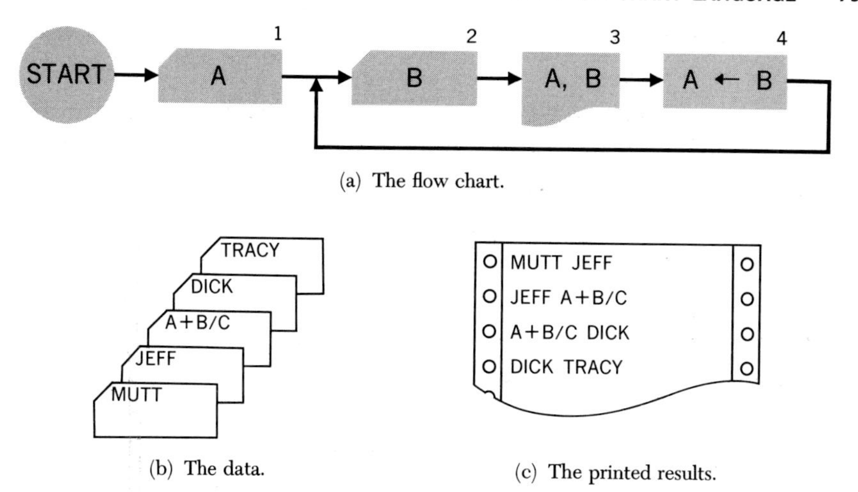

(a) The flow chart.

(b) The data.

(c) The printed results.

Figure 2-21 A questionable process.

Example *a* shows a "conventional" assignment of a constant value to a variable. Example *b* shows an assignment of the character string "BLUEFIN" to the variable FISH. Any quantity in quotes is to be regarded as an alphanumerical constant.

The parallel with numeric values has come to an end. More complicated expressions to the right of the assignment arrow will, for the time being, be considered meaningless and will not be permitted. For example,

FISH ← 2 × "BLUEFIN"

or

FISH ← "BLUEFIN"+"REDFIN"

is, as far as we are concerned, meaningless.

Only two forms of alphanumeric assignment are allowed:

variable ← variable

and

variable ← alphanumeric constant

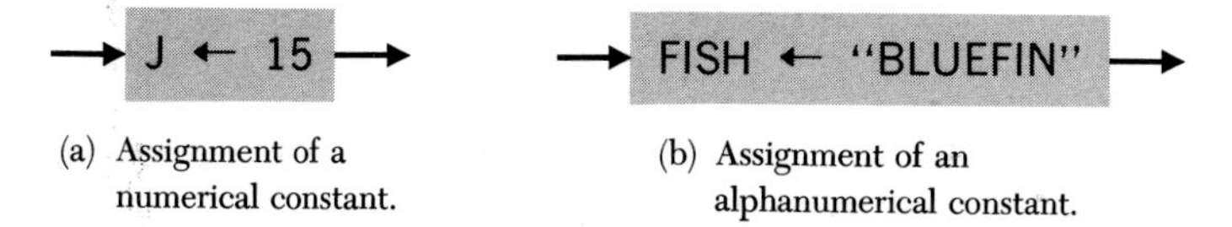

(a) Assignment of a numerical constant.

(b) Assignment of an alphanumerical constant.

Figure 2-22 Two kinds of assignment.

It should also be clear that the following are *invalid:*

NUMBER ← 2+"4"

or

PRODUCT ← "5" × "5"

Now suppose we are carrying out the following input step of a flow chart.

A data card like the following one arrives in position to be read.

How do we specify in our flow-chart language whether it is to be read as a number or as an alphanumeric symbol? The answer is this. If any box in the flow chart contains an operation on the data that can be performed *only* on numbers, then the value on the card *must* be read as a number, but if there are no such operations, then you may choose *either way* to read it. However, before the card is read, this decision must already have been made. There is no ambiguity when the card arrives in position to be read.

Let us look at some examples of input and output of symbols and numbers to illustrate this thought. First, suppose we have the flow chart shown in Figure 2-23, for the input of two values, X and Y, and the output of their sum, Z.

Two different data cards are presented for input, as shown in Figure 2-24. If the first card is read, everything works perfectly. The output for input values of 4 and 3 is 7.

If the second card is read, what happens? Something is obviously wrong because we cannot add "R" to "T". A perfectly valid flow chart, when used with data that can be interpreted as numerical, becomes utterly meaningless for data that is clearly *not numerical.*

Next let us look at a second flow chart (Figure 2-25), which inputs two

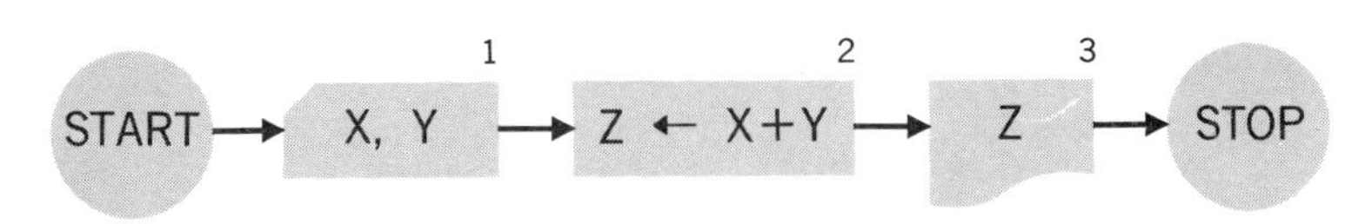

Figure 2-23 First flow chart.

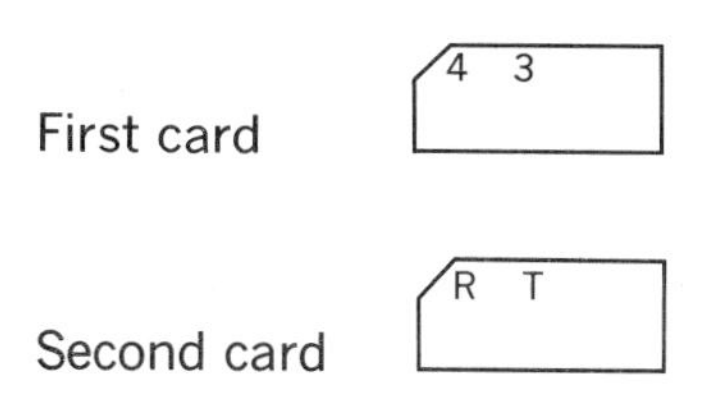

Figure 2-24 Two data cards.

values X and Y, assigns Y to Z and then prints the values of X, Y, and Z. If we present the first card as input, there is no problem. The computer prints three values, "4", "3", and "3". If we present the second card as input, there is again no problem. The computer prints three values, "R", "T", and "T".

Here then is a flow chart that is meaningful whether the data is numerical or alphanumerical. When you look at the first flow chart (Figure 2-23), you can clearly say it is intended to work on numerical values only, or in other words, that the window boxes for X, Y, and Z are to store numbers only. Box 2 alerts you to this crucial fact. But if you look at the flow chart in Figure 2-25, you cannot say which type of value is to be stored in the window boxes.

We see, then, that the flow chart alone will not always make clear what kind of data is to be assigned to each of the variables. If you feel this is intolerable, we could agree to "flag," in our flow charts, those input variables to be treated alphanumerically. For instance, in Figure 2-25 we could revise box 1 as follows, putting a little notch under each variable of the input list whose input value is to be treated as alphanumerical:

1

→ X, Y →

On the other hand, you may be willing to live with the situation as it is because:

(a) In this case (Figure 2-25), it simply doesn't matter.
(b) In an actual computer programming language like FORTRAN or

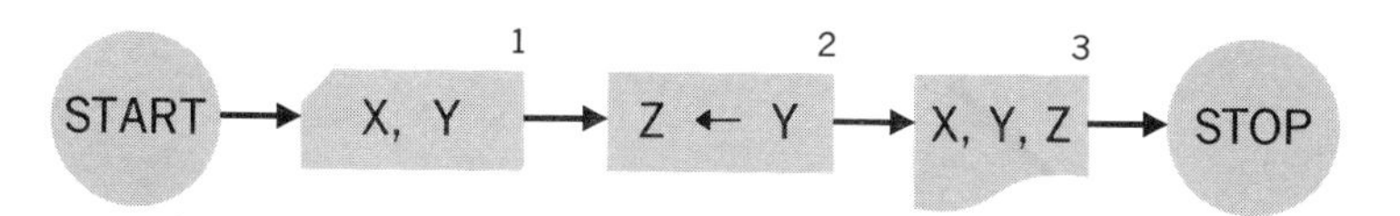

Figure 2-25 Second flow chart.

ALGOL, simple steps are taken to remove such ambiguities. You will understand this when you consult your language manual.

In any event, remember to use quote marks around numerals or character groups when you mean them to be character groups, as in

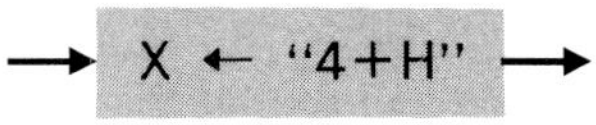

→ X ← "4+H" →

or

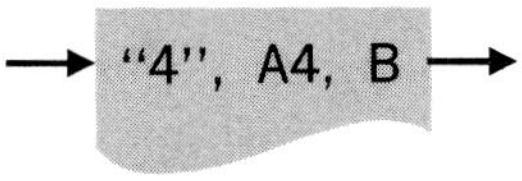

→ "4", A4, B →

CHAPTER 3

ADDITIONAL FLOW-CHART CONCEPTS

3-1 PROBLEM SOLVING—SOME SIMPLE EXAMPLES

The construction of algorithms and their flow charts is essentially a problem-solving process. In order to teach problem solving, we must proceed in a manner quite different from the one to which you are accustomed. It is not adequate merely to present the straightforward development of an elegant flow chart. We must instead show how the final solution was evolved by its creator. You must see how we choose a place to start on a problem. You must see some of the false starts and oversights, some of the awkward algorithms we obtain on our first attempts. Above all, you must learn that in constructing algorithms, we first attempt to get some kind of a solution of the problem—good or bad. Then we look at our solution critically, trying to find ways to improve it. Trying to draw the best flow chart on your first attempt can lead to confusion and exasperation. (Some programmers may tell you that they always get the best algorithms the first time. Don't believe them!)

Finding the Largest of Several Numbers

Consider the problem of inputting values for A and B, determining which value is the larger, and outputting the larger value. This problem may seem trivial, but it occurs over and over again as part of more complicated algorithms. In Figure 3-1 we see one solution of this problem.

The message inside the quotes is to be printed out just as it stands, while the variables will have their values printed out. Thus, the output from this flow chart would have some such form as is shown in Figure 3-2.

Each word message is just a single element of the output list and must be separated from the variables by commas.

Let's try to generalize this method to find the largest of three numbers. We see that whichever is the larger of A and B must now be compared with C. Thus, we have the flow chart in Figure 3-3*a*.

By now perhaps you get the feeling that things are not going too well. Each time we increase the number of values to be compared, we add another row of decision boxes twice as long as the preceding row. Thus, if we wanted to find the largest of five values, we would have

$$1 + 2 + 4 + 8 = 15$$

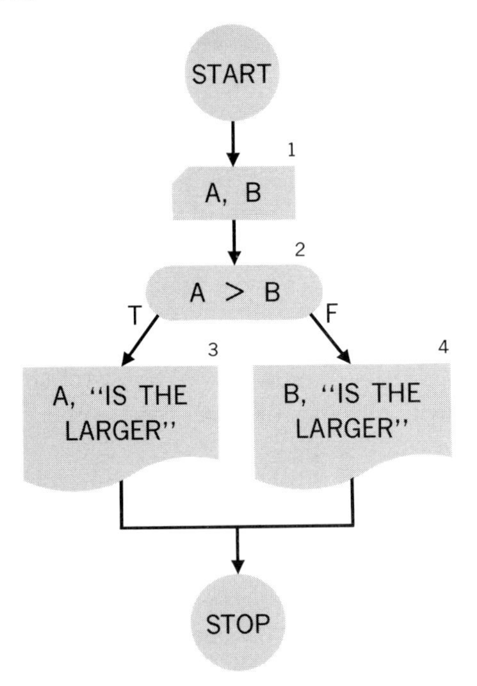

Figure 3-1 Larger of two numbers.

decision boxes; the largest of eleven values would require

$$1 + 2 + 4 + 8 + 16 + 32 + 64 + 128 + 256 + 512 = 1023$$

decision boxes. Surely there is a better way.

If we tried to describe the process of Figures 3-3*a* and 3-3*b* in words, we might say, "Each new value must be compared with the largest value

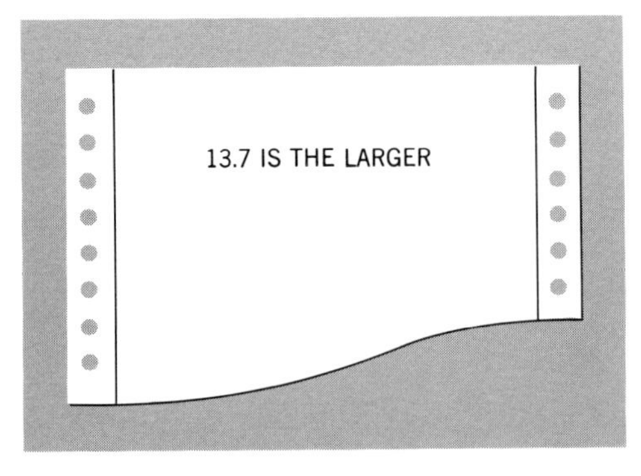

Figure 3-2

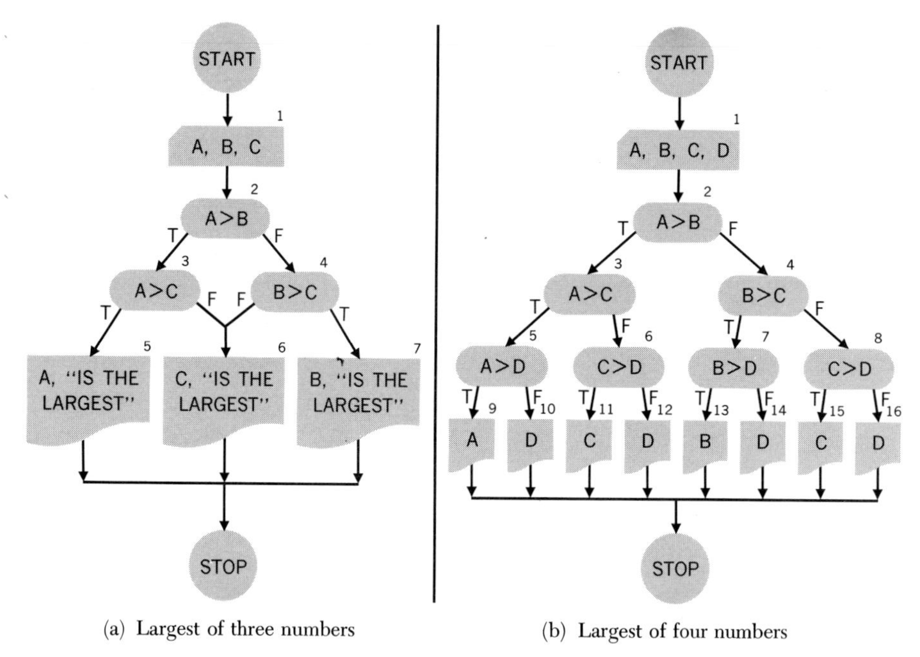

(a) Largest of three numbers

(b) Largest of four numbers

Figure 3-3 Progressively more distasteful flow charts.

found so far." The phrase,

"The largest value found so far"

is the key. The number described by this phrase can be represented in our flow chart by a variable. Let's then introduce the *auxiliary variable* LRGST to represent the largest value found so far.

LRGST certainly starts out with the value of A:

LRGST ← A

Next we compare B with LRGST:

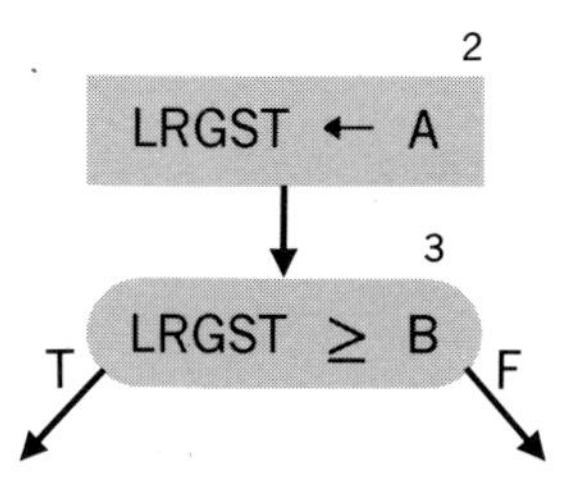

If this assertion is false, then LRGST must be assigned the value of B as its new value, before going on to compare with C. This gives us the flow-

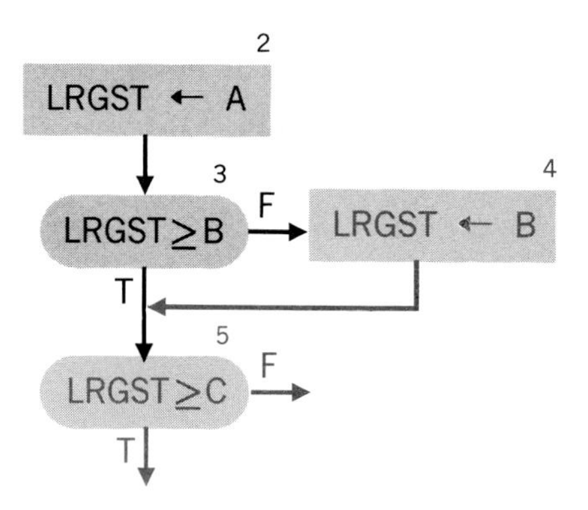

Figure 3-4

chart fragment in Figure 3-4. To complete the flow chart, we repeat this process as many times as necessary, as seen in Figure 3-5.

Here we can see that the number of decision boxes is one less than the number of input values. Thus, finding the largest of 11 numbers would require 10 decision boxes in our flow chart instead of the 1023 required by the previous method. The lesson to be learned from all this is that we must constantly be on the alert for the possibility of introducing additional variables to simplify our work.

The flow chart in Figure 3-5 can be still further simplified if the numbers to be searched for the largest are input from a stack of data cards, one value per card. The reason for this simplification is that it is no longer necessary to denote each number being tested by a separate variable. Thus, a *loop* may be used to replace the list of similar flow-chart boxes.

This flow chart is seen in Figure 3-6. Here the input value of N is the number of cards in the stack. The value of N is decreased by one each time through the loop and so indicates the number of cards still to be read.

Tallying Grades

The final flow chart of this section, Figure 3-7, shows how a computer may be used to tally data read from cards.

Recall Section 2-2, which dealt with the analysis of grade results from the advanced placement examination. Another type of analysis we could perform would be to tabulate the number of grades falling in the high

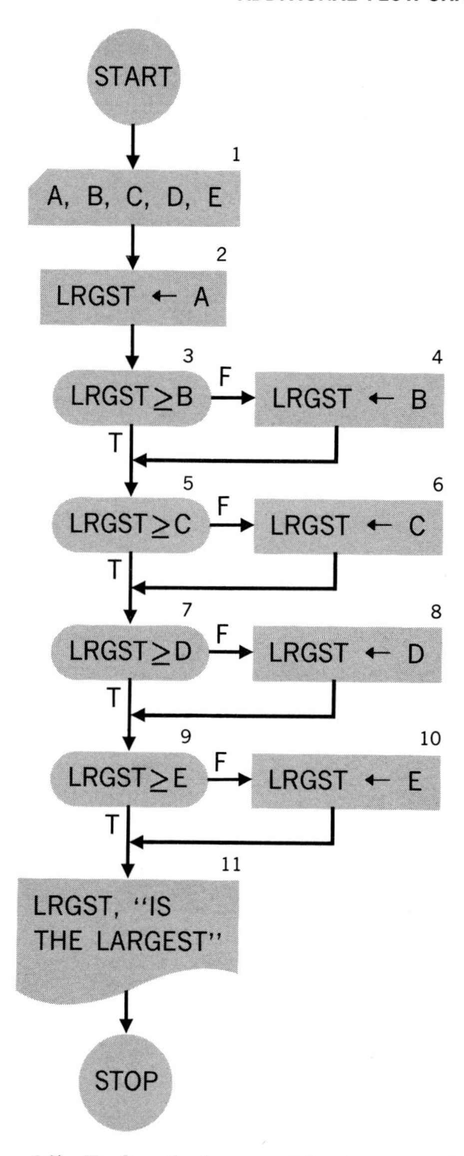

Figure 3-5 Finding the largest of five input variables.

range ($100 \leq$ GRADE ≤ 150), the middle range ($50 \leq$ GRADE < 100), and the low range (GRADE < 50). The variables HIGH, MID, and LOW are counting or "tallying" variables. For each input value of GRADE, one of the three counters clicks up one notch. Another variable, N, keeps a count of the number of grades read. Again we put a card with an im-

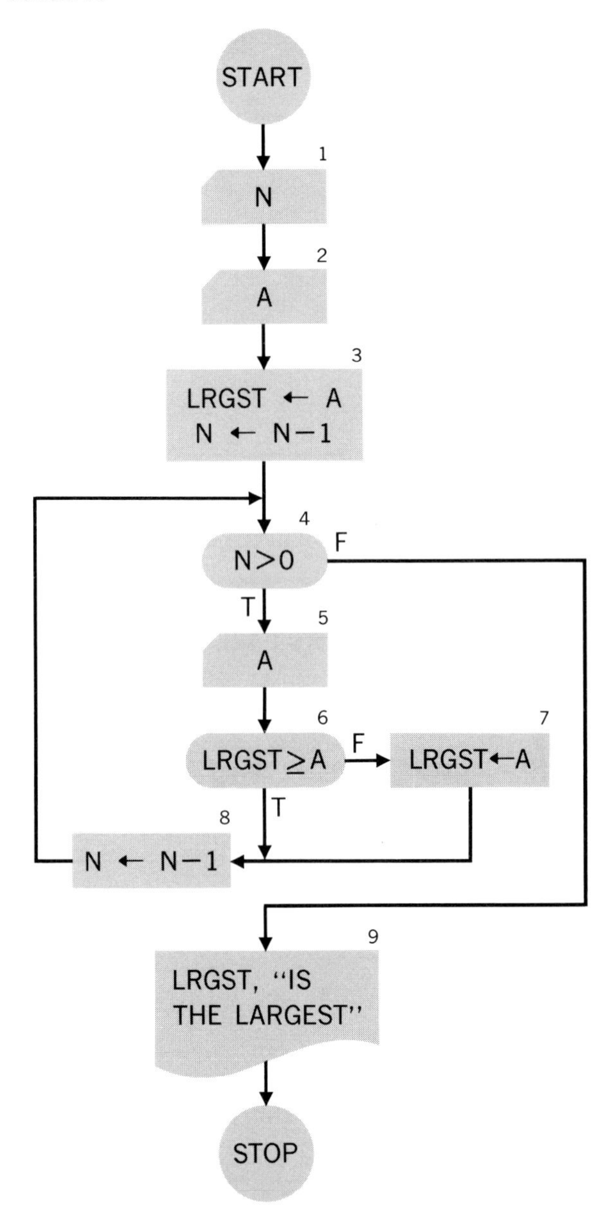

Figure 3-6 Finding the largest of an arbitrary set of numbers stored outside the computer's memory.

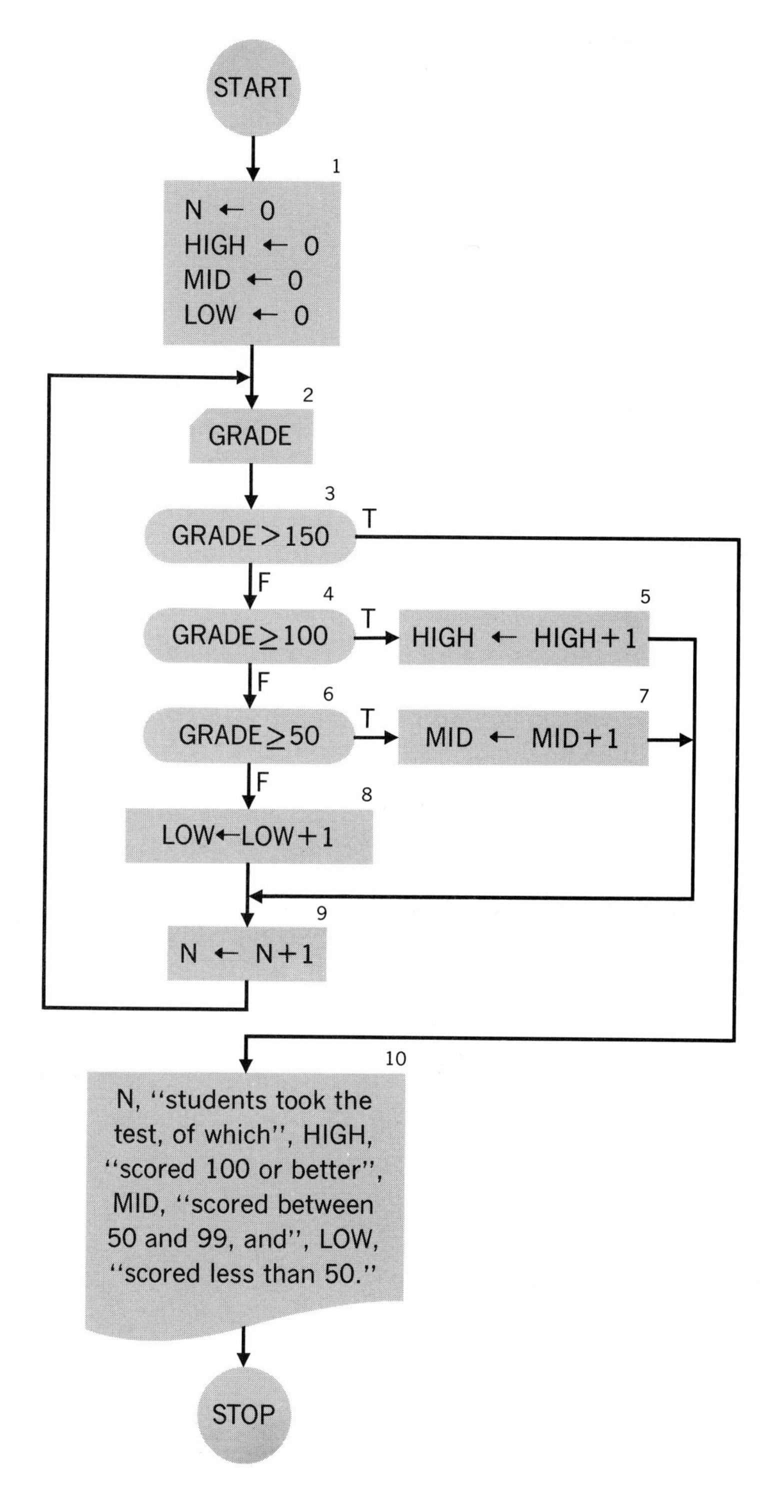

Figure 3-7 Illustrating the use of two million dollar computer for tallying.

possible grade (anything greater than 150) at the end of the stack. The test in box 3 will alert us to stop tallying when this card is reached.

Notice the printing in box 10 that gives an idea of some of the possibilities in this direction.

EXERCISES 3-1, SET A

1. Modify your postal regulation flow chart of Section 2-2 (Problem 3) to handle the case when the dimensions of the box are not punched on the data cards in any particular order (i.e., longest not necessarily first).

Hint. In both problems, you can imagine the flow chart begins with an input step of the form

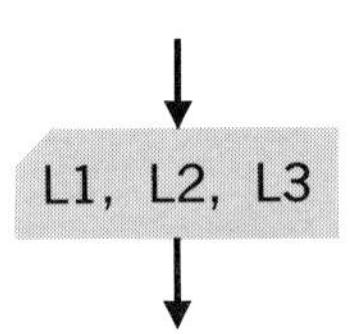

where L1, L2, and L3 represent the measured lengths of the three sides. In the original problem, the L1 was known in advance to be the largest, so the girth was $2 \times (L2 + L3)$. In this problem the girth is

$$2 \times (L1 + L2 + L3 - x)$$

where x is the largest of L1, L2, and L3.

2. Draw a flow chart to input values of b and c, output both values immediately, and then perform the following.

(a) If $b = 0$ and $c \neq 0$, output "bx+c=0 has no root."
(b) If $b = 0$ and $c = 0$, output "every real number satisfies bx+c=0."
(c) If $b \neq 0$, compute the root of the equation $bx + c = 0$. Output "the root of bx+c=0 is", followed by the root.

Finally, return to the input step for more data.

EXERCISES 3-1, SET B

In the tallying problem, Figure 3-7, we saw how a computer might be asked to examine and tally a series of values for T that are input from data cards. There are many similar things we may want to do with a series of input values. For example, we may wish to sum all the values of T, or sum the squares of T, or sum the absolute values of T, etc. In the following exercises, develop a flow chart for the described operation on a series of input values for T. Always print some appropriate message that identifies the numerical result that is also to be printed. The basic ingredients for the desired flow charts can be found by restudying Figure 3-7.

1. Sum the cubes of 100 values of T. Call this SUMCUB.

2. Without reading the input values more than once, develop all three sums: SUMALL, SUMCUB, and SUMNEG, where SUMALL is the sum of all the values, and where SUMNEG is the sum of the values that are less than zero.

3. For each of the 100 values that are input, print the cumulative sum to that point. Call it CUMSUM. Thus, after reading the fifth value for T, we print the sum of the first five values. After the sixth value of T has been read, we print the sum of the first six terms, etc.

4. Think of the one hundred input values mentioned in the preceding exercises as representing the plays of a game that has two players. If a number is ≥ 0, it means player A has won that play. If the number is negative, player B has won that play. Now suppose the game is scored as follows (like badminton or volley ball): player A begins by serving. If the server wins a play, a point is added to his score. If the server loses a play, the other player becomes server and the score does not change. Prepare a flow chart to print which player wins and the score after 100 plays.

3-2 THE EUCLIDEAN ALGORITHM

The Euclidean algorithm is found in the fifth book of Euclid, dating back at least to 300 B.C. This algorithm is a method for finding the *greatest common divisor* of two whole numbers. It plays a central role in mathematics and is thus well worth our study.

Review

You have often used common divisors, also called "common factors," in simplifying fractions. Consider the problem of simplifying

$$\frac{54}{72}$$

One way of doing this is to *cancel* out prime factors one at a time.

$$\frac{54}{72} = \frac{\not{2} \times 27}{\not{2} \times 36} = \frac{27}{36} = \frac{\not{3} \times 9}{\not{3} \times 12} = \frac{9}{12} = \frac{\not{3} \times 3}{\not{3} \times 4} = \frac{3}{4}$$

Another way would be to determine that 18 is the greatest common divisor (GCD) of 54 and 72, and divide it out all at once.

$$\frac{54}{72} = \frac{3 \times 18}{4 \times 18} = \frac{3}{4}$$

One way of defining the GCD of two numbers, say 54 and 72, is first to consider the sets of divisors of each number:

$$S = \text{set of divisors of } 54 = \{1,2,3,6,9,18,27,54\}$$
$$T = \text{set of divisors of } 72 = \{1,2,3,4,6,8,9,12,18,24,36,72\}$$

The *intersection* of the two sets

$$S \cap T = \{1,2,3,6,9,18\}$$

is the set of common factors of the two numbers. The greatest number of this set of common factors is the greatest common divisor.

One way of finding this greatest common divisor is to factor each number completely:

$$54 = 2 \times 3 \times 3 \times 3$$
$$72 = 2 \times 2 \times 2 \times 3 \times 3$$

Then, by taking as many factors of each kind as are common to both these factorizations (here one 2 and two 3's), we form the factorization of the GCD

$$\text{GCD} = 2 \times 3 \times 3$$

However, in case the given numbers are very large, finding their factorizations can be very difficult. The Euclidean algorithm is a technique for finding the GCD *without the necessity of finding these complete factorizations.*

Developing the Algorithm

In the equation

$$364 = 245 + 119$$

suppose we know that two of the numbers (say 364 and 245) have 7 as a common divisor. Then we can be sure that the third number is also divisible by 7. This is a simple consequence of the distributive property, since writing 364 as 7×52 and 245 as 7×35, we have

$$119 = 364 - 245 = 7 \times 52 - 7 \times 35 = 7 \times (52 - 35)$$

In general, suppose that three integers, A, B, and C, are so related that one can be expressed as the sum of the other two. That is,

$$A = B + C$$

or equivalently,

$$C = A - B$$

Then any number that is a common divisor of two of these integers is also a divisor of the third.[1]

Thus, any pair selected from these three numbers will have the same set of common divisors as any other pair.

Let's see how this statement helps us in looking for the GCD of two numbers, say 943 and 437. Now

$$943 - 437 = 506$$

According to our statement, the pair

506, 437

will have the same set of common divisors as the pair

943, 437

Thus our problem can now be replaced by that of finding the greatest common divisor of 506 and 437, which is simpler than the given problem because one of the numbers is smaller. Repeating this process,

$$506 - 437 = 69$$

Again, if we now consider the pair

437, 69

the set of common divisors is again unaltered. A third application yields

368, 69

This process is quite clearly algorithmic.

Constructing the Flow Chart

The basic step consists of replacing the larger of the two numbers by the difference of the larger and the smaller. In flow-chart terms, letting L represent the larger and S the smaller, we have the basic assignment step

L ← L−S

which is repeated over and over, as given in Figure 3-8.

[1] The verification is the same for the preceding example. If $A = D \times M$ and $C = D \times N$, then $B = A - C = D \times M - D \times N = D \times (M - N)$.

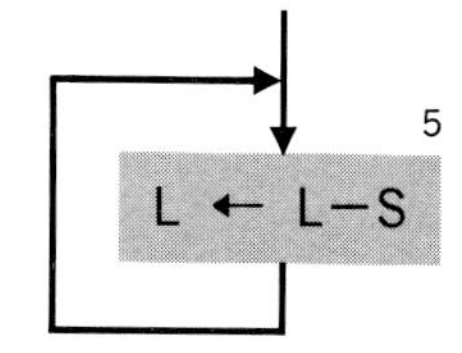

Figure 3-8 Endless Loop.

Of course, we have to provide a way out of this loop. But first, let's trace it with the example considered above (Table 3-1); that is, we enter the loop with L = 943 and S = 437.

Starting with step 3, L is assigned negative values and will take on larger and larger negative values as the process continues. What went wrong is that after step 2, L was no longer the larger number of the pair (L,S). This can be rectified by interchanging the values of L and S before resuming the subtraction process. This requires testing to see whether L≥S.

The interchanging seen in the cloud at the right in Figure 3-9 will occur in many other algorithms throughout the book. How are we to implement this idea in our flow-chart vocabulary? The first idea that comes to us is

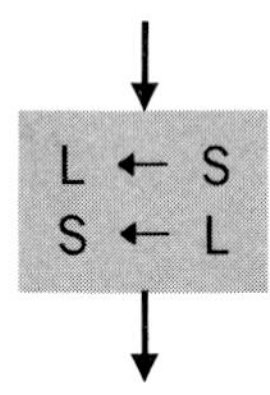

But it doesn't work, since after the first assignment, L and S will have the same value so that the second assignment has no effect whatsoever.

TABLE 3-1 Trace of Figure 3-8

Step	Flow-Chart Box	Values of Variables	
		L	S
Start		943	437
1	5	506	437
2	5	69	437
3	5	−368	437
4	5	−805	437

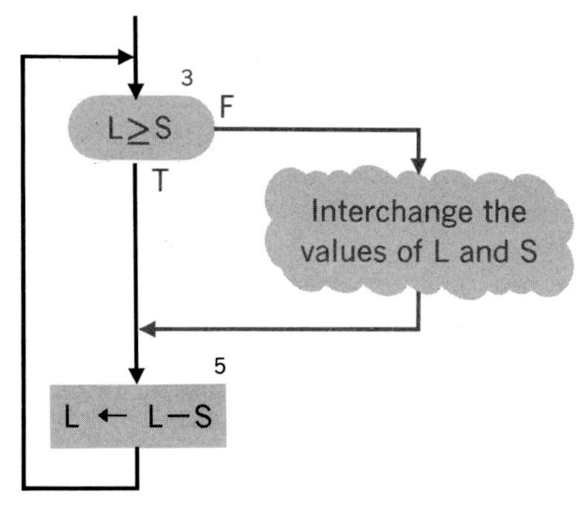

Figure 3-9

Equally ineffective is

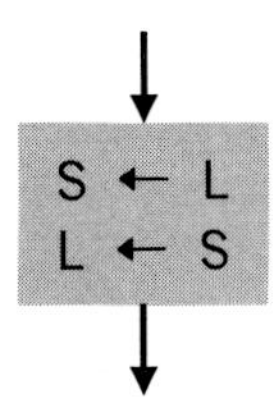

What can be done? This impasse dynamically illustrates an important consequence of the destructive nature of assignment. We can state the principle this way.

Assigning a new value to a variable destroys all record of the old value, *unless we have made a copy of the old value prior to the assignment.*

Applying this principle to the problem at hand, we introduce a variable COPY and implement the cloud in Figure 3-9, as shown in Figure 3-10.

Let's trace this flow chart with the same initial values of L and S as before (Table 3-2).

A study of Table 3-2 shows this: upon completing step 26, the repeated execution of box 5 will have reduced the value of L to zero. From this point on, execution will begin to cycle through boxes 3 and 5 over and over without changing the values of any variables.

We must be done, but what is our answer? Since we have not altered our set of common divisors at any point in the process, the set of common divisors of 23 and 0 must be the same as the set of common divi-

TABLE 3-2 Trace of Figure 3-10

Step	Flow-Chart Box	Values of Variables			Test	T or F
		L	S	COPY		
Start		943	437			
1	3				$943 \geq 437$	T
2	5	506				
3	3				$506 \geq 437$	T
4	5	69				
5	3				$69 \geq 437$	F
6	4	437	69	69		
7	5	368				
8	3				$368 \geq 69$	T
9	5	299				
10	3				$299 \geq 69$	T
11	5	230				
12	3				$230 \geq 69$	T
13	5	161				
14	3				$161 \geq 69$	T
15	5	92				
16	3				$92 \geq 69$	T
17	5	23				
18	3				$23 \geq 69$	F
19	4	69	23	23		
20	5	46				
21	3				$46 \geq 23$	T
22	5	23				
23	3				$23 \geq 23$	T
24	5	0				
25	3				$0 \geq 23$	F
26	4	23	0	0		
27	5	23				
28	3				$23 \geq 0$	T
29	5	23				

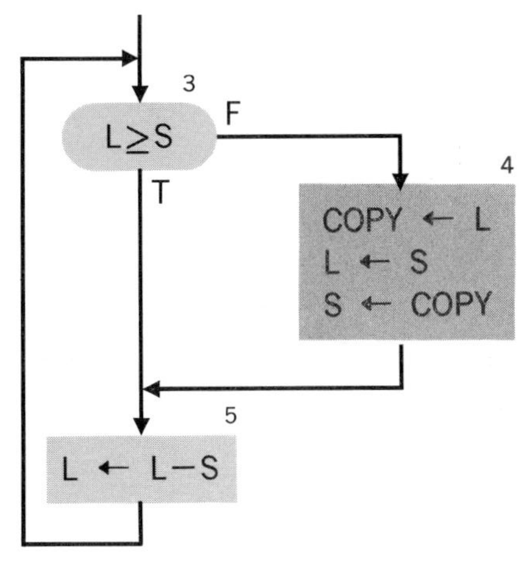

Figure 3-10 Closing in on Euclid's algorithm.

sors of 943 and 437. But what are the common divisors of 23 and 0? The number 23 is a divisor of both 23 and 0. That is,

$$23 = 23 \times 1 \qquad 0 = 23 \times 0$$

Moreover, no number larger than 23 is a divisor of 23. Thus, we can output 23 (the final value of L) as the GCD. The complete flow chart is seen in Figure 3-11.

In preparation for the next section, think about this algorithm and see whether you can arrive at any improvements that will reduce the number of steps in the trace.

3-3 REFINING THE EUCLIDEAN ALGORITHM

By studying the trace (Table 3-2) of the Euclidean algorithm, we see that the value of L was reduced by 437 two times, then reduced by 69 six times, and finally reduced by 23 three times. A lot of needless repetition can be cut out.

We can, for example, replace

$$\left.\begin{array}{r} 437 \\ -\ 69 \\ \hline 368 \\ -\ 69 \\ \hline 299 \\ -\ 69 \\ \hline 230 \\ -\ 69 \\ \hline 161 \\ -\ 69 \\ \hline 92 \\ -\ 69 \\ \hline 23 \end{array}\right\} \text{ by } \begin{cases} \mathrm{CHOP}\left(\dfrac{437}{69}\right) = 6 \\ \\ 437 - 6 \times 69 = 23 \end{cases}$$

The values here are obtained from the division algorithm of grade school arithmetic (mentioned in Section 2-4):

$$\begin{array}{rl} 6 & \longleftarrow \textit{Quotient} \\ \mathsf{S} \longrightarrow 69 \overline{)437} & \\ \mathsf{L} \longrightarrow \quad 414 & \\ \hline 23 & \longleftarrow \textit{Remainder} \end{array}$$

In general, then, variables Q and R are introduced as the quotient and remainder on dividing L by S. According to the division algorithm, the remainder, R, will always be less than the divisor, S.

These computations are represented in flow-chart language by the assignments

$$\begin{array}{l} \mathsf{Q} \leftarrow \mathrm{CHOP}\left(\dfrac{\mathsf{L}}{\mathsf{S}}\right) \\ \mathsf{R} \leftarrow \mathsf{L} - \mathsf{Q} \times \mathsf{S} \end{array}$$

which accomplish at once all the subtractions using the same value of S.

The present value of S will become the next value of L and the present value of R becomes the next value of S (Figure 3-12).

No test of whether $\mathsf{L} \geq \mathsf{S}$ is necessary, since, as was remarked above, the division algorithm assures us that the new value of L will always be greater than the new value of S.

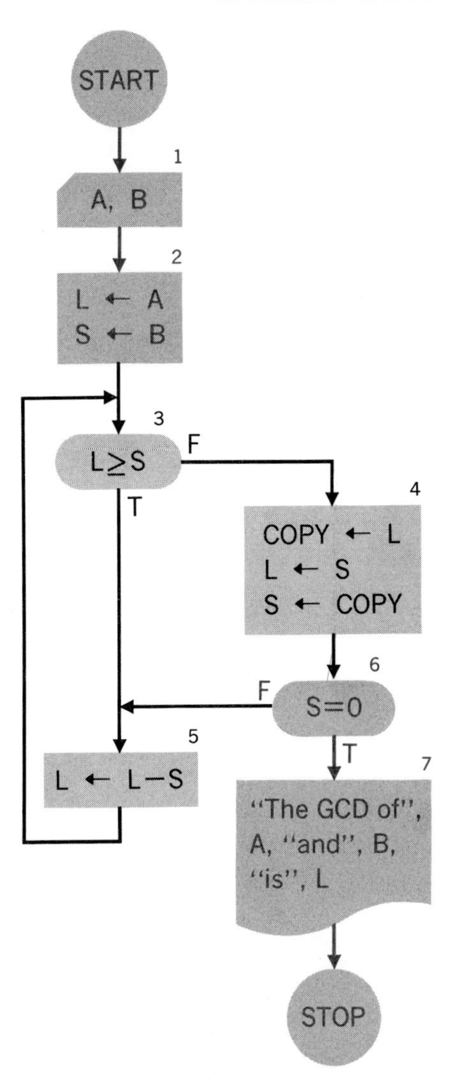

Figure 3-11 Euclidean algorithm (subtraction form).

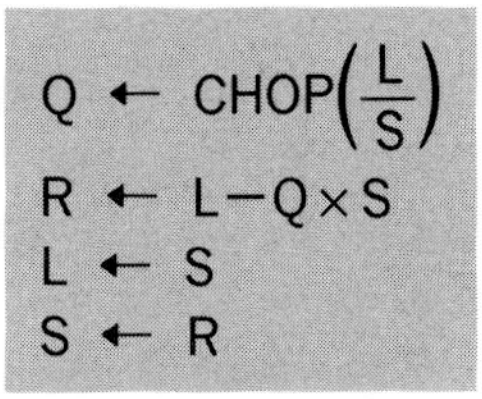

$$Q \leftarrow \text{CHOP}\left(\frac{L}{S}\right)$$
$$R \leftarrow L - Q \times S$$
$$L \leftarrow S$$
$$S \leftarrow R$$

Figure 3-12

When S attains the value zero, then the value of L is the GCD. Our final flow chart appears in Figure 3-13.

Comparing a trace of Figure 3-13 with the trace (Table 3-2) of the version in the preceding section will make the saving evident. The same input values of A and B are used for easy comparison. Table 3-3 gives the new trace.

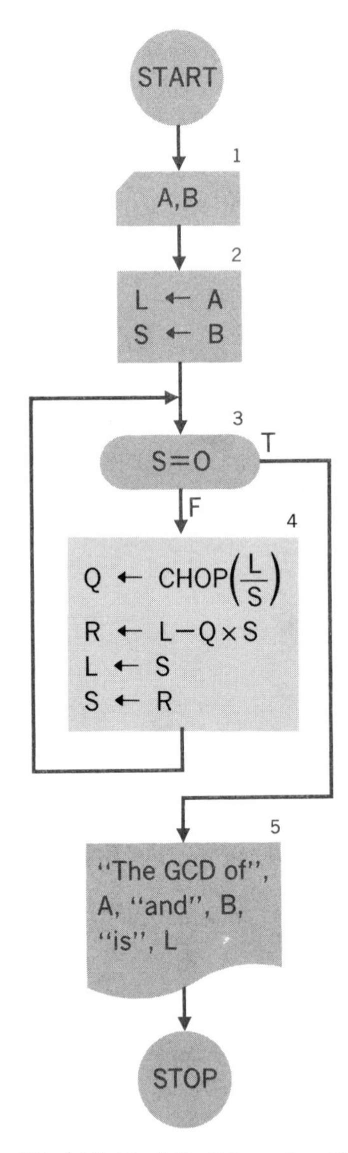

Figure 3-13 Final (division) Euclidean algorithm flow chart.

TABLE 3-3 Trace of Figure 3-13

Step	Flow-Chart Box	Values of Variables						Test	T or F
		A	B	Q	R	L	S		
1	1	943	437						
2	2					943	437		
3	3							437 = 0	F
4	4			2	69	437	69		
5	3							69 = 0	F
6	4			6	23	69	23		
7	3							23 = 0	F
8	4			3	0	23	0	0 = 0	T
9	5	943	437			23			

Using hand computation on this problem without following the flow chart, we have

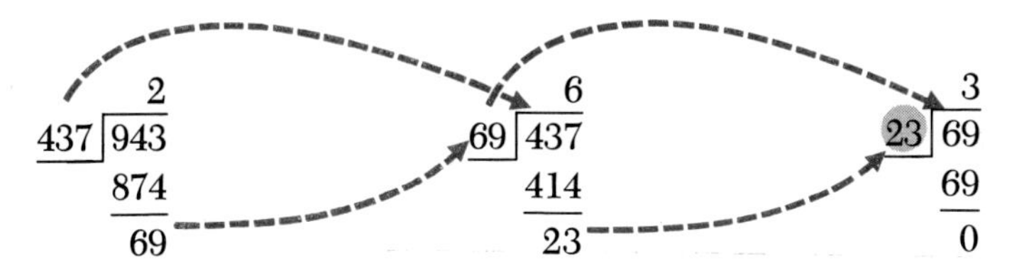

Thus, the algorithm is a succession of division problems in which the divisor of one is *promoted* to dividend of the next and the remainder is promoted to divisor. When the remainder finally becomes zero, the divisor is the GCD.

EXERCISES 3-3

1. Prepare a flow chart to print only the three right-most digits of one hundred terms of the Fibonacci sequence beginning with the seventeenth term. Make guesses at how many of these hundred numbers will be even, how many greater than 500, and how many between 300 and 400. Save these guesses to see how they compare with results when you run the program on a computer. (*Hint.* Use the CHOP Function.)

In Exercises 3-1, Set B, a series of 100 values of T were input from data cards. In the following two exercises develop a flow chart for the described operation on this same series of input values of T. Always print some appropriate message identifying the numerical result printed.

2. For each input value after the first value, sum and print the two most recently input values of T and their sum. Call this sum TWOSUM.

3. For each input value after the kth (where the value of k is itself supplied as data and where $3 \leq k \leq 100$), print out the average of either the most recent three values or, if the most recent value is lower than its predecessor, print the average of the preceding two values (omitting the most recent one from this average).

4. Prepare a flow chart to calculate and print the first 15 rows of a table according to the following rules.

(a) The table is to have four columns called N, A, B, C.
(b) The values in the first row of the table are 0, 1, 1, 1.
(c) The value of N is one greater than its value in the preceding row.
(d) The value of A is one greater than its value in the preceding row.
(e) The value of B is one greater than the sum of the values of A, to and including the preceding row.
(f) The value of C is one greater than the sum of the values of B, to and including the preceding row.

3-4 COMPOUND CONDITIONS AND MULTIPLE BRANCHING

Often, we may encounter or wish to write condition boxes such as

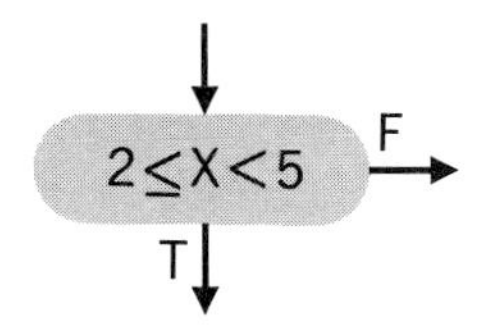

The statement appearing in this box is called a "compound" statement and is obviously equivalent to

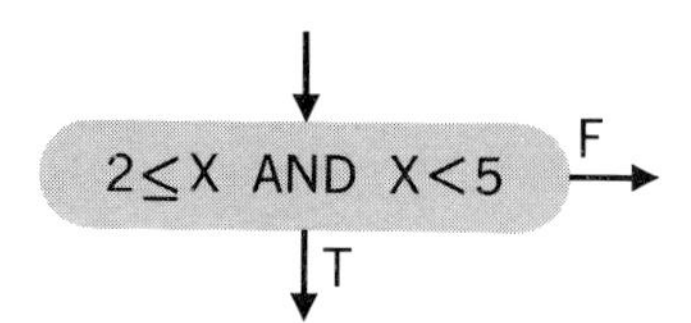

This means that we leave by the bottom if *both* the conditions $2 \leq X$ and $X < 5$ hold. Otherwise, we leave by the side. It is important to see

how to express this compound condition in terms of the simpler components:

In this way we will be able to make flow charts more readily translatable into computer language, the reason being that each condition may have to be tested in a separate step.

Since the compound statement is true only if *both* simple relations are true and is false if *either* simple relation is false, we can clearly connect the simple condition boxes as in Figure 3-14*b*.

In any flow chart in which it appears, the box in Figure 3-14*a* may be replaced by the combination in Figure 3-14*b*, the connections being made as indicated by the arrows. Neither *a* nor *b* is the "more correct." The combination in *b* is the more detailed and perhaps more readily translated into machine language. In that respect *b* is better. But, on the other hand, the single box in *a* is more easily scanned by a reader who wishes to know what the flow chart is doing.

In contrast to this example where we want to know whether both of two conditions are true, there are places where we might want to know whether either of two conditions is true. The decomposition of the latter type of compound condition into simple conditions is shown in Figure 3-15*b*.

Clearly, compound condition boxes could grow to any degree of com-

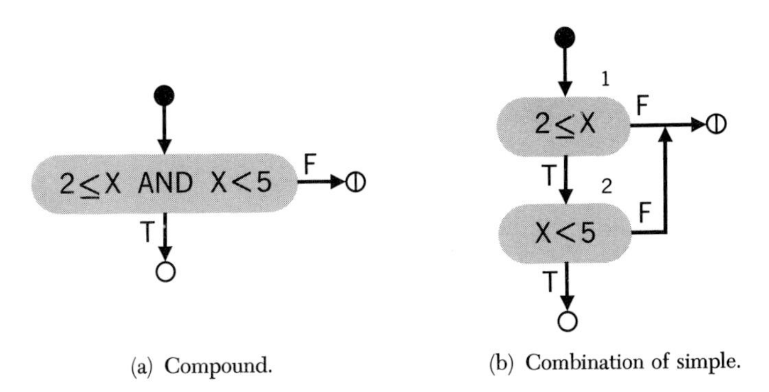

(a) Compound. (b) Combination of simple.

Figure 3-14 Compound condition box and an equivalent combination of simple boxes.

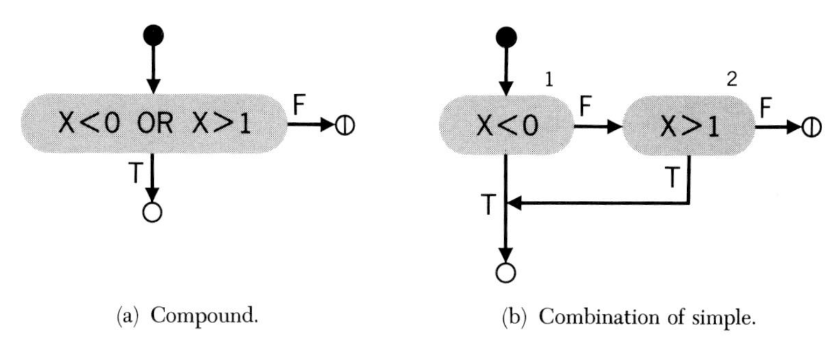

(a) Compound. (b) Combination of simple.

Figure 3-15 Another compound condition box and its equivalent combination of simple boxes.

plexity demanded by the problem, with any number of conditions to be satisfied and any number of variables involved.

For example, if we want to know when both X and Y are positive or Z is zero, we can draw the compound box and its decomposition as in Figure 3-16.

Notice that the decomposition in Figure 3-16 can be accomplished in two stages. We first use the method shown in Figure 3-15 to decompose the "or" statement in 3-16*a* to obtain Figure 3-16*c*. Now the method of Figure 3-14 is used to replace box 4 of Figure 3-16*c* by the "cloud" in Figure 3-16*b*.

A compound condition box may be regarded as shorthand for a combination of simple condition boxes. There is another type of shorthand associated with condition boxes that can be extremely helpful in the

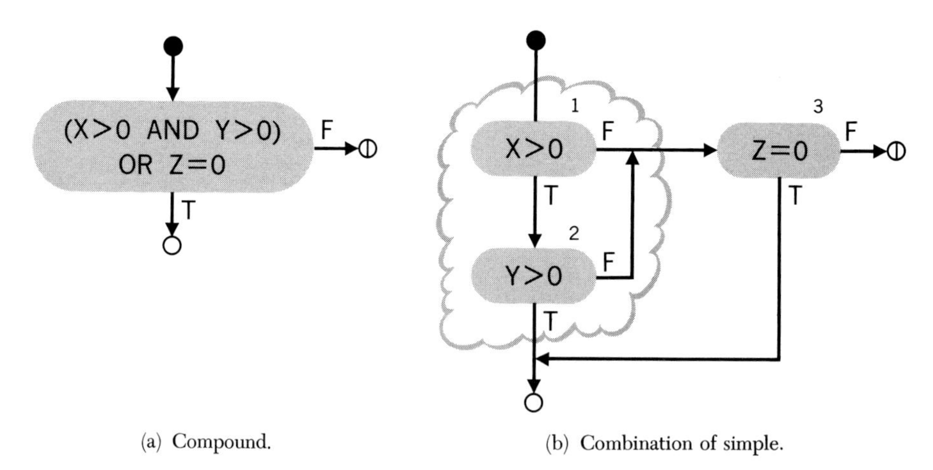

(a) Compound. (b) Combination of simple.

Figure 3-16 Composition of condition boxes.

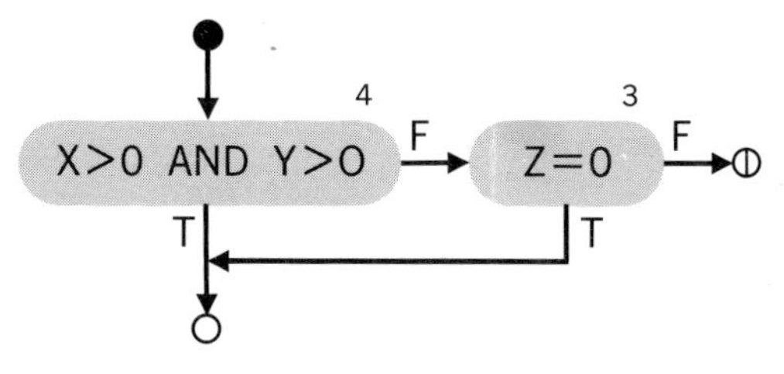

Figure 3-16*c*

process of gradually building up complicated flow charts. This shorthand technique is called "multiple branching."

To indicate multiple branching, we will draw compound condition boxes with several exits. Each exit must be clearly labeled to show what condition would cause its use. For example,

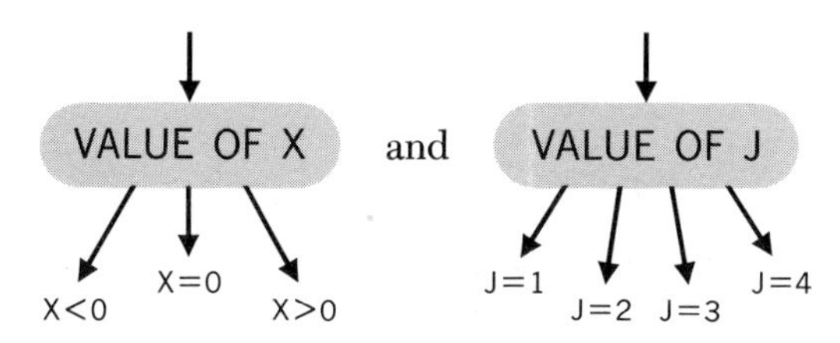

Two important warnings are in order.

1. The conditions on the exits must not be overlapping. If one exit were labeled "$3<X<7$" and another were labeled "$5\leq X<10$", and if we come into this box with a value of X between 5 and 7, we will not know which branch to take on leaving.
2. All possibilities must be exhausted. If the conditions on the exits were "$X\leq 3$", "$6\leq X<9$", and "$9\leq X$", and if we come into the box with a value of X between 3 and 6, we will have no way to get out. Then we really will be in a box.

We should note in passing that any box indicating a multiple branch of n ways can be broken down into a chain of n − 1, 2-way branches. Thus the 4-way branch on the value of J may be viewed in more detail as the chain of three 2-way branches (Figure 3-17*a*).

An example of the usefulness of multiple branching is provided by the example in Section 3-1 of tallying test grades as flow-charted in Figure 3-7. The way in which this same problem might have been handled with multiple branching is shown in Figure 3-17*b*. We simply "collapse" the chain

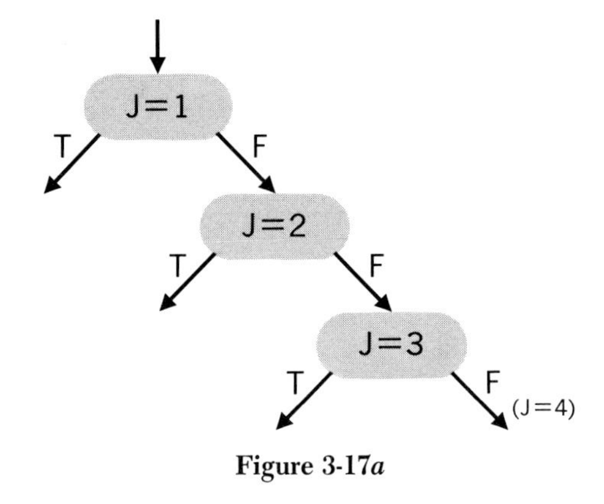

Figure 3-17*a*

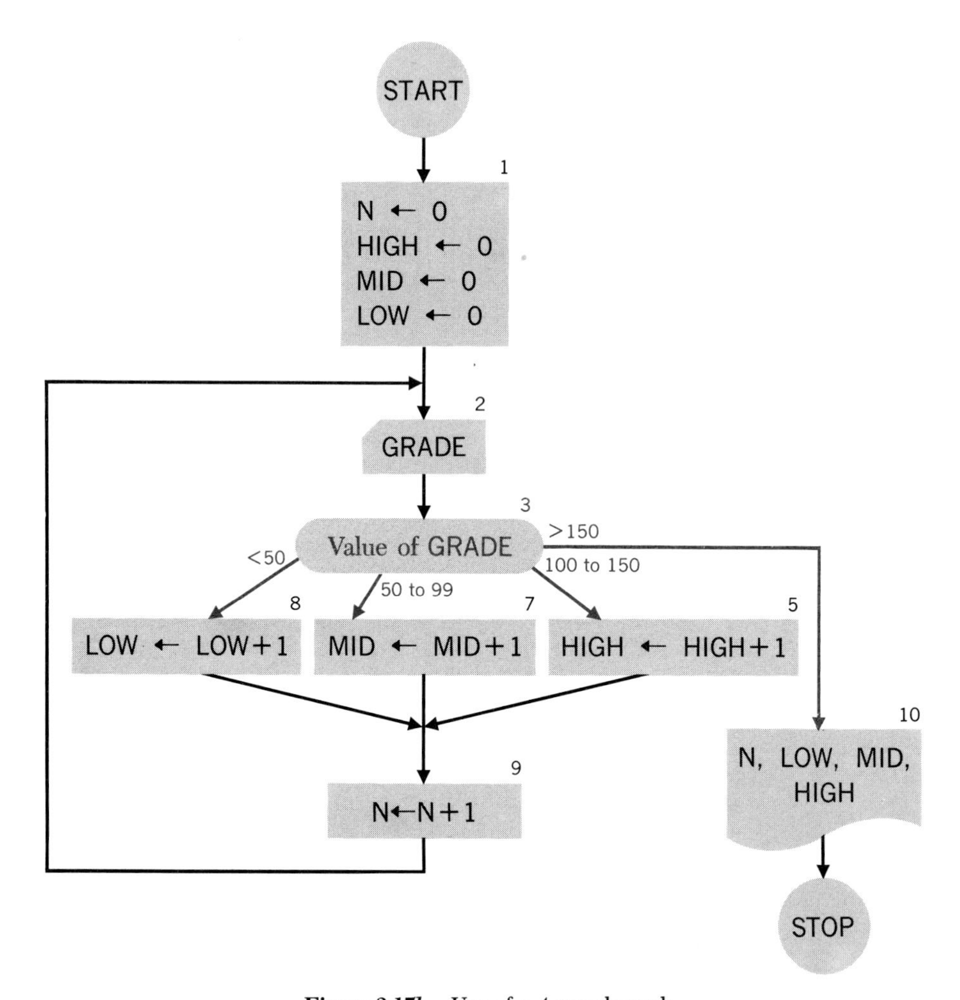

Figure 3-17*b* Use of a 4-way branch.

of 2-way branches (boxes 3, 4, and 6 of Figure 3-7) into a single 4-way branch (box 3 of Figure 3-17*b*).

In the normal course of events this multiple branching flow chart would have been given first. It represents our first formulation of the problem. After we had first drawn this flow chart, we would then have given our attention to the problem of decomposing the multiple condition box into a combination of simple conditions.

EXERCISES 3-4

In each of the next seven exercises your job is to construct the flow chart equivalent to the given assertion using only simple condition boxes. The "true" path of the flow chart should lead to box 20 and the "false" path to box 30.

Example. *The assertion is:* X1 is less than X2 and either P exceeds G or T equals S or both.

The required flow chart is shown in Figure 3-18.

1. x lies between 2 and 7, inclusive.

2. Either 7 is less than Q, or 7 is less than R, or 7 is less than S.

3. x lies between 1.7 and 8.4, and y lies between −3.9 and +5.4 (Figure 3-19).

4. Given the shaded region inside the two straight lines (Figure 3-20) whose equations are

$$y = 2 \times x$$

and

$$y = \tfrac{1}{2} \times x$$

(a) The point (x1,y1) lies inside the shaded region of quadrant I.

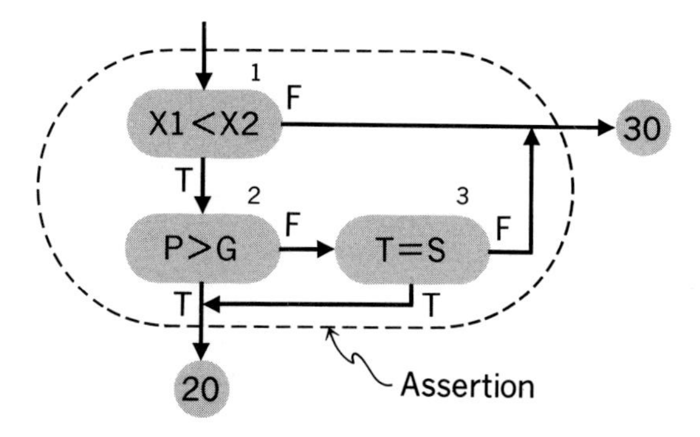

Figure 3-18

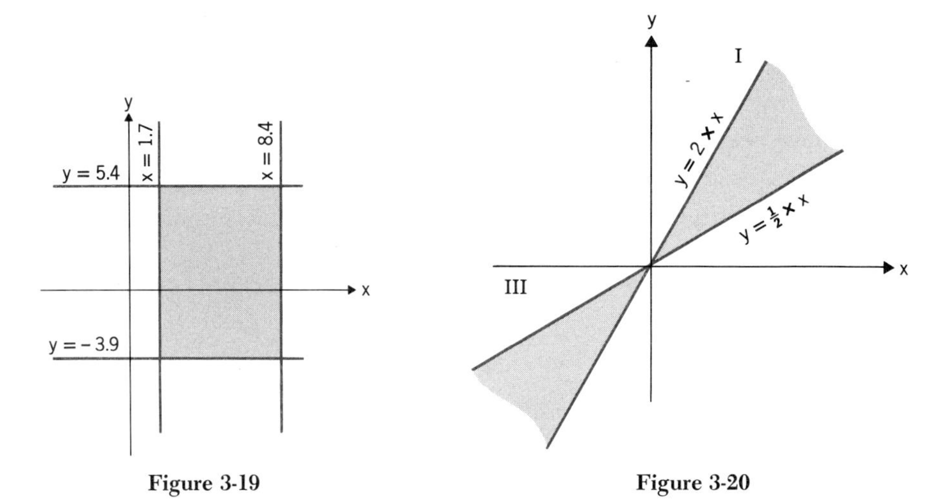

Figure 3-19

Figure 3-20

(b) The point (x1,y1) lies inside the shaded region of quadrant III.
(c) The point (x1,y1) lies somewhere inside the shaded region of quadrants I or III.

5. The point (x1,y1) lies inside the shaded triangle in the first quadrant formed by the straight line $y = -\frac{2}{3}x + 2$ and the coordinate axes (Figure 3-21).

6. The point (x1,y1) lies in the shaded area (or on its boundaries) formed by the curve, $y = \sin x$, and the straight line, $y = \frac{1}{2}(\pi - x)$ (Figure 3-22).

7. The intersecting straight lines

$$y = 4 \times x - 12 \qquad \text{and} \qquad y = -4 \times x + 16$$

determined four regions, one of which, region A, lies entirely in the upper half-plane. We assert that the point (x1,y1) lies in the interior of region A or on its boundary.

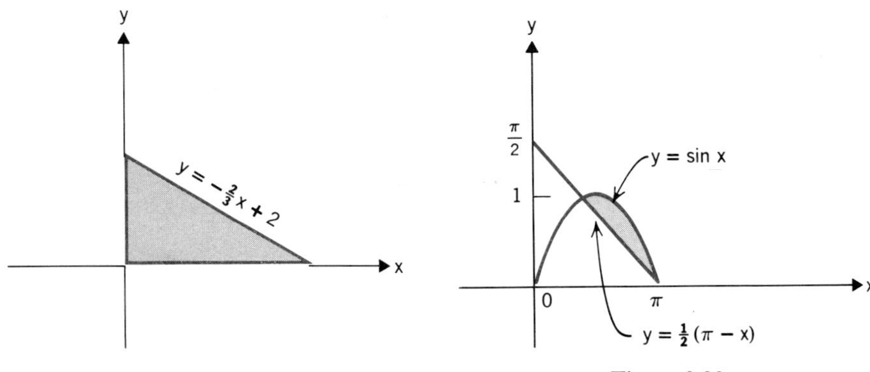

Figure 3-21

Figure 3-22

For each of the following flow-chart assertions, certain x, y pairs lead to box 20. These pairs define a region in the x-y plane. Your job is to draw the graph of this region.

8.

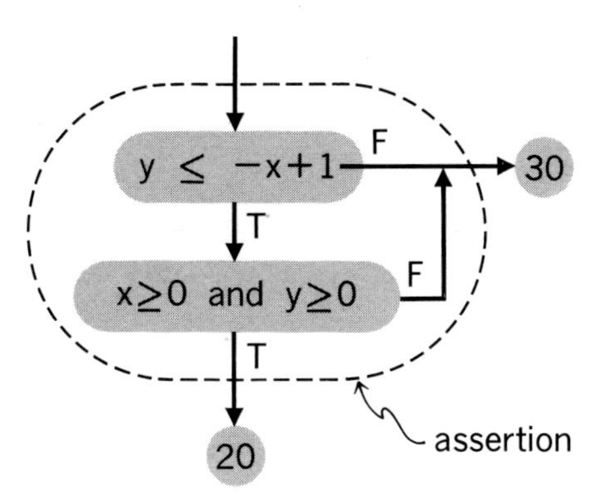

9.

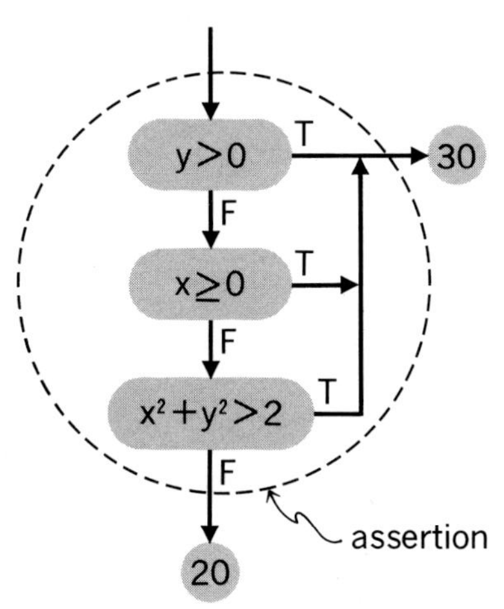

10. Draw a flow chart that computes and prints the numbers 1, 2, 3, or 4 as a message to indicate in which quadrant a point P lies. The coordinates (x1,y1) of P are given. What happens if P lies on one or both axes?

11. We return to the carnival wheel problem (Exercise 9, Section 2-4). We now suppose the rule is modified. Recall that p, the number of points won or lost, was originally a straight-line function of k, the position number in the repeated group of four sectors. We now want a new point rule where p is an arbitrary function of k. For example,

k	Old Point Rule	New Point Rule
0	lose 30	lose 20
1	lose 10	lose 30
2	win 10	win 0
3	win 30	win 50

Draw a revised flow chart to show p as a function of the same data pair s and m but with the new point rule given above. (s is the sector position of the wheel at rest, and m is the number of sector positions the wheel is spun.)

3-5 EVALUATION OF RELATIONAL EXPRESSIONS

We pause here to look in a more formal way at the statements that we have been writing inside the oval condition boxes and to see how they are evaluated. When the lines emanating from the oval are marked true (or T) and false (or F), we have been referring to the statement that appears inside as an *assertion*.

Here is a restatement of the *method for determining whether the assertion is true or false*, originally given in Section 2-1.

1. Look up the current values of the variables.
2. Evaluate the arithmetic expressions on each side of the relation symbol, obtaining for each a numerical value.
3. Determine whether the relation in question holds between the numerical values obtained in 2.

It follows, for example, that the expression

$$X^2+2\times X+1 \;<\; 2\times A\times B$$

will be read as though parentheses were inserted as follows:

$$(X^2+2\times X+1) \;<\; (2\times A\times B)$$

We can convey the same idea by saying that when reading expressions having no parentheses, relational symbols have a lower precedence than any of the arithmetic operators. We can expand the precedence table, Table 2-1, to include the relational symbols, as shown in Table 3-4.

TABLE 3-4 Precedence Levels for Relational Expressions

Levels		Symbol
High	First	$\uparrow$
↑	Second	$\times$, /, $-$ (unary)
↓	Third	+, $-$ (binary)
Low	Fourth	$<, >, \leq, \geq, =, \neq$

Nothing need be said about scanning left-to-right for symbols of the fourth level, since in a properly written expression there can be, at most, one such symbol. Such an expression as

$$3 < X < 5$$

(frequently encountered in mathematics) is actually a compound expression, that is, in this case

$$3 < X \qquad \text{and} \qquad X < 5$$

We have seen how to deal with such compound statements in the preceding section.

Perhaps you would be interested in seeing how a machine might find out whether one of the above inequalities is true or false. Consider, for example, the SAMOS computer of Chapter 1. It has only the one conditional branching instruction, BRANCH ON MINUS. We consider for our example the condition box

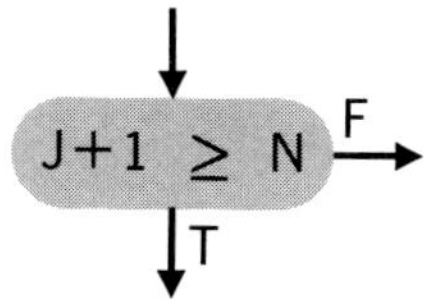

with the current values of the variables, given by

Variable	J	N
Current value	7	10

First, the values of the variables in the condition box are looked up and the arithmetic expressions on either side of the relation symbol are evaluated. The condition box may now be visualized as

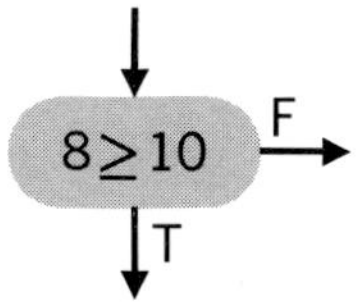

Because $8 \geq 10$ is equivalent to the relation $8 - 10 \geq 0$, the expression $8 - 10$ is evaluated and we may now visualize the condition box as

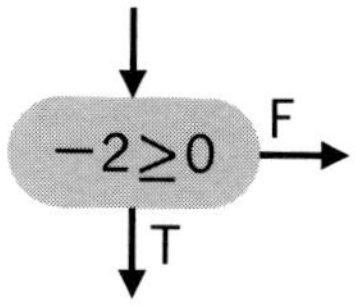

The machine determines the truth or falsity of the relation $-2 \geq 0$ by effectively examining the first character in the numeral on the left. This character being a minus, we "branch on minus," that is, we go to an address specified in the branching order to pick up our next instructions corresponding to the false side of the flow-chart box. Otherwise, the next instruction after the branch on minus will be executed. This corresponds to emerging from the true side of the flow-chart box.

3-6 SUBSCRIPTED VARIABLES

It is now appropriate to introduce into our flow-chart language an extremely powerful tool, the subscripted variable.

We admit as variables inscriptions of the sort

$$X_1, X_2, X_3, X_4, X_5$$

Here the thing occupying the position of X may be the inscription for any properly written variable while the subscript must be an integer.

Each subscripted variable is provided with a window box as with ordinary variables, as suggested in Figure 3-23.

We do not introduce these subscripted variables just for the purpose of having more variables available. If that were all we wanted, we could use

X1, X2, X3, X4, X5

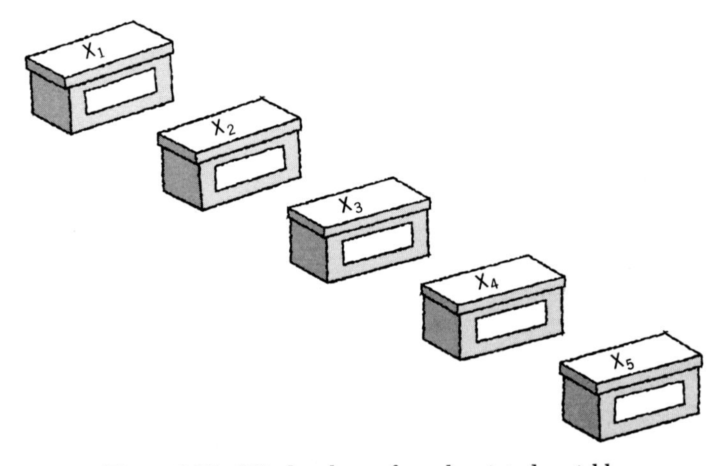

Figure 3-23 Window boxes for subscripted variables.

The application of subscripted variables lies in our ability to write expressions like

$$X_K$$

in our flow chart boxes. K is a variable which can have only an agreed set of consecutive values, like 1, 2, 3, 4, and 5. Let us see how we interpret such an inscription. Suppose we find in a flow chart the assignment box

$$\rightarrow \boxed{X_K \leftarrow 19} \rightarrow$$

Evidently, we are supposed to put 19 somewhere. But where? If we look at the window boxes of Figure 3-23, we find boxes labeled X_1, X_2, X_3, X_4, and X_5, but none labeled X_K. We do the obvious thing. We look up the current value of K. Say it is 4. Then we interpret the assignment box shown above to mean

$$\rightarrow \boxed{X_4 \leftarrow 19} \rightarrow$$

Thus X_K is a subscripted variable that unambiguously designates one window box from the set inscribed with X_1, X_2, X_3, X_4, or X_5. Which window box is designated depends on the current value of the variable K.[2]

The domain of permissible values of the subscript K can, of course, be as large as is necessary. Generally we will limit K to the nonnegative integers. The real power of subscripted variables becomes evident when we consider problems having a large number of related variables. The next example begins to illustrate the power of this notation.

Consider the problem of *finding* and printing the *largest* value of a group of input variables. You recall that we considered this problem in Section 3-1. Now we shall see how subscripted variables may be utilized in dealing with this same problem.

First, we show in Figure 3-24*a* a slightly modified copy of Figure 3-5 for finding the largest of six numbers after storing them in memory.

We see a certain monotonous repetition in the left-hand flow chart. Think how much worse the situation would have been if there were a hundred input variables instead of only six. The problem would get out of hand (as well as off the paper).

[2] Note that X_K is *very* different from XK. The latter case can only designate one window box—that inscribed with XK.

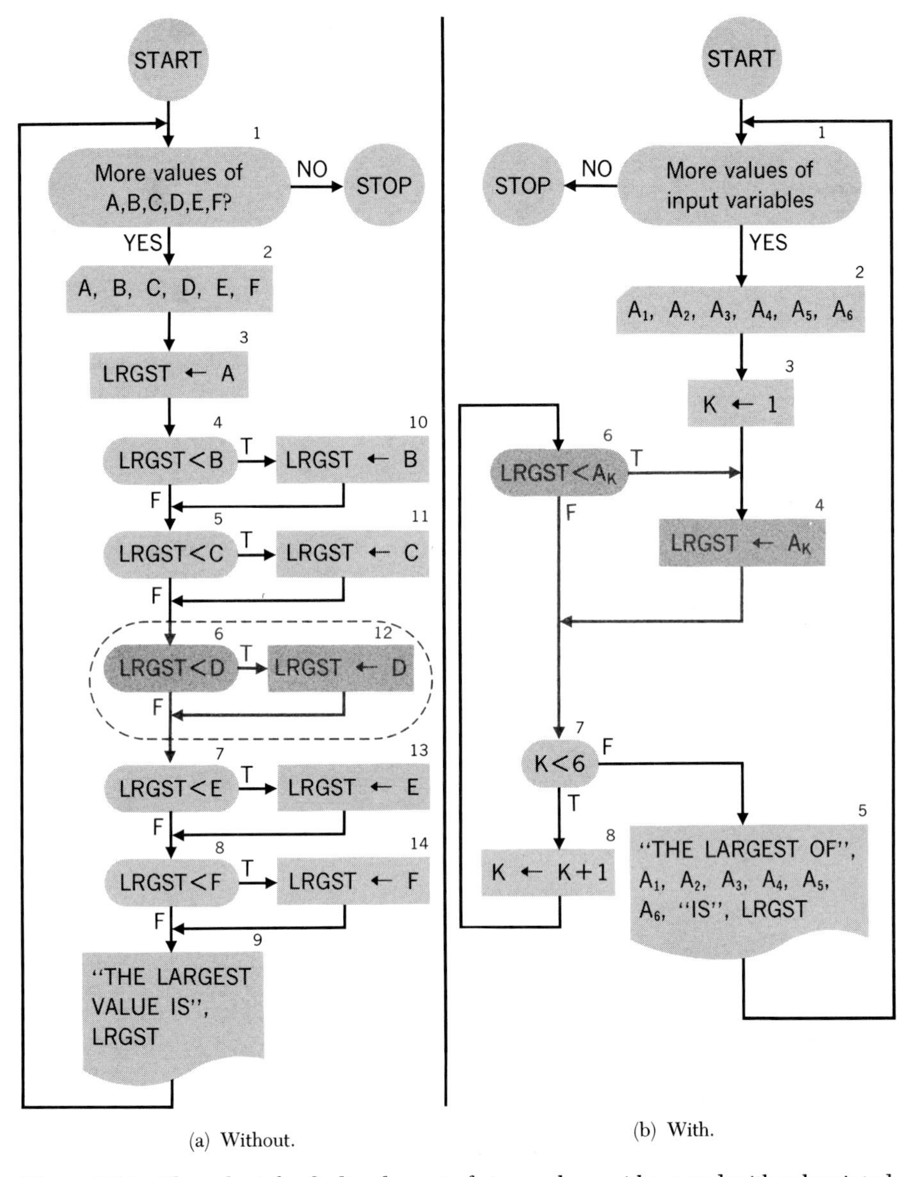

(a) Without. (b) With.

Figure 3-24 Flow chart for finding largest of six numbers without and with subscripted variables.

We will now see how to treat the same problem with subscripted variables. We let the input variables be

$$A_1, A_2, A_3, A_4, A_5, A_6$$

We have put a dashed line around one of the repeated "blocks" that go into making up this flow chart. The general form of such a block, when using subscripted variable notation, would be

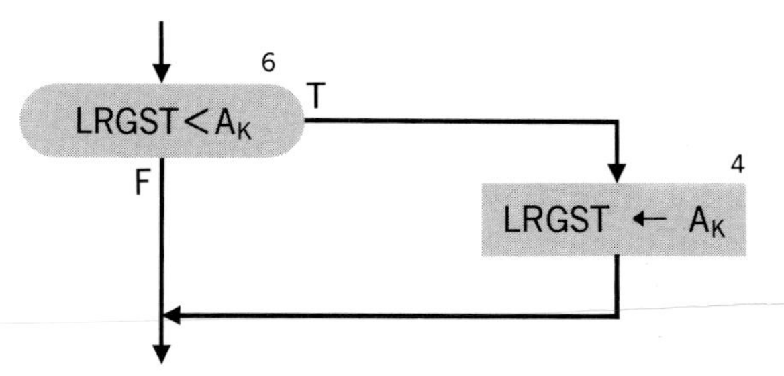

With suitable values assigned to K this configuration can represent any of the five "blocks" in Figure 3-24*a*. But how do we get to the next step? Clearly, *unless* K already has the value 6, we augment K by 1 and come back to the top of the block. We display these additional boxes (7 and 8) in Figure 3-25. What we have so far described represents the *body* of Figure 3-24*b*. All that remains is to attach the head and tail.

To start, we must input the data, assign the initial value of 1 to the variable K, and hook in at the top of box 4 of Figure 3-25. If we leave box 7 at F we print the current value of LRGST and go back for more data (if any). The complete flow chart is given in Figure 3-24*b*.

Careful study of the development of the flow chart in Figure 3-24*b* and comparison with that in Figure 3-24*a* will show better than any number of words the importance of subscripted variables and the way we use them.

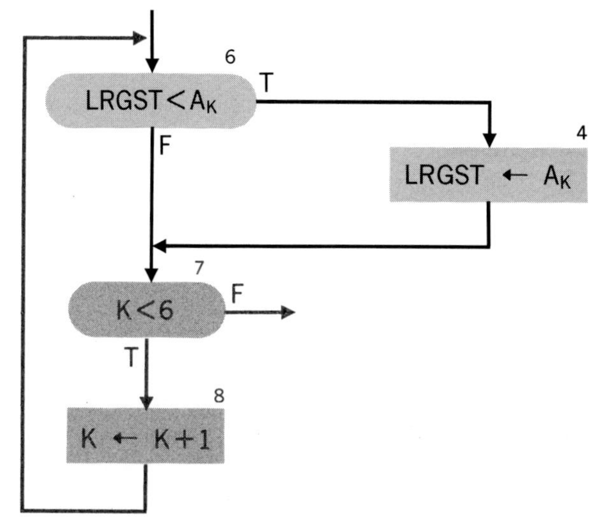

Figure 3-25 Partial flow chart for largest of a set of numbers.

An important thing to observe about the flow chart of Figure 3-24*b* is that it would only be changed in the most minor way if we had 30 input variables rather than a mere six. In box 7, the 6 would be replaced by 30. In the input and output boxes, 2 and 5, A_1, A_2, A_3, A_4, A_5, A_6 would be replaced by A_1, A_2, A_3, A_4, A_5, A_6, A_7, A_8, A_9, A_{10}, A_{11}, A_{12}, A_{13}, A_{14}, A_{15}, A_{16}, A_{17}, A_{18}, A_{19}, A_{20}, A_{21}, A_{22}, A_{23}, A_{24}, A_{25}, A_{26}, A_{27}, A_{28}, A_{29}, A_{30}.

We could avoid all of this writing by introducing a more compact notation. The real point is that the *structure of the flow chart,* that is, the way the boxes are connected, *does not depend on the amount of data.*

In the input and output boxes we are really dealing with a *set* of variables, and there is a convenient notation in common use that we can adopt. The notation

$$\{A_K,\ K=1(1)30\}$$

is a shorthand equivalent to listing every element A_1 through A_{30}. Explanation of this notation is given below.

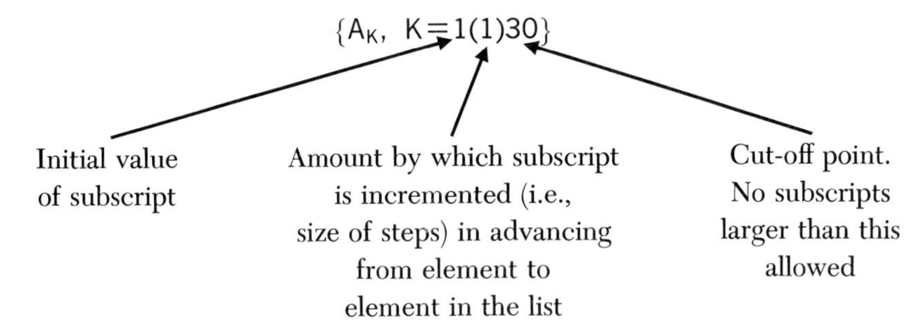
{A_K, K=1(1)30}
Initial value of subscript
Amount by which subscript is incremented (i.e., size of steps) in advancing from element to element in the list
Cut-off point. No subscripts larger than this allowed

Example. The notation

$$\{A_J,\ J=7(5)23\}$$

denotes

$$A_7,\ A_{12},\ A_{17},\ A_{22}$$

This type of notation may be used either in an input or in an output box. In nearly all uses in this text, the initial value and the increment will both be one. The input and output boxes, 2 and 5 of Figure 3-24*b*, for example, could be replaced by

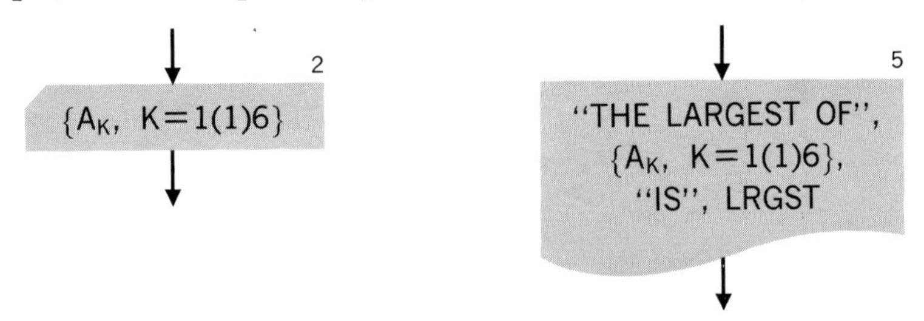
2
{A_K, K=1(1)6}
5
"THE LARGEST OF",
{A_K, K=1(1)6},
"IS", LRGST

Any variable of an algorithm may be employed as a subscript. Thus, A_J, B_L, C_i, X_m are all perfectly acceptable forms. The variable used as a subscript in the set notation may also be chosen arbitrarily. Thus, $\{P_i,\ i=1(1)4\}$ and $\{P_s,\ s=1(1)4\}$ are both acceptable. Moreover, they are also equivalent in meaning. Both define the set: $\{P_1, P_2, P_3, P_4\}$.

EXERCISES 3-6, SET A

Problems 1 and 2. When we revised the carnival wheel problem in Exercise 11, Section 3-4, we could have employed a multi-way condition box to model the new point rule. In Figure 3-26*a* you can see one way to achieve that objective.

A student now proposes an alternative solution, shown in Figure 3-26*b*. He claims it is simpler, equivalent, and an inherently more general solution. Study these two flow charts carefully and answer the two questions given below.

1. Under what circumstances are the flow charts equivalent?
2. In what sense can *b* be construed to be more general than *a*?

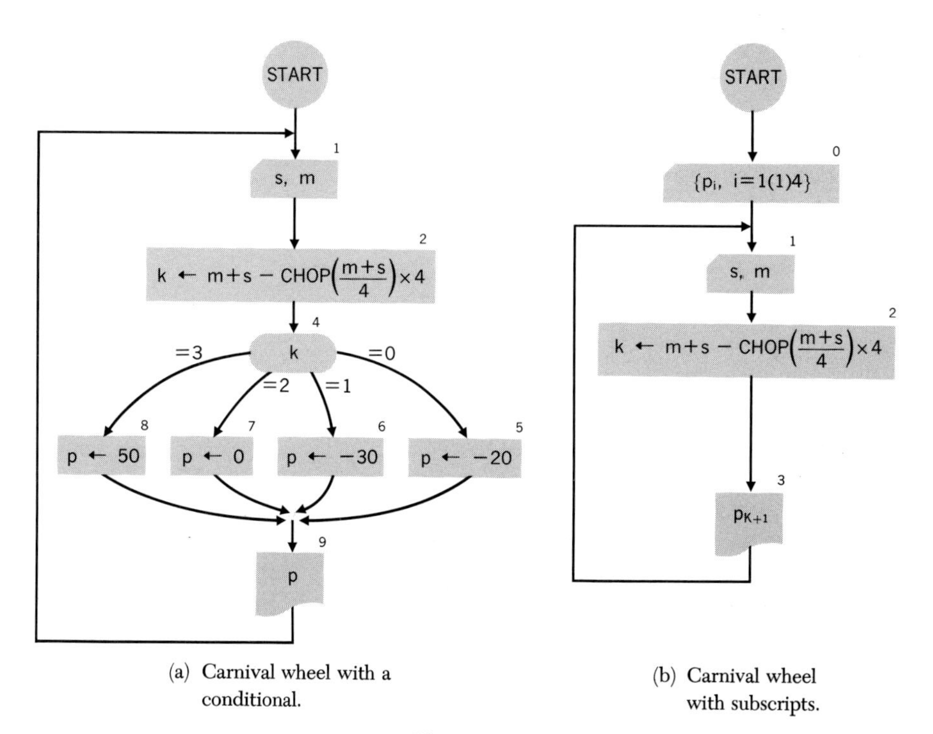

(a) Carnival wheel with a conditional.

(b) Carnival wheel with subscripts.

Figure 3-26

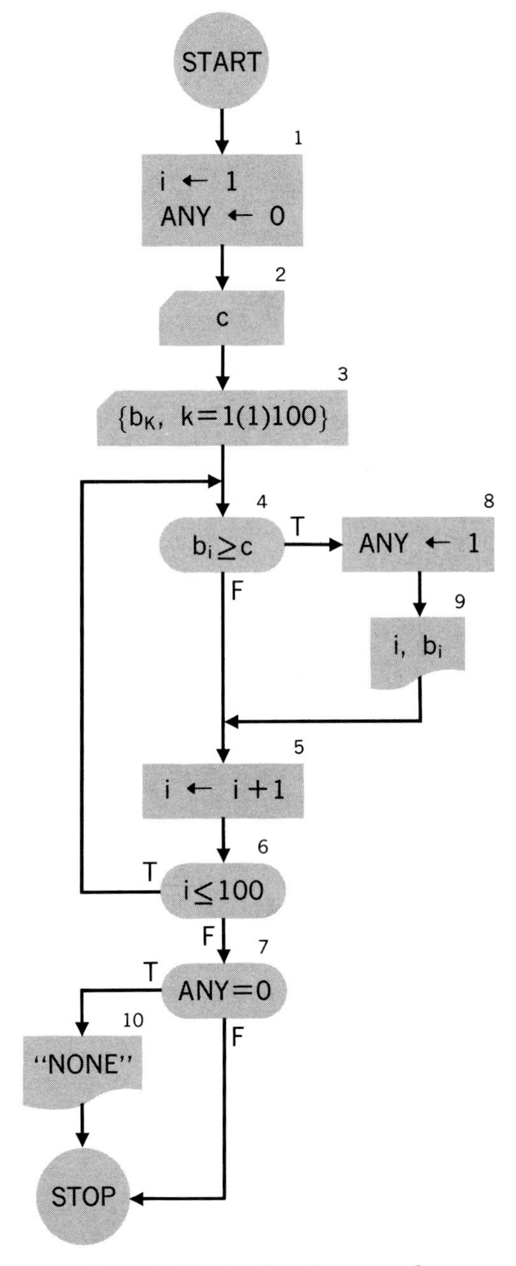

Figure 3-27 An algorithm to study.

Problems 3 through 7. The flow chart in Figure 3-27 is an algorithm that accomplishes the following steps.

(a) Inputs a number c.
(b) Inputs 100 numbers $b_1, b_2, \ldots, b_{100}$.
(c) Determines and prints a list of the b_i that satisfy the relation

$$b_i \geq c$$

Study the flow chart carefully and answer the following questions.

3. How many times is box 6 executed?

4. How many times is box 8 executed?

5. Under what circumstance will box 10 be executed? The remark is made that ANY is a "switch variable"; that is, it is used like railroaders use a rail switch. Explain.

6. Is it really necessary for there to be more than one value of b in memory at any given time in order to achieve the same output objectives for this program? Another way of asking this question is, "Are subscripts really necessary in this algorithm?" If your answer is no, redraw the flow chart accordingly, putting a check mark next to each box you change.

7. How would you modify either Figure 3-27 or your modified version, resulting from 6, to generalize the flow chart, so that instead of reading 100 elements for b we read any given number n of them?

8. Draw a flow chart for inputting n and a vector $a_0, a_1, \ldots, a_n$. The a's are considered to be the coefficients of the polynomial

$$a_0 + a_1x + a_2x^2 + \cdots + a_nx^n$$

and n is its apparent degree. However, some or all of the coefficients may be zero. Construct a flow chart to determine the actual degree, m, of the polynomial. Of course, $m \leq n$ and m can be determined by searching the set of coefficients for the nonzero element with the highest subscript. Output m and the coefficients from a_0 through a_m inclusive. If all the coefficients are zero, do not print any coefficients but let the printed value of m be -1.

Additional Remarks on Subscripts

Based on our previous discussions, the variable X_N designates one of a set of window boxes inscribed with $X_1, X_2, X_3, \ldots$. Which box is designated depends on the current value of the variable N. Now, what do we mean by X_J? By the same reasoning, X_J designates one of the boxes $X_1, X_2, X_3 \ldots$, depending on the current value of the variable J. X_N and X_J may designate different boxes (if $N \neq J$) or may designate the same box (if $N = J$).

Now, what do you think X_{N+1} should mean? Apparently, it should designate one of the boxes inscribed with X_1, X_2, X_3, ... Which of these is designated should depend on the current value of the variable N. Suppose the value of N is 3. Then $N+1$ is 4 and X_{N+1} really means X_4. From this example you will correctly guess that arithmetic expressions can be used as subscripts. However, procedural languages sometimes place limits on the complexity of expressions used as subscripts (see your language supplement). In this text we will normally avoid expressions more complicated than $N+1$ (or $N+K$) as subscripts.

In summary, if the subscript of a variable is an expression, it must be possible to compute the value of this subscript each time the subscripted variable is encountered in a flow-chart box. The subscript expression must be *integer*-valued. Like any expression, a subscript expression is "computable" if we have previously assigned values for every variable that appears in the subscript expression.

Sorting Example

Frequently in computing we have to put numbers (or other things, like names) into some kind of order. This "sorting" seems like a very simple thing, but the problem arises so often as part of larger problems that much effort has been spent to be able to do sorting as efficiently as possible. Many algorithms have been invented and many refinements made for this purpose. Now we will develop one of many possible algorithms for sorting. We will study other sorting algorithms later.

In sorting, the problem is this: if we input a set of numbers:

5 7 2 6 5 9

we should output:

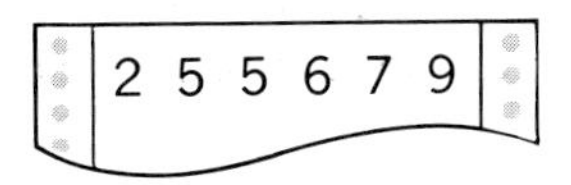

Consider a list of input variables with values:

A_1	A_2	A_3	A_4	A_5	A_6
5	7	2	6	5	9

We scan the values from left to right until we encounter the first place where the values decrease. (If there is no such decrease, then the values are already in increasing order.) In the above example, we find this first decrease when going from A_2 to A_3. Interchange these values:

A_1	A_2	A_3	A_4	A_5	A_6
5	2	7	6	5	9

What next? We seem to have made some progress, so let's treat this list just like a brand new one, that is, go back to the beginning and scan from left to right, etc.

This almost seems too simple to work. Nevertheless, we observe that as long as the list is not in increasing order, there will always be another interchange to do. Each interchange affects the relative order of just one pair of values and, since there are only finitely many such pairs, the algorithm must terminate. Perhaps you would like to try the process with some playing cards.

Next, we do a flow chart for this algorithm. The basic idea is the interchange of A_K and A_{K+1} which, experienced as we have become, we know to represent as

$$\begin{aligned} \text{COPY} &\leftarrow A_K \\ A_K &\leftarrow A_{K+1} \\ A_{K+1} &\leftarrow \text{COPY} \end{aligned}$$

We execute this interchange only if $A_K > A_{K+1}$. Thus, the condition box:

$$A_K > A_{K+1} \quad (\text{T} \rightarrow;\ \text{F} \downarrow)$$

If false, we go to the next position in the list,

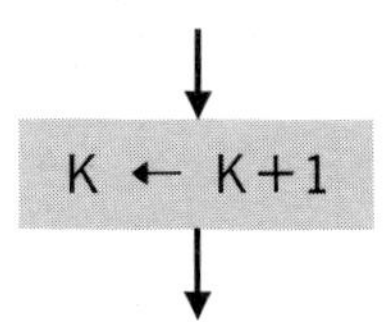

and repeat the test (that is, return to the condition box). On emerging from the interchange box, we set K back to 1 and start over. We now have the skeleton of Figure 3-28.

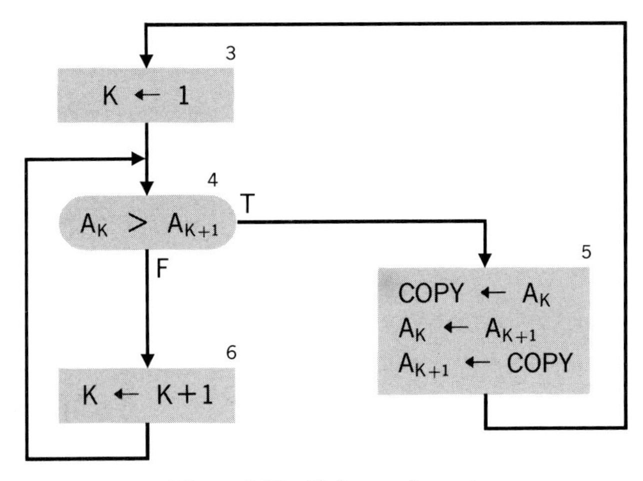

Figure 3-28 Skeleton of a sort.

Only input, output, and stopping mechanisms are needed. We should also decide on how large a list of numbers the flow chart should be set up to handle. One time we may want to sort 13 numbers, another time 200, or perhaps 1000. Why not let the variable N denote the length of the list? This is all put together in Figure 3-29.

"Vectors"

Before we leave this section, there is a terminology we would like to introduce in connection with subscripted variables. Let's suppose we have a subscripted variable such as

$$\{X_I, I = 1(1)6\}$$

It is then customary to refer to the list (or linear array):

$$X_1, X_2, X_3, X_4, X_5, X_6$$

or the list of values of these variables:

$$7, 9.2, 32, 17, -2.73, 0$$

as a "*vector*." The individual entries in this list are referred to as the "*components*" of the vector. This is in agreement with mathematical usage. Engineers and physicists often speak of a vector as having a magnitude and direction, but that view is really just a special example of our mathematical description of a vector.

Mathematical notation requires that the list of components comprising a vector be enclosed in parentheses; as

$$(X_1,\ X_2,\ X_3,\ X_4,\ X_5,\ X_6)$$

We will not insist on these outer parentheses in our computer work.

We will frequently use terminology such as "the vector X," to designate the list

$$X_1, X_2, X_3, X_4, X_5, X_6$$

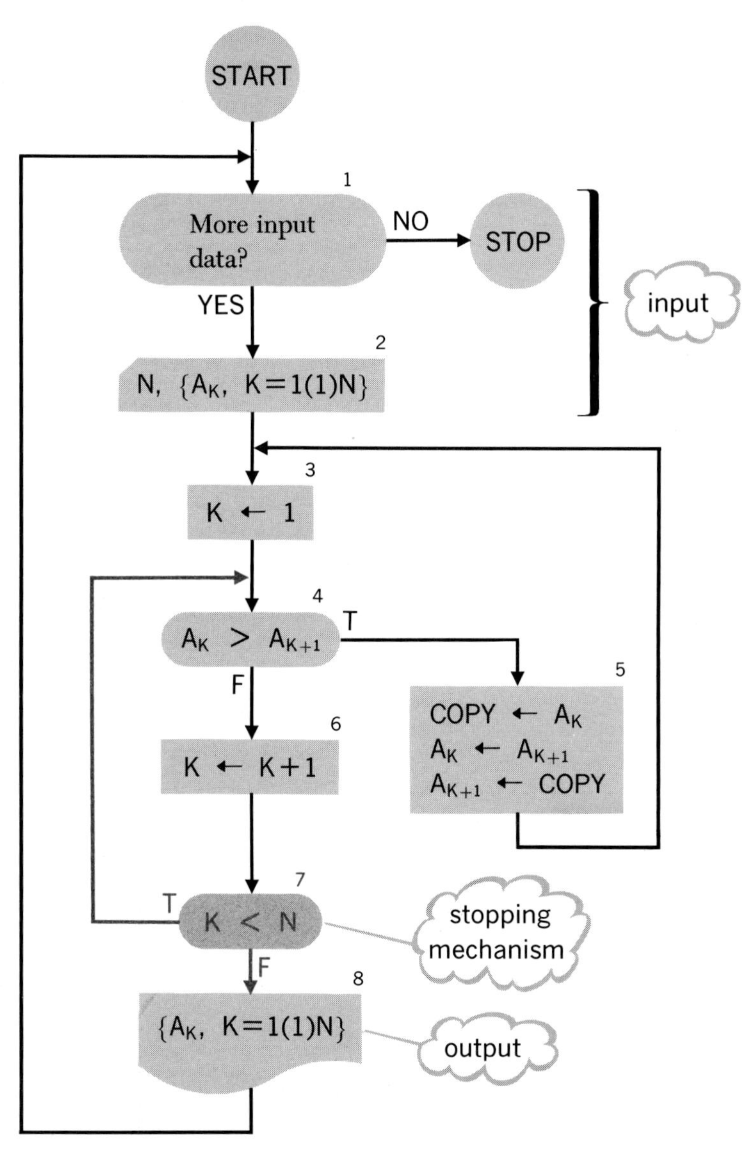

Figure 3-29 Sort.

EXERCISES 3-6, SET B

This group of exercises concerns the sorting algorithm given in Figure 3-29.

1. Suppose you want to test the algorithm by determining whether the list

$$7 \quad 2 \quad -5 \quad 4$$

will be properly sorted in ascending order, i.e.,

$$-5 \quad 2 \quad 4 \quad 7$$

(a) What are the values of the input data at box 2?

(b) With these input data, trace through the algorithm beginning at box 3, showing the box numbers in the sequence they are actually executed until box 8 is reached. Use a table like the one given here. It is partially filled for this problem to help you get started.

Sequence \ Box	3	4	5	6	7	8	Assigned Value of K
1	√						1
2		√					
3			√				
4	√						1
5		√					
6				√			2
7							
8							
9							
.							
.							
.							

Scratch Pad for a Vector

1	~~7~~	2
2	~~2~~	7
3	−5	
4	4	

(c) How many times in this sequence has a flow-chart box (including box 8) been executed before returning to box 1?

(d) How many times is box 4 reached?

2. By now you should be thoroughly convinced this algorithm will work every time. Suppose the values to be sorted are

$$-9 \quad 5 \quad 9 \quad 12$$

That is, they are already in ascending order. How many times will box 4 be executed before box 8 is reached?

3. What if the input values are already sorted but in opposite order, say,

$$12 \quad 9 \quad 5 \quad -9$$

How many executions of box 4?

Save your results for problems 1, 2, and 3. In the next chapter we will look at another sorting algorithm and will wish to compare with corresponding results of the new algorithm.

EXERCISES 3-6, SET C

1. There are 101 members in a youth symphony orchestra about to make a concert tour. A reporter asks the conductor, "What is the median age of your members?" The conductor answered, "I don't know, but here is an alphabetical list of the players' names and ages."

(a) For the purposes of this exercise we will define the median of an ordered set of numbers to be the "middle" one of the set—in other words, there are as many preceding it as following it. For example, in the set

$$3, 7, 24, 35, 67, 81, 97$$

the median is 35.

Draw a flow chart to find the median age of the players from the list of ages provided, which cannot be assumed to be in numerical order.

(b) The definition of the median given above does not work if the number of items is even. For example, there is no "middle" number in the sequence

$$4, 17, 31, 43, 57, 68.$$

In this case the median could be defined to be the mean of the two numbers adjacent to the "split"—in the above case $(31 + 43)/2 = 37$.

Develop an expression that will determine the median of an ordered set of n numbers $a_1, a_2, \ldots, a_n$. Your answer should be one expression that gives the correct answer for n either odd or even. (*Hint.* You will find the CHOP function useful.)

(c) Prepare a flow chart similar to the one prepared in part *a*, but designed to work for an orchestra containing an arbitrary number of players, and to produce not only the median age, but also the ages of the oldest and youngest players.

2. In Figure 3-7 we tallied advanced placement exam scores in three categories: LOW, MID, HIGH. Draw a new flow chart for an algorithm that tallies the exact number obtaining each score from 0 to 150. In order to do this use a subscripted variable S_1, S_2, S_3, . . . , where S_{84}, for example, keeps a tally of the number of tests with a score of 84. Output the final values in this tally.

3. Revise the flow chart in the preceding exercise to output the *decile points* instead of all the tallies. The first decile is that score such that ten percent of the students had scores greater than or equal to it and ninety percent had scores less than it; the second decile is that score such that twenty percent of the students had scores greater than or equal to it and eighty percent had scores less than it, and so on.

3-7 DOUBLE SUBSCRIPTS

Once you have mastered the use of subscripted variables in computing you will find that double subscripts offer very little additional difficulty.

In mathematics, data often come to us in a "rectangular array" of rows and columns, as illustrated in Figure 3-30.

The mathematical term for such a rectangular array is "*matrix.*" It is hard to believe how often these matrices crop up.

One way in which such a matrix as the above might occur is as the "coefficient matrix" of a system of equations:

$$\begin{aligned} 5W + 2X + 7Y &= 1 \\ 9W - 4X + 0Y &= 2 \\ 6W + 7X + 3Y &= -2 \end{aligned}$$

The above matrix has three rows and four columns. Columns are vertical like the columns on a Greek temple. The individual numbers appearing in the array are called "entries." When you want to discuss the entry in a certain position, you can specify the position by giving the row and the column.

We see in Figure 3-31 that a matrix is essentially a "table."

Double subscripts make their appearance when we introduce the no-

$$\begin{matrix} 5 & 2 & 7 & 1 \\ 9 & -4 & 0 & 2 \\ 6 & 7 & 3 & -2 \end{matrix}$$

Figure 3-30 Matrix.

Column / Row	1	2	3	4
1	5	2	7	1
2	9	−4	0	2
3	6	7	3	−2

Figure 3-31 The matrix as a table.

tation used in talking about entries in a matrix. We use a variable with two subscripts

$$A_{I,J}$$

to indicate the entry in the I row and the J column. *The row is always given first and the column second.* Thus, if we let A represent the matrix at the beginning of this section, as tabulated in Figure 3-31, then the value of $A_{2,3}$ is 0 while that of $A_{3,2}$ is 7.

As in the case of singly subscripted variables, we consider that there is a window box associated with each of the twelve variables $A_{1,1}$, $A_{1,2}$ and so forth, as suggested in Figure 3-32.

If we wish to input a table into these window boxes, we could indicate this on a flow chart by the input box in Figure 3-33.

It would be good to have some notation (as in the last section) to refer to an entire matrix or to portions thereof. An extension of our previous notation is shown in Figure 3-34.

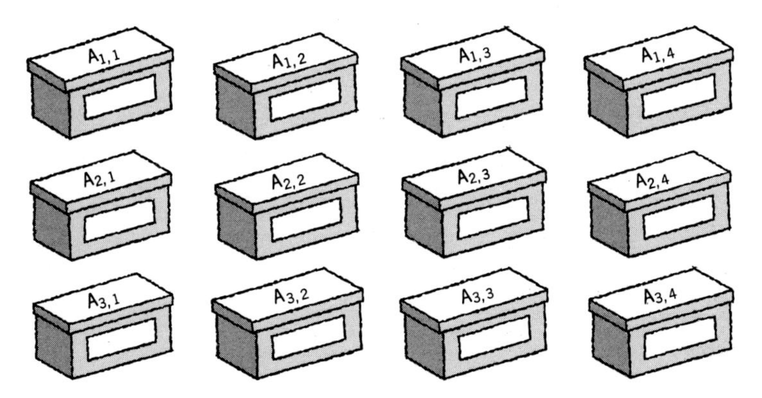

Figure 3-32 Window boxes for subscripted variables.

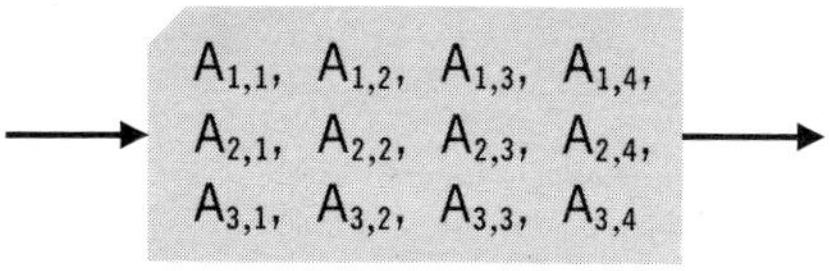

$$\longrightarrow \begin{array}{l} A_{1,1}, A_{1,2}, A_{1,3}, A_{1,4}, \\ A_{2,1}, A_{2,2}, A_{2,3}, A_{2,4}, \\ A_{3,1}, A_{3,2}, A_{3,3}, A_{3,4} \end{array} \longrightarrow$$

Figure 3-33 Input box for subscripted variables.

This notation is an abbreviation for what appears in Figure 3-33. Mathematicians and computer programmers like to use such notation because it allows naming particular ordered subsets of matrix elements in an exact way. Thus, the way the braces are used in Figure 3-34 indicates that each row is read in completely (left to right) before going on to the next row. This could be important to know if the table is too large to put onto one card. We would then put each row (rather than each column)on a separate card. For our flow-chart language, however, this information is quite superfluous. All we need to know is that an input box like that in Figure 3-34 will cause entries of a matrix like that in Figure 3-30 to be assigned to the appropriate variables represented in Figure 3-32.

Significant computations with doubly subscripted variables usually involve complicated looping and will, therefore, be left to the next chapter. We content ourselves here with a very simple example illustrating the use of double subscripts in flow charts.

Example. A zero sum game

We are given the matrix:

$$\begin{matrix} 6 & 2 & 5 & 4 & 3 & 1 \\ 9 & 0 & 8 & 3 & 2 & 6 \\ 1 & 8 & 5 & 4 & 1 & 1 \\ 8 & 3 & 7 & 3 & 6 & 3 \\ 5 & 5 & 4 & 8 & 1 & 2 \\ 3 & 2 & 1 & 6 & 4 & 8 \end{matrix}$$

We now describe a game employing this matrix. We have two dice, one green and one red. We roll the dice and let K denote the number on the green die and L that on the red die. Now we increase our score by the sum of the entries in the Kth row and we deduct from our score the sum of the entries in the Lth column. Can you see why this is called a "zero sum" game? *Hint.* Around what total score will the game hover after a large number of rolls of the dice?

We will construct a flow chart for this game. An outline of the steps involved in the problem is as follows.

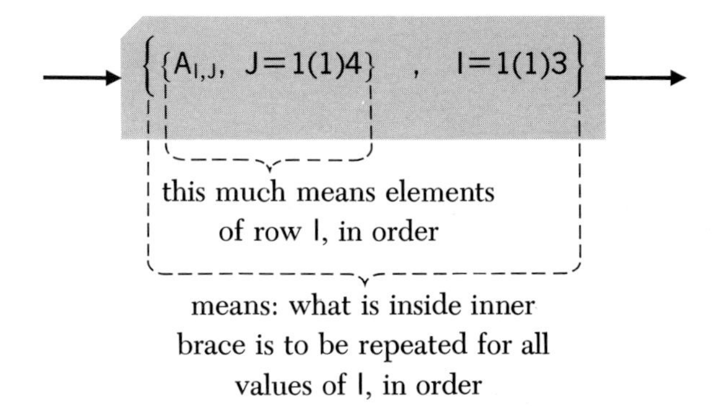

Figure 3-34 Abbreviated input statement for doubly-subscripted variables.

1. Input the given matrix.
2. Input values for K and L.
3. Calculate the sum of the entries in the Kth row.
4. Calculate the sum of entries in the Lth column.
5. Compute the difference of the values in steps 3 and 4.
6. Print out this difference.

After a detailed analysis of step 3, the flow chart should offer little difficulty. The analysis of this detail is given in Figure 3-35.

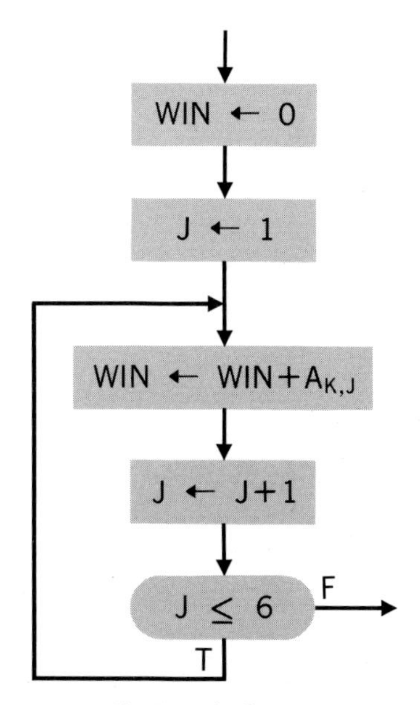

Figure 3-35 Detail of zero sum game.

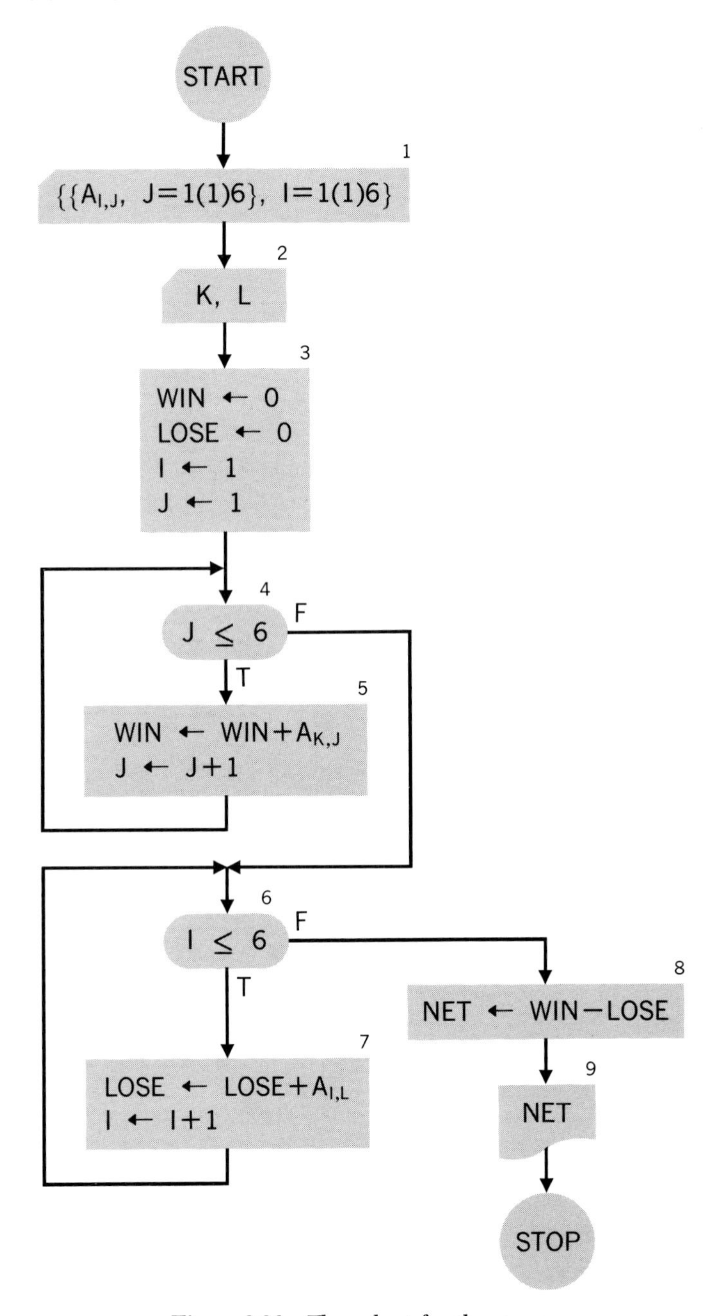

Figure 3-36 Flow chart for the game.

You should see that when we finally come out of this loop the value of WIN is the sum of the entries in the Kth row of the matrix. Notice that the value of K, which determines the row in which entries are summed, remains the same during any one execution of the loop.

Now we exhibit the entire flow chart for this game in Figure 3-36.

It may be well to point out for contrast an alternative flow chart to Figure 3-36, which makes a sensible use of subscripted variable methods, for this problem and leads to a simpler program (Figure 3-37).

However, we lose some potential generality with this approach. Notice that in principle this game could also be played using larger matrices, say, 8×8, 10×10, etc. Of course, for each new size we would need either dice with more faces, like octahedrons, or some other device for generating pairs of numbers. To generalize Figure 3-36 for any size array we need change only the 6's (where they appear in boxes 1, 4, and 6) to N and add a box 0 to the flow chart at the start to read in this value of N—which could vary from game to game. Such generalization is not possible with the approach used in Figure 3-37. In short, while producing a shorter program, Figure 3-37 captures less of the spirit of our algorithmic method.

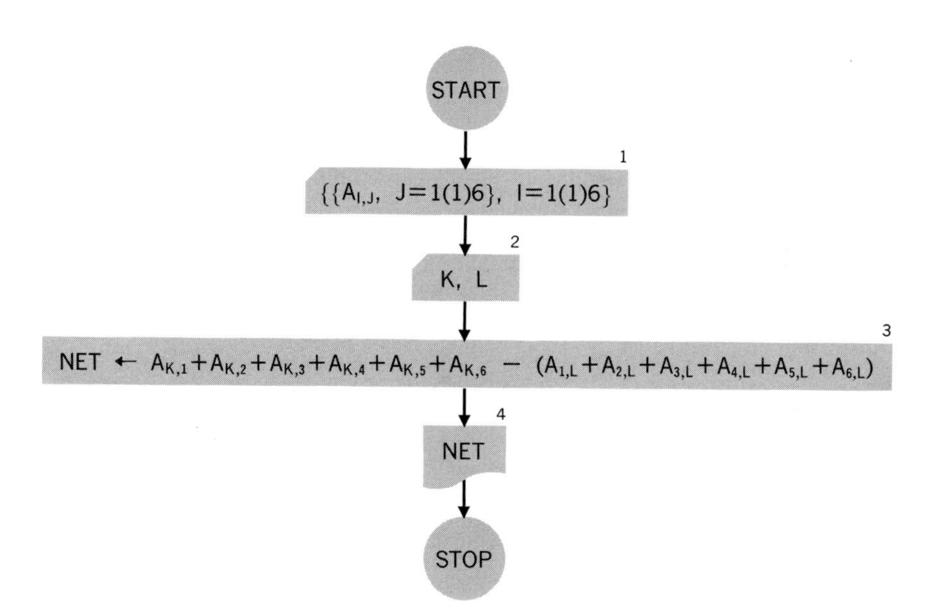

Figure 3-37 Less instructive alternative.

EXERCISES 3-7

In each of the following five exercises, assume that all the variables or matrix entries that are mentioned are already assigned initial values. Your job is to flowchart the action described. (These are some of the elementary operations often performed with matrices. They are usually pieces of larger problems.)

For example, the matrix P has 22 rows and 27 columns. Find the sum of the absolute values of all entries in row L, where L has already been assigned a value.

A possible answer is shown in Figure 3-38.

1. For the same matrix P, find the sum of all but one of the entries in the Kth column. The exception is the entry in row 12 of that column. Call the sum being generated COLSUM.

2. For the same matrix P, add to each entry in row L the value of the corresponding entry (same column) of row M. As an actual example with a much smaller matrix, Q, we would have:

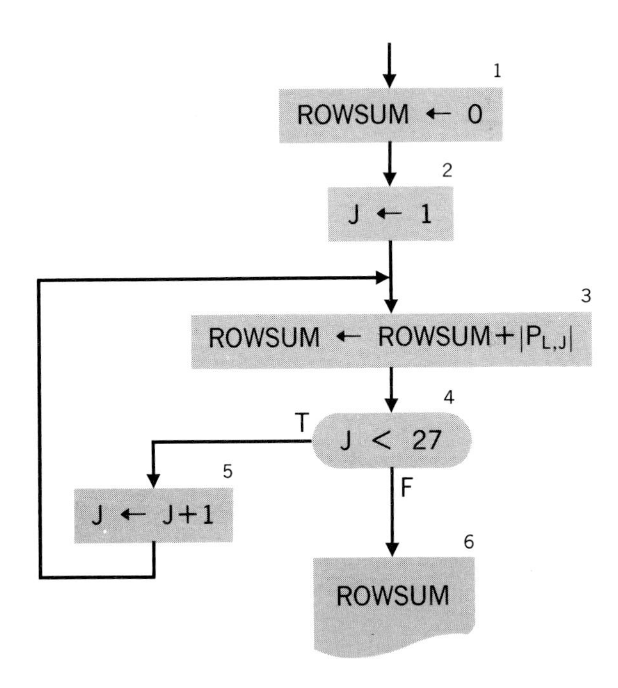

Figure 3-38

	Before						After				
	3	4	2	5	−4		3	4	2	5	−4
Row L	3	9	1	2	−4	⇒	4	10	3	5	−2
Row M	1	1	2	3	2		1	1	2	3	2

3. For the same matrix P, add to each entry in row L, *except in the* K*th* entry, two times the corresponding value of the Mth row.

4. For the same matrix P, interchange row L with row M.

5. For the same matrix P, find the entry in row L having the largest magnitude. Divide every entry in row L by the entry of largest magnitude.

CHAPTER 4

LOOPING

4-1 LOOPING

Study of the concept of *branching* in preceding chapters enabled us to develop some fairly complicated flow charts involving looping. "Looping" refers to the kind of "connections" that result in passing through the same box twice or many times during the course of a computation.

In this chapter we will study looping in more detail. Then we will develop a systematic way of treating one very important kind of looping.

We commence by putting down side-by-side in Figure 4-1 two different flow charts for the Fibonacci sequence problem of Section 1-2. Remember that the Fibonacci sequence,

$$1, 1, 2, 3, 5, 8, 13, 21, 34, \ldots$$

has the property that each term (after the two 1's) is the sum of its two immediate predecessors.

The flow chart in Figure 4-1*a* represents an algorithm for computing and printing in order all terms of the Fibonacci sequence that are less than 10000. The flow chart in Figure 4-1*b* represents an algorithm for computing and printing a numbered list of the first 1000 terms of the Fibonacci sequence.

We can see that box 5 is exactly the same in each flow chart. This box contains the fundamental computation in this algorithm.

Each flow chart has a loop, i.e., boxes 3, 4, 5 in the first flow chart and boxes 3, 4, 5, 6 in the second. These sequences of boxes are passed through (or "executed") over and over again. Each loop is equipped with an absolutely certain exit. In Figure 4-1*a* we exit or *branch out* of the loop as soon as the variable LTERM exceeds 10000. In Figure 4-1*b* we exit when J exceeds 1000. In Figure 4-1*b* the loop will be executed 1000 times. In Figure 4-1*a* it is not at all clear how many times the loop will be executed.

The reason that we can tell the number of times the loop will be executed in Figure 4-1*b* is that the loop is *controlled by a counter*, whereas this is not the case in Figure 4-1*a*. The variable J works exactly like a counter (Figure 4-2). It is augmented, stepped-up, or incremented by one each time we pass through the loop. This is represented by box 6 in Figure 4-1*b*. Furthermore, box 2 in this figure sets the counter to 1 at the start. Thus, the value of J gives us the number of transits through the loop we have made (including the one we are currently making).

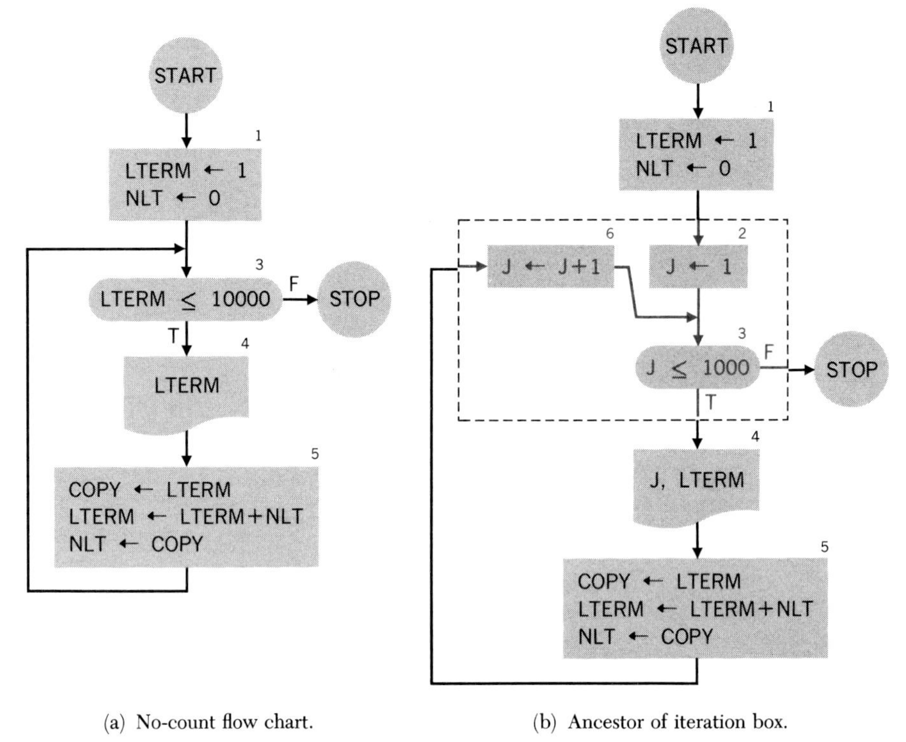

(a) No-count flow chart. (b) Ancestor of iteration box.

Figure 4-1 Two flow charts for the Fibonacci sequence.

In addition to acting as a counter, J has one additional duty; it controls the exit switch. When J counts up to 1000, it throws the switch allowing us to exit from the loop. Here we exit to a → STOP, but we could as well have gone to some other task. This "controlling" duty of the variable J is seen in box 3.

To emphasize the distinction, we present still another flow chart, Figure 4-3, in which a counter has been added to Figure 4-1*a* to print out a numbered list. We see that the variable J in Figure 4-3 has the same counting duty as the variable J in Figure 4-1*b*, but it does not control the exit switch.

We see then that the variable J in Figure 4-1*b* has both counting and switching duties. You can conceive of J as a switchman who has been given the instructions. "Let the first 1000 through and then throw the switch."

The situation within the dashed lines of Figure 4-1*b* occurs so often that we introduce a special box to do the work of all three boxes.

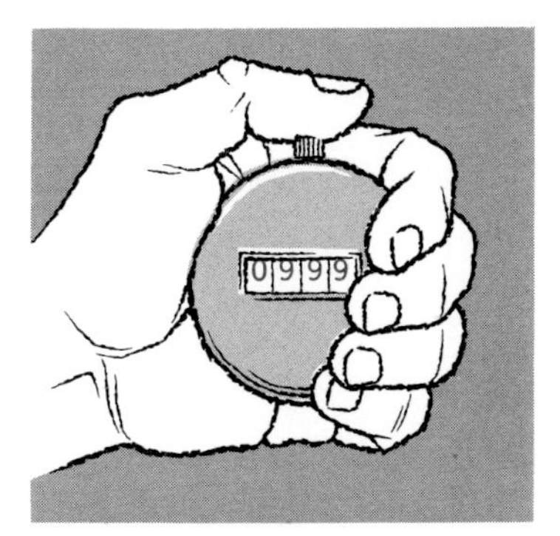

Figure 4-2 The variable J.

The three-compartment box in Figure 4-5 is shorthand for the three boxes in Figure 4-4. Such a box can be used whenever a counter controls (the exit switch for) a loop. The exits from the two compartments on the

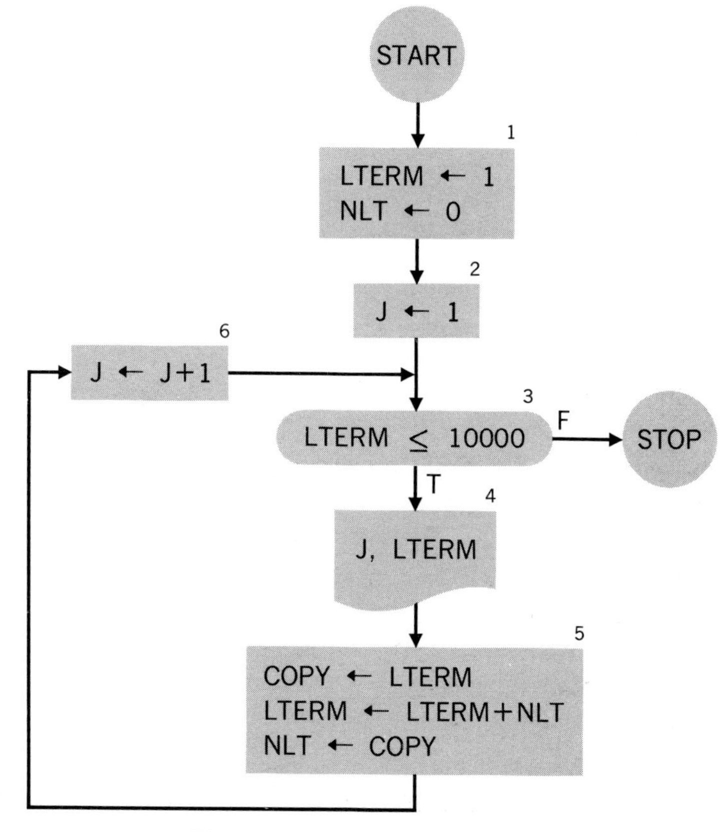

Figure 4-3 Noncontrolling counter.

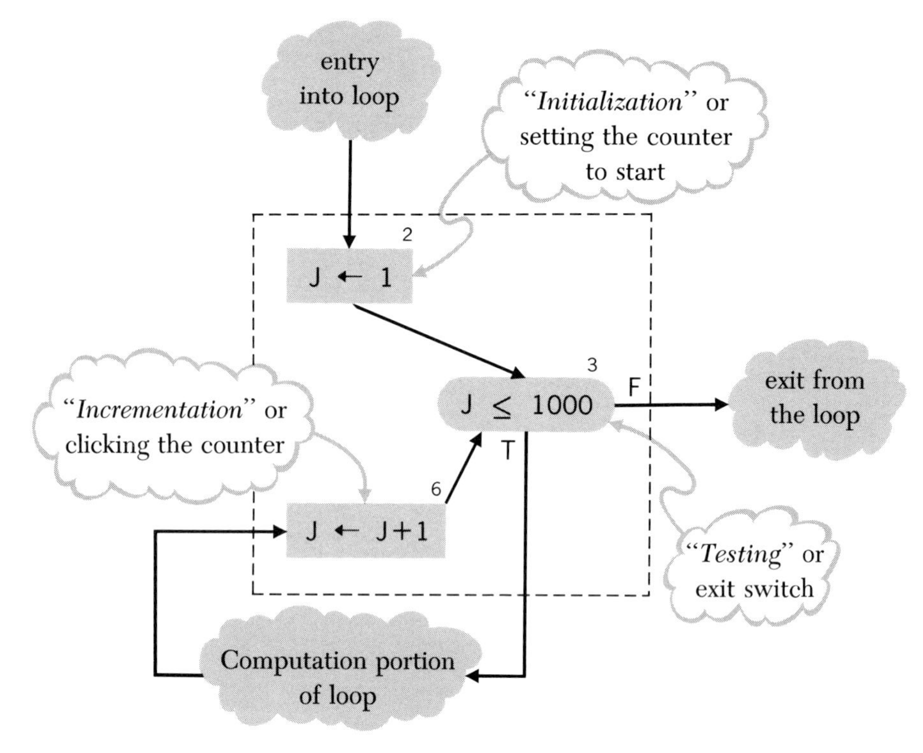

Figure 4-4 Embryo iteration box.

left lead into the larger compartment on the right. We draw a schematic *iteration box* to fix the names of the compartments (Figure 4-6). Returning to our example of the Fibonacci sequence, we find that Figure 4-1*b* can be replaced by Figure 4-7.

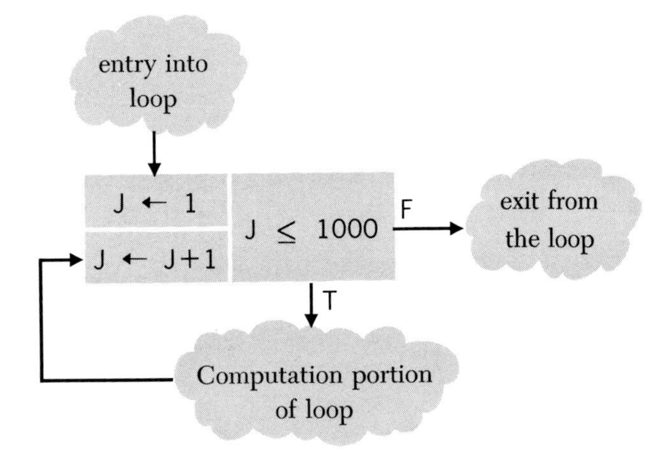

Figure 4-5 Birth of the iteration box.

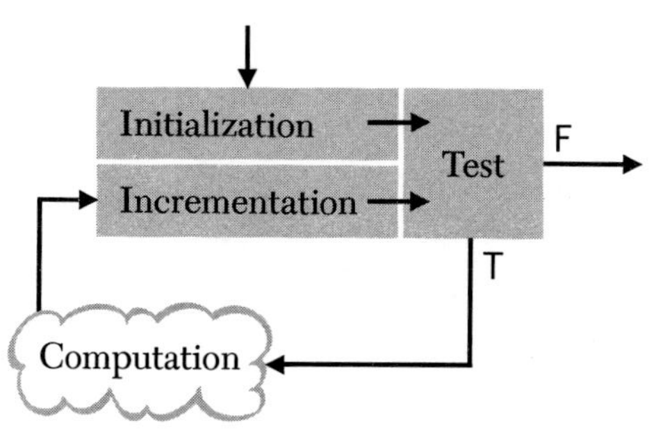

Figure 4-6

In Figure 4-7 box 2 replaces boxes 2, 3, and 6 of Figure 4-1*b*. If you have understood what it is that an iteration box does, then Figure 4-7 should be easier to read than Figure 4-1*b*. We will soon see that iteration boxes make flow charts easier to write, too, since, whenever we realize (or even suspect) that we have a loop controlled by a counter, we draw the iteration box and try to hang the loop on it.

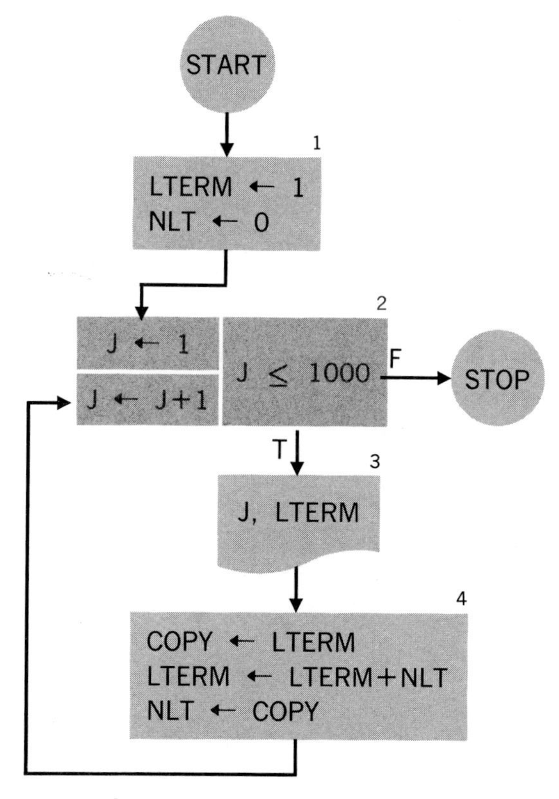

Figure 4-7 Fibonacci sequence algorithm with an iteration box.

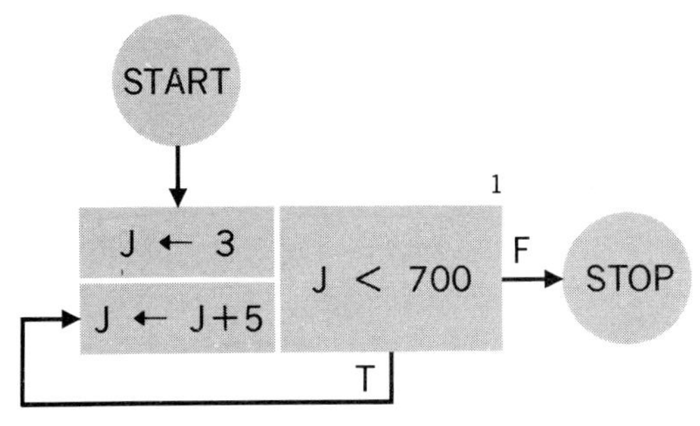

Figure 4-8 The "Little Dandy" flow chart.

We must remember that the heart of the loop is in the computation portion. The iteration box merely represents the in and out mechanism. Conceivably, however, the computation portion could be omitted, as is suggested in Figure 4-8. The best that can be said of this "algorithm" is that having no output, it saves paper. This flow chart does show us that we can initiate with integers other than 1, increment with integers other than 1, and exit on integers other than 1000. We give, in Figure 4-9, a diagram showing the most general forms of iteration box used in this course.

EXERCISES 4-1

1. Using an iteration box, write a complete algorithm that does the following.

(a) Inputs M numerical values for a vector beginning at VEC_1. These input values are already arranged in nonascending numerical order.

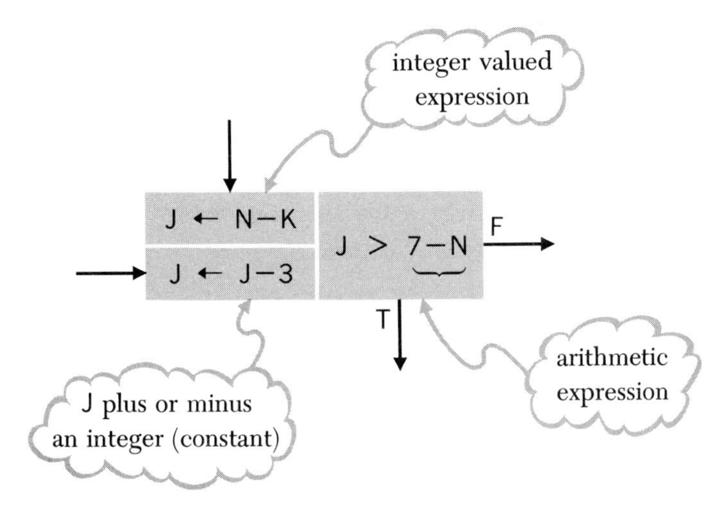

Figure 4-9

(b) Searches, beginning at VEC_1, for a pair of duplicate values.
(c) If a pair of duplicate values is found, prints out the duplicated value and the index value (subscript) of the first element of the duplicate pair and stops.
(d) If no pair of duplicates is found, prints out an appropriate message and stops.

2. You are given a flow chart in Figure 4-10.

(a) What, in simple terms, does this algorithm do? Give a clear description.
(b) Suppose the following six input values are assigned to the A vector at box 1:

$$3, -4, 6, 6, 7, 12$$

What values, if any, will be printed at box 6?

3. Study the flow chart in Figure 4-11, and answer the following questions.

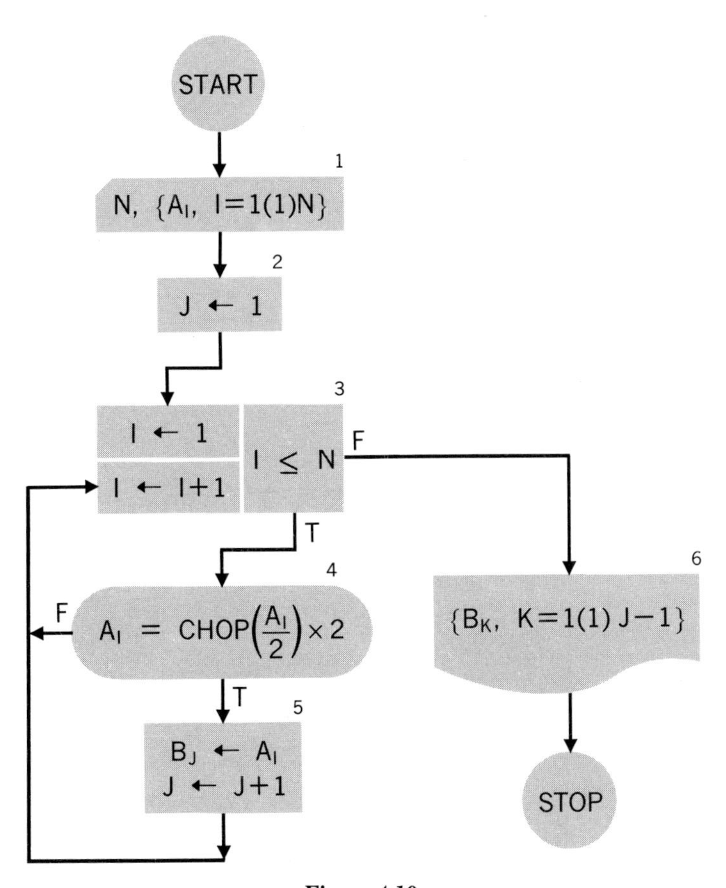

Figure 4-10

(a) Show what is printed on the first five lines of the output from this algorithm.

(b) Redraw this flow chart employing an iteration box.

4. A toy distributor has made a bargain purchase of 10,000 small toys packaged in rectangular boxes of varied size. He intends to put the boxes into brightly colored plastic spheres and resell them as surprise packages. How-

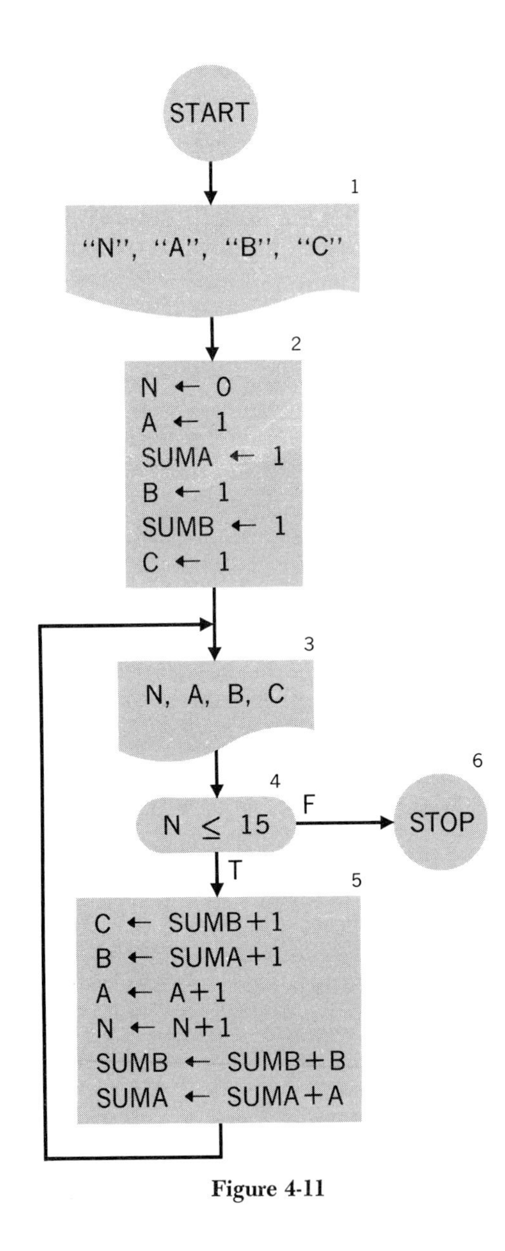

Figure 4-11

ever, he needs to know how many spheres of each diameter (4, 6, 8, 10, and 12 inches) he will need. Since the diagonal

$$D = \sqrt{A^2 + B^2 + C^2}$$

of a rectangular box having sides A, B, and C is its largest measurement, the distributor needs to calculate the diagonal lengths of the boxes and then to determine the number of diagonals that are of 4 inches or less, the number of diagonals that are between 4 and 6 inches, and so on.

In this problem we imagine that the distributor decides to calculate D for each of the 10,000 boxes. He has given each box an identification number (ID) and has measured A, B, and C in each case. Your job is to draw a flow chart that would produce a printed table, each line having five entries, i.e., numbers consisting of the input values for ID, A, B, and C, and the computed value of D. Each line of the printed table is to correspond to one packaged toy. Use an iteration box. Only four flow-chart boxes are needed—not counting

START and STOP .

5. This problem is an extension of Problem 4. Here we shall assume the toy distributor realizes that there is an easier way to tally the desired number of plastic spheres of each diameter than by a manual scan of a 10,000-line table produced by the computer. We leave it to you to modify the flow chart prepared in Problem 4 so that instead of printing the long table, the algorithm tallies the number of spheres needed of each size and prints these tallies after processing the 10,000 data sets.

6. In Figure 4-7 we studied a way to generate the terms of the Fibonacci sequence. Now you are to flowchart a related algorithm: generate both the Fibonacci sequence and its sum sequence. Let F_J be the Jth term of the Fibonacci sequence. Thus, F_3 is 2, F_4 is 3, F_5 is 5, etc. Let S_J be the sum of all terms of the Fibonacci sequence up to and including the Jth term.

$$S_5 = 1 + 1 + 2 + 3 + 5 = 12$$
$$S_6 = 1 + 1 + 2 + 3 + 5 + 8 = 20, \text{ etc.}$$

Each term of the S-sequence is a cumulative sum. Your flow chart should generate pairs of values of these two sequences and print the pairs as they are generated. The first pair to be printed is F_3, S_1, and the second is F_4, S_2, etc. The algorithm should terminate after printing 60 such pairs.

As an added challenge, see if you can write the flow chart without using subscripts.

7. Recall Figure 3-26*b*, which was an algorithm for computing the points won or lost in one spin of the carnival wheel (i.e., for one data pair s and m).

This algorithm allowed us to have an arbitrary point rule by input of four values into vector elements p_1, p_2, p_3, p_4.

Now suppose we are interested in determining our score after a large number, say N, of the arbitrarily chosen data pairs s, m. For the moment we won't concern ourselves with where these data pairs came from. Your job is to revise the flow chart in Figure 3-26*b* so that it now does the following.

(a) Inputs values of p_i for a 4-point rule.
(b) Determines a point value for each of N data pairs, s, m and, instead of printing these values, forms their sum (in SUM).
(c) After the N data pairs have been "processed," prints N and SUM using appropriate literals to explain the significance of the values that are printed. For example, "After 35 spins your score is 552 points."

If you can't fight your way through this exercise just yet—postpone it until after you have done several of the exercises in Set A of the next section.

8. *Simplified Model of Payroll Computation.* The workers in a plant are assigned numbers from 1 to N. Let T_i be the number of hours worked by worker number i and let R_i be his hourly rate of pay. The payroll department wishes to input the time data obtained from the Timekeepers' Department and the rate figures obtained from the Personnel Department and output the weekly wages for each worker and the total payroll.

(a) Draw a flow chart to do this job. You may assume that the Timekeepers' data comes in the form of an ordered list of the T_i's from 1 to N and that Personnel's data is a second and separate ordered list of the R_i's from 1 to N.
(b) In actual payroll applications, it is often found that N is so large that it is impractical to input the entire T and the entire R vector. Assuming this condition to be the case here, what procedural changes would you suggest in the flow chart so that the computer would not need to input more than one T_i and one R_i at a time?
(c) What role does the subscript play, if any, in the solution of part *b*?
(d) How does your part *b* solution compare with Figure 1-12?

9. Study the flow chart in Figure 4-12, which has the effect of assigning values to certain elements of the array C modeled as the 8 × 8 checkerboard.

(a) What is the *range* in values that can possibly be assigned to k in box 3? Assume that the data value for r can be any five-digit integer. All data are to be integers.
(b) If 3 is the value computed for k in box 3, what values will be assigned for s during the repeated execution of box 7?
(c) Place in the squares of C the values that are assigned to the corre-

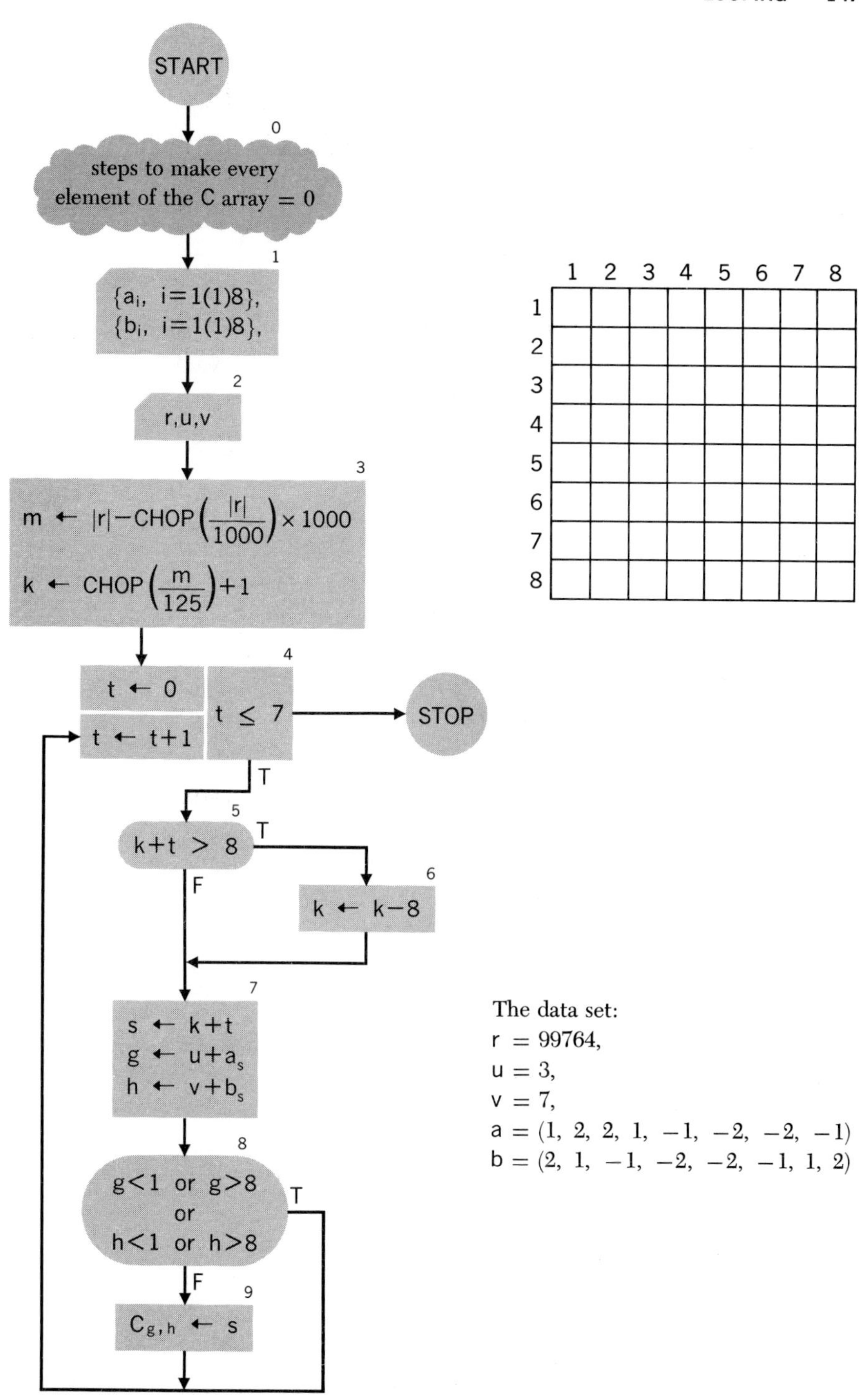
START
0
steps to make every element of the C array = 0
1
{a_i, i=1(1)8},
{b_i, i=1(1)8},
2
r,u,v
3
m ← |r|−CHOP(|r|/1000) × 1000
k ← CHOP(m/125)+1
4
t ← 0
t ← t+1
t ≤ 7
STOP
T
5
k+t > 8
T
F
6
k ← k−8
7
s ← k+t
g ← u+a_s
h ← v+b_s
8
g<1 or g>8
or
h<1 or h>8
T
F
9
C_g,h ← s
1 2 3 4 5 6 7 8
1
2
3
4
5
6
7
8
The data set:
r = 99764,
u = 3,
v = 7,
a = (1, 2, 2, 1, −1, −2, −2, −1)
b = (2, 1, −1, −2, −2, −1, 1, 2)

Figure 4-12

sponding array elements as a result of executing the flow chart, using the given set of data.

(d) Is there any chess piece that you know of that could reach the positions into which values have been placed from (u,v) in one move? If so, which one?

4-2 ILLUSTRATIVE EXAMPLES

In this section we wish to present a portfolio of examples illustrating the iteration box. We present them at a rather brisk pace, and they will get gradually more complicated. In order to make what we wish to emphasize stand out, we will usually present only fragments of flow charts. Consider the task: given N numbers, print out these given numbers and their cubes, thus, in effect, constructing a table of cubes.

Suppose the list is already stored in the computer's memory, in locations belonging to a subscripted variable, X_J. Then we will run through the subscripts, reading out of memory the values of the X_J and making the desired computations. This suggests the use of an iteration box with the loop variable doing the *running*, as shown in Figure 4-13*a*. In Figure 4-13*b* the same computation is performed with the data stored on cards rather than in the machine.

Notice that in Figure 4-13*b* the loop variable is nowhere to be seen in the computation portion of the loop. Figure 4-13*a* provides our first experience with a common occurrence, that of a loop variable going click,

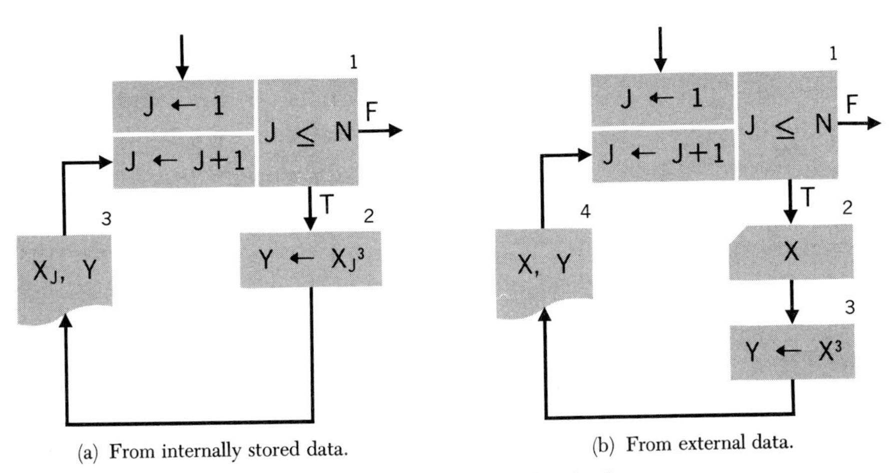

(a) From internally stored data. (b) From external data.

Figure 4-13 Making a table of cubes.

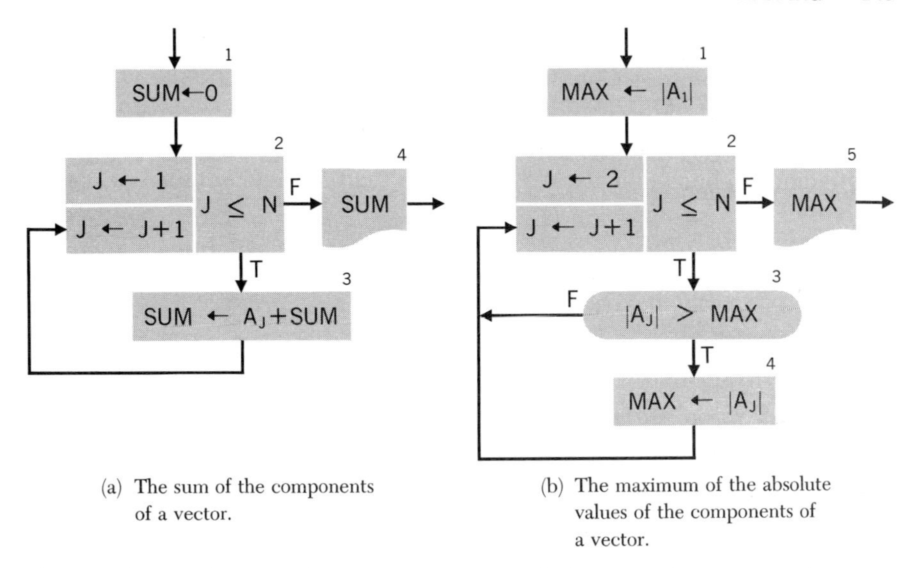

(a) The sum of the components of a vector.

(b) The maximum of the absolute values of the components of a vector.

Figure 4-14 Application of iteration boxes to calculation with vectors (subscripted variables).

click, click through the subscripts of a subscripted variable.

We see this again, in fact, in our next two examples: adding up a list of numbers already stored in memory, and second, finding from a list of numbers in memory the maximum of their absolute values. These are flowcharted in Figure 4-14. If you have trouble understanding the loop in Figure 4-14*b*, review Figures 3-24*b* and 3-25, where we first discussed an algorithm like this one.

There is a fundamental difference between the algorithm of Figure 4-14 and those of Figure 4-13. In any transit of the loops of Figure 4-13, no use is made of calculations made in previous transits, while that is certainly not the case in Figure 4-14.

We find in Figure 4-15 two variants of Figure 4-14*b*. The first shows the modification of Figure 4-14 which must be made if we wish to print out the value of J for which $|A_J|$ is the maximum. The second shows the algorithm for finding the maximum value of $|A_J|$, but over only the even values of J. Notice that the counter we used in *b* of Figure 4-15 counts by 2's and not by 1's.

The first of the loops of Figure 4-16 exhibits the calculation of factorials, and the second is borrowed from the Fibonacci sequence algorithm of Figure 4-7. These algorithms share the property that no new data values are needed after the loop is entered.

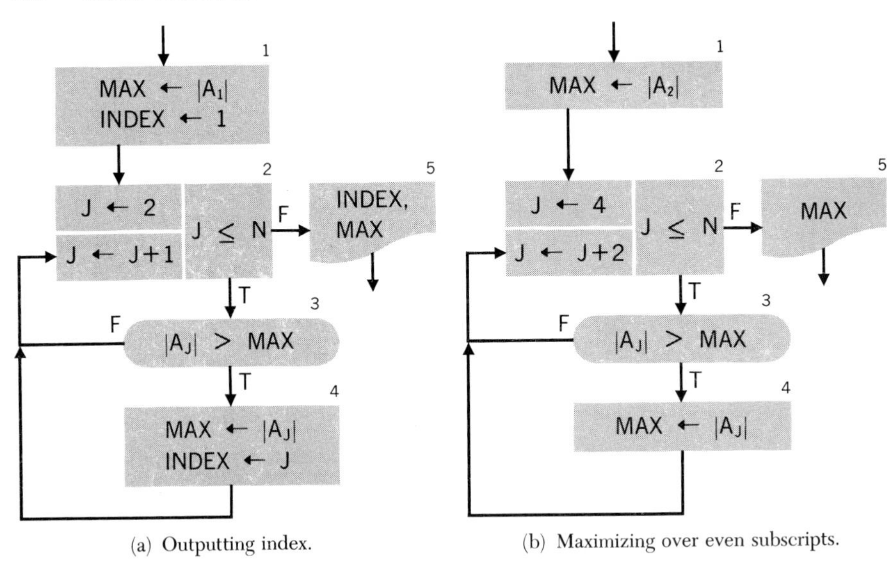

(a) Outputting index.

(b) Maximizing over even subscripts.

Figure 4-15 Two variations of Figure 4-14*b*.

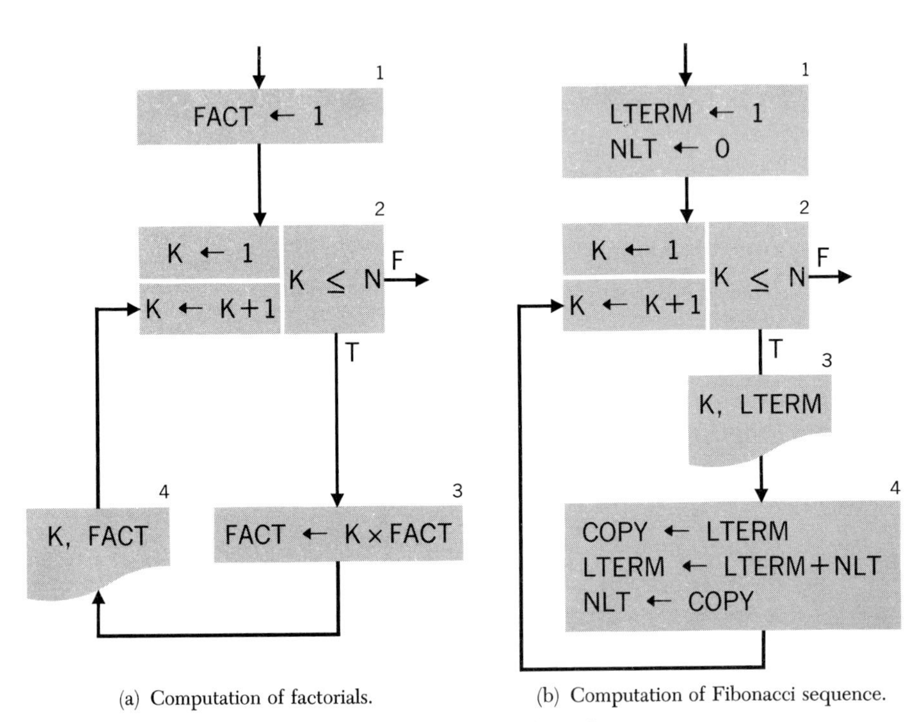

(a) Computation of factorials.

(b) Computation of Fibonacci sequence.

Figure 4-16 Loops without data.

EXERCISES 4-2, SET A

1. Construct a flow chart to calculate and output a table of four columns. The first column is to contain the integers from 1 to 100. The second column is to contain the squares of the corresponding integers in the first column. The third and fourth columns are to contain the cubes and fourth powers of the integers in the first column. For example, the second line of output should be

2 4 8 16

In the following problems you have in storage two columns of N numbers each. One column is called P, the other Q. For each problem in this set your job is to convert the word statement to an equivalent partial flow chart. You should find the iteration box helpful. You may wish to first flowchart the computation part of the loop, then hang it from the proper iteration box and, finally, precede the iteration box, if appropriate, by an initializing box.

2. Think of the Ith value of P and the Ith value of Q as the pair P_I, Q_I. Interchange the values in every such pair.

3. Modify the flow chart drawn for Problem 2 so that only even-indexed pairs are interchanged. Does it matter whether N is even or odd?

4. Modify the flow chart drawn for Problem 2, assuming you wished to interchange only every third pair of values beginning with the fifth pair.

5. Move the first CHOP(N/2) elements of the vector P to the vector Q. See picture (Figure 4-17).

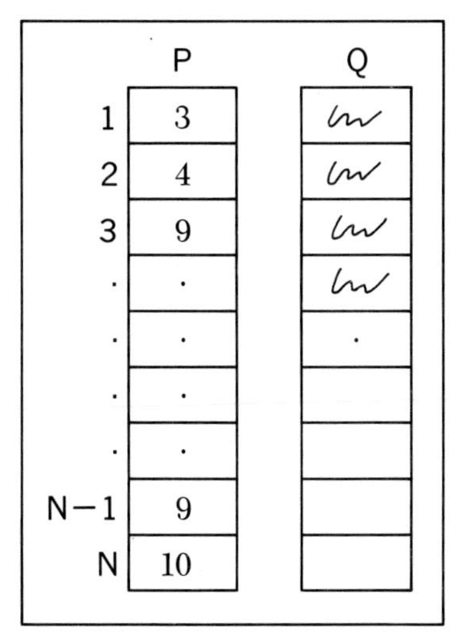

(a) Picture of memory before "move."

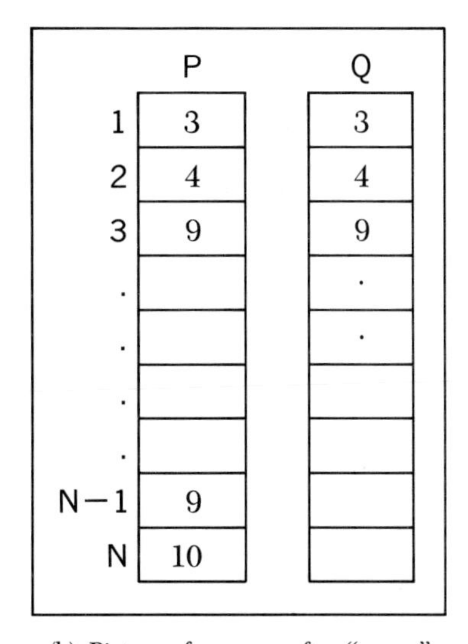

(b) Picture of memory after "move."

Figure 4-17 Moving elements of a vector.

6. Move the last CHOP(N/2) elements of the vector P to the first CHOP(N/2) positions of vector Q. Assume N is even. *Hint.* What is the index of the first element of P that is to be moved?

7. Same problem as Exercise 6—but don't assume N is even.

8. Let each of the last K elements of the N-element vector P be "shifted" or moved two positions in memory to make room for the later insertion of two new values at positions N − K + 1 and N − K + 2 (see Figure 4-18).

9. You have already stored 100 input values for elements P_1, P_2, . . . , P_{100}.

(a) Form the sum of their cubes (in SUMCUB).
(b) Form the sum of the negative values (in SUMNEG).
(c) Form the sums SUMCUB, SUMNEG, and SUMBIG (where SUMBIG is the sum of the absolute values greater than 50 in magnitude).

10. Refer to the flow chart you constructed in Problem 1, Exercises 3-7. Redraw the flow chart using an iteration box (sum of entries in the Kth column of the matrix P except for the element in row 12).

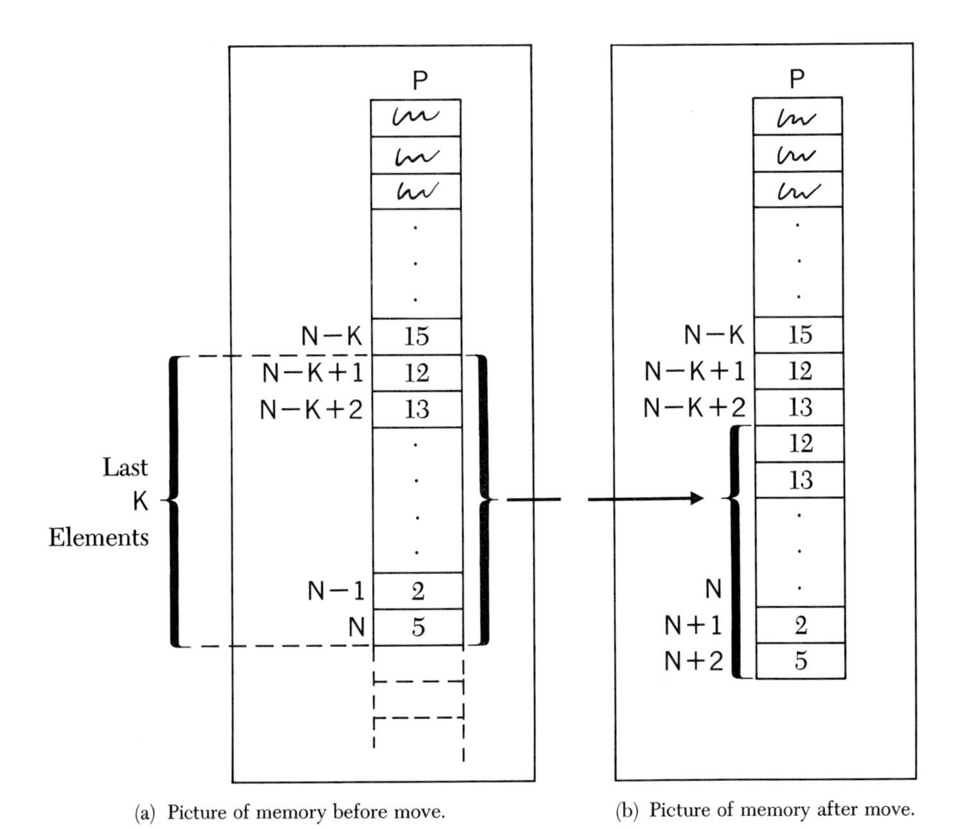

(a) Picture of memory before move. (b) Picture of memory after move.

Figure 4-18 Shifting elements of a vector.

11. Refer to the flow chart you constructed for Problem 2, Exercises 3-7. Redraw the flow chart using an iteration box (replacing entries of the Lth row of matrix P by the sum of row L and row M entries).

12. Refer to the flow chart you constructed for Exercises 3-7, Problem 3. Redraw the flow chart using an iteration box (replacing entries of the Lth row by the sum consisting of the row L entry and 2 × row M entry, but leaving the column K entry of row L unchanged).

In each of the following two exercises, assume there are N values currently assigned to the P vector in memory.

13. Search the list in the forward direction, that is, P_1, P_2, P_3, etc., for the first value greater than 50 in magnitude, assigning this value to W and 1 to ANY. If no such value is found, assign 0 to ANY. In either case, now proceed to the same point in the flow chart.

14. Search the list in the backward direction, that is, P_N, P_{N-1}, P_{N-2}, etc., for the first value greater than 50 in magnitude, assigning this value to W. If no such value is found, assign 50 to W. In either case, now proceed to a common point in the flow chart.

15. Search the N elements of the P vector for the nonzero element of largest magnitude less than $|M|$. Assume the value of M has already been stored in memory. Assign the value of the vector element found in this search to T. If no such value is found, print the message "NONE" and stop.

16. Search all N elements of the P vector for the element that is the largest in value and is still less than the value currently assigned to M. Assign the value found to T. If none is found, print "NONE" and stop.

In the following two exercises assume that all entries of a matrix Q are stored in memory. Q has M rows and N columns.

17. Search the Lth row of Q for the smallest value. Assign this value to SMALL.

18. Search the Rth column backwards (that is, from bottom to top) for the first entry, if any, that is at least as large as the current value of T. Assign the row value for this entry to ROW and the value itself to BIG. If no such value is found, assign the value zero to ROW.

We have now seen a number of examples illustrating the use of iteration boxes. But how, in the course of drawing a flow chart, can we tell whether an iteration box will be useful? The answer is that *we will want to use an iteration box whenever we have a loop controlled by a counter.* Whenever this situation exists (or when we strongly suspect that it does), we draw the iteration box and try to hang a loop on it. We may draw the iteration box before knowing everything that goes inside it.

As an example, consider the problem of finding all the integer factors of a given integer N. If N is large, this task is very tedious, as you will know if you have ever tried it. We will be very glad, therefore, to have a computer do the job for us.

The word statement of the algorithm for this problem is very simple.

Go through the integers, 1, 2, 3, 4, etc., checking each one to determine whether it is a divisor of N, and if it is, write it down.

Now for the flow chart. Since for each integer we must check whether it divides N, we have a repetitive process, a loop. Because we perform the calculation for 1, 2, 3, 4, etc., it would seem that our loop is controlled by a counter. Now we draw our iteration box, noting that we are not yet sure where to stop.

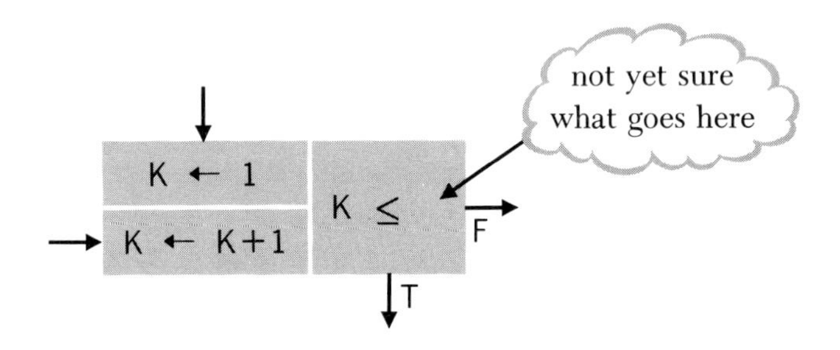

Of what does our calculation consist? Of determining whether K is a divisor of N. But how shall we express this question? Well, for K to be a divisor of N means that N/K is an integer or, equivalently, CHOP(N/K) = N/K. Thus,

K is a divisor of N

is equivalent to

$$N = K \times \text{CHOP}(N/K)$$

We put this in our flow chart! (See Figure 4-19.)

Now we come to the important question of where to stop our computation. We could go all the way to N, i.e., we could put N in the empty space in the test compartment of the iteration box. Then if N were a million, we would have to go through the loop a million times. Must we do that? At this point, a look at the mathematics of the situation will help.

Whenever we find one integer factor of N, say K, we have really found two because N/K is also an integer factor. Moreover, these two factors

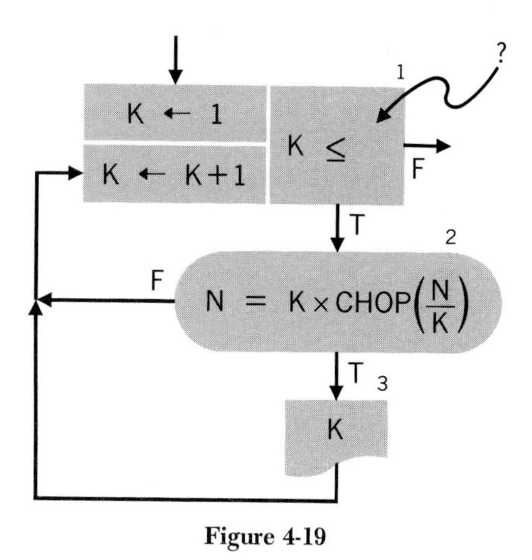

Figure 4-19

cannot both be less than $\sqrt{N}$, or else we would have

$$N = K \times (N/K) < \sqrt{N} \times \sqrt{N} = N$$

which is a contradiction. By the same reasoning, K and N/K are not both greater than $\sqrt{N}$. If they were, we would have a similar contradiction:

$$N = K \times (N/K) > \sqrt{N} \times \sqrt{N} = N$$

Thus, whenever we express N as the product of two factors, one of these factors is $\leq \sqrt{N}$ and the other is $\geq \sqrt{N}$. This means that we only have to go as far as $\sqrt{N}$ in our search for factors if, in our output step, we print out the value of N/K along with each factor K.

Our complete flow chart is then seen in Figure 4-20.

We see that if N were 1,000,000 we would now pass through the loop only 1000 times. Quite a saving over our original plan to pass through the loop a million times! You can make still other improvements in this algorithm after a bit of study. But, unfortunately, additional improvements will not be so spectacular. (The algorithm still has one minor logical flaw which you are invited to correct. Note that when N is a square, the algorithm prints two identical factors, i.e., $\sqrt{N}$).

The last example of this section is the problem of evaluating a polynomial. We will illustrate our methods with a third-degree polynomial and then generalize to Nth degree. Consider the expression

$$A_0 + A_1 \times X + A_2 \times X^2 + A_3 \times X^3$$

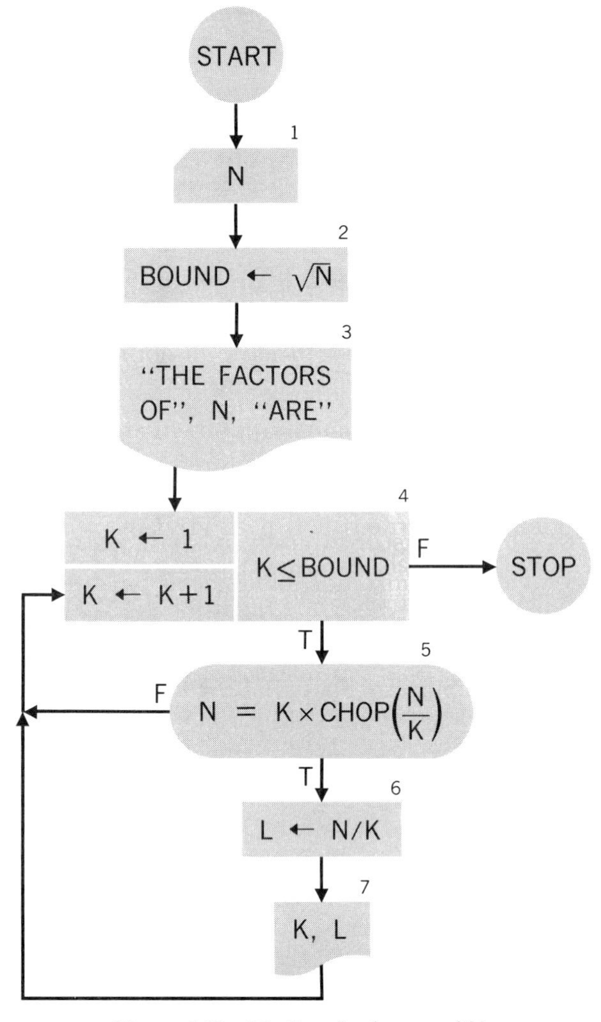

Figure 4-20 Finding the factors of N.

After values are assigned to the components of the vector A, this expression represents a polynomial of degree no greater than three. When a value is assigned to X, the polynomial can be evaluated.

We first describe the usual method of performing this evaluation. We evaluate each term in the order written, adding this value to a cumulative sum of the terms computed so far. We also keep the last power (PWRX) of X computed to simplify the computation of the next higher power. This process is obviously controlled by a counter that runs through the subscripts of A. But should we initiate the loop variable at

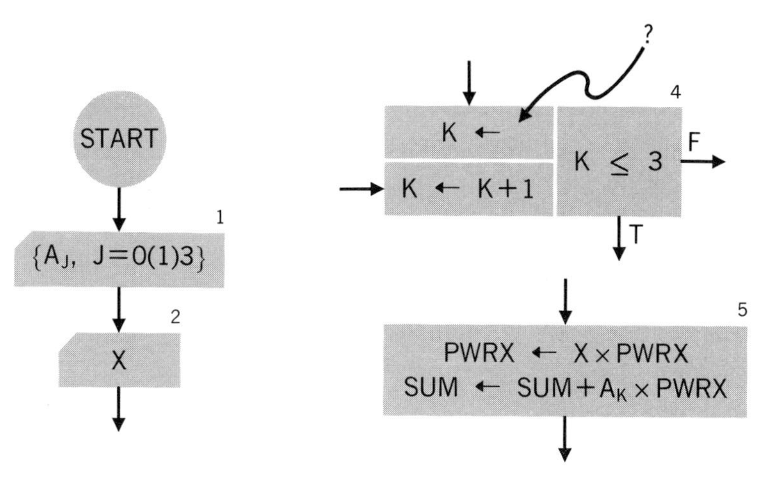

Figure 4-21 Pieces of polynomial evaluation.

0 or at 1? There doesn't seem to be much computation at 0. Our thoughts so far are shown in Figure 4-21.

Box 5 in Figure 4-21 contains the entire loop calculation. Our decision about what initial values to assign to SUM and PWRX decides the question of how to initialize K in box 4. Now we can draw our flow chart (Figure 4-22). It should be obvious how we can generalize this flow chart to work for polynomials of arbitrary degree. We have only to replace the occurrences of "3" in boxes 1 and 4 by "N", and input N, either in box 1 or ahead of that box. Instead of stopping we could, of course, go back to get another value of X or another polynomial.

Now that we have solved the problem, we ask (as usual), "Is there another way to do it?" There is, in fact, another way, and a most elegant one. We take a polynomial

$$B_0 \times X^3 + B_1 \times X^2 + B_2 \times X + B_3$$

and express it in the following way:

$$((B_0 \times X + B_1) \times X + B_2) \times X + B_3$$

Satisfy yourself that these two expressions are equivalent. The second of these expressions is in very inconvenient form for all mathematical purposes except evaluation.

In constructing the flow chart, at each step the variable VALUE represents the number by which X is being multiplied. You might enjoy trying to draw the flow chart yourself before looking at the solution in Figure

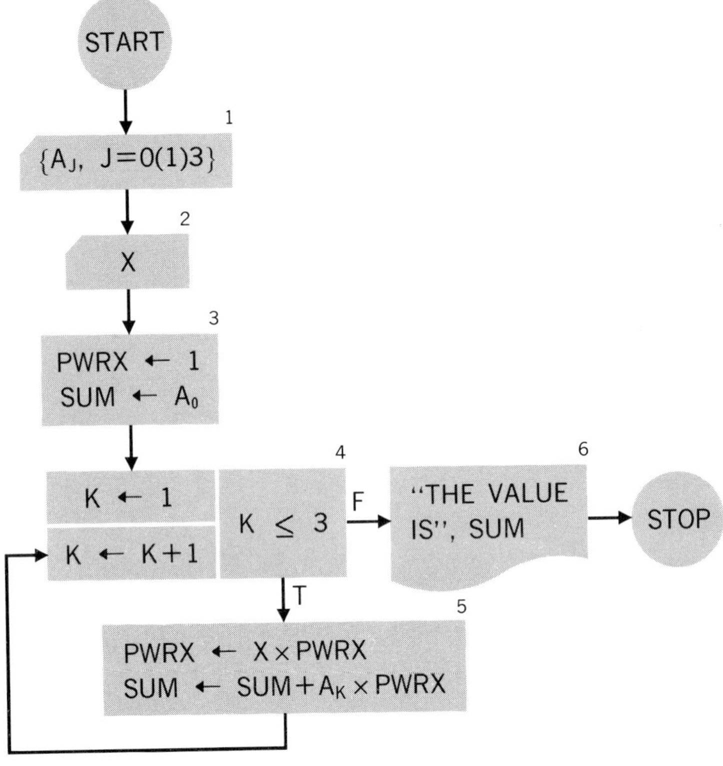

Figure 4-22 Evaluation of polynomial, everyday method.

4-23. Again, of course, we can generalize to degree N by replacing the occurrences of "3" in boxes 1 and 4 by "N" and inputting N prior to (or in) box 1.

Let us compare the two algorithms. Certainly, the simplicity of the computation in box 5 of Figure 4-23 appeals to our esthetic sense but, in the last analysis, the key question is, "Which algorithm uses the least computer time?"

To answer this, compare the computation portion (box 5) of the two loops. In the first method there will be two multiplications and one addition for each transit of the loop. In the second method there will be one multiplication and one addition in each transit of the loop. The second (Sunday) method is therefore shorter. If the polynomial were of degree N, it would save N multiplications. And if you intend to use this algorithm to evaluate many polynomials, then the second method will save a number of multiplications equal to the sum of the degrees of all the polynomials to be evaluated.

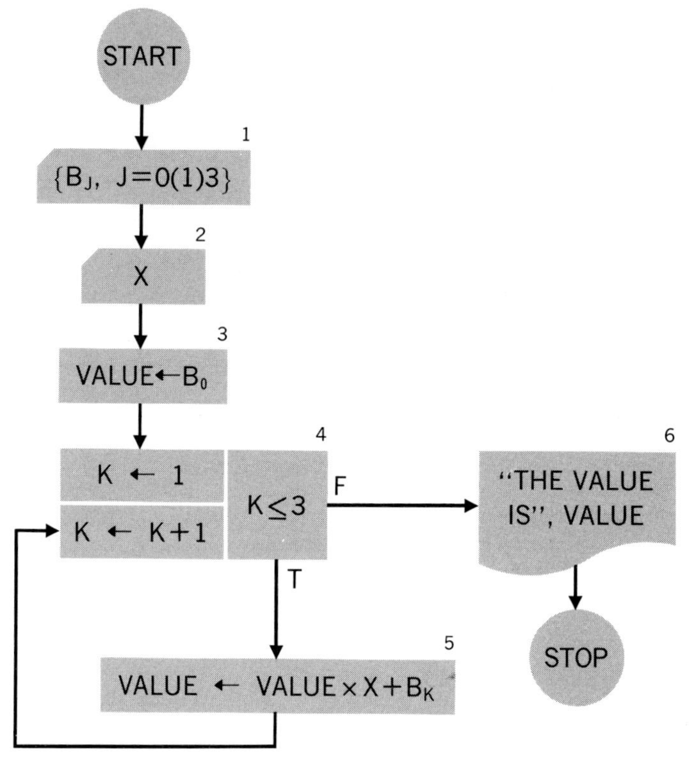

Figure 4-23 Evaluation of polynomial, Sunday method.

EXERCISES 4-2, SET B

1. Given a set of N values of a vector X, i.e., X_1, X_2, . . . , X_N, and given a value A.

(a) Draw a flow chart for the computation of NUM defined mathematically as an N-term product:

$$\text{NUM} = (X_1 - A) \times (X_2 - A) \times (X_3 - A) \times \cdots \times (X_N - A)$$

Show input and output of all required data and results.

(b) Same as *a* except that NUM has the Kth one of the N terms omitted.

2. Suppose that in the preceding exercise you were told that the given value of A is equal to X_K. What data value, required as input in 1*b*, is no longer needed? Redraw the flow chart to display the computation of DEN, which is defined the same as NUM, except $X_K = A$ and the term $(X_K - A)$ is omitted.

3. Develop an algorithm to test the first 500 integers and output only those that are *perfect.* A perfect number is one that is equal to the sum of all its factors. The smallest perfect number is $6 = 1 + 2 + 3$. (By definition, the number 1 is excluded from the perfect numbers.)

4. (a) *Preliminary.* In Problem 7, Exercise 4-1, you were asked to spin the carnival wheel N times. Did you finish this exercise? If not, do so now before going on to the main task described in the next paragraph.

(b) *Main.* We begin now to develop more seriously the concept of simulating the playing of a game for the purpose of predicting, with the aid of a computer, something about its outcome. It is a "spinning wheel game." Imagine you are given an inexhaustible supply of data pairs, s, m, for input. These data are somehow representative of what a person might actually experience if he were to take turns spinning the wheel with one or more other players. We will say that a "game" consists of a series of spins for a given player and terminates whenever the magnitude of his score, |SUM|, exceeds some given critical value, CV. We shall say that the "length" of the game is the number of spins in the series. The question we really want to ask is, "How many turns 'on the average' can a player be 'expected' to take before CV ≤ |SUM|?"

In this exercise you are preparing the groundwork to answer the question later. Your job now is to draw a flow chart that simulates one complete game. The paragraph below contains some guidelines—to be consulted only after you have experimented with a plan of your own.

(1) As in the earlier exercise, first input the four values constituting the "point rule" to be used.
(2) Next input a value for CV, the critical value.
(3) Then input a series of data pairs, s, m.
(4) After each pair the new value for the net winnings (SUM) is computed and a counter L of the number of spins is updated.
(5) Whenever the absolute value of SUM exceeds the CV, we print the values of L, CV, and SUM and then stop.
(6) For insurance against an endless loop, we print out an error message and stop if L ever exceeds 1000.

Remember to use an iteration box where you think it can help to keep the flow chart simple in structure.

4-3 TABLE-LOOK-UP

Now we begin an algorithmic investigation into the subject of table-look-up; the looking up of values of a tabulated function, as when we "go to the tables" to find the value of sin (.3217) or of $\sqrt{147.62}$.

Example 1. Table-look-up by matching

Our first example of table-look-up does not even involve an iteration box. We have a function, F, and, as in common mathematical notation, we write

$$Y = F(X)$$

We also have a stack of cards, each card punched with a value of the variable X and the corresponding value of Y.

X,Y

This means that each card represents an ordered pair of numbers (X,Y), related by $Y=F(X)$. No two cards then can have the same value of X punched on them unless the values of Y are also the same. This is what is meant by saying that "Y is a function of X." The stack of cards can be regarded as a table of values of the function, F.

To look up the functional value of a certain number, one method would be to go through the cards comparing this number with the value of X on each card and, when equality is found, to print the corresponding value of Y. Figure 4-24 is a flow chart for this process.

Any flow chart that reads a whole table into storage will use subscripted variables. We suppose that we have a stack of cards with two numbers, X_K, Y_K, punched on each, and with X_K and Y_K satisfying

$$Y_K = F(X_K)$$

Notice that the subscript changes each time a card is read. Data from different cards goes into different window boxes. If 1000 cards are to be

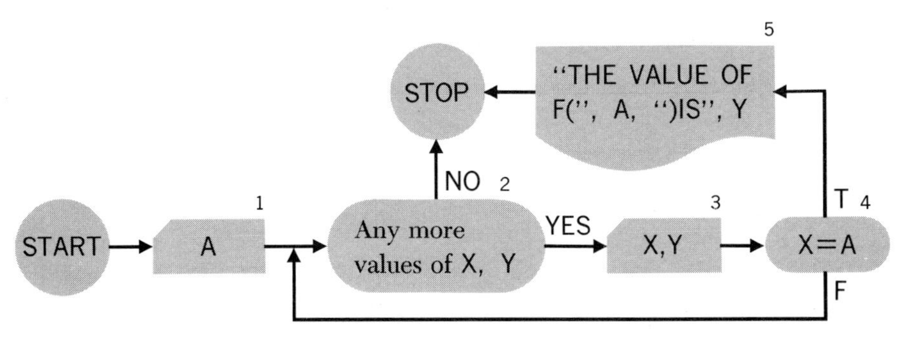

Figure 4-24 Primitive table-look-up.

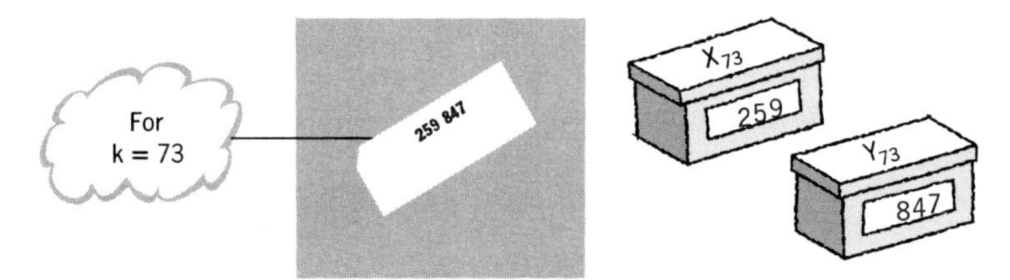

Figure 4-25

read, then 2000 window boxes must be made available to receive the data on them (Figure 4-25).

For our flow-chart language we introduce a slightly different type of input set notation (Figure 4-26).

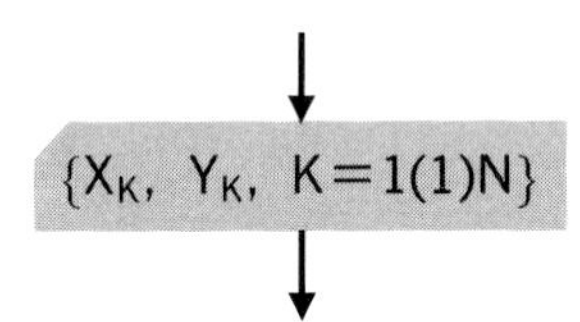

Figure 4-26 An input step for a stack of N ordered pairs of subscripted variables.

Though we have not seen an input instruction quite like this before, it is clear that its effect is equivalent to the combination of boxes shown in Figure 4-27.

Once the table has been read in, we select (i.e., input) a value for which F is sought. We compare this value with each of the X_I until we find equality; then we print out the value of Y_I. The flow chart is seen in Figure 4-28.

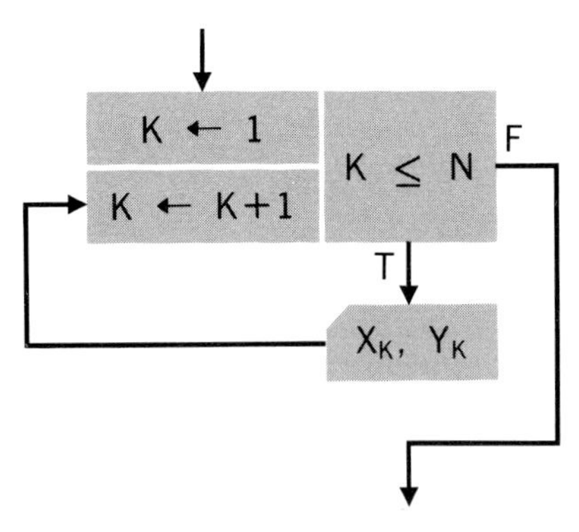

Figure 4-27

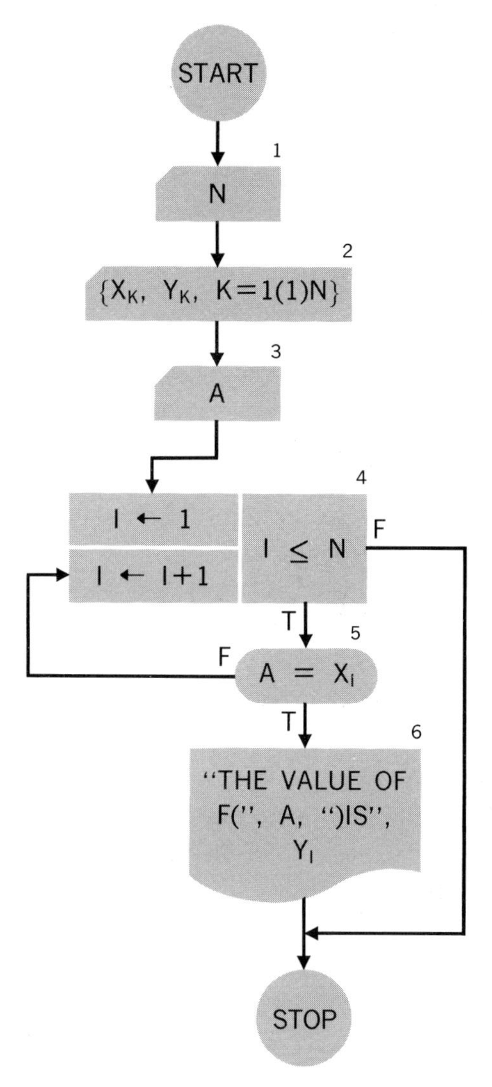

Figure 4-28 Look-up from an internally stored table.

What is important here is the way in which the iteration box helped us to draw the flow chart. Notice, however, that there is a second exit from the loop besides the one from the iteration box.

In Figure 4-28 we could have gone back for more values of A instead of stopping.

Example 2. Table-look-up: bracketing entries in an ordered set

Have you ever had to look up values in a table? Suppose you are given a value of X and you want to find the value of sin (X). What happens, of

Your given value ↝ .5836 of X

X	sin (X)
⋮	⋮
.5760	.5446
.5789	.5471
.5818	.5495
.5847	.5519
.5876	.5876

(a) What you see in the table.

.5818	.5495
.5836	?
.5847	.5519

(b) What you write down.

Figure 4-29 Reading a table.

course, is that you don't find your value of X listed. So you note the nearest listed values above and below, and write these down together with their functional values, as in Figure 4-29.

Usually you "interpolate" a value between the two tabulated values of sin (X) in the same proportion as that interpolated between the two tabulated values of X.

We will construct a flow chart for instructing a computer to do everything except the final interpolation. It would be easy to instruct the machine to perform this step, too, but we want to focus our attention on the table-look-up problem. We will print as output the number whose functional value we wish to find, the closest tabulated values of X, above and below, and the corresponding values of Y.

We will assume in this problem that the values of X are arranged (indexed) in increasing order. We input the table

$\{X_K,\ Y_K,\ K=1(1)N\}$

and the value we are looking up in the table

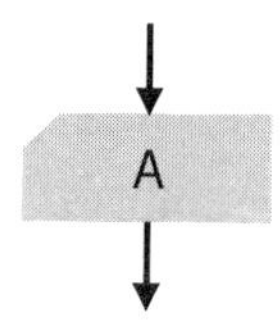

Our task involves comparing A with successive values of X. Again, we have a loop that can be controlled by an iteration box. The computation consists merely of comparing A and X_I and printing out the desired information when we bracket A between two tabulated values of X. Of course, if we hit A on the nose we output that information, too. The flow chart in Figure 4-30 is self-explanatory.

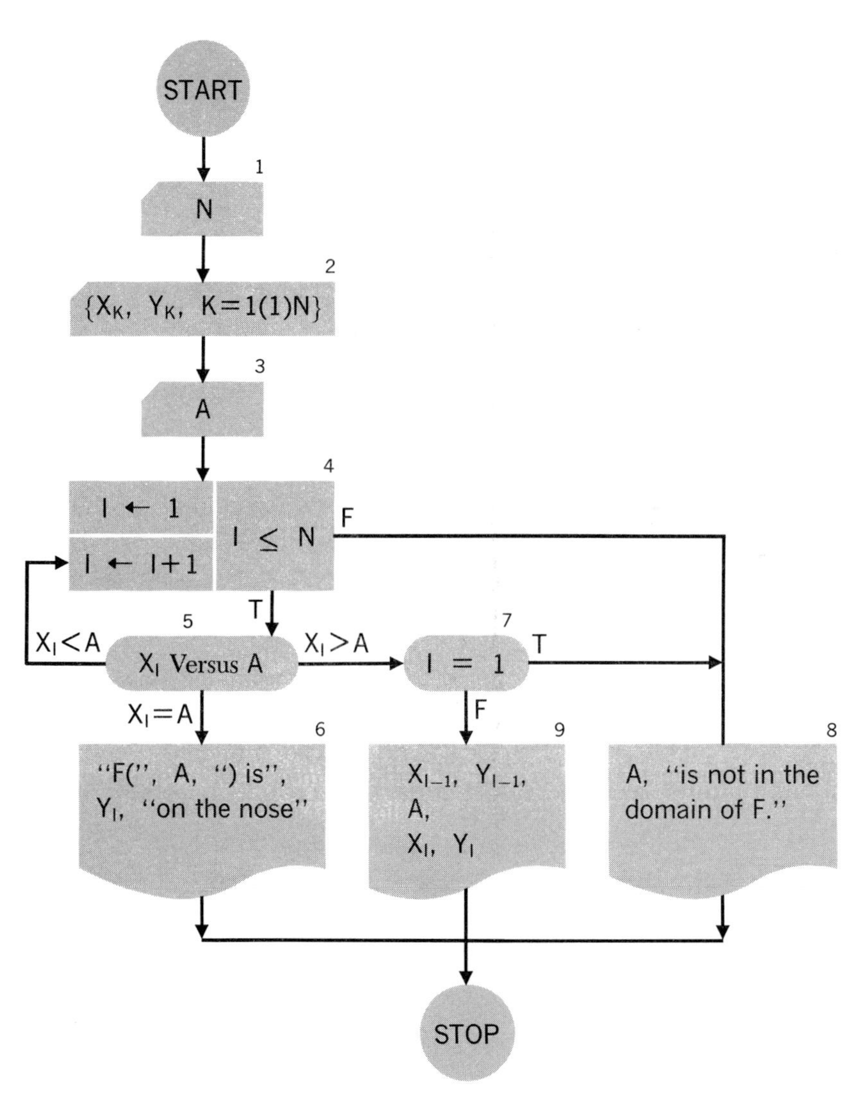

Figure 4-30 Simple scan table-look-up in an ordered set of values.

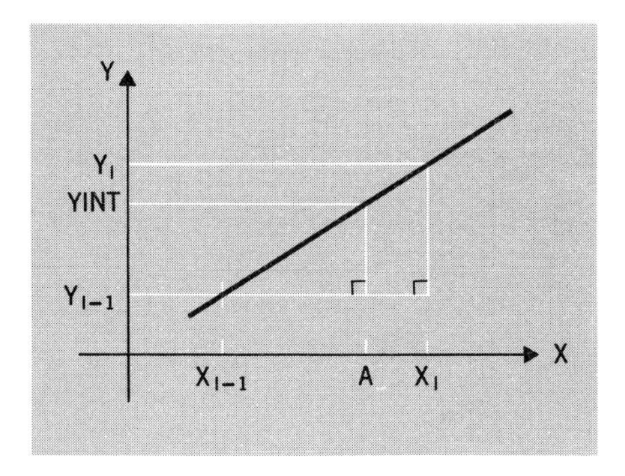

Figure 4-31 Illustration of straight-line interpolation.

EXERCISE 4-3, SET A

Improve the flow chart in Figure 4-30 so that in place of box 9 we will print the interpolated value of Y (call it YINT) along with the value of A. *Hint.* Figure 4-31 should help you to see how YINT may be computed.

[1] Example 3. Table-look-up: bisection method

And now we ask the familiar question: can we improve on the algorithm? Let's compare the algorithm with what we do in real life. In the algorithm we take a value of A and start at the beginning of the table and compare with each entry. Is this what we would really do? Take the analogy of a telephone book. We want to find the number of Tom Spumoni. Do we start at the beginning (Figure 4-32) and compare Spumoni with each entry? Certainly not! What we do is split the book in the middle and check to sce which "half" thc namc is in. Then wc split that "half" and so on. Just as this is a faster way for you to look things up, so it is for a computer.

The flow chart for this algorithm is presented in Figure 4-33. We use two auxiliary variables, LOW and HIGH, to indicate the lower and upper indices of the part of the table to which we are currently confined.

On each loop we find the midpoint of LOW and HIGH, that is,

7

$$\rightarrow \boxed{\text{MID} \leftarrow \text{CHOP}\left(\frac{\text{LOW} + \text{HIGH}}{2}\right)} \rightarrow$$

[1] If time is short, the rest of Section 4-3 can be omitted without loss of continuity.

A

AAAA Cleaners	234-5678
AAA Auto Club	355-2320
Aardvark Motors	591-4378
Aaronson, Don	567-8901
Abacon, James	456-7890
Abernathy, P.	288-1108
Ace	

Figure 4-32 In search of Spumoni.

and test to see whether

$$A \leq X_{MID}$$

If so, MID becomes the new HIGH (box 9) and, if not MID becomes the new LOW (box 10). Box 4 determines at the outset whether A is in the range of the table. Box 6 is the stopping mechanism. When $HI - LO = 1$ we know that A is bracketed between two table entries with consecutive subscripts, i.e., that

$$X_{LO} \leq A \leq X_{HI}$$

The computation portion of the loop (boxes 6 to 10) exhibits the "bisection technique." Study this computation until you are sure you understand it. The idea occurs over and over again in computing and often represents maximum efficiency. You will see bisection again in Chapter 7.

It is interesting to compare the efficiency of the algorithms in Figures 4-30 and 4-33. The loop of Figure 4-30 (boxes 4 and 5) will be passed through N/2 times, on the average. The loop in Figure 4-33 will be executed a number of times equal to or one less than the number of digits required to express N in the binary system. For example, if N is 1,000,000, Figure 4-33 requires 19 or 20 transits, since $2^{19} < 10^6 < 2^{20}$.

There is no iteration box in the flow chart of Figure 4-33. The reason is that the loop in this algorithm is not controlled by a counter. There is a valuable lesson here. You should *not* try to force algorithms into iteration box form when it seems difficult to do so. Iteration boxes are *not* useful in all loops. They are useful only when the loop is controlled by a simple counter.

EXERCISE 4-3, SET B

You may have noticed that the algorithm in Figure 4-33 lacks one feature exhibited by the one in Figure 4-30. That is, in the latter, if an exact match

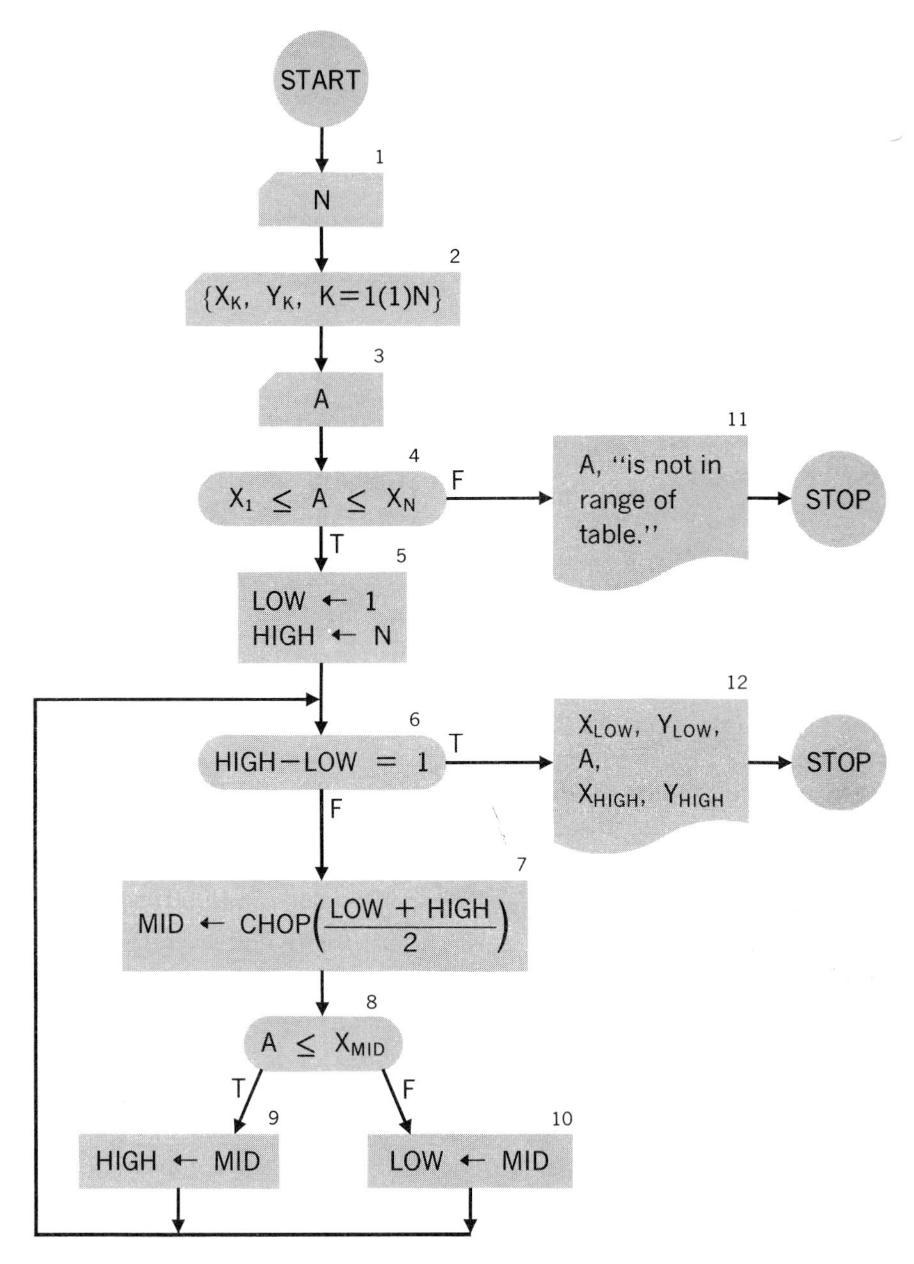

Figure 4-33 Table-look-up in an ordered set of data using bisection technique.

is found, a message like

"F(24.2) is 39.25 on the nose"

is printed.

Your job in this exercise is to redraw Figure 4-33, or whatever portion is necessary, with the "on-the-nose" feature added.

Example 4. Table-look-up in an unordered set of values

Suppose that the values of X_I had *not* been indexed in increasing order. This sort of thing might happen if the table were constructed out of empirical data collected by a number of investigators.

There are two different plans we could follow.

1. We could look up our value in the table as it stands.
2. We could first sort the data according to increasing values of X_I and then look up in the sorted table.

The first plan would be followed to look up a very small number of values in the table. When many values are to be looked up, the second plan is much shorter.

If we sort the data first, the sorting process would be followed by a bisection look-up algorithm, as in Figure 4-33. Sorting has already been discussed in Section 3-6 and will be discussed further in Section 4-4. We turn our attention now to the first plan.

Our goal here is the same as in the algorithm of Figure 4-30. That is, we want to squeeze A as tightly as possible between two tabulated values of X_I,

$$X_{LO} \leq A \leq X_{HI}$$

The difference here is that we will know that we have attained our result *only* after we have scanned the entire table. Furthermore, no bisection technique can be used here since the values of X_I are not indexed in any order.

In constructing this algorithm, it is assumed that the maximum and minimum values of X_I are known.

We want to input these extreme values in such a way that they can easily be compared with other values of X_I. This is best done if they are input as *additional* values of X_I. Since we have already used subscripts 1 to N for the table values, we start by assigning the minimum value to X_0 and the maximum to X_{N+1}, but we call them X_{LO} and X_{HI}. By doing it this way, we actually use X_{LO} and X_{HI} as a *vise* within which we *clamp*

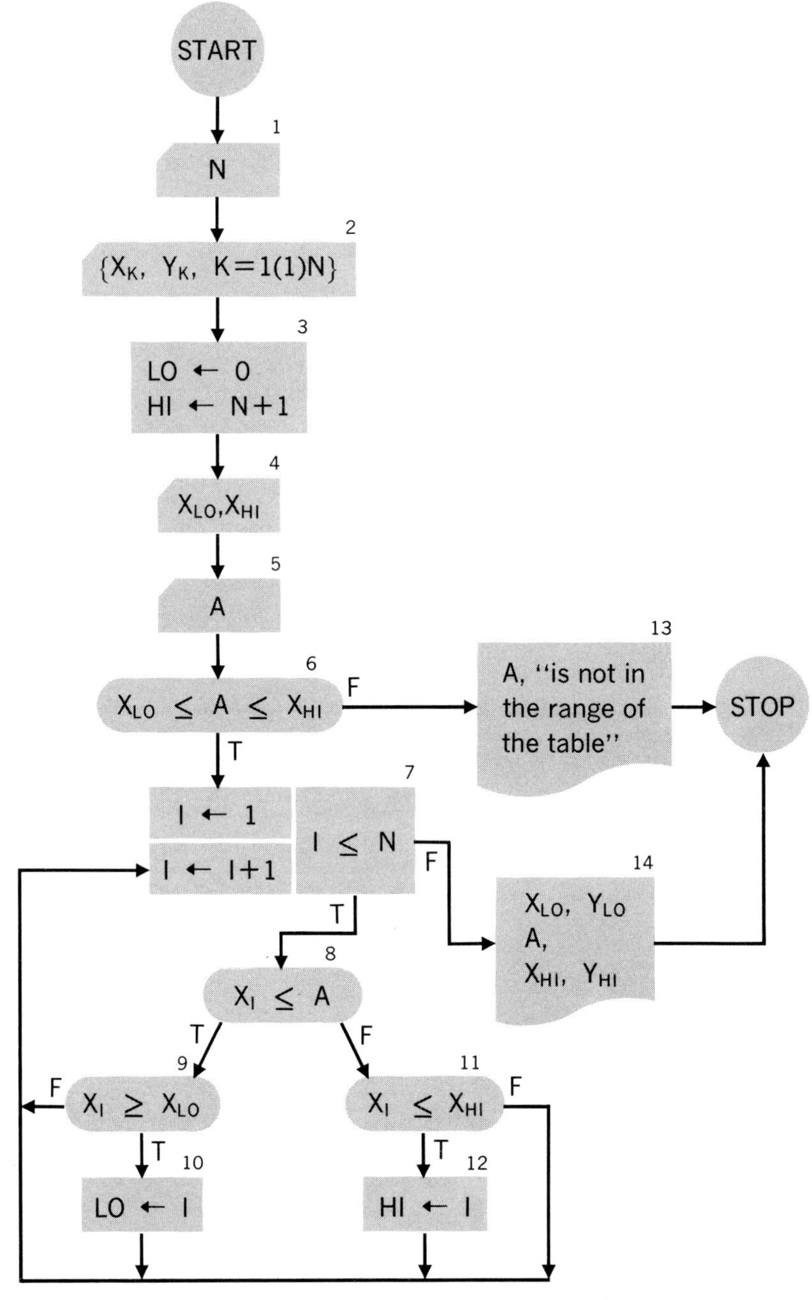

Figure 4-34 Look-up in an unsorted table.

the value of A. At the beginning, the vise is, of course, opened as wide as possible, with X_{LO} equal to the minimum of all values and X_{HI} equal to the maximum. At the end, if A is within the range of the table, X_{LO} is the closest value *less than or equal to* A, and X_{HI} is the closest value *greater than or equal to* A. Since we are scanning the entire table, we clearly have a loop controlled by a counter; therefore, an iteration box is useful. The algorithm is seen in Figure 4-34.

4-4 NESTED LOOPS

By the term "nested loop" we refer to algorithms that have, like the silhouette shown in Figure 4-35, a *loop within a loop*. In this silhouette,

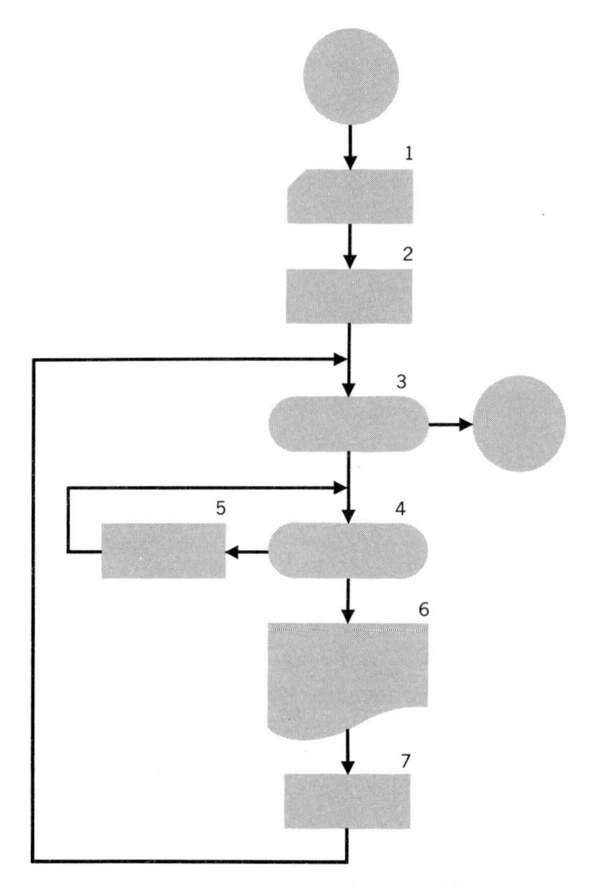

Figure 4-35 Silhouette of a nested loop.

boxes 3 through 7 constitute one loop, while boxes 4 and 5 form an *inside loop*. Remember that in a flow chart, whenever an arrow goes back to a box already passed through, you then have a loop.

You have already seen numerous examples of nested loops of a rather trivial kind in which the "return" on the "outer" loop merely involved coming back for more data, as in the next silhouette (Figure 4-36). Here the inner loop consists of boxes 3, 4, and 5. The outer loop consists of boxes 1, 2, 3, 4, and 5. Clearly, box 1 is supposed to be

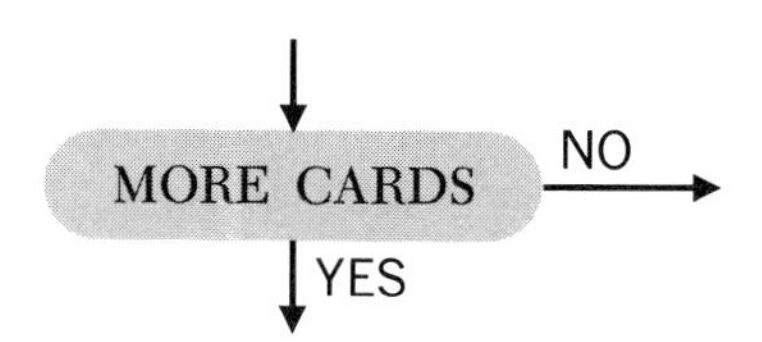

and the return on the outer loop is merely for the purpose of coming back to repeat the same calculation with new sets of data.

The sorting algorithm of Section 3-6 had a nontrivial use of a nested loop although we did not call your attention to it at the time. It is quite possible to construct valid algorithms containing nested loops without being conscious of the existence of this nesting. But when both the inner and outer loops are controlled by iteration boxes, we will usually be conscious of the nesting.

A simple but classically beautiful illustration of nested loops is the solution of the following problem. You will recognize this problem as being of a type often encountered in algebra courses (and puzzle books).

> *Stickler.* Find all the three-digit numbers that are equal to the sum of the cubes of their digits.

The reason such a problem emphasizes the power of a computer is that this problem, although possible, is extremely tedious to do by hand calculation. However, it is a trivial problem for a computer and the algorithm is absurdly easy to write.

If we let the digits of the number be H, T, and U, then the three-digit number is

$$100 \times H + 10 \times T + U$$

The problem then is to find and print out all the triples of digits (H, T, U) that satisfy the condition:

$$100 \times H + 10 \times T + U = H^3 + T^3 + U^3$$

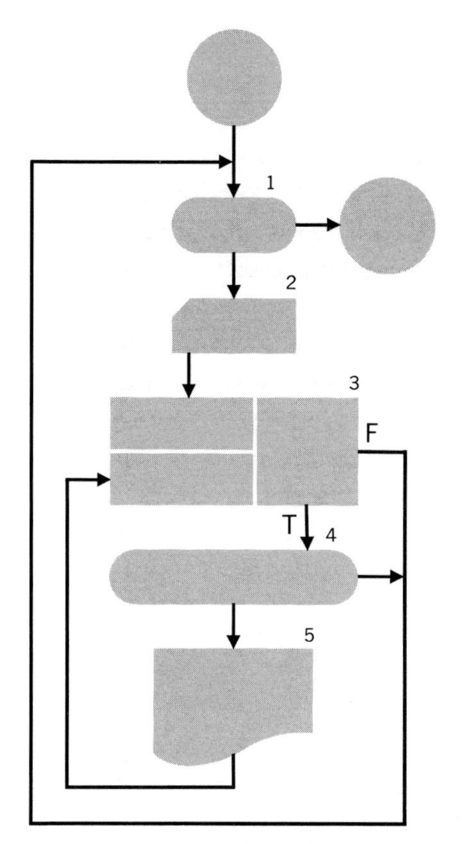

Figure 4-36 Silhouette showing nesting formed when returning for more data.

Consequently, we would expect to find in our flow chart the structure shown in Figure 4-37.

This is, in fact, the only computation performed in this algorithm. The rest of the problem merely makes the various values of H, T, and U available for the test of Figure 4-37. The process of making these values available

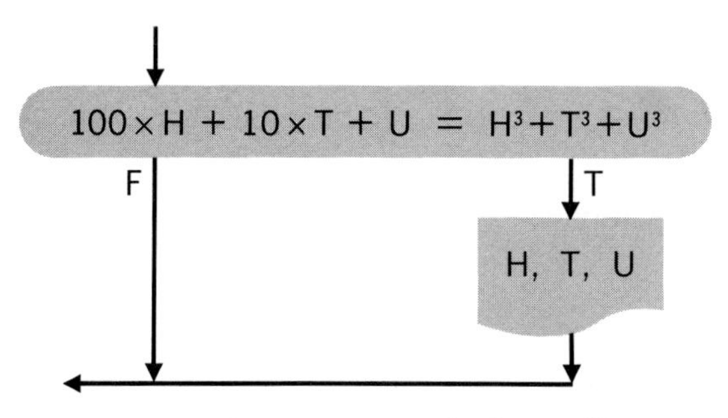

Figure 4-37 Computation for the Stickler.

involves nested loops. This process can be described somewhat vaguely this way. When a value is assigned to H we then let T "run through" the digits from 0 to 9, and when values are assigned to both H and T we then let U "run through" the digits from 0 to 9. In this explanation we are trying to explain briefly the process of counting as performed by the odometer on a car, where we consider each rotating wheel of the odometer as a variable and the value showing as the value of that variable.

This commonplace idea becomes even clearer in the flow chart for the algorithm given in Figure 4-38. The initial value of H is 1 rather than zero because we are looking for three-digit numbers.

The stickler does not require any ingenuity—merely brute force. The 900 computations required in the algorithm would probably take all day by hand, but a fast computer would complete the calculation in less than a second.

EXERCISES 4-4, SET A

Reexamine Figure 4-38 and answer the following questions.

1. How many multiplications are required from START to STOP ?

2. How many different values of H^3 are computed from START to STOP ?

3. How many different values of T^3 are computed from START to STOP ?

4. Revise the algorithm so that the same value of H^3 is never recomputed and the same value of T^3 is not recomputed more than 10 times.

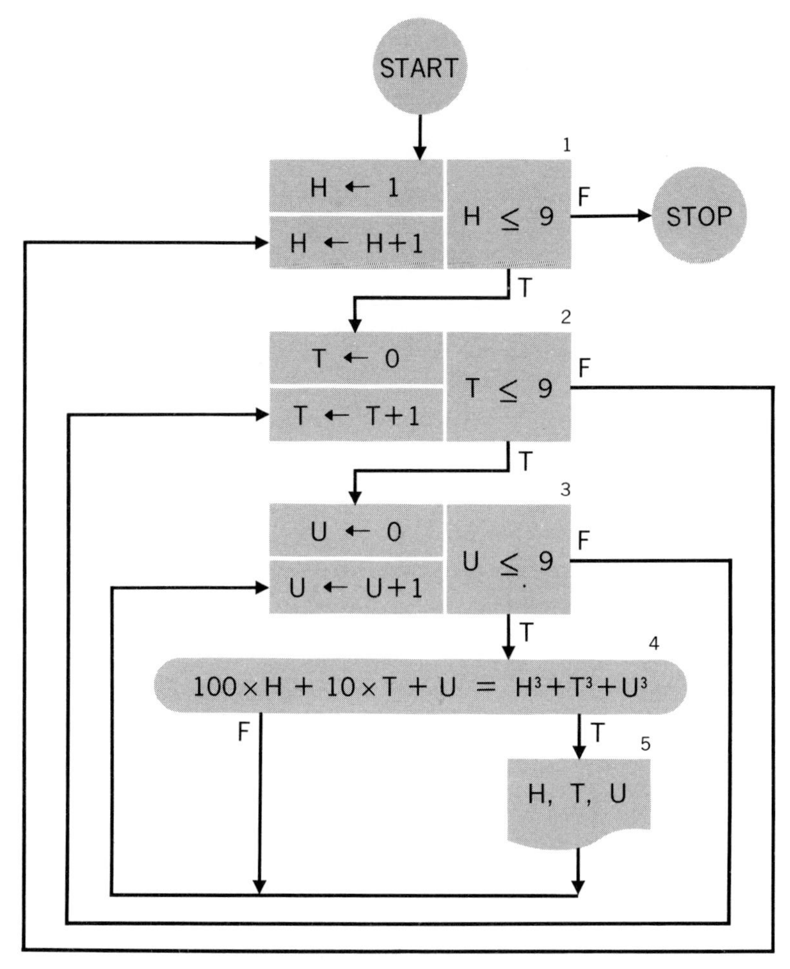

Figure 4-38 Flow chart for the stickler.

5. How would you revise the algorithm so that no value of H^3, T^3, or U^3 is ever computed a second time? *Hint.* Compute all values, $0^3, 1^3, 2^3, \ldots, 9^3$, and store them in a separate CUBE vector having 10 elements.

6. See if you can reduce the total number of multiplications to 119 using no more than nine different boxes in the flow chart.

Nested loops develop most naturally out of the systematic processing of the entries in a matrix. Suppose we wish to find the sum of all entries in a matrix having M rows and N columns. First we add up each row, and then add the resulting sums.

In this example we can mentally separate the calculations in the two loops. The inner loop, adding up the entries in a given *row,* say the Ith, is given by Figure 4-39.

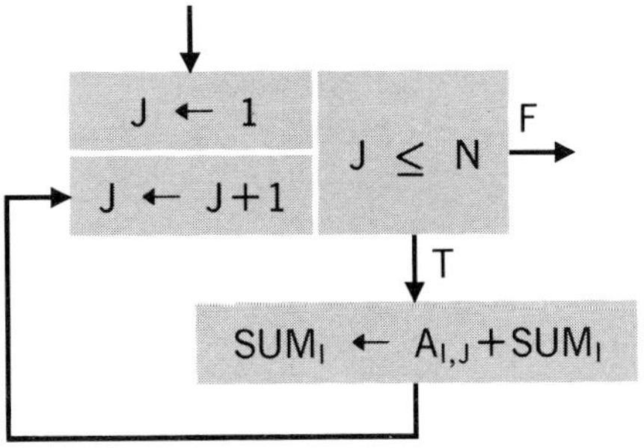

J ← 1
J ← J+1
J ≤ N
F
T
SUM_I ← $A_{I,J}$+SUM_I

Figure 4-39

And then the outer loop is shown in Figure 4-40. The rust-colored oval, "COMPUTE SUM_I" is to be replaced with the inner loop. There is nothing left to do but to input the matrix, initialize the various SUMs and TOTAL to zero, and output the final answer. The flow chart is Figure 4-41. The return arrow for the inner loop goes from box 7 to box 6, while that for the outer loop goes from box 9 to box 4.

Many computations that involve matrices have similar flow charts. Several will be seen in the next set of problems.

EXERCISES 4-4, SET B

In the following exercises, you are to draw a flow chart equivalent to each word problem. Each involves a nested loop, and you will find iteration boxes

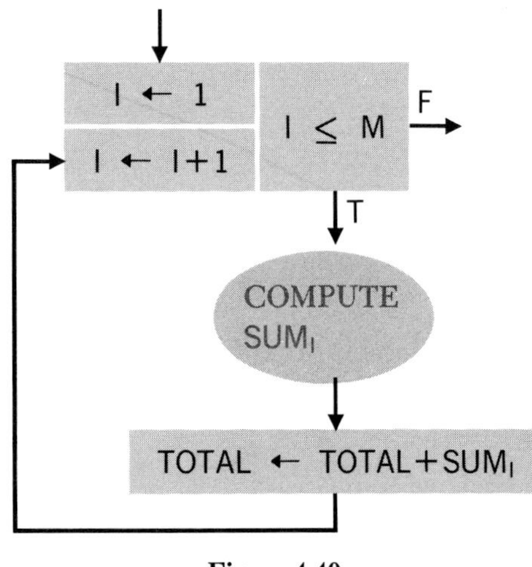

Figure 4-40

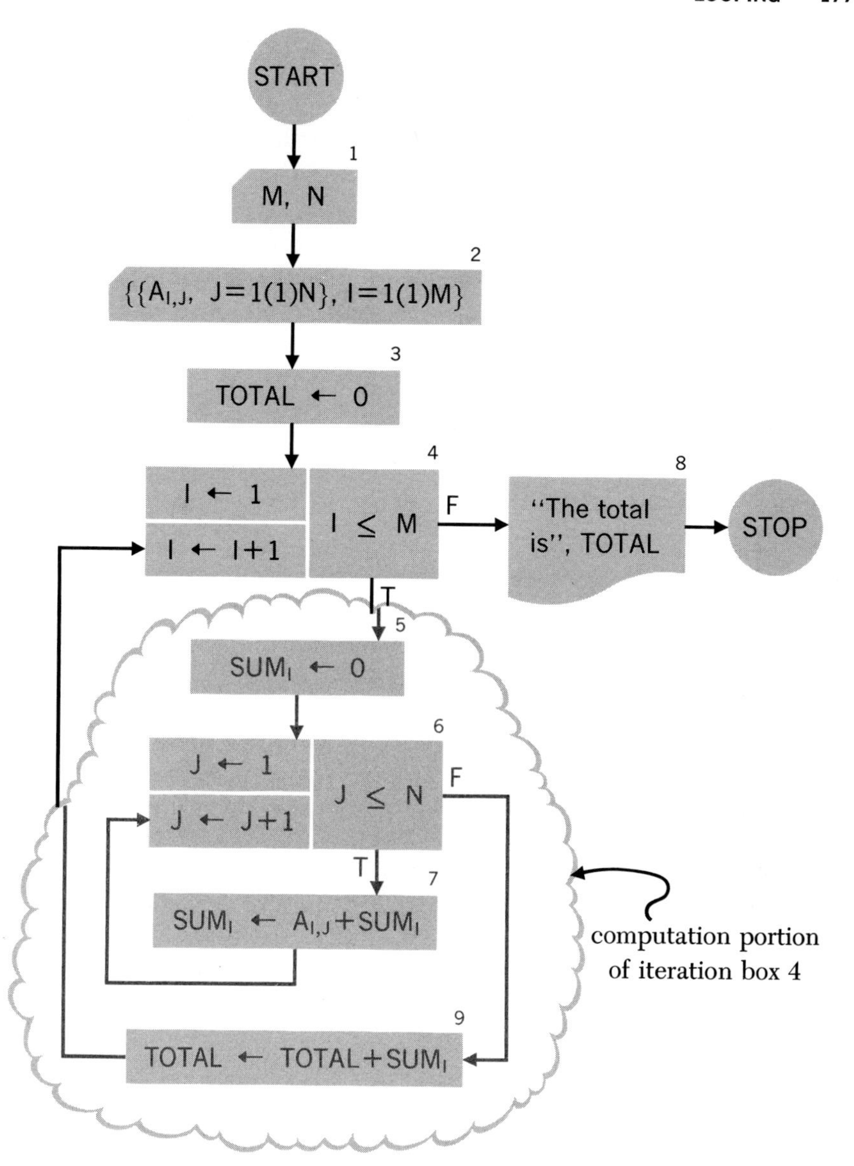

Figure 4-41 The sum of the entries of a matrix showing nested iteration boxes.

helpful. Assume in each case that the matrix P, having M rows and N columns, is *already* stored in memory.

1. Write a flow chart to *clear* the matrix P, that is, set every element to zero, row by row.

2. Search P for the element of largest absolute value. Assign this element to BIG and print the value of BIG. *Hint.* Start by assuming that the entry of largest magnitude is zero.

3. Search P for the element of largest value (not absolute value), assigning it to LARGE. Print the value of LARGE and the row number ROW, and column number, COL, where this value was found. *Hint.* Start by assuming the largest value is $P_{1,1}$.

4. Search for the algebraically least nonzero element in odd-numbered rows and even-numbered columns, and assign its value to LEAST. While conducting this search, keep a tally of the number of zeros found, ZTALY, and then print values for LEAST and ZTALY. If all elements are zero, the value printed for LEAST should be zero.

5. Add a multiple, T, of the first row entries to the entries of all other rows of P. For example, if T = 2, we show the action on a 4-row by 4-column matrix P.

$$\text{before action} \begin{cases} 1 & 2 & 1 & 1 \\ 3 & 4 & 2 & 5 \\ 1 & 2 & 1 & 2 \\ 3 & 1 & 3 & 2 \end{cases} \qquad \begin{matrix}\text{after adding} \\ 2 \times \text{row 1 to} \\ \text{each of the} \\ \text{other rows}\end{matrix} \begin{cases} 1 & 2 & 1 & 1 \\ 5 & 8 & 4 & 7 \\ 3 & 6 & 3 & 4 \\ 5 & 5 & 5 & 4 \end{cases}$$

6. Determine the minimum value in each column, MIN, of the matrix P and print it out with its row and column identification, ROW and COL. If there is more than one occurrence of the minimum value, report the last one found. For the 4 × 4 array shown in the preceding exercise in the "before" state, the desired output for this exercise would be:

MIN	ROW	COL
1	3	1
1	4	2
1	3	3
1	1	4

7. A matrix that has the same number of rows and columns is called a "*square matrix.*" In the next three exercises we shall assume that P is square (M rows and M columns). The "*main diagonal*" of a square matrix is the set of entries having equal row and column subscripts, i.e., $P_{1,1}$, $P_{2,2}$, $P_{3,3}$, etc. The ith element on the main diagonal can therefore be referred to as $P_{i,i}$.

Assign to SUM1 the sum of all entries to the *left* of the main diagonal of the square matrix P, accumulating the terms row by row. *Hint.* Make yourself a picture of the triangular group of entries that fall in the category to be summed. What is the first row involved? What is the last column involved? For any row to the left of the main diagonal, what are the subscripts of the rightmost entry?

8. Form the sum of all entries that are situated to the *right* of the main diagonal of P, accumulating the terms row-by-row. (See Problem 7.)

9. The "triangle" to the left of the main diagonal that you worked with in problem 7 is often called the "lower triangle," and the one to the right of the main diagonal is often called the "upper triangle." In this exercise we wish to search the upper triangle column-by-column starting from the *last* column. We will search each column from top to bottom for the first entry that is at least twice as large in magnitude as its immediate predecessor in the same column. An entry that exhibits this increased magnitude will be termed a PIG.

A PIG can occur in any but the leftmost column of the upper triangle. Print all values of PIG as they are discovered, along with their row and column subscripts I and J. If no PIG is found, print "NONE." What is the smallest matrix that can have a PIG? (*Answer.* A 3 × 3.) *Hint.* Can the top element of a column be a PIG? What is the row subscript for the bottommost element in the Jth column?

EXERCISES 4-4, SET C

1. Study the flow chart in Figure 4-42 and answer the following questions.

(a) Give, in your own words, a summary of what this algorithm is designed to accomplish.

(b) If a 4-row by 17-column matrix is input as a result of executing box 1, how many times will the false exit from box 4 be taken?

(c) Referring to the same 4 × 17 matrix, how many times will box 5 be executed?

(d) Assume that the following A array is input at box 1:

3	4	6	−2	1	9
2	5	6	1	7	1
8	15	1	2	9	8
6	1	8	3	4	7

Show the array that is printed as a result of executing box 3.

2. Redraw the flow chart for the sorting algorithm shown in Figure 3-29, using an *iteration box* for control of the *inner* loop. The inner loop consists of boxes 3, 4, 5, 6, and 7.

3. Draw a flow chart to do the following.

(a) Find the number of distinct (i.e., no two congruent) triangles with sides of integer length and no side greater than 100 in length.

(b) Find the sum of the perimeters of the triangles in part *a*.

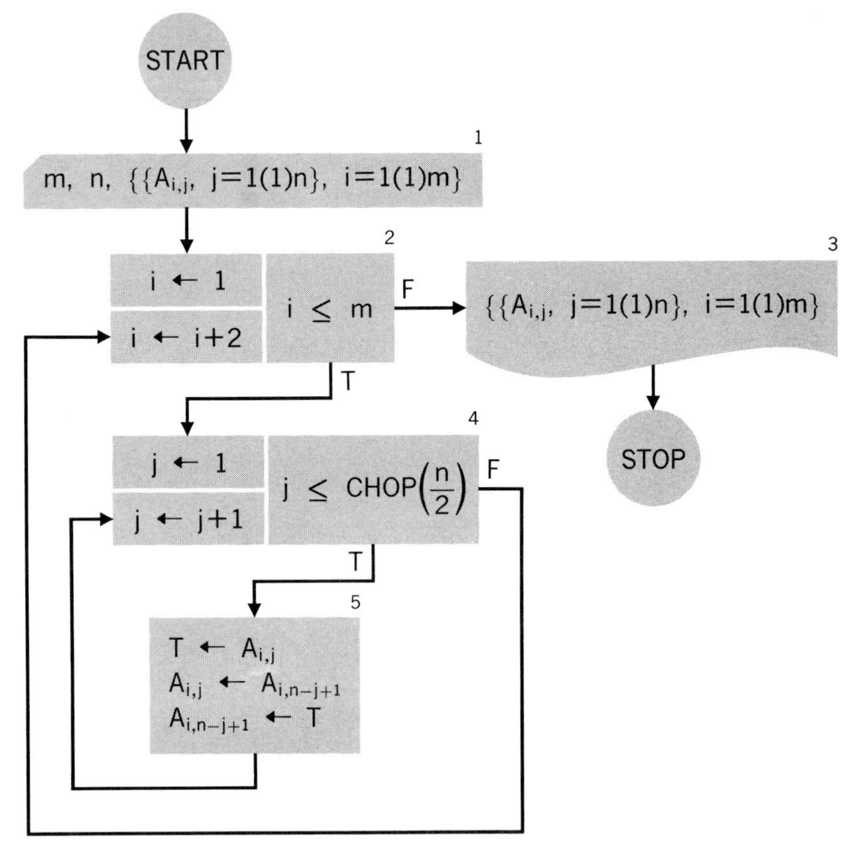

Figure 4-42

(c) In part *a* replace the condition "no side greater than 100 in length" by "with perimeter ≤ 100" and redraw the flow chart.
(d) Redraw *b* with the replacement condition specified in part *c*.

4. Study the flow chart in Figure 4-43.

(a) Describe in simple terms the overall objective of the algorithm represented by the flow chart.
(b) If the algorithm can be simplified without altering its net effect, show the changes that you would propose.
(c) If the following data sets were given as input to the algorithm, what values of COUNT would be printed?

Set 1

$$\mathsf{A} = \begin{pmatrix} 3 & 1 & 2 \\ -5 & 0 & 7 \\ 4 & 2 & -8 \end{pmatrix} \qquad \mathsf{V} = (2, -2, 4)$$

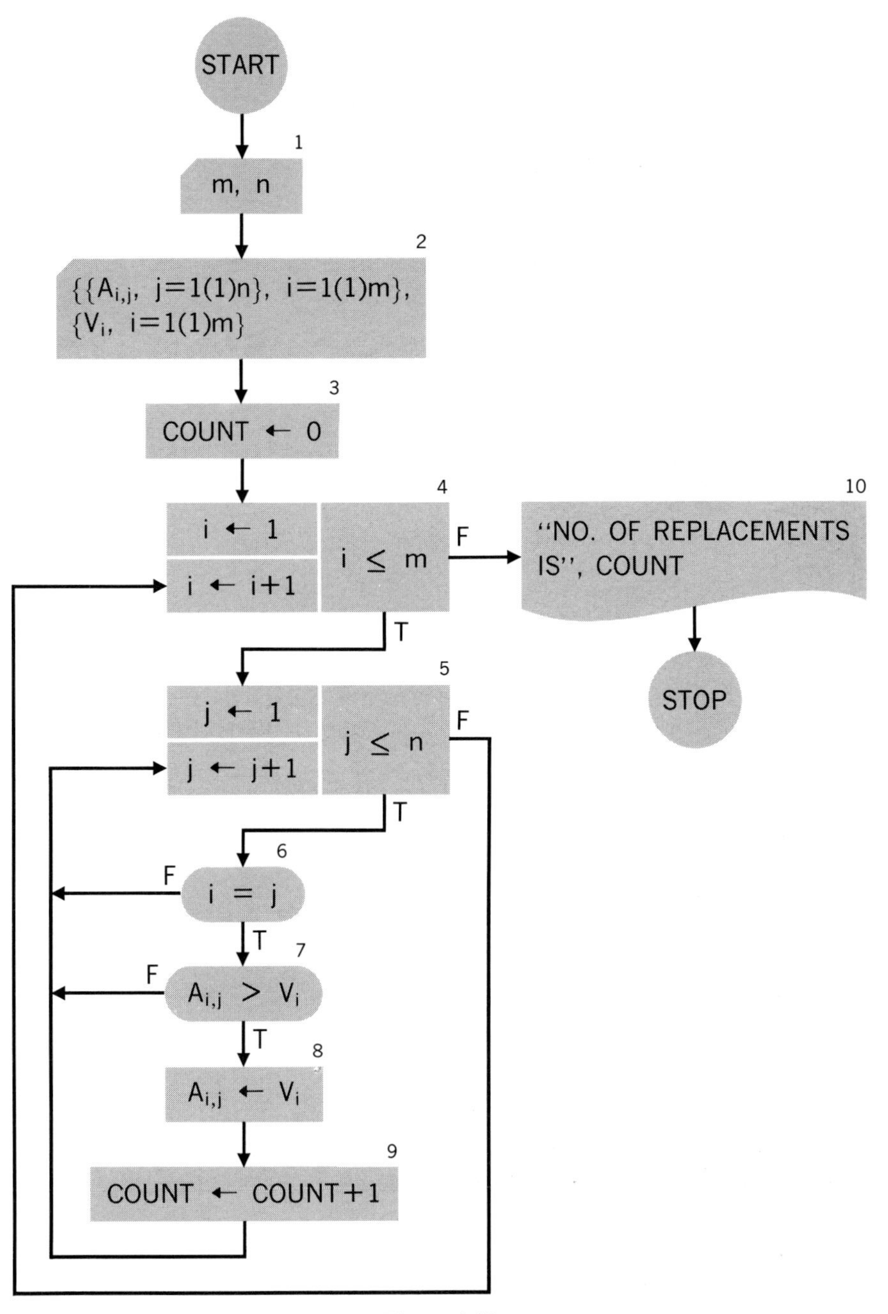
START
1
m, n
2
{{A_{i,j}, j=1(1)n}, i=1(1)m},
{V_i, i=1(1)m}
3
COUNT ← 0
4
i ← 1
i ← i+1
i ≤ m
F
T
10
"NO. OF REPLACEMENTS
IS", COUNT
STOP
5
j ← 1
j ← j+1
j ≤ n
F
T
6
F
i = j
T
7
F
A_{i,j} > V_i
T
8
A_{i,j} ← V_i
9
COUNT ← COUNT+1

Figure 4-43

Set 2

$$A = \begin{pmatrix} 3 & 1 & 2 & 5 & 6 \\ -5 & 0 & 7 & 1 & -5 \end{pmatrix} \qquad V = (2, -1)$$

5. The flow chart fragment in Figure 4-44 represents a special summing process on a portion of a matrix A having n rows and n columns.

Now assume the A matrix stored in memory is as follows:

$$A = \begin{bmatrix} 6 & -2 & 5 & 4 & -3 & 1 \\ 9 & 0 & -8 & 3 & -2 & 6 \\ 1 & 8 & 5 & -4 & 1 & -1 \\ 8 & -3 & 7 & -3 & 6 & 3 \\ 5 & -5 & 4 & -8 & 1 & 2 \\ 3 & 2 & -1 & 6 & -4 & 8 \end{bmatrix}$$

and assume that n has been assigned the value 6.

(a) What is the range of rows from which elements can be taken for the summing process in box 5?

(b) Will any matrix elements actually be retrieved (for summing) from row 2; yes or no? If not, why not?

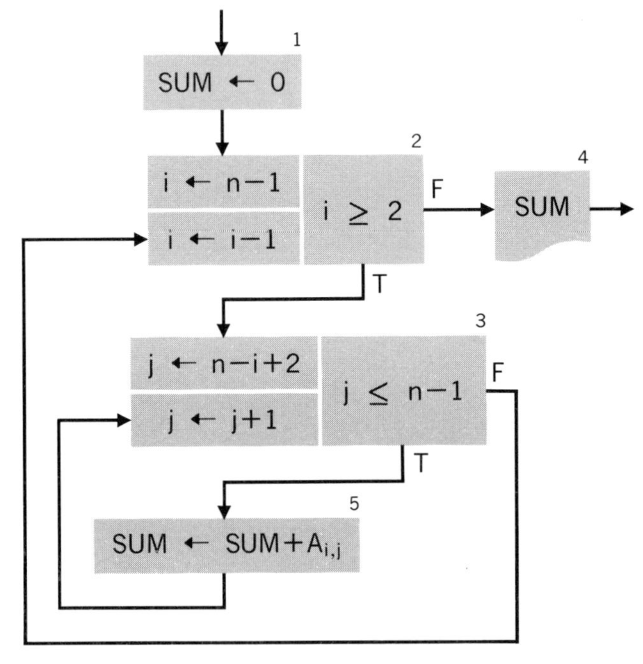

Figure 4-44

(c) Draw a border around that portion of the matrix that identifies the group of elements that will be included in the sum for this particular matrix A.

6. The following is a problem statement and a student's flow chart solution. The student's solution is related to but is *not* really what is wanted. Your job is to modify the student's solution so that it *is* what is wanted.

The problem statement. The computer is to be given two lists of numbers,

$$\{PREC_i,\ i=1(1)15\}$$

and

$$n,\ \{TYPE_i,\ i=1(1)n\}$$

Elements in the vector called TYPE are integers that range in value from 1 to 15.

Elements in the vector called PREC are also integers, but range in value from -3 to 6.

Following the input of this data, the computer is to examine successive pairs in the vector called TYPE, i.e., $(TYPE_k,\ TYPE_{k+1})$, for $k = 1, 2, \ldots, n-1$ and then print out values of k and $TYPE_k$ for each pair examined for which the following condition is satisfied. The condition is

$$PREC_{TYPE_k} \geq PREC_{TYPE_{k+1}}$$

The student's flow chart solution is shown in Figure 4-45.

The Prime Factor Algorithm

In Section 4-2 (Figure 4-20) we considered the problem of finding the factors of an integer N. Now our problem is to represent N as a product of prime factors. These problems may sound similar to you. To see how they are different, compare the following. The list of factors of 360 in the order output by Figure 4-20 is

1, 360, 2, 180, 3, 120, 4, 90, 5, 72, 6, 60, 8,
45, 9, 40, 10, 36, 12, 30, 15, 24, 18, 20

On the other hand, the complete factorization of 360 as a product of primes is

$$2 \times 2 \times 2 \times 3 \times 3 \times 5$$

When we output the results from our algorithm, the multiplication operators will be omitted.

We will work out the algorithm following the same steps we would use doing the computation by hand. In the hand method we would

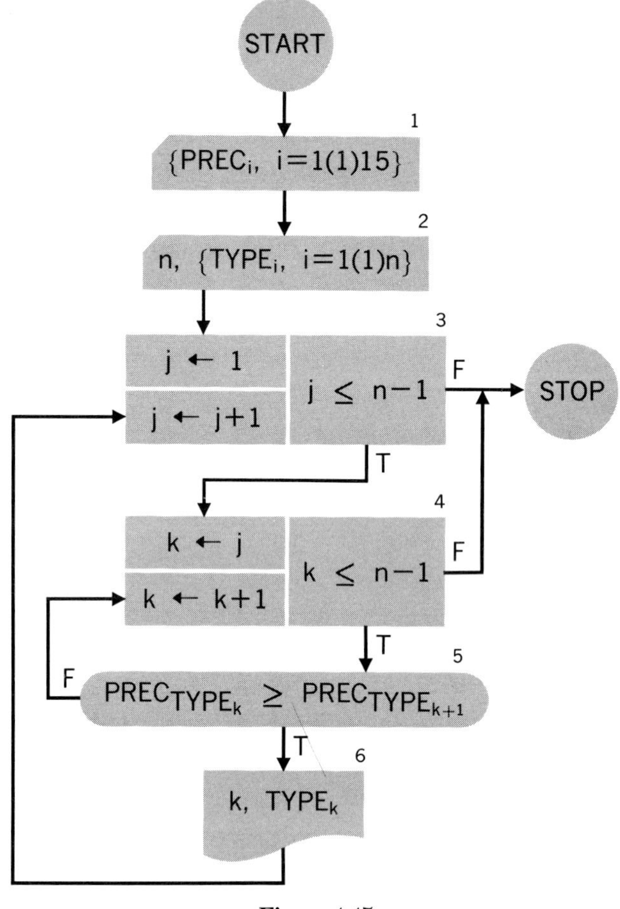

Figure 4-45

check to see whether K is a divisor of N. (Start by letting K be 2.) If K is *not* a divisor of N, increment K by 1 and check again. If K *is* a divisor

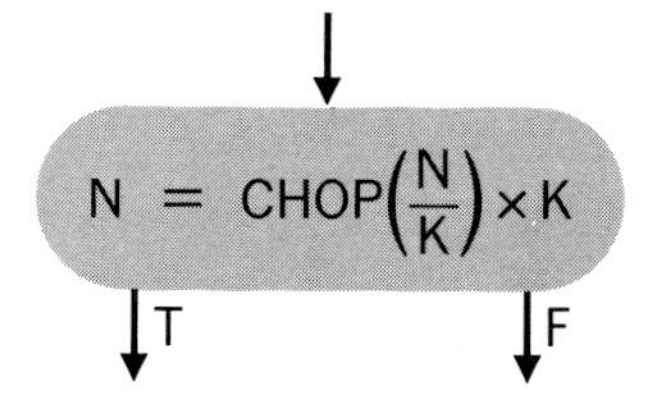

of N, then do the following.

1. Print out K.
2. Replace N by N/K (so that we can now look for factors of the smaller number obtained by dividing N by the factor K).

3. Before incrementing K, check whether K is a divisor of the new value of N (remember that repeated factors are possible).

Finally, as soon as K exceeds $\sqrt{N}$, N can have no factors other than itself (and 1) so N must be prime, or equal to 1. You should satisfy yourself that, in the process we describe, the present value of N can never have factors less than the present value of K.

Since K starts at 2, is incremented by 1, and is not to exceed $\sqrt{N}$, we evidently have the iteration box,

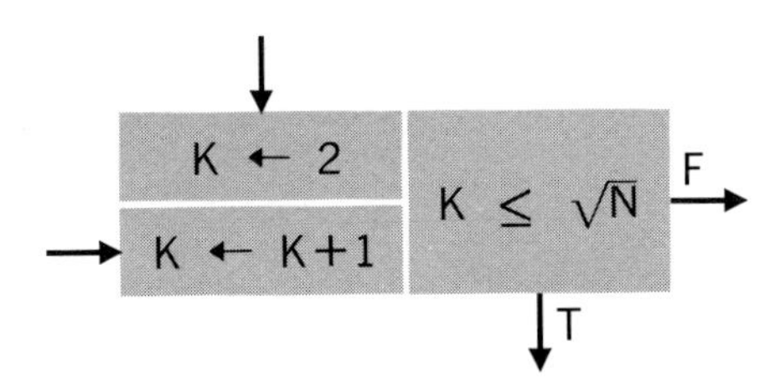

The rest of the algorithm has been discussed in the preceding sentences, so we exhibit its flow chart in Figure 4-46. We can see in this flow chart that as K goes up toward N, N comes down toward K. The inner loop, boxes 3, 4, and 5, involves the check for repeated factors. The necessity for box 6 arises from the possibility that, at some point, N might be a power of K. In this case successive repetitions of the inner loop would eventually have reduced the value of N to 1. If $N \neq 1$ at box 6, it means the current value of N must then be a prime, a fact that calls for printing this value at box 7. It is left to the student to check that nothing but primes can occur in the output. If a list of the primes less than $\sqrt{N}$ were available to be input into the computer, the computation would be considerably shortened.

EXERCISE 4-4, SET D

One of the students who studied the algorithm in Figure 4-46 wondered about ways to improve its efficiency. In particular, he was unhappy with the fact that in repeating the test in box 2,

$$K \leq \sqrt{N}$$

we must repeatedly compute $\sqrt{N}$ even though the value of N might remain un-

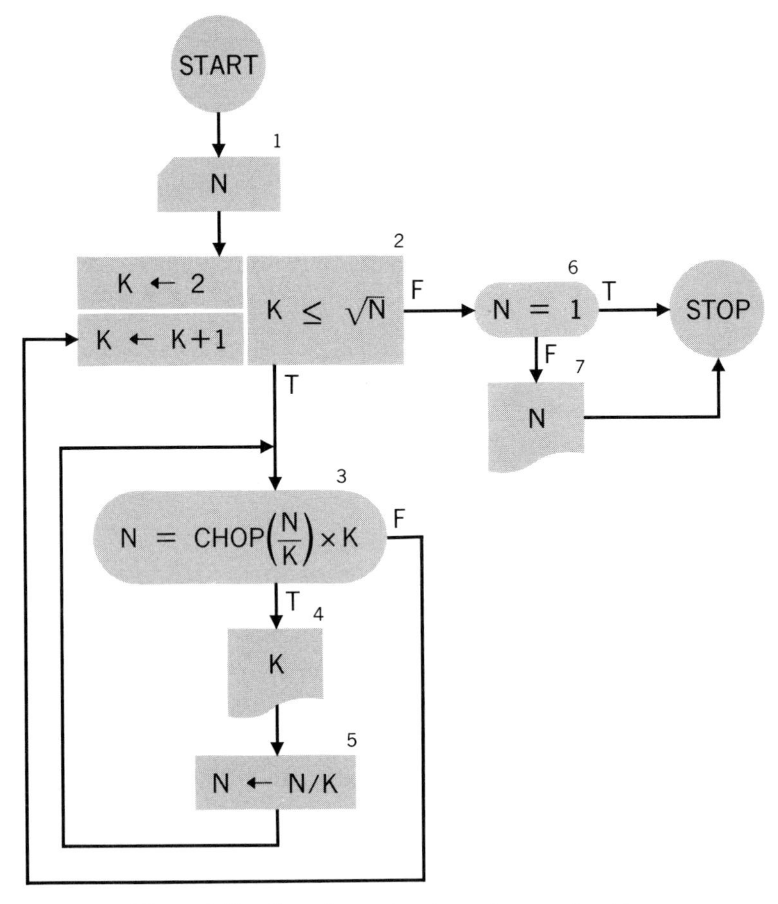

Figure 4-46 Complete prime factorization algorithm.

changed during a number of transits through the loop. As an alternative, the student developed the algorithm in Figure 4-47, claiming:

(a) It is equivalent to Figure 4-46 as far as results are concerned.
(b) While perhaps slightly more difficult to understand, it is more efficient in that $\sqrt{N}$ is computed only once for each value of N.

Your job in this exercise is to study the proposed alternative and either verify the claims made by the student, *a* and *b*, or show where he is wrong. To verify or refute claim *a*, you should trace through the flow chart finding the factors of several numbers such as 10, 11, 12, and 24.

Shuttle-Interchange Sorting Algorithm

Look back at the sorting algorithm of Section 3-6, Figure 3-29. The purpose of the algorithm was to take a given list of numbers and "sort" or "rearrange" it in increasing order. We went through the list from left to right looking for a consecutive pair out of order.

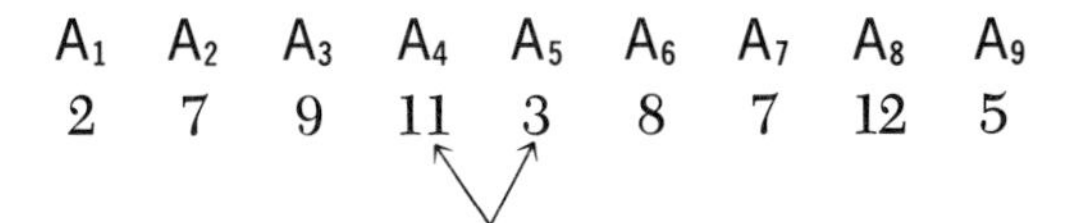

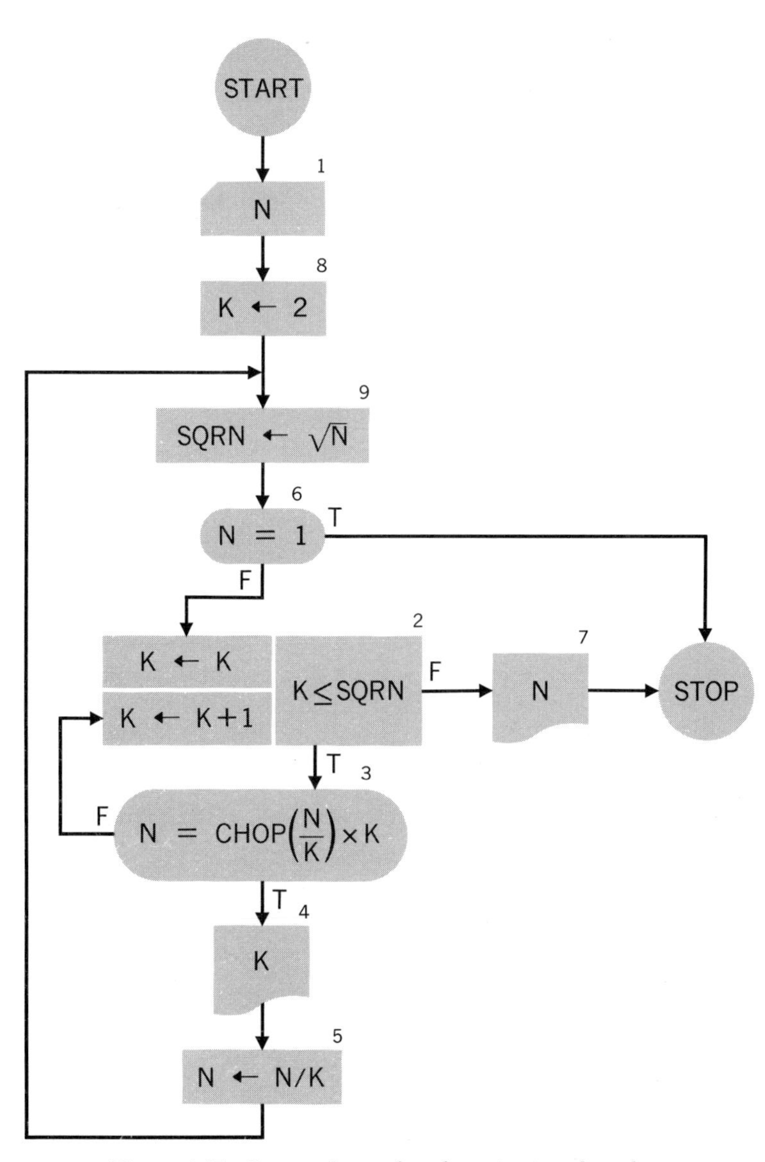

Figure 4-47 Proposed complete factorization algorithm.

As soon as we found two adjacent numbers out of order we interchanged them.

A_1	A_2	A_3	A_4	A_5	A_6	A_7	A_8	A_9
2	7	9	3	11	8	7	12	5

Then we started over again treating this "interchanged" list as a brand new problem. The algorithm was easy to describe but rather wasteful. The reason for this wastefulness is the rechecking of pairs preceding the interchanged pairs. These are already known to be in increasing order! We look for an algorithm to eliminate this waste.

In the example above we see that the 3 is still out of place. Holding a finger on the position of 11, so as not to lose our place, we first take care of 3. Using three tests and two interchanges, we work 3 back to where it belongs between 2 and 7.

A_1	A_2	A_3	A_4	A_5	A_6	A_7	A_8	A_9
2	3	7	9	11	8	7	12	5

Now we come back to 11 where our finger was and compare it with the next entry, and so on. To translate this into a flow chart, we input N and a vector with N components.

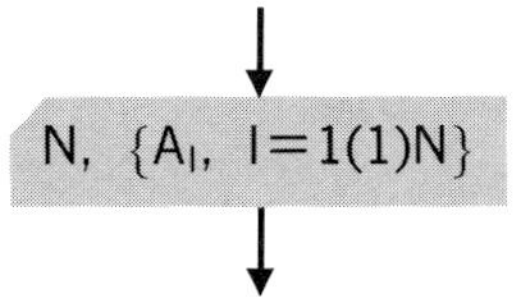

$N, \{A_I, I=1(1)N\}$

Now we introduce a variable J, which runs through the subscripts, picking out $N-1$ pairs A_J, A_{J+1} to be compared.

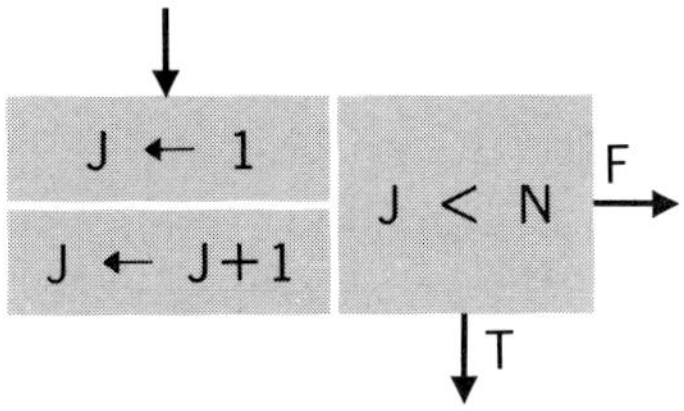

$J \leftarrow 1$; $J \leftarrow J+1$; $J < N$ (F →, T ↓)

Then we must have a variable K which, after an interchange located by

J, works the smaller of the two interchanged numbers back to its proper location.

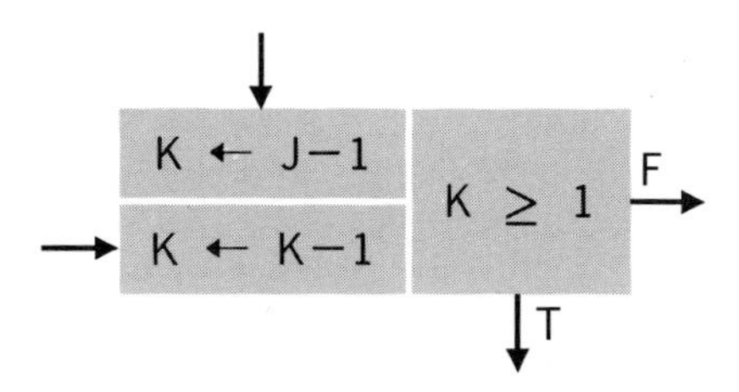

There are two surprises in this box. First, there is a variable on the right side of the initiation compartment. Second, incrementation is negative. Both of these novelties are permissible.

Now we draw the flow chart in Figure 4-48. This sorting algorithm is quite efficient and has, therefore, been named. It is variously called the "shuttle-interchange" algorithm or the "pushdown and bubble" algorithm.

EXERCISES 4-4, SET E

1. In order properly to compare the primitive sorting algorithm (Figure 3-29) with the one in Figure 4-48, redraw the former, using an iteration box for control of the inner loop. In redrawing Figure 3-29, you can simply omit box 1, letting box 8 lead to a STOP.

2. In order to appraise the efficiency of the shuttle-interchange method and to compare it with the primitive sort, we will again equate the work of sorting to the number of comparisons required. In this case, the sorting work would be proportional to the total number of times boxes 4 and 7 (Figure 4-48) are executed.

(a) How many times are boxes 4 and 7 executed from START to STOP if the values to be sorted are 7, 2, −5, 4?

(b) How many times are boxes 4 and 7 executed if the values to be sorted are −9, 5, 9, 12?

(c) How many times are boxes 4 and 7 executed if the values to be sorted are 12, 9, 5, −9?

3. What changes would be required in the flow chart of Figure 4-48 to make it serve for sorting numbers into descending order?

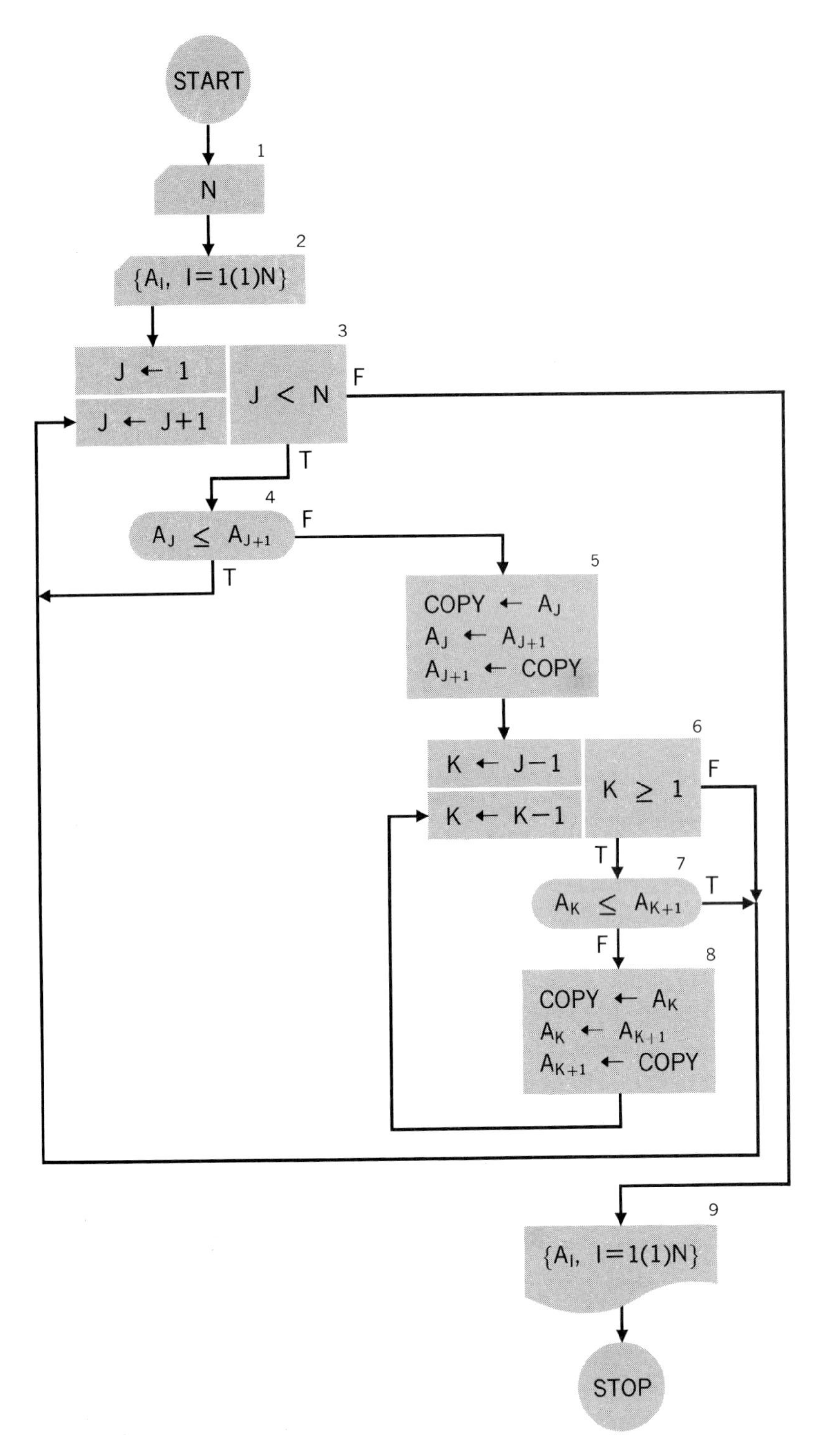

Figure 4-48 Shuttle-interchange sort.

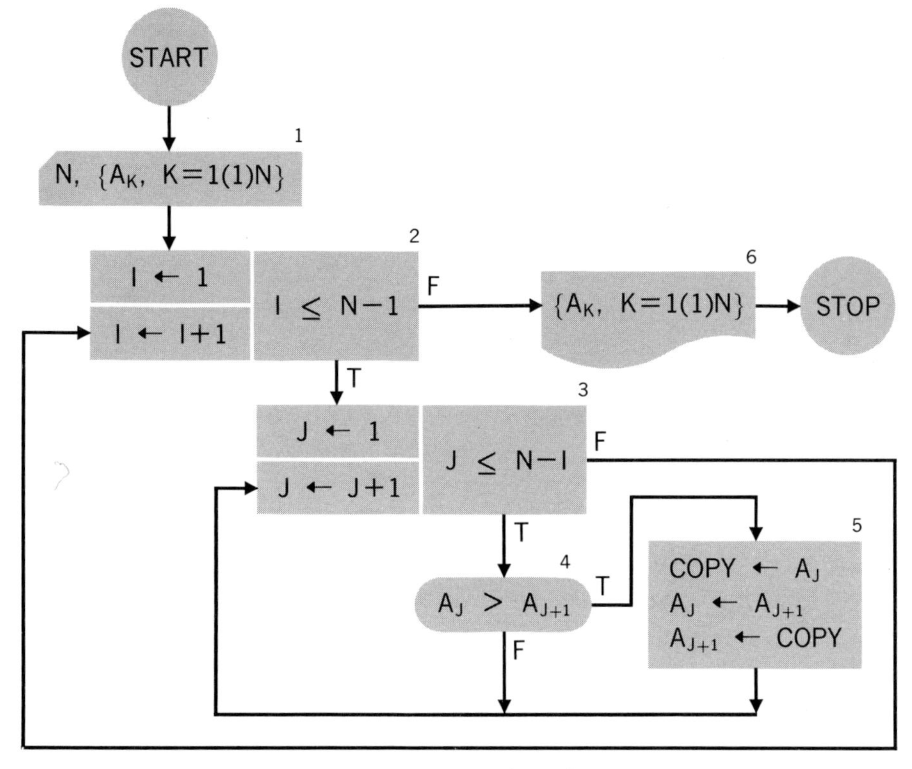

Figure 4-49 A sleeper?

4. A student brings into class the algorithm shown in Figure 4-49. He makes the following claims.

(a) It is an algorithm for sorting numbers in ascending algebraic order.
(b) It is more efficient than the algorithm in Figure 4-48.

Your job is to verify or refute each claim.

[2] 4-5 AN INTERESTING USE OF LOOPING: THE MONOTONE SEQUENCE PROBLEM

A few years ago a charming little problem was making the rounds of mathematics departments. It was a true stickler in contrast with the pseudostickler we met earlier in Section 4-4. New terms used in the statement of the problem are explained below.

[2] This section can be omitted without loss of continuity.

Problem. Suppose you are given a sequence (that is, a list) of N numbers, all guaranteed to be different. Prove that the length of the longest monotone subsequence is at least $\sqrt{N}$.

By a sequence we mean a list of numbers like the components of a vector. The order in which they are written is very important. For example:

5 0 9 6 1 12 3 7 2

By a subsequence we mean the list that remains after "crossing out" some numbers in the original list. We show one of the 512 possible subsequences of the sequence exhibited above:

~~5~~ ~~0~~ 9 6 ~~1~~ 12 3 ~~7~~ 2

The reason for explaining this idea in terms of "crossing out" is to make it absolutely clear that the order of the remaining terms is not altered. By a *monotone* subsequence we mean one in which either the values are increasing from left to right or one in which they are decreasing.

Thus, the preceding subsequence is not monotone but the following two are, the first being increasing and the second, decreasing.

~~5~~ 0 ~~9~~ ~~6~~ 1 ~~12~~ 3 7 ~~2~~
5 ~~0~~ ~~9~~ ~~6~~ ~~1~~ ~~12~~ 3 ~~7~~ 2

You can check that the increasing subsequence is the longest possible; that is to say, there is no increasing subsequence with more than four terms. The decreasing one is not the longest possible, since the subsequence

9 6 3 2

is longer.

In this example the longest increasing subsequence had length 4 and so did the longest decreasing subsequence. Thus, in this example the length of the longest monotone subsequence is 4.

The problem concerning the longest monotone subsequence is actually one of proving a theorem. It may not be possible to get a computer to prove this theorem, but still this problem suggests an interesting task that a computer can perform. Namely, for a given sequence, find the length of its longest increasing subsequence.

We look for an algorithm, and the first one we not only find very quickly, but also quickly reject. It begins this way. List all possible subsequences. Check each to see whether it is increasing. Make a note of the length of each one that is increasing. Pick out the greatest of these recorded lengths. That is a valid way of attacking the problem, and the flow chart is not difficult to draw. What, then, is wrong with this solution? We reject it because of the monstrous amount of computation. If the original sequence had 60 terms, then the number of subsequences would be 2^{60} or 1,125,899,898,650,624. For all intents and purposes, such a number of calculations may as well be infinite. An algorithm that calls for this many calculations may be of theoretical interest but is of no practical use whatsoever.

Finding a usable algorithm for this problem is a more difficult undertaking than any we have tried so far. We will not get the idea all at once.

Let's take another look at the previous example.

I	1	2	3	4	5	6	7	8	9
A_I	5	0	9	6	1	12	3	7	2

For each value of I from 1 to 9, we want to figure out the *length* (call it B_I) of the longest increasing subsequence having A_I as its last term. This is not difficult for the short sequence in this example. The answers are tabulated here.

I	1	2	3	4	5	6	7	8	9
A_I	5	0	9	6	1	12	3	7	2
B_I	1	1	2	2	2	3	3	4	3

How did we find the values of B_I? By eye—just by looking. And yet we are sure we are right. Still, there is a systematic way (an algorithm) for finding the values of the B_I. But first, note that the desired length of the longest increasing subsequence is now simply the maximum of the values of the B_I; in this case, then, it is 4.

In order to expose this systematic method, consider the preceding table only partly filled out. We will show how to find the value of B_7. We will see that the computer-inspired concept of reassignment is of great help to us in explaining this algorithm. We start by giving B_7 the initial value 1. We know that B_7 must be at least 1.

I	1	2	3	4	5	6	7	8	9
A_I	5	0	9	6	1	12	3	7	2
B_I	1	1	2	2	2	3			

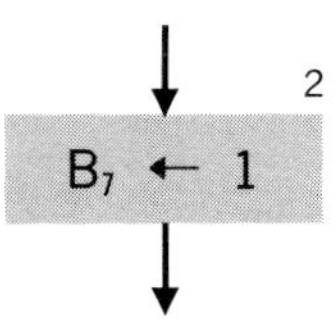

How can we find increasing subsequences ending with A_7 (i.e., ending with 3)? One way is simply to tack A_7 onto the end of a subsequence terminating with some A_K coming earlier in the list. This "tacking on the end" can only be done when it will not destroy the increasing property of the subsequence; that is, only when $A_K < A_7$. This suggests the test

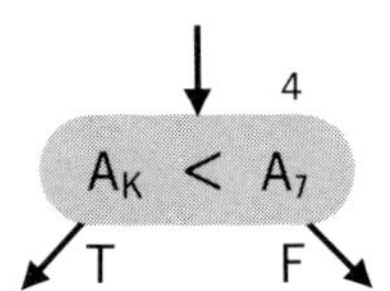

Suppose the answer is "T" (as occurs for the first time in our example when the value of K is 2). Then we know that there is an increasing subsequence whose last two terms are A_K and A_7. What is the longest such subsequence? We obtain it by finding the longest increasing subsequence terminating with A_K and then tacking A_7 on the end. The length of this "extended" subsequence will then be B_K+1. To be sure we have the longest extended subsequence ending with A_7, we must compare each candidate value of B_K+1 with the current value of B_7.

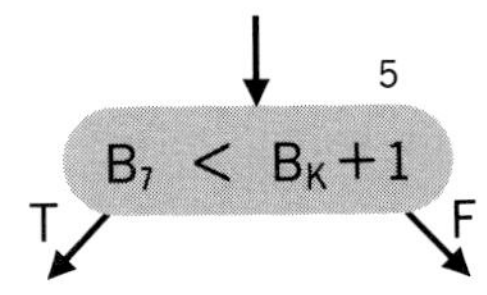

If true, we assign the value of B_K+1 to B_7.

6

$B_7 \leftarrow B_K+1$

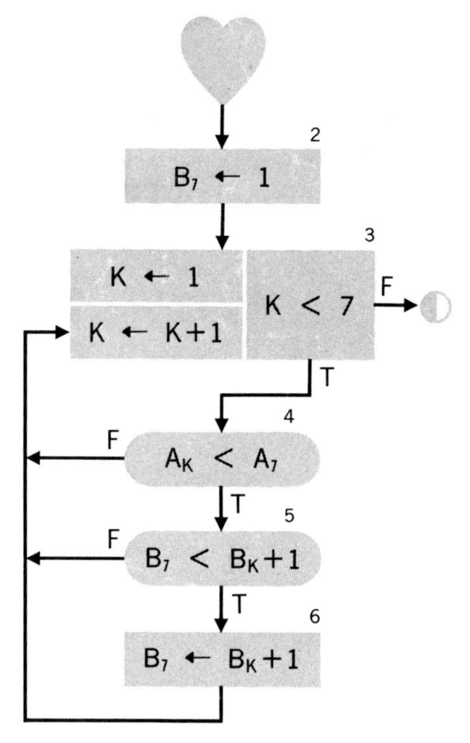

Figure 4-50 Heart of the algorithm.

If either of the inequalities in decision boxes 4 and 5 is false, then no reassignment takes place. In any event we now increment K by 1 and repeat the test in box 4. We perform this process for all values of K from 1 to 6.

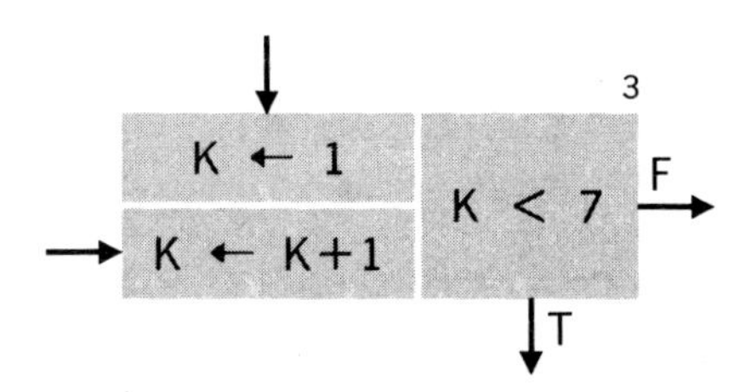

All this together constitutes the heart of our algorithm, as seen in Figure 4-50.

It is clear now that each of the B_J is calculated in this same way, not just B_7. In order to get this same calculation made for each B_J, we replace each occurrence of 7 in Figure 4-50 by J and hang the heart from the following iteration box, with the connections as indicated. (We are

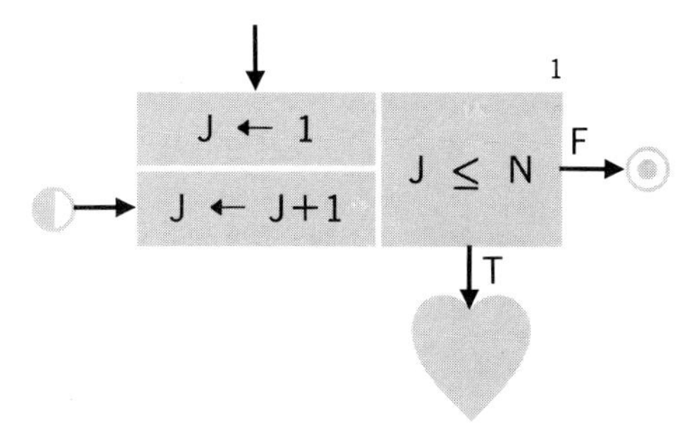

assuming here that $\{A_I,\ I=1(1)N\}$ has been input.) In Figure 4-51 we see where we stand so far.

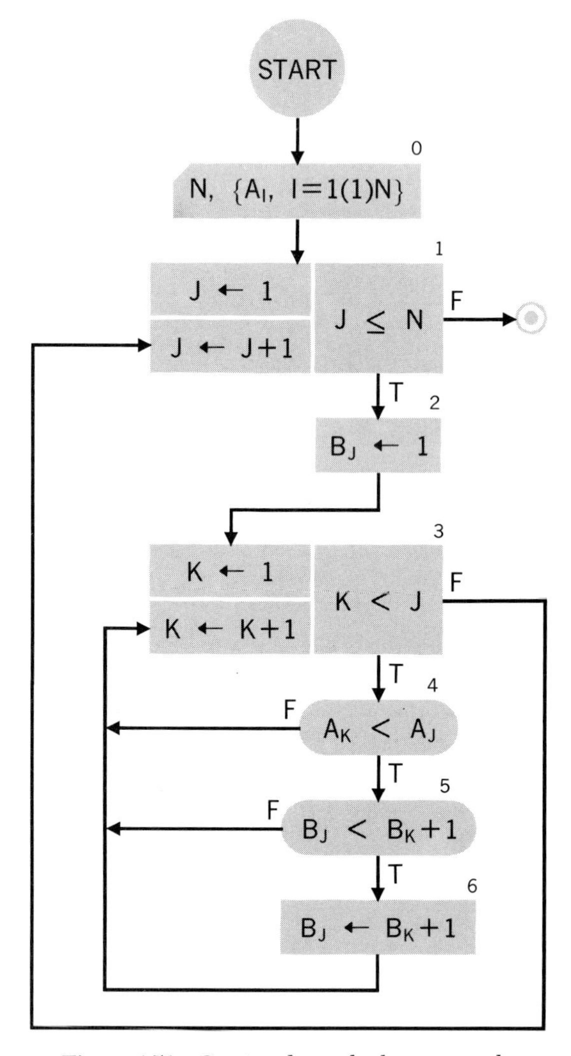

Figure 4-51 Coming down the home stretch.

We have done just about everything now except get the answer. The answer, you recall, is the largest of the values of the components of B. We have done such a computation before, and it will be "child's play" to reconstruct it. The variable MAXINC is taken from MAXimum of the lengths of INCreasing subsequences.

If we join the two flow charts (Figure 4-51 and Figure 4-52) together at the bullseye, the algorithm is complete.

As usual, we ask the question, can we make any improvements? And, as usual, the answer is yes. It would produce a simpler looking flow chart, as well as a slightly shorter computation, to keep a "running" record of the value of MAXINC instead of introducing it after all the values of the B_J's are computed. We mean that after a given B_J is finally computed we should compare it with MAXINC and then reassign B_J to MAXINC if B_J is larger. This eliminates one iteration box from our flow chart. The

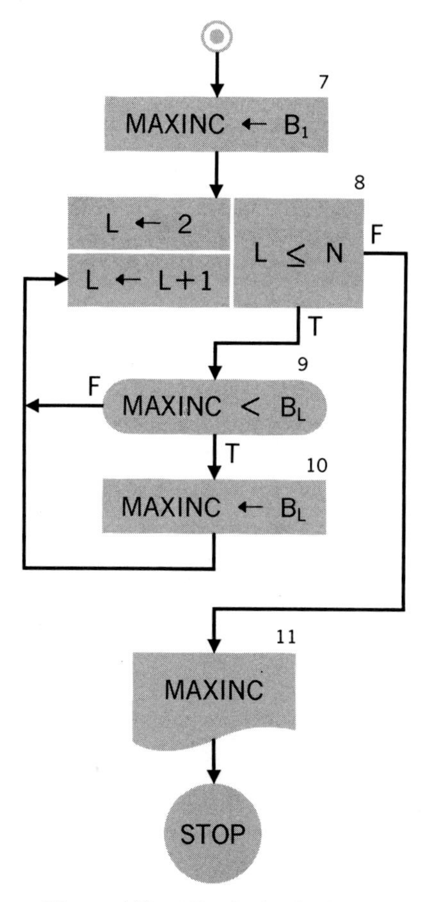

Figure 4-52 The final calculation.

comparison and possible reassignment are seen in boxes 13 and 14 of Figure 4-53. It is now necessary to assign an initial value to MAXINC prior to box 1.

As a final surprise we find that some of the machinery developed in our algorithm will inspire a proof of the theorem proposed in the original problem. This is discussed in Exercises 2 and 3 of Set A below. Exercise 3 offers one of the most interesting challenges in this book.

EXERCISES 4-5, SET A

1. What changes are needed in Figure 4-53 to convert the algorithm to one that finds the length of the longest *decreasing* subsequence? Let C_I represent the length of the longest such sequence terminating with A_I.

2. Show that if $J < K$, then the pairs of output values

$$(B_J, C_J) \qquad \text{and} \qquad (B_K, C_K)$$

cannot be the same (i.e., not both $B_J = B_K$ and $C_J = C_K$).

3. Use the result of Exercise 2 to show that the length of the longest monotone subsequence is at least $\sqrt{N}$.

4. Now that we have succeeded in producing an algorithm (we will call it MAXY for short) that finds the length of the longest increasing subsequence, how do we find the *sequence* itself? We ought to be able to search through the B-vector for clues that will point to the A's belonging to this sequence. If you are on your toes, you will be able to draw a flow chart for the process of searching out and printing elements of this subsequence. The flow chart can then be tacked onto box 11 of Figure 4-53.

To get you started we'll give you two hints.

(a) Although MAXY developed the value of MAXINC, it did not tell you where the top or "head" of the longest (or one of the longest) subsequence may be found. Your flow chart must search for it.

(b) We will show you a picture that should suggest a plan for systematically retrieving elements of the subsequence once you have found its head. Here it is.

K	1	2	3	4	5	6	7	8	9
A_K	5	⓪	9	6	①	12	③	⑦	2
B_K	1	[1]	2	2	[2]	3	[3]	[4]	3

the head (pointing to K = 8)

The desired subsequence in this case is 0, 1, 3, 7.

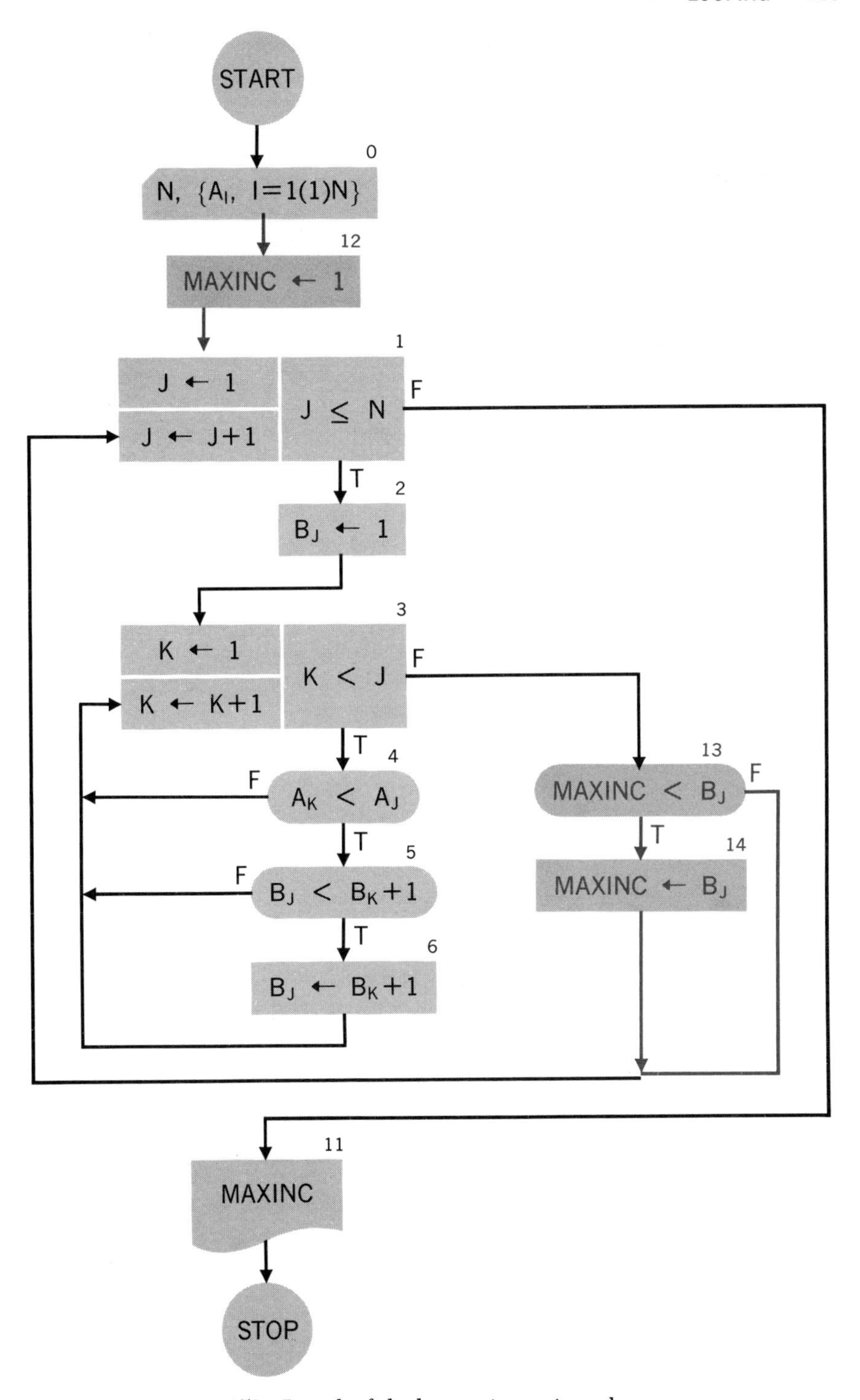

Figure 4-53 Length of the longest increasing subsequence.

EXERCISES 4-5, SET B

Problem Set on Intersection, Union, and Merge. Here we focus on a group of operations that are of fundamental importance in the real world of information processing (on or off the computer). In each of the following four problems, A is an m-element vector of numbers and B is an n-element vector of numbers. Moreover, values in each vector are already sorted in numerically ascending order prior to input. Algorithms for intersection, union, and merge have certain structural similarities. The descriptive flow chart in Figure 4-54 will prove helpful as a guide in detailing the flow charts for each of the next four problems.

1. *Intersection.* Given the two vectors A and B, develop a detailed flow-chart algorithm that forms a new vector int whose elements comprise the *intersection* of the sets defined by A and B. We assume here that no duplicate values occur within any one vector. By *intersection* we mean that int is to contain copies of those values that are *common* to both A and B. Values

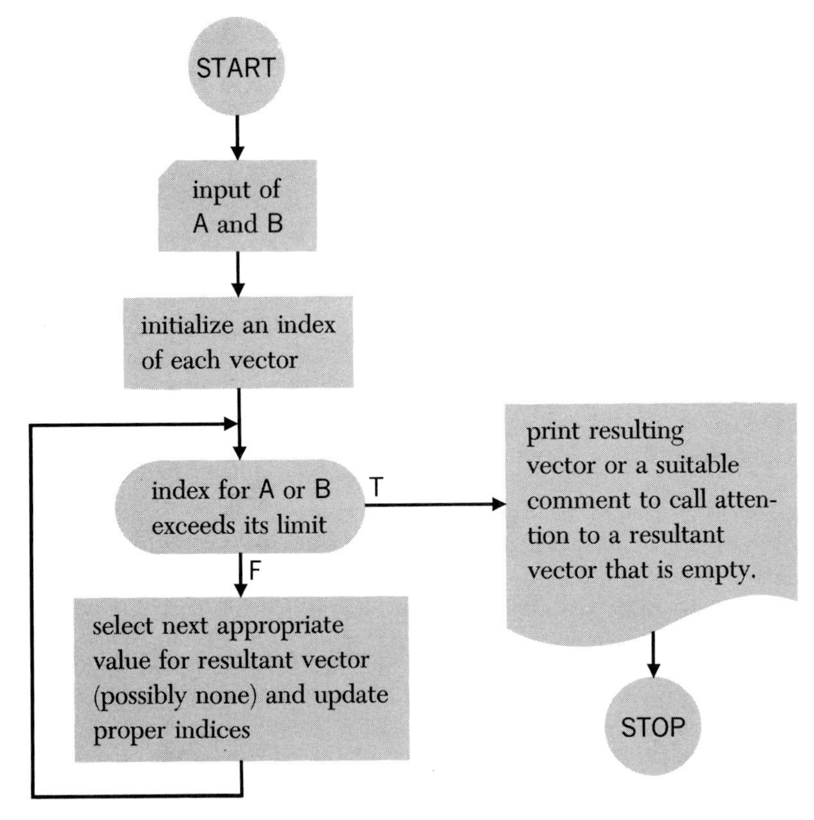

Figure 4-54

placed in int should be in ascending numerical order. Note that the maximum number of components that can occur in the intersection vector int is limited to the minimum of m and n, the dimensions of A and B, respectively.

2. *Union.* Given the two vectors A and B, develop a flow chart algorithm that forms a new vector U whose elements comprise the *union* of the sets defined by A and B. We assume here that no duplicate values occur within any one vector. By *union,* of course, we mean that U is to contain one copy of each distinct value found in the course of scanning all of A and all of B. Values placed in U should be in ascending numerical order. Note that the union U will contain at most m+n elements.

3. *Merge.* Given the two sorted vectors A and B, develop a flow chart algorithm that forms a new vector W whose elements comprise combined values, still sorted, of A and B. Thus, if

$$A = \{1,2,4,5,10\}$$

and

$$B = \{2,6,10,12\}$$

then

$$W = \{1, 2, 2, 4, 5, 6, 10, 10, 12\}$$

(a) In your first approach assume that no duplicates occur within any one vector.

(b) Now decide what changes, if any, are required for consideration of the case where duplicate values may occur within A and/or B.

4. *Union and intersection at the same time.* In cases where we want both the union U and the intersection int for the same vector pair A,B, certain economy can be gained by combining parts of the algorithms for Problems 1 and 2 to form a single algorithm that develops both U and int while making one scan of A and B. Develop the detailed flow chart for this double-purpose algorithm.

CHAPTER 5

APPROXIMATIONS

5-1 INTRODUCTION

When we have constructed an algorithm for solving a class of problems, sometimes with considerable effort, we are able to delegate the execution of the algorithm to someone else. Indeed, this ability to delegate is a very strong argument in favor of the algorithmic approach. Most of the time we think of the computer as that *someone else.*

A computer is an obedient and docile servant of mankind but, like most servants, it has certain peculiarities and idiosyncrasies that can be exasperating and sometimes lead to difficulties. In this chapter we will explore some of the problems that arise when algorithms are executed on digital computers. The particular problems that we will discuss arise out of the way in which computers handle numbers.

You have been accustomed to using numbers for at least as long as you have been in school and so are quite familiar with them. Familiarity often breeds contempt, and you may therefore not appreciate the elegance and sophistication with which you treat numbers.

In your earlier study of mathematics you have learned about the *system of real numbers.* From the mathematical point of view, this "society" of real numbers is extremely democratic in the sense that any real number is just as good as any other. However, when you have to write numerals representing these numbers, certain differences appear. The real numbers that you encountered first were whole numbers that had rather simple names such as 1, 347, and 5763897. You also learned about fractions like 1/2, 17/32, etc. Then there were decimal fractions such as those occurring in 3.1416, 0.9823, and 6.17. Finally, you learned that there are real numbers that cannot be expressed in any of the previous forms. The most popular example of this kind of number is π. At this point, things become more involved. We can *approximate* the number π by means of ordinary fractions such as 22/7, or by decimal fractions such as 3.14, 3.1416, or 3.141592, and many others. You also learned about numbers like the square root of two, cube root of three, fourth root of twenty-six, etc., which could be approximated but not expressed exactly in any of the previous three forms.

The use of digital computers imposes restrictions on our freedom to express numbers. In a computer like SAMOS numbers may be expressed in only two forms. The first of these is the integer form. The second is the so-called floating-point form, which is designed to represent a series of digits with a decimal point. Examples of this form were given in Figure 1-34. At this point, review carefully Section 1-8. Numbers that are not in one of these two forms have to be converted to one of them, or if this is not possible, suitable approximations must be found.

Even with these two forms there are limitations. A natural property of integers is that their size may be as large as you please. In a computer, however, there is always a limitation on size because the machine cannot handle arbitrarily large numbers. The maximum size of the integer that may be expressed in a computer depends on the particular machine used and is a function of how the machine was designed. Most computers can handle integers whose expression requires up to ten decimal digits. If larger integers are necessary in the solution of certain problems, then special steps have to be taken to accomplish the task. In the case of floating-point expressions, there are also limitations that depend on the machine used. In most cases, machines will normally handle numerals requiring up to about seven or eight decimal digits and a decimal point. This is sufficient to handle the majority of problems but, again, special procedures may be developed if greater accuracy is required. You may think that such a degree of accuracy is sufficient, since you probably have not had any occasion to do problems requiring greater accuracy. This may be explained by the fact that the manual procedures you have been taught to use are extremely messy with large numerals. Of course, this is one reason why computers are so useful. In the remainder of this chapter, we show you examples in which greater accuracy is required.

EXERCISES 5-1

1. For each of the numerals listed below, tell whether the number can be expressed exactly in digital form (base 10) or not. If the answer is yes, express the number digitally.

(a) $\sqrt{2}$	(f) $\sqrt[3]{27}$
(b) 34.2	(g) 250,827.36
(c) 3426.	(h) 0
(d) $\frac{1}{9}$	(i) $\frac{22}{7}$
(e) $\frac{5}{64}$	(j) π

5-2 THREE-DIGIT FLOATING-POINT ARITHMETIC

We now intend to show you how computers can occasionally accumulate sizable errors. If possible, algorithms should always be constructed so as to minimize these errors. Since computers often carry out millions of consecutive arithmetic operations, the errors generated can become quite large. Do not be frightened. We purposely are about to show you fairly simple and yet horrible examples illustrating what can happen. Things do not often get this bad, but you ought to be on guard against them if you are going to use computers on which numbers in floating-point form carry seven or eight decimal digits.

To make the arithmetic relatively easy to follow, we will work with a floating-point word length of three or four digits in our examples. The results will then be somewhat analogous to what would happen if you used, say, eight-digit data in an eight-digit word length computer. So, if your computer does eight-digit arithmetic and you have, say, three-digit data, then in some algorithms you may have a built-in cushion guarding against accumulation of error. But in other problems, the results are independent of word size in both computer and data, as you will see.

How does a computer do arithmetic with floating-point numbers? Since the memory word length is fixed, that is, assumed to be three digits, not only each number but *each intermediate result* is also limited to three digits. Otherwise it would not be convenient to *store* an intermediate result. We hasten to point out that a *single* multiplication operation is considered to have no "intermediate results." For example, in multiplying 92.7 by .876, our three-digit chop computer would first find all six digits of the product and *then* chop off to three digits. To illustrate:

Right	*Wrong*
92.7	92.7
.876	.876
5562	5562
6489	6489
7416	7416
81.2052	81.0

Thus, in our computer arithmetic,

$$92.7 \times .876 = 81.2$$

In the problem

$$92.7 \times .876 \times 4.35$$

the computer will replace $92.7 \times .876$ by 81.2 and then multiply 81.2 by 4.35.

In general, computers do not *automatically* round the results of arithmetic computations, although many computers have instructions in their repertoire that can perform the rounding operation upon request. The last part of the execution of a single arithmetic operation usually consists of ignoring those digits of the results that would not fit into a standard floating-point word in memory. Of course, this causes an error that accumulates. Let's continue looking at examples of how a three-digit computer would do arithmetic if it chopped rather than rounded the intermediate results.

ADDITION

Example 1 $\qquad 3.72 + 2.91 = 6.63$

Since the answer fits into a three-digit word, it appears correctly.

Example 2 $\qquad 3.72 + .476 = 4.196$

The computer result is 4.19.

Example 3 $\qquad 14.6 + .0673 = 14.6673$

The computer result is 14.6.

SUBTRACTION

$8.64 - 2.79 = 5.85$	Computer result: 5.85
$3.67 - 4.03 = -.36$	Computer result: −.360
$-18.3 - .0983 = -18.3983$	Computer result: −18.3
$1.23 - 1.22 = .01$	Computer result: .0100

Note the *terminal* zeros that have been inserted where necessary to achieve a three-digit word.

MULTIPLICATION

$4.27 \times 3.68 = 15.7136$	Computer result: 15.7
$27.3 \times .00364 = .099372$	Computer result: .0993
$.999 \times .999 = .998001$	Computer result: .998

DIVISION

$54.3/4.55 = 11.934+$	Computer result: 11.9
$.0632/.00412 = 15.339+$	Computer result: 15.3
$27.5/.00987 = 2786.2+$	Computer result: 2780

EXERCISES 5-2

Work each problem using computer arithmetic as above. First round all the given numbers to three digits where necessary. Chop all intermediate results to three digits.

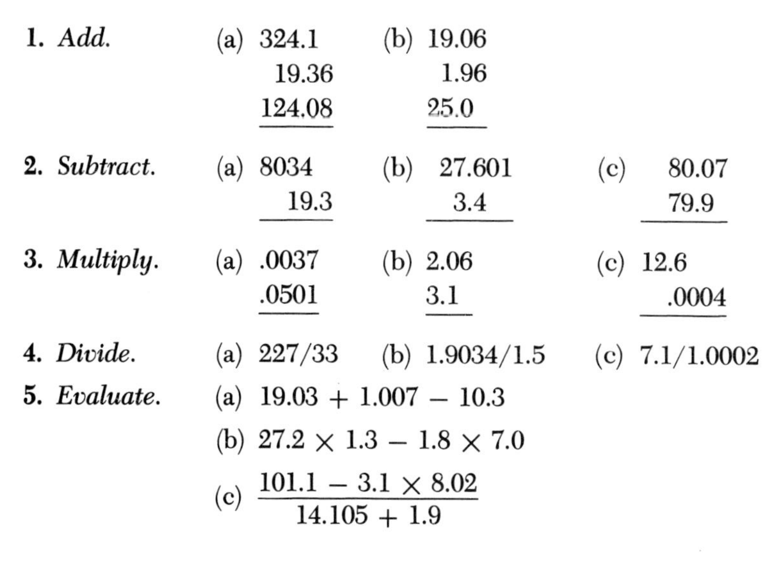

1. *Add.* (a) 324.1, 19.36, 124.08 (b) 19.06, 1.96, 25.0

2. *Subtract.* (a) 8034 − 19.3 (b) 27.601 − 3.4 (c) 80.07 − 79.9

3. *Multiply.* (a) .0037 × .0501 (b) 2.06 × 3.1 (c) 12.6 × .0004

4. *Divide.* (a) 227/33 (b) 1.9034/1.5 (c) 7.1/1.0002

5. *Evaluate.* (a) $19.03 + 1.007 - 10.3$

   (b) $27.2 \times 1.3 - 1.8 \times 7.0$

   (c) $\dfrac{101.1 - 3.1 \times 8.02}{14.105 + 1.9}$

5-3 IMPLICATIONS OF FINITE WORD LENGTH

In the preceding examples we saw how errors may be introduced as a result of the *execution* of algorithms. In addition, there are surprising consequences of the fact that we have a fixed, finite word length for *all* numbers. Let's see what this means. With our three-digit computer, the number 1/3 can best be represented as .333. Suppose we add $1/3 + 1/3$. The computer result is .666 and not .667 as it should be. In other words, *when using a computer, the sum of the best representations of two numbers is not necessarily the best representation of the sum of the two numbers!*

Another example of the same sort is 3/16 + 3/16, which, when performed in the three-digit computer, is .187 + .187 and yields .374 instead of .375, the best representation of 3/8. We might think that if we took .188 as the best approximation to 3/16, it would help but, alas, .188 + .188 = .376 and we are no closer to .375 than we were before.

Of course, if the word length were eight digits, rather than three, the inaccuracy would not be as great. In using computers, however, we often repeat calculations many times. Let's see what happens if we add 1/3 ten times successively, using three-digit computer arithmetic.

$$
\begin{array}{r}
.333 \\
+\ .333 \\
\hline
.666 \\
+\ .333 \\
\hline
.999 \\
+\ .333 \\
\hline
1.332
\end{array}
$$

which becomes

$$
\begin{array}{r}
1.33 \\
+\ .333 \\
\hline
1.66 \\
+\ .333 \\
\hline
1.99 \\
+\ .333 \\
\hline
2.32 \\
+\ .333 \\
\hline
2.65 \\
+\ .333 \\
\hline
2.98 \\
+\ .333 \\
\hline
3.31
\end{array}
$$

As you can see, the error builds quite rapidly. We could have obtained a better result by multiplying .333 by 10, getting 3.33.

In Chapter 4 you learned how to devise algorithms for the construction of tables of values of a function. Suppose you had the task of constructing such a table of f(x) for values of x from 0 to 100 at intervals of 1/3. You might be tempted to incorporate the following iteration box into your flow chart.

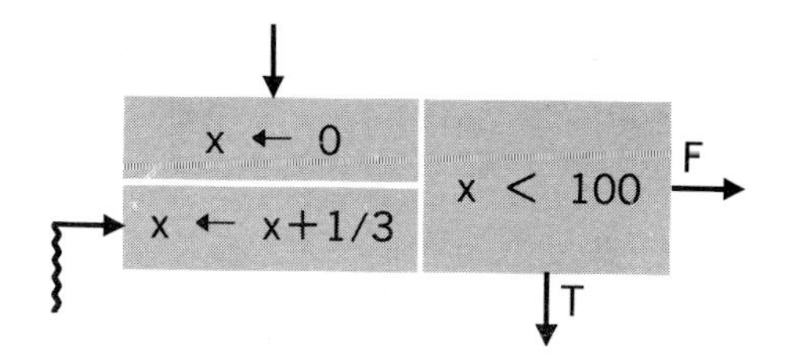

With a three-digit computer, the result of adding .333 successively 300 times is 90.9, instead of the desired 100. Moreover, you would get to 100 after 331 additions. In other words, your table would have 331 lines rather than the desired 300. Interestingly enough, no matter how often you add .333 to 100 thereafter, the result would always be 100 in three-digit computer arithmetic. Thus, had your problem been the task of producing a table to 200 rather than 100, the three-digit computer would get caught in a loop and patiently print out identical consecutive lines with the value of x equal to 100 until someone stopped the machine.

If you had eight-digit word length, the same infinite loop could occur, but only after x reached a very large value, so that things would not be quite as bad.

Fortunately, as is usually the case, when the source of a difficulty has been identified, we can think of ways to improve things. Part of our trouble comes from repeated additions. We have seen that multiplication reduces the error, so we can rewrite the box above as follows:

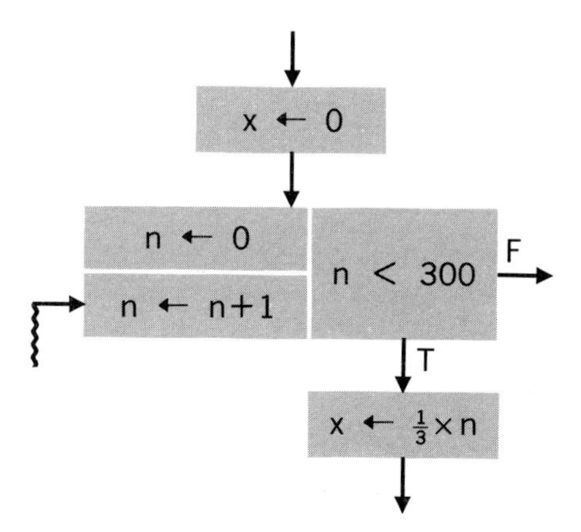

Another part of our trouble arises from the fact that we introduce an error as soon as we use 1/3 as the interval, since this number cannot be exactly represented in floating-point form. Could we eliminate this particular error by using, say, .5 as the interval? To decide this point we must determine whether the answers using an interval of .5 are, in fact, more accurate. If so, then indeed we have overcome another source of error in the solution to this problem.

Many digital computers use the *binary* representation of numbers, and it just so happens that the number 1/2 has finite representations in both the decimal and binary systems of numeration, .5 and .1, respectively. On the other hand, the number 1/10, which has .1 as its decimal representation, does *not* have a finite binary representation. When choosing an increment like .1, this easily overlooked fact can have considerable effect on the accuracy of our results when our machine converts to binary for its actual computations.

To see that 1/10 does not have a terminating representation in the binary system, we express 10 in binary form as $10 = 2^3 + 2^1 = 1010_{\text{two}}$ and divide 1 by it:

$$\begin{array}{r l}
 & .000110011001\ldots \\
1010 & \overline{)\,1.000000000000} \\
 & \underline{1010} \\
 & 1100 \\
 & \underline{1010} \\
 & 10000 \\
 & \underline{1010} \\
 & 1100 \\
 & \underline{1010} \\
 & 10000 \\
 & \underline{1010}
\end{array}$$

We see that we are in a repeating cycle and that

$$\tfrac{1}{10} = .00011001100110011001100\ldots_{\text{(base)two}}$$

If our computer chops to six binary digits, then

$$\tfrac{1}{10} = .000110011_{\text{two}}$$

in our computer arithmetic. Now if we compute

$$\tfrac{1}{10} \times 10$$

after converting to binary arithmetic using a six-digit chop, we have

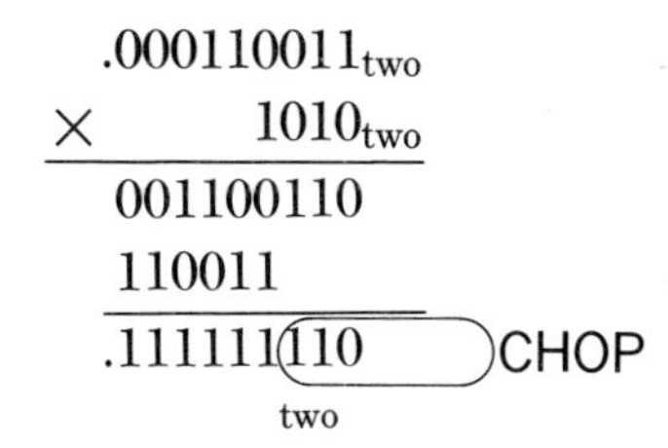

In our computer arithmetic we will then have

$$\tfrac{1}{10} \times 10 = .111111_{\text{two}}$$

instead of

$$\tfrac{1}{10} \times 10 = 1$$

The value of $.111111_{\text{two}}$ in more usual numeration is

$$\tfrac{1}{2} + \tfrac{1}{4} + \tfrac{1}{8} + \tfrac{1}{16} + \tfrac{1}{32} + \tfrac{1}{64} = \tfrac{63}{64}$$

Finally, if the computer outputs the answer in the decimal system, it will convert $.111111_{\text{two}}$ to $.984375_{\text{ten}}$ which will be chopped to $.984_{\text{ten}}$.

In adding 1/10 ten times with a six binary digit chop after each addition, the situation is much worse. Here we would have the binary result

$$.111101_{\text{two}} \text{ or } \tfrac{61}{64}$$

This is .953125 in base ten, which would then be chopped to .953.

All of this shows us that we must know some details of how our computer works internally if we expect to use it effectively.

Problems with Polynomials

Now let us look at another kind of difficulty that arises out of the peculiarities of computer arithmetic. This process occurs very frequently in a large variety of scientific problem areas. In Section 4-2 we discussed the evaluation of polynomials and showed that the nested evaluation (or "Sunday") method is preferable because repeated computation of powers of x is avoided.

Since fewer multiplications are required in the preferred method, you would expect greater accuracy and, indeed, this is *usually* the case. But look at the following example.

Using three-digit computer arithmetic, it is required to evaluate the polynomial $x^3 - 6x^2 + 4x - .1$ for $x = 5.24$. For purposes of later discussion, imagine that this calculation is done as part of the larger problem of finding a root of the polynomial. Computation of the exact value, without rounding, alongside the same calculations in three-digit computer arithmetic are displayed below.

Exact Arithmetic	*Computer Arithmetic*
$x = 5.24$	$x = 5.24$
$x^2 = 27.4576$	$x^2 = 27.4$
$x^3 = 143.877824$	$x^3 = 143.$
$4x = 20.96$	$4x = 20.9$
$-6x^2 = -164.7456$	$-6x^2 = -164.$
$x^3 - 6x^2 = -20.867776$	$x^3 - 6x^2 = -21.0$
$x^3 - 6x^2 + 4x = .092224$	$x^3 - 6x^2 + 4x = -.100$
$x^3 - 6x^2 + 4x - .1 = -.007776$	$x^3 - 6x^2 + 4x - .1 = -.200$

Something seems to be terribly wrong here. Notice that we are not using the Sunday method. Let's try that one. Naturally we will use computer arithmetic because, in exact arithmetic we would get the exact same result as before. Here goes!

$$x - 6 = -.76$$
$$(x - 6)x = x^2 - 6x = -3.98$$
$$(x - 6)x + 4 = x^2 - 6x + 4 = .02$$
$$((x - 6)x + 4)x = x^3 - 6x^2 + 4x = .104$$
$$x^3 - 6x^2 + 4x - .1 = .004$$

This does not look good either. The last result, using the nested parentheses method, is a lot closer than the previous method but has the disadvantage of having the *wrong sign*. This could cause havoc if we are trying to find a root of the polynomial (see the discussion of bisection in Section 7-1), but the previous result, which does have the correct sign, is too much in error to be acceptable. This problem could be solved with reasonable accuracy on a real computer having, say, eight-digit words. But if you stop to consider that it is not uncommon to use computers to solve and evaluate polynomials of very high degree, the problem of accuracy is right back with us again. Unfortunately, no simple answer to this problem is known.

EXERCISES 5-3

1. Verify the value given in the text for adding $\frac{1}{10}$ ten times in a binary machine with a six binary digit chop.

2. Compute the binary values of $\frac{3}{10}$, $\frac{7}{10}$, $\frac{9}{10}$ by dividing and chopping to six binary digits.

3. How can the values of $\frac{2}{10}$, $\frac{4}{10}$, $\frac{6}{10}$, and $\frac{8}{10}$ (chopped to six binary digits) be obtained from previous results without using division? Find these values.

4. Verify the assertion in the text that in three-digit computer arithmetic the result of adding .333 successively 300 times is 90.9 instead of 100. (*Hint.* Study the pattern of the process before plunging into 300 additions!)

5. In three-digit arithmetic, what would be the effect of the stopping condition x=4 in the following iteration box?

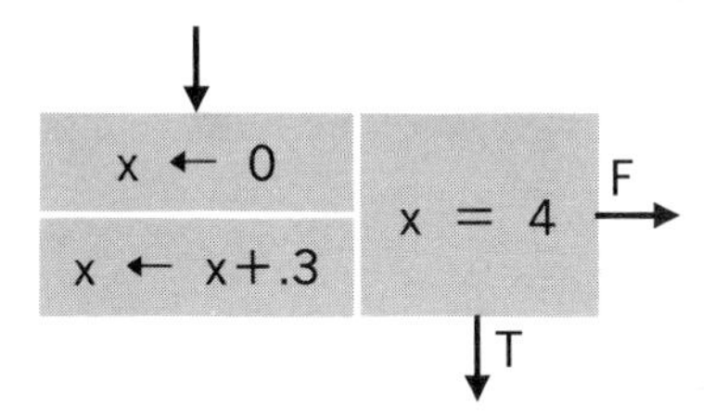

How would you change the condition to avoid the difficulty?

5-4 NONASSOCIATIVITY OF COMPUTER ARITHMETIC

There are other problems and difficulties that arise in the process of doing arithmetic on computers. In the first method of evaluating the polynomial $x^3 - 6x^2 + 4x - .1$ for $x = 5.24$, we had computed the computer results for the first three terms as 143., 164., and 20.9, respectively. Evaluating $143. - 164. + 20.9 - .1$ from left to right, we get $-.200$ as the result. Since addition of real numbers is commutative and associative, we might have wanted to rearrange our work as follows:

$$(143. + 20.9) - (164. + .1) = 163. - 164. \quad = -1.00$$

This is the most surprising result yet! Since the exact value of the polynomial is .007776, the result above is certainly the worst of the several approximations that we have yet obtained. But this result was found by simply changing the *order* of the addition, which does not affect the theoretical results. Comparing the intermediate results, it is, of course, easy to see that the difficulty lies in the chopping process after each operation.

Let's explore this phenomenon further.

Suppose we wish to compute

$$\sum_{n=1}^{10} \frac{1}{2^n}$$

In Table 5-1 we have computed the exact decimal equivalents of the ten terms to be added, as well as their three-digit computer equivalents. We have also summed the exact values.

Now let us add in the "normal" way, from top to bottom, using three-digit computer arithmetic.

$$\begin{aligned}
.500 + .250 &= .750\\
.750 + .125 &= .875\\
.875 + .0625 &= .937\\
.937 + .0312 &= .968\\
.968 + .0156 &= .983\\
.983 + .00781 &= .990\\
.990 + .00390 &= .993\\
.993 + .00195 &= .994\\
.994 + .000976 &= .994
\end{aligned}$$

This result differs from the exact value by .005, which is not very good. Now let us try adding the same values in the reverse order.

TABLE 5-1

n	$1/2^n$	Exact Decimal Equivalent	Three-Digit Computer Equivalent
1	1/2	.5	.500
2	1/4	.25	.250
3	1/8	.125	.125
4	1/16	.0625	.0625
5	1/32	.03125	.0312
6	1/64	.015625	.0156
7	1/128	.0078125	.00781
8	1/256	.00390625	.00390
9	1/512	.001953125	.00195
10	1/1024	.0009765625	.000976
		.9990234375	

$$
\begin{aligned}
.000976 &+ .00195 = .00292\\
.00292 &+ .00390 = .00682\\
.00682 &+ .00781 = .0146\\
.0146 &+ .0156 = .0302\\
.0302 &+ .0312 = .0614\\
.0614 &+ .0625 = .123\\
.123 &+ .125 = .248\\
.248 &+ .250 = .498\\
.498 &+ .500 = .998
\end{aligned}
$$

Here the error from the exact result is only .001, or one-fifth of the previous error.

Again, it must be pointed out that you have been given examples with three-digit arithmetic only so that you might be able to follow the step-by-step execution of the process with greater ease. Similar effects occur in real operations on real computers, where we perform much longer series of calculations. As an example, we have computed the sum of the first 10,000 terms of the series $\sum \frac{1}{n^2}$ by two algorithms. First, is the one displayed in Figure 5-1. The result of executing this algorithm with eight-digit arithmetic is *1.6444743*. Now, using the algorithm shown in Figure 5-2, we get *1.6448339*, a difference of .0003596.

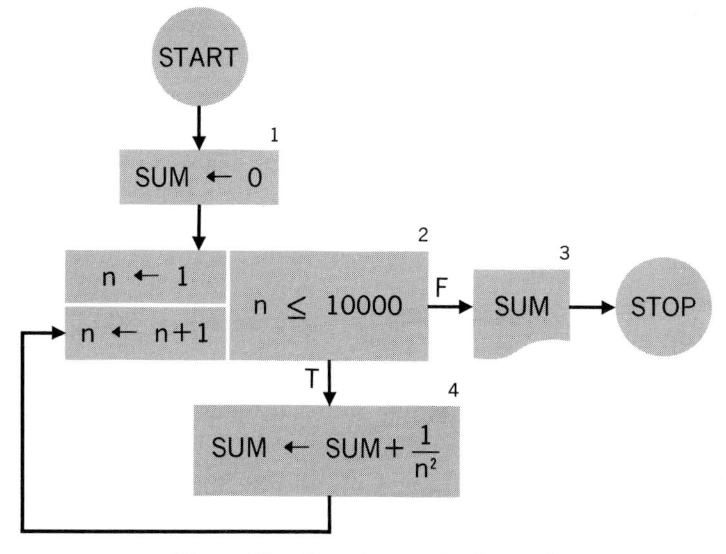

Figure 5-1 Summing a series forward.

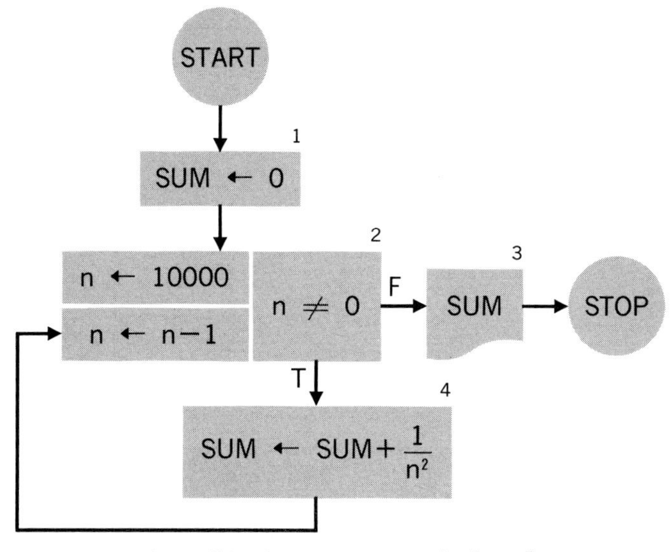

Figure 5-2 Summing a series backward.

Even if we modify these algorithms so as to add only 1000 terms of the series, the corresponding results are 1.6438868 and 1.6439344, differing by .0000476. Clearly, we seem to have established a valuable principle. *The associative law does not work for computer arithmetic; therefore, the order in which computer operations are performed has a definite effect on the accuracy of the result.*

In particular, it should be noted from the above examples that *adding terms in order of increasing magnitude is distinctly preferable to the reverse order.* By adding in the preferred way, the cumulative effect of a large number of small terms has a better chance to make itself felt.

Batch Adding

A generally more satisfactory method of dealing with these difficulties is provided by "batch adding." The basic idea is very simple. It presumes we are adding up a large number of terms, each very small compared with the grand total. The idea is to add up terms in small *batches,* say, ten terms to a batch. Once the sum for one batch of ten has been computed, it is summed with the totals of other such batches of ten to form the sum, say, for a batch of 100. This process is continued to produce sums for batches of 1000 terms, 10,000 terms, 100,000 terms, etc. In this way the effect of each new term or each new batch is significant because it is always added to a group of terms or to groups of batches that are of approximately the same magnitude.

We can develop an algorithm for the above process by first noting that batch adding is closely modeled on our *method of counting* in the decimal system. The algorithm shown in Figure 5-3 is an algorithm for count-

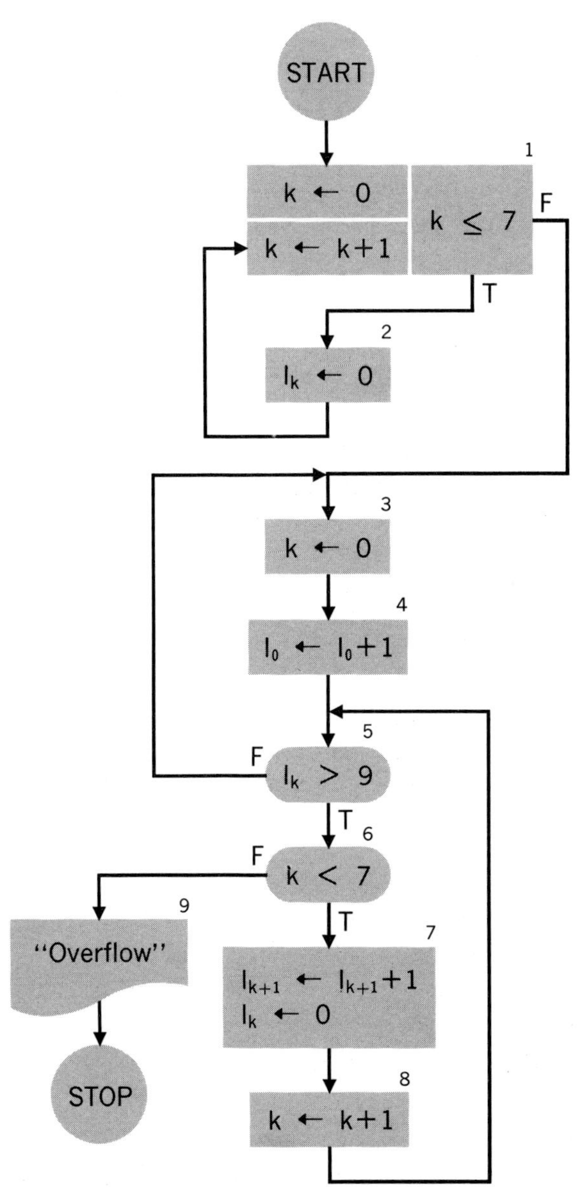

Figure 5-3 Counting.

ing from 1 to 99,999,999. It works just like an automobile odometer. The variables I_7, I_6, . . . , I_0 play the roles of the wheels on the odometer. Each time the value on one of these wheels goes over 9 (in box 5), this wheel is set back to zero and the value on the next wheel is incremented by 1 (in box 7). At any stage in the process, the variables I_0, I_1, I_2, . . . record,

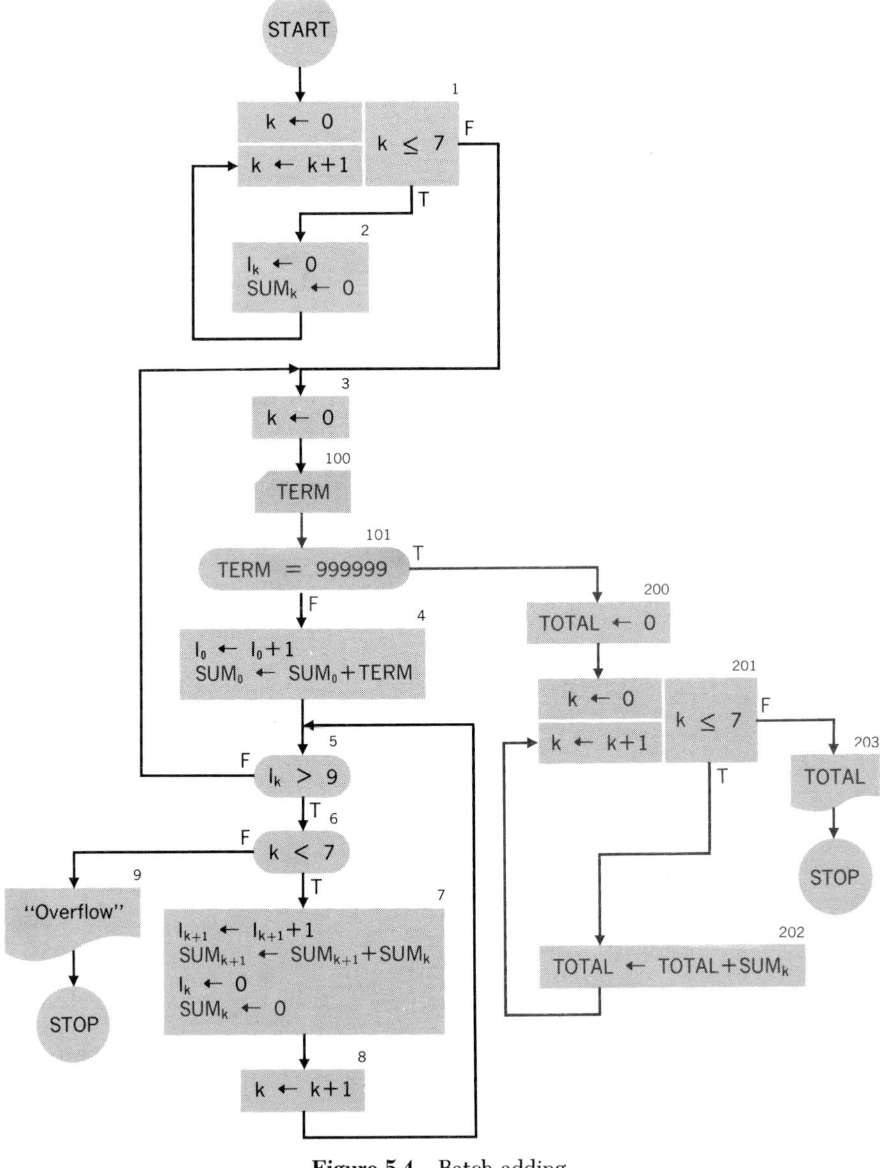

Figure 5-4 Batch adding.

respectively, the units digit, tens digit, hundreds digit, etc. of the number to which we have counted. In other words, at any stage, the number to which we have counted is $I_0 \times 10^0 + I_1 \times 10^1 + I_2 \times 10^2 + I_3 \times 10^3 + I_4 \times 10^4 + I_5 \times 10^5 + I_6 \times 10^6 + I_7 \times 10^7$.

In "batch adding" we use the same basic flow chart but introduce "sum registers," SUM_0, SUM_1, SUM_2, . . . , SUM_7. Each time we increment I_0 by 1, we read a term and add it to SUM_0 (as seen in box 4 of Figure 5-4). Each time we increment I_{K+1} by 1 in box 7, we also increment SUM_{K+1} by SUM_K and "reset" SUM_K to zero.

In this way, terms are added in SUM_0 until ten terms are added to form a *batch*. These batches are in turn added up in SUM_1, until ten additions are performed, thus obtaining a batch of 100, and so on. We can expect that all terms being added will not differ excessively in magnitude, thus holding down the round-off error.

The number 999999 in box 101 is used to signal the end of the list of input values to be added.

The mechanism in boxes 200 through 203 calculates and outputs the grand total by adding up the values in all the registers SUM_0, SUM_1, SUM_2, . . . SUM_7.

The values of TERM need not necessarily be input; they might as well be obtained by calculation. Thus, boxes 100 and 101 could be replaced by any flow-chart fragment for computing successive values of TERM. The idea will be especially useful in certain numerical methods to be developed later. One of these methods is for computing areas by adding up what may be a very large number of computed values, each representing a small part of the total area.

5-5 SOME PITFALLS

For our next example, let us consider the problem of solving two simultaneous linear equations, i.e., a system.[1]

$$a_{11}x + a_{12}y = b_1$$
$$a_{21}x + a_{22}y = b_2$$

In earlier mathematics courses you have undoubtedly solved many such systems of equations and have learned several methods of doing so. Hope-

[1] From here on the comma between double subscripts and the multiplication symbol between multiplicands will often be omitted.

fully, you have also developed some shortcuts and tricks that simplify this job. Such procedures depend on an examination of the system, on some insight, and sometimes on a hunch.

For a computer-oriented algorithm, it is often possible, and even interesting, to develop a master algorithm that examines the system and, depending on the results of this examination, chooses one of several available subordinate algorithms for the actual solution of the system. When you have finished studying this section, you may want to attempt the construction of such an algorithm. For the time being, we will select a fixed method of solution in order to see what can go wrong.

Our method will eliminate the variable x from the second equation by dividing all coefficients in the first equation by a_{11}, multiplying the resulting coefficients by a_{21}, and then subtracting the first equation from the second.

Let us first illustrate the algorithm by an example. To solve

$$\left.\begin{array}{l}(1)\ 2x + 3y = 12\\(2)\ 5x - 2y = 11\end{array}\right\}$$

we divide all coefficients of Equation 1 by 2, obtaining

$$(3)\ x + \tfrac{3}{2}y = 6$$

Next, we multiply all coefficients of Equation 3 by 5 and subtract the results from the corresponding coefficients of Equation 2, yielding

$$(4)\ -\tfrac{19}{2}y = -19$$

Dividing both sides of this equation by $-19/2$, we get

$$(5)\ y = 2$$

We now have a new system of equations (1 and 5), which is equivalent to the original system. Since the second component of the desired solution is the right-hand member of Equation 5, we can substitute this value into Equation 1 to get the first component, 3. Thus, the required solution is the ordered pair (3,2).

Figure 5-5 displays this algorithm as a flow chart. In order to take care of contingencies, we must check before each division that the divisor is not zero.

It would probably help you to trace through this flow chart with our earlier example, or one of your own, to verify that this flow chart is indeed a description of the previously discussed algorithm and, moreover, that the process does indeed produce the correct solution.

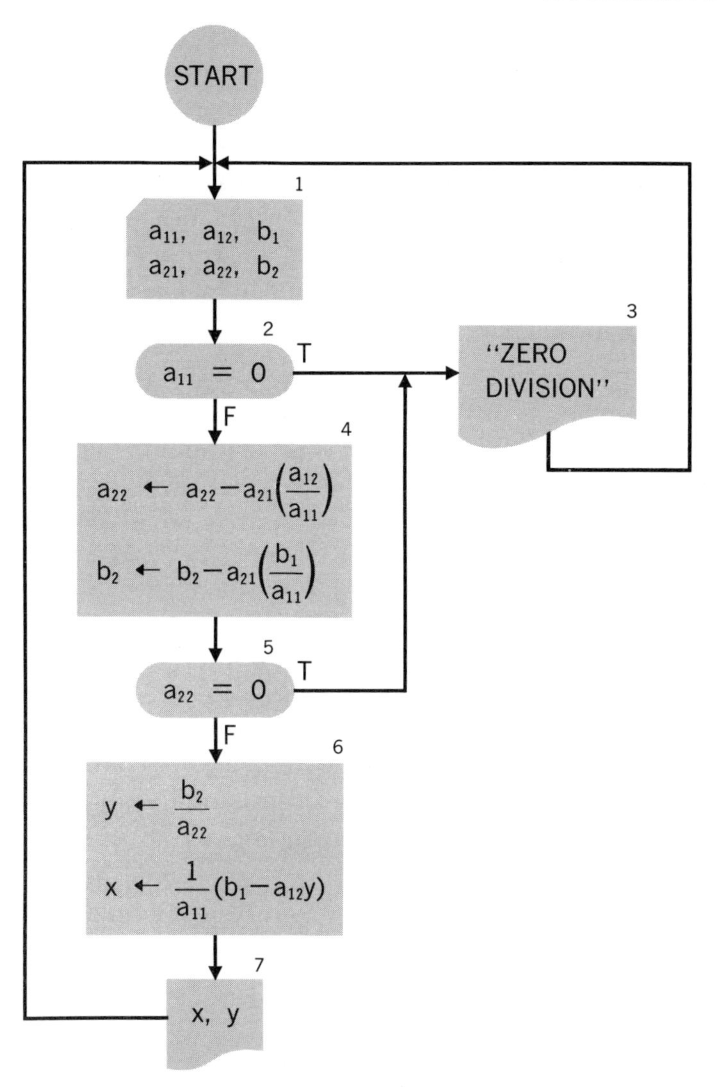

Figure 5-5 Solving two linear equations.

Now for a troublesome example. Consider the system

$$\begin{aligned} .0001x + y &= 1 \\ x + y &= 2 \end{aligned}$$

Let us first apply our algorithm using exact arithmetic to get the exact solution. At box 4, a_{22} will be assigned $1 - 10000$, i.e., -9999, and b_2 becomes $2 - 10000$, i.e., -9998. Thus the second equation becomes

$$-9999y = -9998$$

At box 6, y is assigned the value $\frac{9998}{9999}$. Then x is assigned the value of $\frac{1}{.0001}(1 - 1 \times \frac{9998}{9999})$ which is the same as $\frac{10000}{9999}$. It is an easy matter to substitute these values into both equations and thus to verify the correctness of the solution.

Of course, neither of these values has an exact finite decimal representation but, chopped to ten significant digits, the solutions for x and y are 1.000100010 and .9998999899, respectively.

Now let us execute the algorithm again, but using three-digit arithmetic. We again obtain the last equation above, but we must chop to three digits, which yields

$$-9990y = -9990$$

so the value assigned to y is 1.00. Consequently, the value assigned to x is $\frac{1}{.0001}(1 - 1 \times 1.00)$ or *zero!* This is a very bad result indeed.

What could have caused this extremely large error? To get at the trouble, let us repeat the trace of the algorithm but this time with the order of the equations interchanged. In other words, let us solve the system

$$x + y = 2$$
$$.0001x + y = 1$$

Here we are to replace a_{22} by $1 - .0001$, which, chopped to three digits is .999. Then we replace b_2 by $1 - .0002$, which, chopped to three digits is also .999. So the value assigned to y is again 1.00. However, the value assigned to x is now $\frac{1}{1}(2 - 1 \times 1.00)$, which is equal to 1.00. Not a bad result!

You are probably wondering why the order of the equations has such importance. The real problem is not the order of the equations but the division by a_{11} in the algorithm that we have used. It happens that the error in the division process is related to the magnitude of the divisor. In solving our system we had a choice of dividing by any one of the four coefficients that appear in the left-hand sides of the equations. We chose, with malice aforethought, to divide by the smallest coefficient we could find, thus maximizing the error. When the equations were interchanged, we divided by as large a coefficient as could be found, which gave us a good result.

You might be interested in knowing that there are many important and very real problems, such as space flight launching or nuclear power plant design, which require the accurate solution of systems of hundreds of simultaneous linear equations. So the problem is worth thinking about. In Chapter 7 you will find a more complete treatment of the important problem of solving simultaneous linear equations.

Lest you think that our preceding discussions have given you sufficient insight into the numerical aspects of solving a system of equations, we give another example of what can go wrong.

Consider the system

$$\begin{aligned} x + .98y &= 1.98 \\ .99x + .98y &= 1.97 \end{aligned}$$

Using exact arithmetic, we get the solution $x = 1$, $y = 1$. Check it! Now suppose we change just one of the numbers involved in the problem slightly, say 1.97 to 1.96; we solve the system

$$\begin{aligned} x + .98y &= 1.98 \\ .99x + .98y &= 1.96 \end{aligned}$$

We get the solution $x = 2$, $y = -2/98 = -.0204$ to three significant digits. Thus, a very minor change in just one coefficient caused an extreme change in the solution.

There is a fairly simple explanation, of course, which involves trying to draw the graphs of the three equations involved in the two systems. We have not drawn these for you, as it would be very difficult to distinguish the three lines with the naked eye. Try to draw the graphs. You will see that they are almost parallel. Since they are not exactly parallel, however, the two pairs of lines have two distinct points of intersection, and you should be able to see why a very small change in a coefficient causes the result that we have observed. Try to construct a similar example of your own. In a real-life problem of this sort, the coefficients of the system of equations to be solved are usually found by prior computations, which themselves are subject to error. This points out again why numerical analysis is such an important adjunct of computational procedure. It also should increase your respect for the courage of astronauts, as well as for the people responsible for the computational problems of a rocket launch.

5-6 MORE PITFALLS

Many numerical difficulties occur in computation as a result of using the number *zero* as a decision criterion. You read earlier that all real numbers are equally good. Nevertheless, some numbers are more important than others. You probably have observed in your earlier studies in mathematics that the number zero occurs more frequently than any other.

In abstract mathematics you may have realized that there does not exist a smallest positive number. To prove this, it is sufficient to observe that if anyone claimed to know such a number, one-half of that number would also be positive, but smaller. In other words, we can find positive numbers arbitrarily close to zero.

In computer mathematics, this is not the case. *For each specific computer system there exists a specific smallest positive number.* Therefore, many mathematical ideas, theorems, and algorithms, whose abstract justification depends on being able to find arbitrarily small positive numbers, must be modified for computer use. While a complete treatment of this distinction is far beyond the scope of this book, we can illustrate some consequences by means of fairly simple examples.

Consider some of the logical problems involved in devising an algorithm to solve an equation of the form $ax^2 + bx + c = 0$, given the coefficients a, b, and c. The *logical* problems include checking to see if a is zero, examining the discriminant $b^2 - 4ac$ to see if it is negative, zero, or positive. Clearly, the number zero plays an important part in this logical analysis. If a is zero, the equation is not quadratic and, therefore, cannot have exactly two roots. If $a \neq 0$, the equation is quadratic and has exactly two roots. Moreover, if the discriminant is positive, the two roots are real. You then know how to find the roots by the quadratic formula.

Suppose we wish to solve the equation $x^2 - 6x + 4 = 0$, which satisfies the above criteria. The exact roots are $3 \pm \sqrt{5}$. Since these roots are irrational, no number representable digitally in a computer can be a solution. In other words, if we asked the question, "Does $x^2 - 6x + 4 = 0$?" the answer given by a computer would always be: NO. We can, however, determine that the value of the left side of the equation is $-.0271$ when x is 5.23, and is .0176 when x is 5.24. Therefore, there is a root *between* 5.23 and 5.24, and we could choose one of these as an approximation to that root. We could also compute closer approximations. The important thing to bear in mind is to ask, not for an exact solution, but for *an approximation with a specified approximation criterion.* Such a criterion might be the value of the left side of the equation. The choice of such a value is not easy, however, and requires considerable analysis for proper determination.

As another example, consider the equation

$$x^2 + 10000x - 1 = 0$$

The discriminant, $b^2 - 4ac = 100000004$; and $\sqrt{b^2 - 4ac} = 10000.00020$, correct to 10 digits. We can compute the roots as -10000.0001 and .0001. Substituting either of these values, the left side of the equation becomes 10^{-8}, which is acceptable. Supposing we can only use eight-digit arithmetic, however, then $\sqrt{b^2 - 4ac} = b$, numerically, and we get -10000 and 0 as roots. While the inaccuracy thus introduced into the computations is relatively small, it is aesthetically disturbing to get zero as a result when the equation does, in fact, have a positive root. This difficulty can be avoided by remembering that if $a \neq 0$, the product of the roots of the equation is c/a. Therefore, we can get the positive root accurately even with four-digit arithmetic if we divide c/a, which is -1, by -10000. In general, whenever b^2 is much larger than $|4ac|$, we can increase the accuracy of computation of the root that lies near zero by dividing c/a by the numerically large root. This avoids getting zero as the result of subtracting the nearly equal quantities b and $\sqrt{b^2 - 4ac}$.

5-7 APPROXIMATING THE SQUARE ROOT AND SINE FUNCTIONS

You have had some experience using mathematical tables in solving problems. Specifically, you probably have used tables of logarithms, trigonometric functions, and logarithms of trigonometric functions. But you may not have given much thought to the origin of these tables or to the methods by which they were created. The mathematical theories used are too involved to be detailed here. On the other hand, the storage capacities of digital computers are limited and preclude the storage of all the tables that users might need for the solution of their various problems. If you are not already familiar with it, you might enjoy looking at *Mathematical Tables,* published by the Chemical Rubber Publishing Company, to get an idea of the multiplicity of tables that it contains. There are in existence many more books of tables. To store all this information in a computer would be too costly. In this section we will discuss one or two methods of obtaining approximate values of the square root and the sine functions.

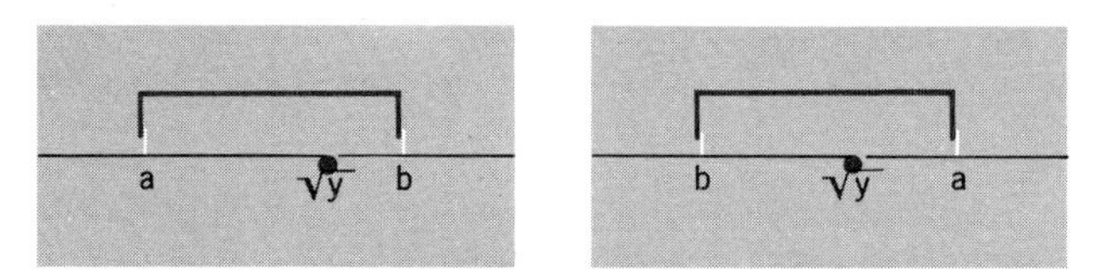

Figure 5-6

Square Root Algorithm

While there are several methods of computing square roots, we choose to use the one attributed to Sir Isaac Newton, and to begin by considering the behavior of two numbers when multiplied together. Suppose the product of a and b is y. Now y is also the product of $\sqrt{y}$ and $\sqrt{y}$, so that

$$a \times b = \sqrt{y} \times \sqrt{y}$$

If a is less than $\sqrt{y}$, then b must be greater than $\sqrt{y}$, or vice versa. In either case, a and b define an interval that must contain $\sqrt{y}$ (Figure 5-6).

Now, keep y fixed, and think of a and b as variables. If the value of a increases (or decreases), the value of b must decrease (or increase) so as to keep the product constant. This is illustrated in Figure 5-7, where we see a changing to c and b changing to d, defining a new interval with endpoints c and d.

With the help of Figure 5-7, we can reach two important conclusions that we will then use to establish the validity of Newton's method. On the number line, consider all intervals for which the product of the endpoints is a given number y. We can assert that:

1. Each such interval contains the square root of y.
2. Each interval containing one endpoint of a second interval *completely contains that second interval.*

Newton's method consists of finding a succession of smaller and smaller intervals, each containing $\sqrt{y}$, such that the length of the inter-

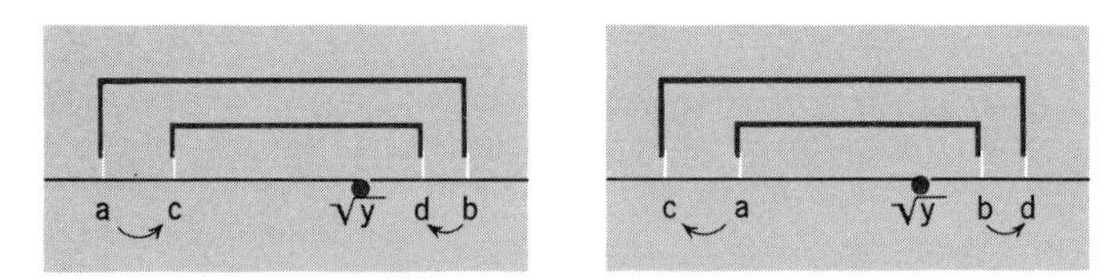

Figure 5-7 Intervals containing $\sqrt{y}$.

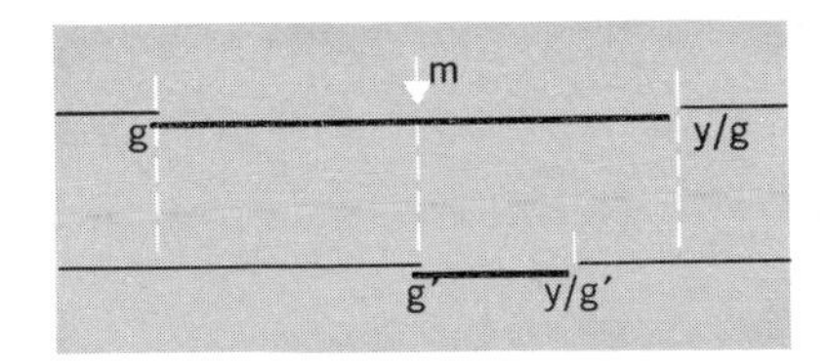

Figure 5-8 First and second Newton guesses.

vals approaches zero. Finding *some* succession of intervals is relatively easy, but we must be careful to choose the intervals so that the length does indeed approach zero.

Starting from any positive real number g (for guess), we can set up a correspondence between g and that interval that has endpoints g and y/g. This interval contains $\sqrt{y}$ since the product of its endpoints is y. The midpoint of this interval makes an excellent choice for our second guess, g′, as illustrated in Figure 5-8.

The second interval, with endpoints g′ and y/g′, is completely contained within the first interval, and still contains $\sqrt{y}$. Furthermore, the length of the second interval is no more than half the first. Continuing this process, the third interval will be less than 1/4 as long as the first, the fourth interval will be less than 1/8 the first, and so on. Thus, the length of the intervals will indeed approach zero, and yet each interval still contains $\sqrt{y}$.

With Newton's method, let us calculate an easy square root, say, the square root of 2, letting the first guess arbitrarily be 1.

The calculation is shown in Table 5-2. In this particular case, the method terminates after four iterations because further iteration will not change the result (in five-digit arithmetic). However, this is not a good criterion to use for termination in the general case, since there is no guarantee that this state of affairs can always be reached. Moreover, even if the value of g does not change in successive iterations, it may not, in fact, be the best approximation to the square root. For example, if we

TABLE 5-2 Newton's Square Root Method

g	y/g	midpoint = $\frac{1}{2}$(g + y/g)	|g − y/g|
1	2/1 = 2	$\frac{1}{2}$(1 + 2) = 1.5	1.0
1.5	2/1.5 = 1.3333	$\frac{1}{2}$(1.5 + 1.3333) = 1.4166	.1667
1.4166	2/1.4166 = 1.4118	$\frac{1}{2}$(1.4166 + 1.4118) = 1.4142	.0048
1.4142	2/1.4142 = 1.4142	$\frac{1}{2}$(1.4142 + 1.4142) = 1.4142	.0000

seek a three-digit approximation to $\sqrt{.709}$ and somehow arrive at .840 as an approximation, then (in three-digit arithmetic):

$$\frac{y}{g} = \frac{.709}{.840} = .844$$

and

$$\frac{1}{2}\left(g + \frac{y}{g}\right) = \frac{1}{2}(.840 + .844) = \frac{1}{2}(1.68) = .840$$

Two successive iterations are .840, and yet .842 is a better three-digit approximation to $\sqrt{.709}$ than is .840. The moral, of course, is that the finite word length of a machine limits the accuracy with which numbers can be represented and thus limits the accuracy of the algorithm.

The Newton square root algorithm is easily drawn as a flow chart. In Figure 5-9 the decision box (to stop iterating) compares the length of the interval with a sufficiently small number, ϵ, which must, however, be large enough to avoid the difficulties of finite precision arithmetic.

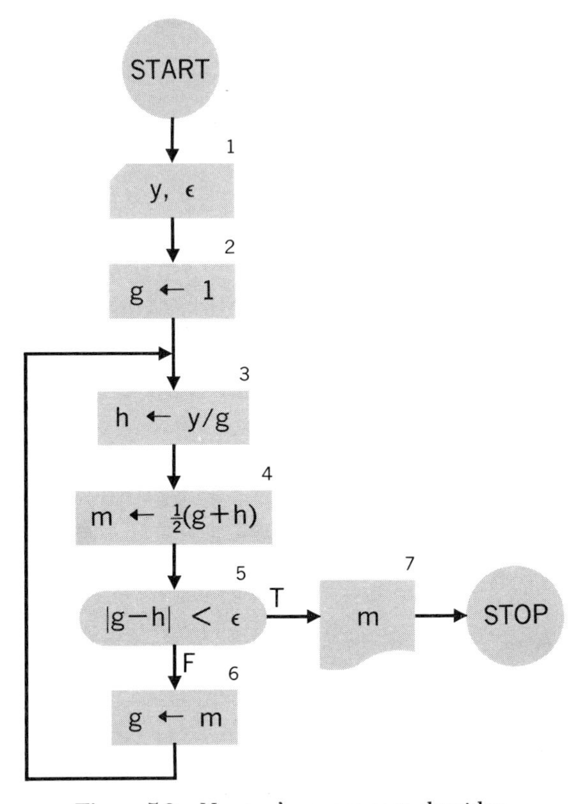

Figure 5-9 Newton's square root algorithm.

Sine Function Algorithm

We will now look briefly at a computation of the sine function. When you first learned about this function, you were told that its values are typically irrational numbers, which could be computed to any desired degree of accuracy by methods developed in calculus. Since you probably have not yet studied much calculus, it is not practical to go into these methods at this point. We can, however, illustrate how values of the sine function can be computed.

We are considering the function sin x, where x is a real number, which you can think of as the radian measure of an angle. It is proved in calculus that the sum of "sufficiently many" terms of the series

$$x - \frac{x^3}{3!} + \frac{x^5}{5!} - \frac{x^7}{7!} + \cdots$$

is a number close to sin x, and that the difference between sin x and the above-mentioned sum becomes numerically smaller as more and more terms are taken.

If we look at the series from a computational point of view, the calculations are not very difficult. Let's look at an easy example, say the calculation of sin (.3).

The first term is, of course, the easiest.

To get the numerator of the second term, we multiply .3 by the value of x^2, in this case, .09. To get the denominator, we multiply the denominator of the previous term, 1, by 2×3.

To get the numerator of the third term, we multiply the numerator of the previous term again by .09, and to get the denominator, we multiply the previous denominator by 4×5.

This seems like a fairly simple procedure, so let us compute the first few terms. To simplify things, let us name the terms as components of a vector, $y_1, y_2, \cdots$.

$$y_1 = x = .3$$

$$y_2 = \frac{-x^3}{3!} = \frac{-x^2}{2 \times 3} \times y_1 = \frac{(-.09) \times (.3)}{6} = -.0045$$

$$y_3 = \frac{x^5}{5!} = -\frac{x^2}{4 \times 5} \times y_2 = \frac{(-.09) \times (-.0045)}{20} = .00002025$$

$$y_4 = \frac{-x^7}{7!} = \frac{-x^2}{6 \times 7} \times y_3 = \frac{(-.09) \times (.00002025)}{42} = -.00000004339$$

Clearly, subsequent terms will be numerically much smaller than those that we have computed. If we stop at this point and compute the sum of these four terms, we obtain .2955202066 as an approximation to sin (.3). Published five-place tables give .29552, so that we have perfect agreement to five digits.

Now let's try to compute sin 5 correct to five digits.

$$y_1 = x = 5$$

$$y_2 = \frac{-x^2}{2 \times 3} \times y_1 = \frac{-25 \times 5}{6} = -20.8333333$$

$$y_3 = \frac{-x^2}{4 \times 5} \times y_2 = \frac{(-25) \times (-20.8333333)}{20} = 26.0416666$$

$$y_4 = \frac{-x^2}{6 \times 7} \times y_3 = \frac{(-25) \times (26.0416666)}{42} = -15.5009920$$

$$y_5 = \frac{-x^2}{8 \times 9} \times y_4 = \frac{(-25) \times (-15.5009920)}{72} = 5.3822889$$

$$y_6 = \frac{-x^2}{10 \times 11} \times y_5 = \frac{(-25) \times (5.3822889)}{110} = -1.2232475$$

$$y_7 = \frac{-x^2}{12 \times 13} \times y_6 = \frac{(-25) \times (-1.2232475)}{156} = .1960333$$

$$y_8 = \frac{-x^2}{14 \times 15} \times y_7 = \frac{(-25) \times (.1960333)}{210} = -.0233373$$

$$y_9 = \frac{-x^2}{16 \times 17} \times y_8 = \frac{(-25) \times (-.0233373)}{272} = .0021450$$

$$y_{10} = \frac{-x^2}{18 \times 19} \times y_9 = \frac{(-25) \times (.0021450)}{342} = -.0001568$$

$$y_{11} = \frac{-x^2}{20 \times 21} \times y_{10} = \frac{(-25) \times (-.0001568)}{420} = .0000093$$

$$y_{12} = \frac{-x^2}{22 \times 23} \times y_{11} = \frac{(-25) \times (.0000093)}{506} = -.0000005$$

Notice that a larger number of terms was necessary to achieve the required accuracy for this larger value of x. We have arbitrarily kept seven digits to the right of the decimal point, which might not always be possible with a digital computer.

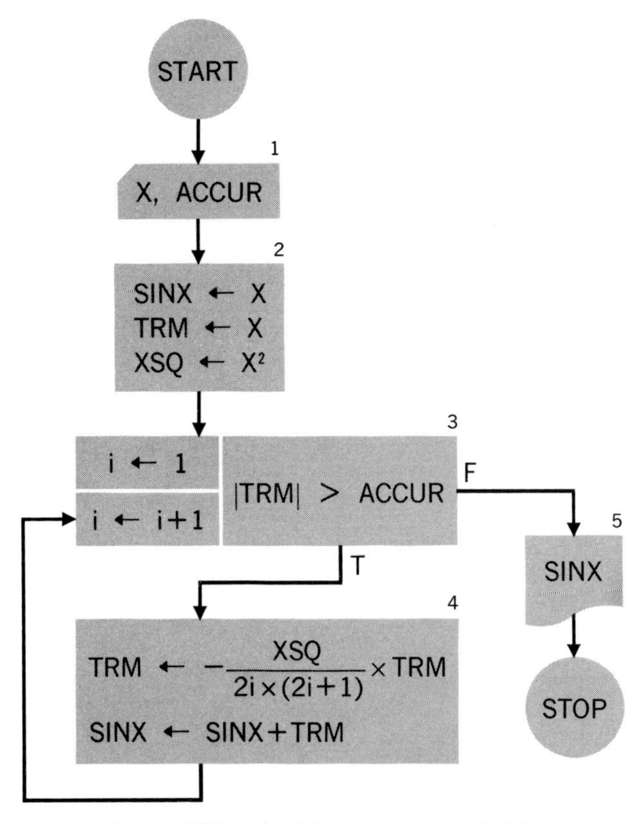

Figure 5-10 Algorithm to compute sin (x).

Adding our 12 terms, we obtain $-.9589243$ as the approximation to sin 5, and we can feel fairly confident of the accuracy of the first five digits.

We give in Figure 5-10 a flow chart for computing the value of sin (x).

Note that we do not store the individual terms of the series. Instead, we sum them as they are computed, keeping a copy only of the very last term, called TRM. In this way, it is possible to avoid the use of subscripts.

We have seen in the preceding examples that when $|x|$ is large, the computation in Figure 5-10 is cumbersome and subject to many numerical inaccuracies. It is desirable, and a relatively easy matter, to convert the problem to one of calculating an approximation for small values of x by using the reduction formulas for trigonometric functions, which you probably have studied in an earlier course. Accordingly, you will be asked in Problem 4 of Exercise 5-7 to draw a modification of Figure 5-10 incorporating this conversion.

EXERCISES 5-7

1. What would be the result of applying the square root algorithm of Figure 5-9 if the input variable y has a value 0?

2. What would be the result of applying the square root algorithm of Figure 5-9 if the input, y, is less than 0?

3. The square root algorithm, Figure 5-9, uses $g = 1$ as an initial approximation no matter what value y has.

   (a) What other initial approximations might be tried?
   (b) Suggest what advantages or disadvantages such approximations might have.

4. Modify the algorithm that computes sin (x), Figure 5-10, so that the value of x is reduced to one between $-\pi/2$ and $\pi/2$, using the relation $\sin x = (-1)^n \sin (x - n\pi)$, for any integer, n.

PART II

NUMERICAL APPLICATIONS

CHAPTER 6

FUNCTIONS AND PROCEDURES

6-1 REFERENCE FLOW CHARTS

In earlier chapters you have frequently seen an assignment box like Figure 6-1. In a general way we know it involves:

1. Sending a reader to find the window box with "y" engraved on its cover and taking the number found there to the master computer.
2. Having the master computer do something with the number delivered to him, thereby producing the square root of that number.
3. Having the master computer give the result to an assigner, who puts it into the window box having "x" engraved on its cover.

In this chapter we will focus on step 2 of this process.

In Section 5-7 we examined Newton's algorithm for finding the square root of a positive number. The flow chart for this algorithm, Figure 5-9, is restated in Figure 6-2 (with the modification that ϵ has a fixed value of .0001).

Someday you will undoubtedly want to find the square root of a number again, so you will be well advised to keep a copy of Figure 6-2 in a notebook where you can look it up and use it again. In fact, if there are other people who also want to find square roots, wouldn't it be a good idea to have a reference book of such flow charts? Now, if we want to have such *reference flow charts*, we must make certain that they are both correct and fully general so that any person can use them at any place in any flow chart—or, in fact, at several places in the same flow chart—with complete confidence. To assist us in making a permanent reference copy of our square root flow chart, we will adopt a few new conventions. We need a way to indicate the argument of the square root, other than by reading a data card as in Figure 6-2. A new flow-chart shape, the funnel shown in Figure 6-3, is used to show both the purpose (taking a square root) of this reference flow chart and the argument, y. We also need a way, in flow-chart language, to state the result and to say that we now return to that box in the flow chart that originated the reference. This shape, replacing the print and stop boxes of Figure 6-2, is the "return" box (Figure 6-4).

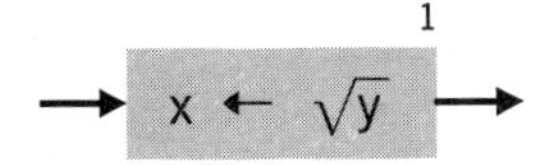

Figure 6-1 An assignment box.

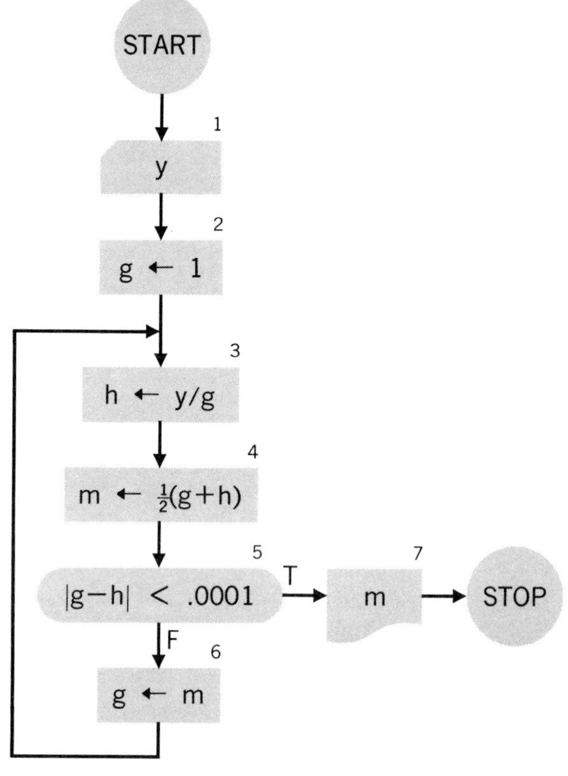

Figure 6-2 Newton's algorithm.

Figure 6-5 shows the use of the funnel and the return box on the ends of a reference flow chart. The first time the reference flow chart is required (by $\sqrt{x}$ in what we will call the "main" flow chart), we enter the funnel via route 1. The inscription on the funnel reminds us that, to use the reference flow chart, we must first assign the value of x to y, so that whenever y appears in the reference flow chart, its initial value will

Figure 6-3 A funnel.

Figure 6-4 Return box.

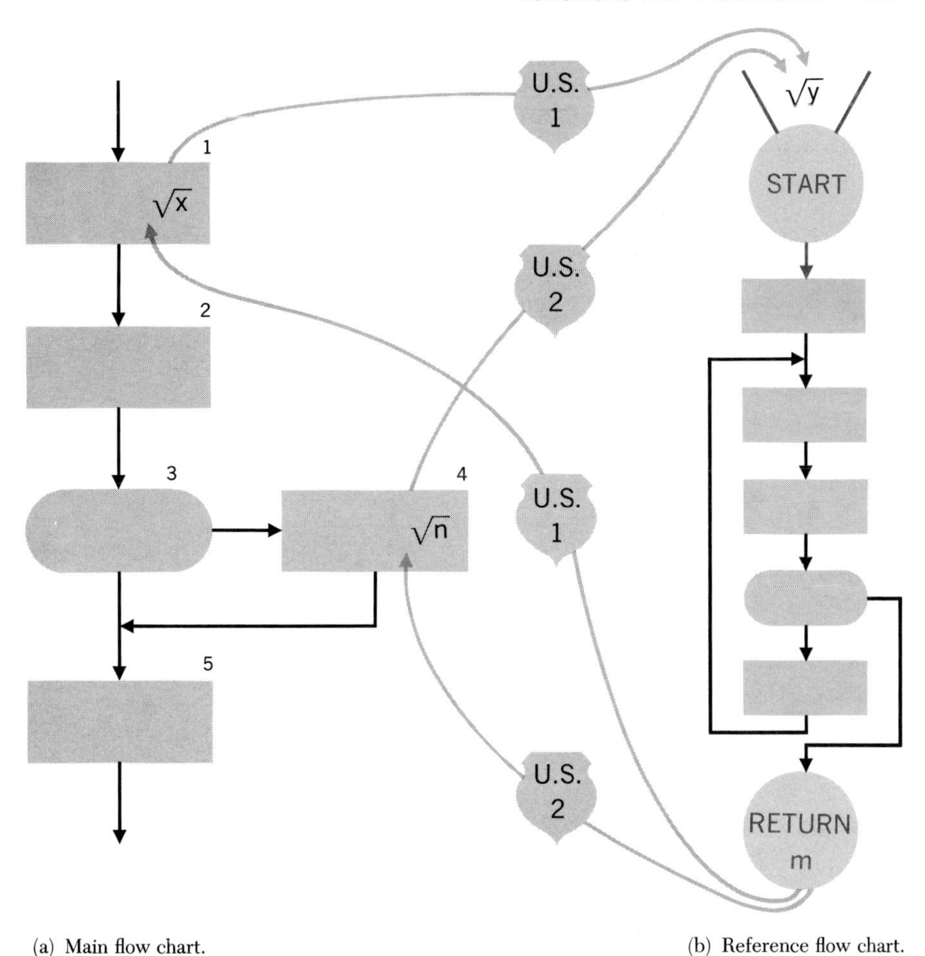

(a) Main flow chart.

(b) Reference flow chart.

Figure 6-5 Use of a reference flow chart.

be the value of x. When execution of the reference flow chart is completed, we are to return via route 1 to the same box in the main flow chart that caused the reference and complete the execution of this box. When we require the reference flow chart again for $\sqrt{n}$ in box 4, we are to go to the funnel via route 2, assign the value of n to y, execute the reference flow chart, and return to the main flow chart via route 2. The flow chart for $\sqrt{y}$ can be referred to as often as necessary by a main flow chart.

Figure 6-6 shows a reference flow chart for Newton's algorithm, which is the best we can do at the moment. Later in this chapter you will be able to improve this reference flow chart further.

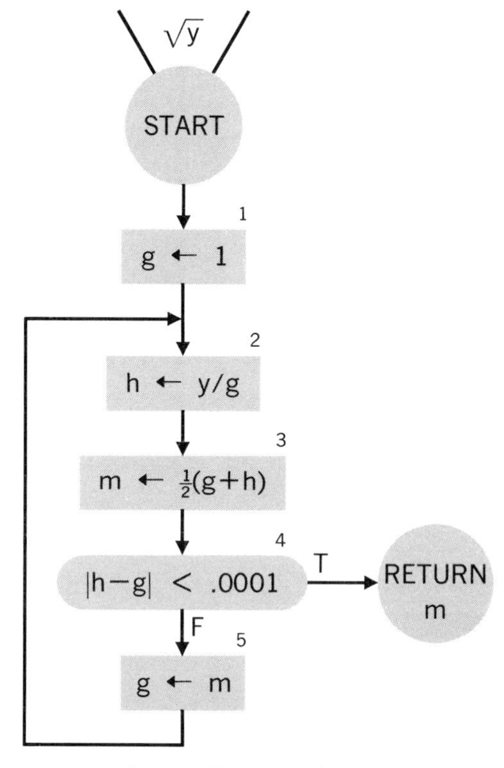

Figure 6-6 Reference flow chart for Newton's algorithm.

EXERCISES 6-1

1. For a cube root, the iteration formula could be

$$m \leftarrow \frac{1}{3}\left(2g + \frac{y}{g^2}\right)$$

Prepare a reference flow chart for the calculation of a cube root.[1]

2. Prepare a reference flow chart for the evaluation of $f(x) = 3x^2 - 2x + 1$.

3. Prepare a reference flow chart for ABSOL(X) that evaluates the absolute value of X.

[1] From the observation that $g^2 \times y/g^2 = y$, it is possible to show that g and y/g^2 lie on opposite sides of $\sqrt[3]{y}$. Once one has convinced himself of this fact, it seems natural to choose the simple average, $\frac{1}{2}(g + y/g^2)$ for the next guess. In later math courses however, it is proved that the weighted average, $\frac{1}{3}(2g + y/g^2)$ is a better choice.

[2] 6-2 MATHEMATICAL FUNCTIONS

Many of you were well introduced to the mathematical concept of functions in earlier courses. Even if you were not, you have probably dealt with particular functions such as the trigonometric, the inverse trigonometric, the logarithm and exponential, and the square root function. In computing, the word "function" is used in a subtly different way than elsewhere. To enable you to appreciate this difference, we will now discuss the mathematical concept of function in some detail. We have, of course, touched casually on the function concept earlier in this book.

The first basic idea involved in the function concept is "unambiguous designation." Suppose we make a remark about Elinor's hat. It turns out that Elinor has a whole closet full of hats and it is not at all clear to which one we are referring. But now a remark is made about Elinor's head. Ah! That is a different matter. Elinor has but one head, so the head being referred to is perfectly clear, that is to say, unambiguously designated (or determined).

We think of a function as being something that performs such unambiguous designations. But a function makes not only one unambiguous designation, but many of them. For example, if we were to say "the hat on the head of X," we would have an unambiguous designation when a particular person's name is inserted for X, and a large set of hats could be designated, depending on the set of names we allow for X.

This is the second basic idea in the function concept. There is a set called the domain of the function, and for each member of this set the function unambiguously designates something.

As an example, consider a function that we will call BRTHDY. The domain of this function is the set of all human beings. Whenever this function is presented with a member of its domain, it designates the birthday of that person. If the function is presented with Abraham Lincoln, it designates February 12. We write

BRTHDY(Abraham Lincoln) = Feb. 12

to indicate that Feb. 12 is the thing designated by the function BRTHDY

[2] If you are already fully familiar with the mathematical concept of a function, you may omit this section and proceed directly to Section 6-3.

on being presented with Abraham Lincoln. Similarly,

$$\text{BRTHDY(George Washington)} = \text{Feb. } 22$$

What is the value of

$$\text{BRTHDY(Tom Spumoni)?}$$

We don't know. But we do know that Tom Spumoni has a birthday (provided he is a real person), and it is this birthday that is designated by the expression

$$\text{BRTHDY (Tom Spumoni)}$$

(In mathematics, as distinguished from computing, we are satisfied here with the existence of Tom Spumoni's birthday and we do not feel the need of being able to exhibit it explicitly.)

Another example of a function is the squaring function, SQR. This function, given any real number, designates the square of that number. Thus,

$$\begin{array}{ll} \text{SQR}(2) = 4 & \text{SQR}(-3) = 9 \\ \text{SQR}(1.7) = 2.89 & \text{SQR}(0) = 0 \\ \text{SQR}(3) = 9 & \end{array}$$

So now we see what a function does. If, to each member X of a given set, a function called F is applied, then an object, F(X), is unambiguously designated. That tells you what a function *does*, but you may well want to know what a function *is*. This, it turns out, is not terribly important to us.

The situation here is somewhat similar to that of *numbers*. We know how numbers behave under various operations; we know numerous properties of the set of numbers, such as order and density; we know properties of various subsets, such as the integers and the rationals. In short, we know almost everything about numbers—except what they are. And we have been able to operate with numbers quite adequately without this knowledge.

And so it is with functions. As long as we know that a function F will, for each member S of its domain, produce for us the *functional value* F(S), we have no need in mathematics of knowing how this is done. There is an analogy with dialing a telephone number. We know that for each telephone number in the "domain" (that is, the set of phone numbers currently in service), a certain telephone is unambiguously determined. When we dial the number, this telephone rings. We are not concerned

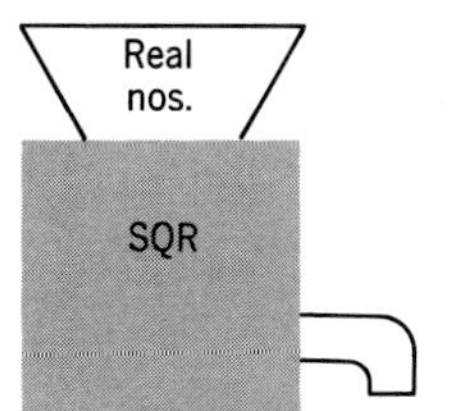

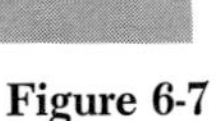
Figure 6-7

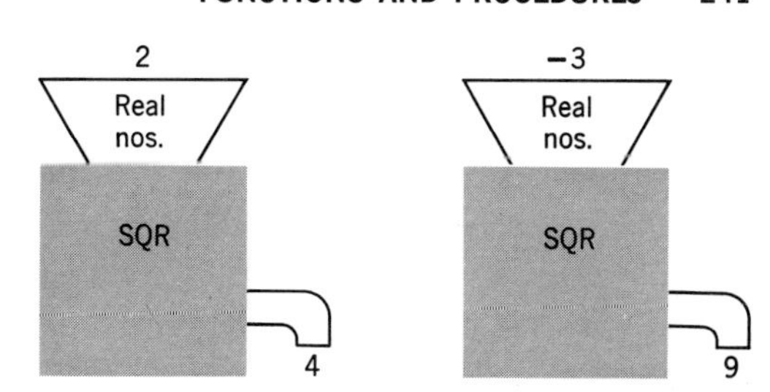

Figure 6-8

with the wiring, the relays, the switches, the computers, and the coaxial cables that may be involved in the process of making the phone ring at the other end of the line. It is only important to us that this phone does ring.

Now that we have been assured that it is not important for us to know what functions *are*, we will discuss three ways of "representing" or thinking about them. This is similar in spirit to our way of representing the real numbers as points on the number line, which means, more or less, that we think of the real numbers as being points on a line.

The representation of a function as a machine is useful as well as popular. Consider, for example, the squaring machine as a representation of the function SQR (Figure 6-7). We see that the machine is equipped with an input funnel and an output spigot. We have indicated the domain of the function (the permissible input) on the input funnel. If we input 2, the machine grinds and cranks and outputs the number 4 (Figure 6-8). If we input -3 the machine whirrs and clanks and outputs 9. In general, for any value of X that we input, the machine outputs X^2. The important thing, the thing that makes SQR a function, is that for each input value there is just one output value.

Figure 6-9 shows another machine, called UNIFAC for UNIque FACtorization. The domain of this function, as we see, is to be the set of positive integers. If we input an integer, the output is the unique decom-

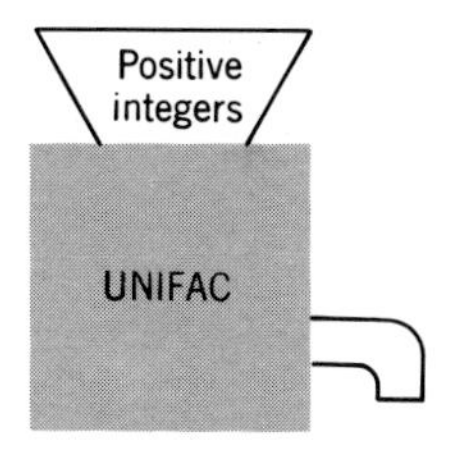

Figure 6-9

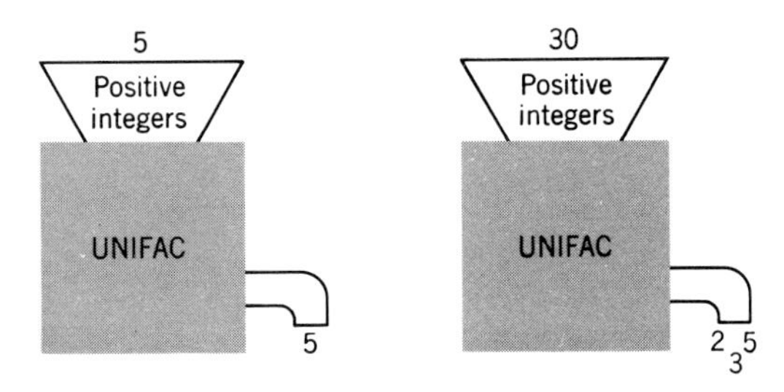

Figure 6-10

position of that integer into its prime factors. So we input 5 and since 5 is prime, 5 is output. That is, UNIFAC(5) = 5. Suppose we input the integer 30 (Figure 6-10). Its prime factorization is $2 \times 3 \times 5$, so what is the value of UNIFAC(30)? Is it 2? or 3? or 5? or do we just take our choice? An ambiguous answer here would mean that UNIFAC would not be a function. We build the machine so as to output, not a cascade of factors, but a single vector having as components the factors arranged in nondecreasing order (Figure 6-11).

An example of a function that accepts vectors as input (Figure 6-12) is the function MAG, which accepts three-element vectors as input and outputs their magnitudes (that is, the square root of the sum of the squares of the components).

Now with SQR, UNIFAC, and MAG we have illustrated functions

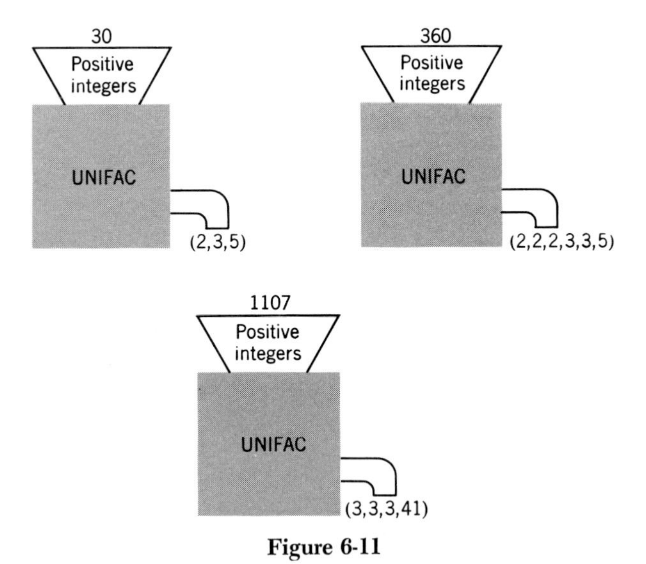

Figure 6-11

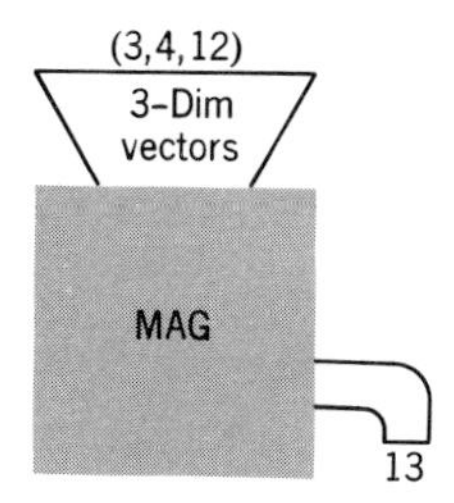

Figure 6-12

which, for an element of the domain (whether its value is a single number or a vector), unambiguously designate an element of the range (either a single number or a vector). In each case, we haven't cared about how this designation happened. However, the fellow who has to design the telephone system, or the UNIFAC machine, or a reference flow chart, must be able to spell out, as a rule or recipe, a way to find a value of F(X) once a value of X is given (Figure 6-13). This is another way of thinking of a function.

When specifying a function, we must be careful to indicate the domain of the function. If no such indication is made, then it will be assumed that the domain is the set of all things for which the rule makes sense. Here are three examples.

Example 1 $F(x) = 3x^2 + 5x - 2 \quad \text{for} \quad -3 \leq x < 5$

Example 2 $G(x) = \dfrac{x^2 - 1}{x^2 + 1}$

Example 3 $H(x) = \sqrt{1 - x^2}$

Figure 6-13 Spelling out a recipe.

In the first of these examples, we see that the domain is specified to be the half-open interval $[-3, 5)$. In Example 2, the domain is not specified and so it is assumed to be the set of all real numbers, since $(x^2 - 1)/(x^2 + 1)$ is meaningful for all real values of x. In the third example, the domain is again unspecified but this time the domain is $[-1, 1]$, since $\sqrt{1 - x^2}$ is not meaningful for values of x taken from outside this interval.

One point that should be clarified at once is: such a rule does not depend on the variables used in expressing it. For example, if we write

$$J(t) = \frac{t^2 - 1}{t^2 + 1}$$

then the function J is identical with the function G of Example 2.

The range of a function is defined to be the set of all values the function is capable of producing. In Example 3 above, the range of the function H is the closed interval $[0,1]$. The range of the square root function is the set of all nonnegative real numbers.

We see that this "rule" viewpoint strongly suggests that of the programmer who is to draw a reference flow chart. The reference flow chart, in Section 6-1, for finding square roots is an algorithm and an algorithm is, after all, a kind of rule or recipe. On the other hand, the "machine" viewpoint suggests more nearly the view that might be adopted by the programmer drawing a main flow chart who wants to *use* the reference flow chart. All he cares about is that if he provides a value of x to the square root reference flow chart, it will return a value he can use as the square root of x.

Whether the "machine" viewpoint or the "rule" viewpoint is adopted in thinking of functions, we can tabulate results, as in Figure 6-14.

The table given in Figure 6-14 is very closely akin to the set of ordered pairs: $(-10,100)$, $(-3,9)$, $(-1.7,2.89)$, $(-1,1)$, $(0,0)$, $(1,1)$, $(1.4,1.96)$, $(2,4)$, $(1.7,2.89)$, $(5,25)$. We call them "ordered" pairs to make it clear, for example, that $(3,4)$ is not to be considered the same as $(4,3)$. In other words, the order is taken into account. The first entry in an ordered pair is called the "abscissa" and the second is called the "ordinate."

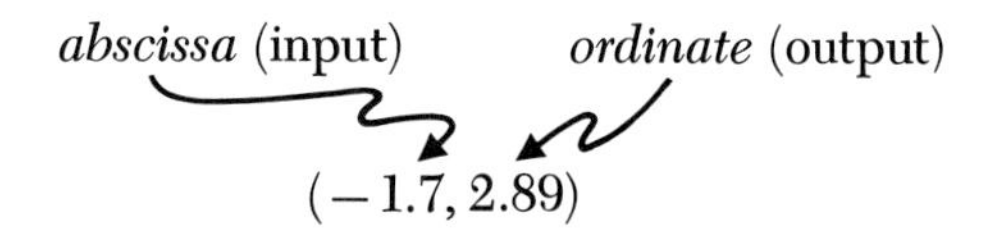

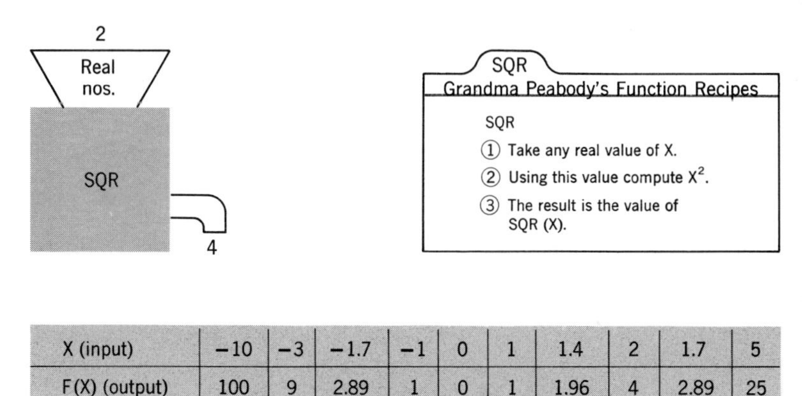

X (input)	−10	−3	−1.7	−1	0	1	1.4	2	1.7	5
F(X) (output)	100	9	2.89	1	0	1	1.96	4	2.89	25

Figure 6-14 Tabulation of SQR.

Although we cannot write out an infinite table, we can conceive of an infinite set of ordered pairs. There is a mathematical notation to describe it. The mathematical notation describing the set of ordered pairs that accompanies the SQR function is

$$\{(x,y) \mid y = x^2\}$$

When you read this out loud you say, "The set of all ordered pairs of the form (x,y) which satisfy the condition that y is equal to x squared."

The rule viewpoint and the set of ordered pairs viewpoint are really equivalent. For, first, the rule determines the set of ordered pairs. And second, the set of ordered pairs itself can be thought of as a rule equivalent to the given one. We shall explain what this means immediately.

Suppose someone asks what the value of SQR(2) is. We could tell him to "go to that set of ordered pairs over there and hunt for the pair whose abscissa is 2. The ordinate of that pair is SQR(2)." This is a rule for finding SQR(X), and this rule is equivalent to the original rule because the two rules always give the same result.

Many people like to think of the function as actually *being* the set of ordered pairs. They then accept the following definition. "A function is a set of ordered pairs with the property that no two pairs in the set have the same abscissa." (The qualification about the abscissa expresses the unambiguous designation property.)

This "set of ordered pairs" viewpoint is evidently closely akin to that adopted in Chapter 4 in the discussion of table-look-up, especially when the table is punched on a stack of cards. In that case, each card may be thought of as an ordered pair.

Whatever viewpoint we adopt, we must agree on one essential fact. That is, if we have two functions, F and G, with the same domain, A, such that

$$F(X) = G(X)$$

for all X in A, then F and G are in fact the *same* function.

We must be especially careful to be clear on this point if we adopt the "rule" viewpoint, since two statements of rules can look quite different but in fact be equivalent. For instance, a rule for finding Q(X) may be stated this way. Take the numbers one more and one less than X and add 1 to their product:

$$Q(X) = (X + 1) \times (X - 1) + 1$$

We then find that Q is the same function as SQR.

Mathematically, every unambiguous designation is a function, so that every computer program can be viewed as a function. The common computing usage of the word function refers to the use of a separate subprogram for the computation of values. Simple functions for which the arithmetic operations of addition, subtraction, multiplication, and division are sufficient are usually computed in the main program (unless they occur so often that a subprogram becomes more economical of memory space). Such simple functions (e.g., $x^2 + 1$) are, of course, recognized as being functions but are seldom called by that name.

Finally, in computing we are not interested in functions for which functional values cannot in principle be computed even when the existence of functional values can be proved, for example, Birthday (Tom Spumoni). The class of functions we are interested in are called "computable functions."

Since computer calculations on real numbers are almost always approximate, you should recognize that, in effect, we replace mathematical functions by computer functions, which are often slightly different.

6-3 GETTING IN AND OUT OF A FUNCTIONAL REFERENCE

We are now ready to tie together the ideas developed in the first two sections of this chapter. In Figure 6-6 we saw a good algorithm for computing approximate values of the square root function. We have said that this algorithm may be "referred to" by another algorithm, and we want to see just how this is done. To save space, we will often substitute the word "subroutine" for "reference flow chart."

Observe that the symbols g, h, m, and y were used in Figure 6-6 to represent variables, and recall that one purpose of reference flow charts is to allow many people to refer to the same flow chart. Since it would be outrageous to have to tell everyone who might refer to Figure 6-6 that g, h, m, and y cannot be variables in *his* flow chart, we must have some means of protection so that a symbol used in a main flow chart cannot possibly be confused with the same symbol in a reference flow chart. We must in effect build a "sterile" boundary between the two flow charts.

In terms of the window-box model, such protection is provided by thinking of subroutines as being carried out inside a sealed brick chamber (see Figure 6-15). The only interactions this chamber has with the outside world are a funnel on the top and a window in the side. When the number to be squarerooted is put into the funnel, the subroutine goes into execution and the desired square root appears in the window.

Inside the sealed chamber, there is a separate staff (master computer, assigner, and reader) and window boxes for each of the variables appearing in the subroutine. These boxes are completely inaccessible to the main flow chart, with two exceptions. When a square root is called for in the main flow chart, we can assign a value to the variable appear-

Figure 6-15 Square root subroutine (exterior view).

Figure 6-16 Square root subroutine (interior view).

ing in the funnel. And, second, we can read from the variable appearing in the RETURN circle.

If some or all of the variables appearing in the subroutine also appear in the main flow chart, then there must be separate window boxes for these variables *outside* the sealed chamber. All references in the main flow chart are to the boxes on the outside. All references in the subroutine are to the boxes on the inside.

In Figure 6-16 we show an interior view of such a brick chamber but without the crew.

There is a slight modification in one of the window boxes. The window box labeled C has windows on both sides. One of them is right up against the outside window. In this way, this box can be read from both the inside and outside of the room. When variable A is assigned a value through the funnel, the subroutine starts up and there is no further contact with the outside world until the subroutine is completed.

In Figure 6-17 we show window boxes as they might be used in a main flow chart and in a subroutine.

By now you should see that nothing within the subroutine will change the values in the window boxes of the main flow chart.

With the subroutine enclosed in thick brick walls, it is almost as though the two flow charts were in different worlds. From inside the subroutine we cannot assign to variables of the main flow chart or even see what these variables are. And from the main flow chart, we similarly have no contact with the variables of the subroutine except for the two previously mentioned points of contact, namely: that we can assign to the variable in the funnel and that we read the value of the variable in the return box. Even in these cases, however, we pay no attention to what symbols are used, only to the location in which they occur. From the point of view of the main flow chart, the variables listed in the funnel and the return box merely play the role of "place holders."

It is sometimes useful to think of the variables in a subroutine as divided into two kinds. There are those which appear in the funnel and provide a link with the outside world. They are called "nonlocal" variables. The others, called "local" variables, do not appear in the funnel and cannot be assigned values directly from the outside.

We are now prepared to finish the description of the interplay between a main flow chart and a subroutine. When the value of SQRT is called for in a main flow chart, the master computer sends out the assigner and the reader as a pair. They hunt for the chamber with SQRT on the funnel. (They pay no attention to the variable that follows SQRT because the less they know about the variables inside the chamber the better.) When they find this chamber, the assigner climbs to the funnel and the reader goes to the window (Figure 6-18). The assigner drops the *value*

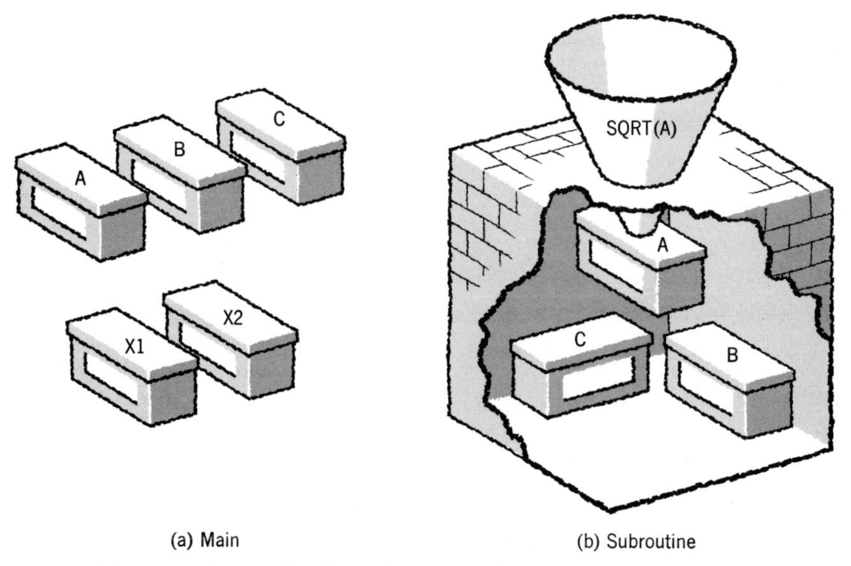

(a) Main (b) Subroutine

Figure 6-17 Window boxes for a main flow chart and subroutine.

Figure 6-18

given to him by the master computer into the funnel (thus assigning this value to the variable A of the subroutine). When the wheels stop turning inside the chamber, the reader notes the value through the window and returns it to the master computer to use in the computation. (In the SAMOS Appendix we explain that this value goes into the Accumulator.)[3]

It is important to be aware that the value of this square root does not get assigned to any of the window boxes of the main flow chart (at least not directly). The master computer, in performing his arithmetic computations, can receive only one numerical value at a time. For this reason, there is always only one window on the functional reference sealed chamber. Hence, the functions with which we are dealing always have for their functional values a single numerical value (never a vector). In present-day mathematical terminology, such functions are called *functionals*. (Vector-valued functions are also very important in computing work, but they will always be evaluated by the use of techniques for "procedures," to be discussed in the next section.)

Functions of more than one variable (that is, functions whose domains are sets of vectors) are treated in almost the same way as above. Recall

[3] Some computers do not have registers called "accumulators." Nevertheless, all computer systems can designate some component to hold the result(s) of a subroutine.

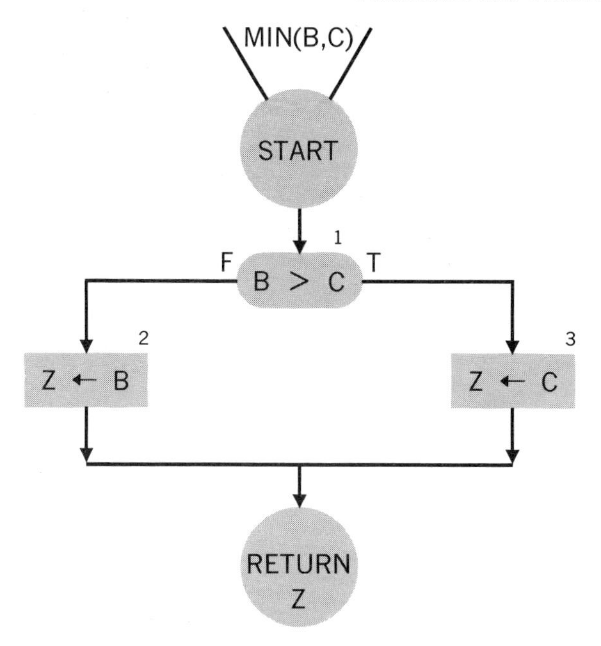

Figure 6-19 Reference flow chart for MIN(B,C).

the function discussed in Chapter 3 for finding the minimum of the values of B and C. The rule expressing this function is

$$\text{MIN(B,C)} = \begin{cases} \text{B}, & \text{if} \quad \text{B} \leq \text{C} \\ \text{C}, & \text{if} \quad \text{B} > \text{C} \end{cases}$$

The reference flow chart for this function, as given in Figure 6-19, follows this rule.

When a main flow chart needs to refer to Figure 6-19, it simply uses the name MIN together with the arguments whose values are to be "put in the funnel."

Figure 6-20 tells us to find a subroutine called MIN, assign the values of R and S, respectively, to the variables in the funnel, and then execute the reference flow chart. Then the value of the variable in the return box is to be read and returned to the main flow chart where 6 will be added and the resulting value assigned to X.

Remember to think of the subroutine as being carried out in a sealed

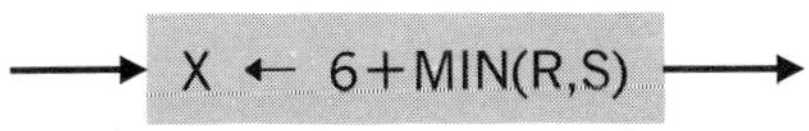

→ X ← 6+MIN(R,S) →

Figure 6-20 A main flow chart box that uses MIN.

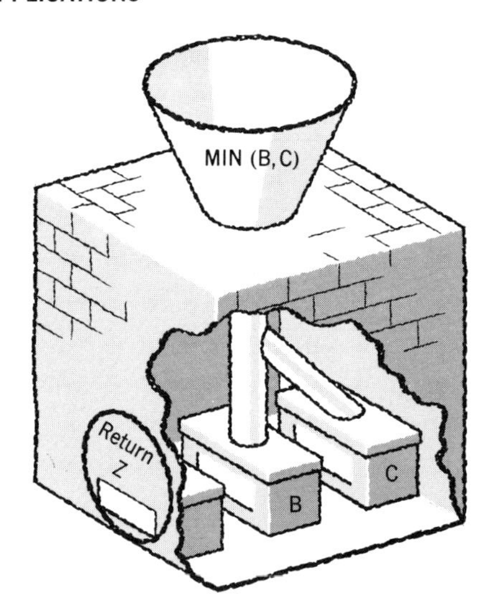

Figure 6-21 Sealed chamber for MIN(B,C).

brick chamber. When the main flow chart calls for the value of MIN(R,S), the values of R and S are dropped in the funnel in that order and are assigned in that order to the subroutine window boxes of B and C (Figure 6-21). Do not be confused by the possible occurrence of the same variables in the main flow chart and in the subroutine.

Whenever we have a function of one or more variables, the name of the function is accompanied by the list of variables. This list (which reduces to one entry for a function of a single numerical variable) is called the "parameter list." Such parameter lists appear both in the funnel of the reference flow chart and at each place where the function is referred to in the main flow chart. Although the same variable will probably not appear in corresponding positions of the various parameter lists for a given function, nevertheless, these lists must match up like the fingers of a hand and a glove. Besides being equal in number, the variables in the parameter lists must also match as to type (numeric, alphanumeric, etc.). A failure to match in type is like trying to put a left-hand glove on a right hand—it doesn't fit.

Composition of Functional References

Suppose two functions F1(x) and F2(x) are given, each with its own definition in the form of a functional reference flow chart. And suppose we are presented with the assignment box:

→ Y ← F1(F2(T)) →

Let us examine in some detail what would take place in a window box model of this situation.

1. The master computer gives the value of T to an assigner, who drops it in the funnel of the chamber labeled F2(x).
2. A reader copies the value that appears in the RETURN window of that chamber and delivers the value to the master computer.
3. The master computer gives the value just delivered to him to an assigner, who drops it in the funnel of the chamber labeled F1(x).
4. A reader copies the value that appears in the RETURN window of that chamber and delivers the value to the master computer.
5. The master computer gives the value just delivered to him to an assigner who assigns it to Y.

Notice that all along we have implicitly assumed that the range of F2 is a subset of the domain of F1.[4]

With this concept of a function-of-a-function, and with each function being thought of as a separate reference flow chart, we should have no trouble in interpreting the following flow-chart boxes:

→ Y ← MIN(|A+B|, 5.4) →

→ Y ← MIN(MIN(F, |T|), Q) →

→ Y ← MIN(SQROOT(B^2-4AC), −B) →

→ Y ← SQROOT(MIN(X, Y)) →

EXERCISES 6-3, SET A

1. (a) Draw a flow chart for function f(x,y) where $f(x,y) = \dfrac{(x^2 + y)^2 + 5}{|x| + 2}$.

   (b) Draw the assignment box that computes Z = f(r,s) + 6t where r, s, and t have been previously assigned values.

[4] Remember that the *range* of a function is the set of all the values that the function is capable of producing.

2. Prepare a flow chart to evaluate the function

$$\text{right (a,b,c)} = \begin{cases} 1, & \text{if a, b, c are lengths of sides for a right triangle} \\ 0, & \text{if they are not lengths for a right triangle} \end{cases}$$

3. (a) Prepare a reference flow chart that assigns to max(x,y,z) the largest (algebraically) of the three values of x, y, and z.

(b) Prepare a flow chart to read in values of A, B, and C, calculate max(A,B,C), assign this value to LARGST, and then print LARGST.

4. Given values of x and y, the function QUAD(x,y) is to return an integer value 1, 2, 3, or 4 according to the quadrant in which the point (x,y) lies. Prepare a reference flow chart for QUAD(x,y).

5. Prepare a flow chart for function INTSCT that takes values of X1, Y1, R1, X2, Y2, and R2 and returns the number of points of intersection that the circle with center (X1,Y1) of radius R1 has with the circle with center (X2,Y2) of radius R2. Allow for the possibility that R1 or R2 is accidentally given with a negative value.

6. For the nth root, an iteration formula corresponding to the cube root formula given in Exercises 6-1 is

$$m \leftarrow \frac{1}{n}\left((n-1) \times g + \frac{y}{g^{n-1}}\right)$$

For larger values of n, the root may be approached very slowly. For this reason, you should not let your computation go beyond ten iterations. Prepare the reference flow chart.

7. Jack Armstrong plans to borrow $100 and wants to compare various loan plans.

(a) Company X will lend him the money at compound interest at 1% monthly. That is, each month 1% of what Jack owes is added to the debt he must someday repay. Draw a reference flow chart for the function IRATE (n,R,L) which computes the amount that must be paid after n months for a loan of L dollars at R percent monthly interest.

(b) Jack finds that Company Y will lend him money at simple interest at $1\frac{1}{8}$% per month. At simple interest Jack pays the interest monthly instead of it being added to the balance owed. Draw a flow chart to compare the amount Jack pays to Company X and Company Y after 12 months, 24 months, 36 months and find the first month (if any) when Jack's total debt to Company X would be more then his total payment and debt to Company Y.

(c) Jack finally wonders how long it will take each company to double its money. Find that period for each company.

EXERCISES 6-3, SET B

1. Redraw the flow chart for the Euclidean algorithm, Figure 3-13, as a reference flow chart. (Is box 5 needed in the new flow chart?)

2. Draw a reference flow chart for finding the GCF (greatest common factor) of three nonnegative integers. [Note that if X = GCD(A,B), then GCF(A,B,C) = GCD(X,C). Hence, use the preceding problem.]

*** 3.** (a) In Section 4-4 you constructed a flow chart for finding the number of triangles having sides whose lengths are integers not greater than 100. Now make a flow chart for solving the same problem with the added restriction that no two of the triangles shall be similar. [*Hint.* Use the preceding problem.]

(b) Modify *a* so as to output the sum of the perimeters of the triangles described in *a* rather than the number of triangles.

[5] **4.** Draw a flow chart to output all numbers less than 10^9 which are expressible as the sum of two cubes in two different ways, together with the two decompositions into the sum of cubes. [E.g., since $12^3 + 1^3 = 1729 = 10^3 + 9^3$, the numbers 12, 1, 1729, 10, 9 would be output.] Eliminate all proportional combinations such as $24^3 + 2^3 = 13832 = 20^3 + 18^3$, which is the same as $2^3(12^3 + 1^3)$ or $2^3(10^3 + 9^3)$.

6-4 PROCEDURES

As we said before, a functional subroutine is used whenever the result is a single numerical value. This value is assigned to the variable named in the return box of the reference flow chart. From there, this value is read by the main flow chart and employed in the appropriate computational step, such as in

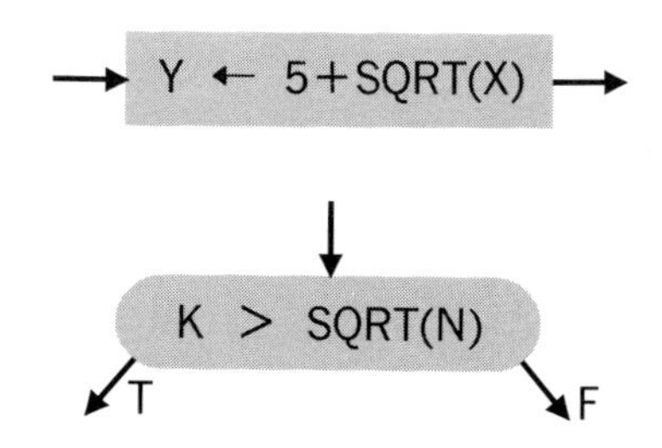

* Exercises marked with an asterisk require extra analysis or imagination beyond that implied in the text.

[5] This problem can be solved by brute force, testing every set of four cubes, requiring 10^{12} trials. You should try to find a more efficient way, requiring about 10^9 trials. Finding this more efficient method will require some ingenuity.

As we have already seen, there are many important functions whose functional values are vectors. These are called *vector-valued functions,* and we will need subroutines for evaluating them. Such subroutines are called *procedures*. As you will see, the operation of a procedure differs from that of a functional subroutine in several respects.

Figure 6-22 is an example of a reference flow chart for a procedure. This flow chart is for a sorting process different from those considered in Chapters 3 and 4.

We see that the procedure reference flow chart again has a funnel in which appears the name of the procedure and a parameter list. There is

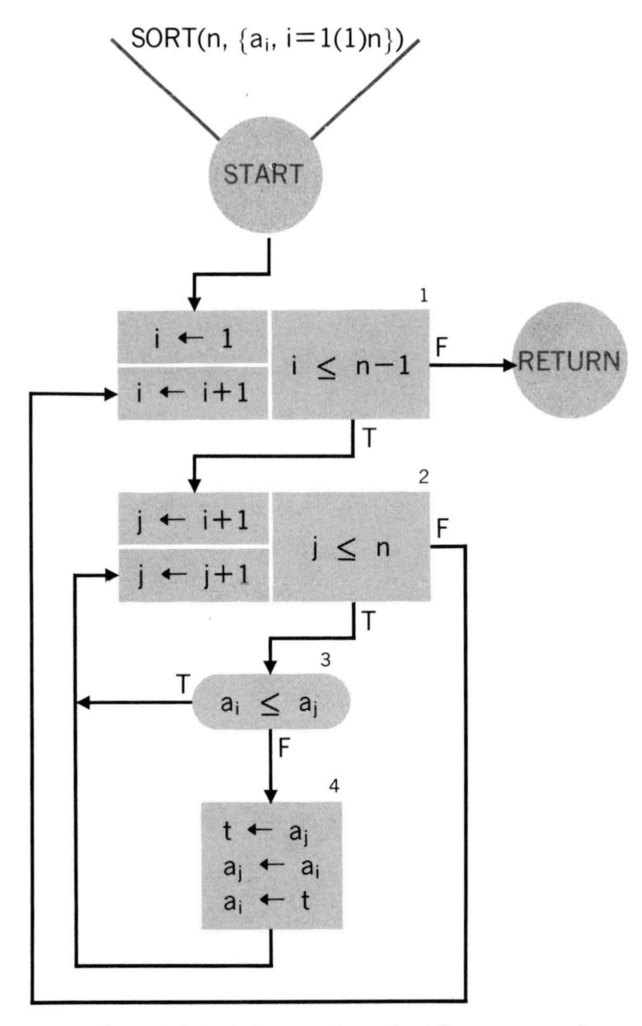

Figure 6-22 Reference flow chart for sort procedure.

a return box but with no variable in it. With your experience, it should be no trouble for you to check that this flow chart will take values assigned to $\{a_i,\ i = 1(1)n\}$ and sort them so they are indexed in nondecreasing order.

But how is the main flow chart to call for such a procedure to be executed? This situation is unlike a functional reference where a single numerical value is returned to be employed in a computational step. Here, a list or vector of values is to be "returned" instead.

What is the "output" of the sort procedure? How is the main flow chart affected? These are the questions we will consider next.

First, we notice that while a call for a functional evaluation always comes during a calculation step, this is never the case with a procedure. Instead, we have a special box:

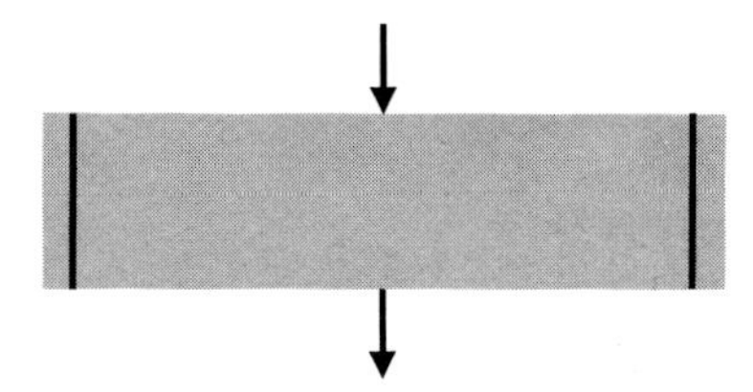

Inside this box is the word EXECUTE, which helps identify it as a call for the execution of a procedure. Also within the box is the name of the procedure to be executed and a parameter list that must correspond to the parameter list in the funnel of the procedure, just as such parameter lists for functionals correspond.

In Figure 6-23 we see a typical call for the sort procedure of Figure 6-22. The *effect* of this procedure on the main flow chart will be to take the values of the vector b and reshuffle them so they are indexed in nondecreasing order. For example, Table 6-1 shows the "after" values of the vector b. This exhibits another difference between the effect of proce-

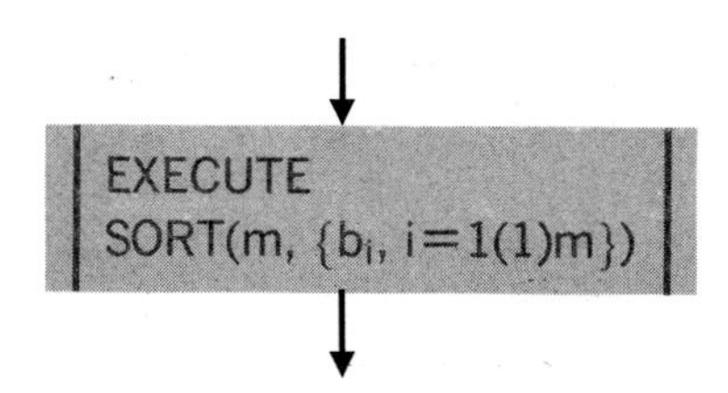

Figure 6-23 Call for sort procedure.

TABLE 6-1

	b_1	b_2	b_3	b_4	b_5	b_6	b_7
Before	7	9	2	1	6.3	−1.5	2
After	−1.5	1	2	2	6.3	7	9

dural and functional flow charts: a procedure *does* change the values of the variables in the main flow chart.

But how shall we visualize the way in which the procedure is carried out, that is, the "coupling" between the main flow chart and the subroutine? The description given below in terms of the old window boxes is in close analogy with what actually goes on in the computer.

Again (as with the functional subroutines), we have the sealed brick chamber in which the procedure is executed. But now there is no window for reading the "functional value"; however, in its place there is a long chute coming out the side (Figure 6-24).

In the interior of the sealed chamber, we are somewhat surprised to see window boxes only for the local variables, none for the nonlocal variables. That is, there are no window boxes for the variables that appear in the parameter list on the funnel. (Note that in the illustrated case, the variable i is not considered to be in the parameter list. This list is considered to consist of n, a_1, a_2, a_3, a_4, etc., with the last subscript being the value of n.)

Figure 6-24 Exterior and interior views of sort procedure of Figure 6-22.

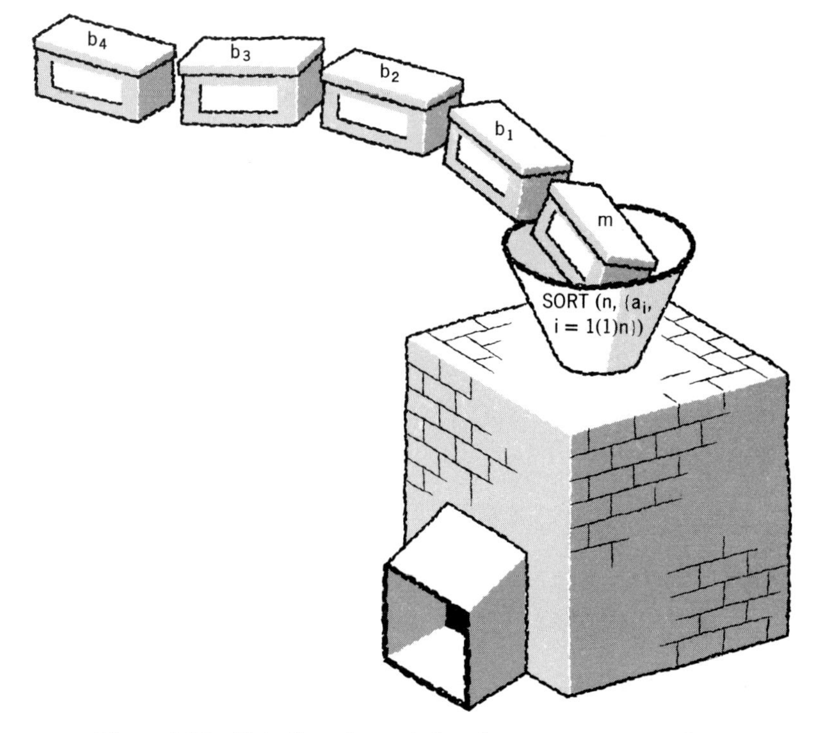

Figure 6-25 Main flow-chart window boxes entering procedures.

In the example under discussion, only boxes for i, j, and t are found inside the brick chamber. And when the procedure is called for by the execute box in the main flow chart, a surprising thing happens. Instead of the values of the variables m, $\{b_i,\ i=1(1)m\}$ being put in the funnel,

```
→ | EXECUTE                    | →
  | SORT(m, {bi, i=1(1)m})     |
```

the *window boxes* belonging to these variables are brought to the funnel and dropped in, in the order in which they appear in the parameter list! (See Figure 6-25.)

As these boxes pass through the funnel, they are received by a staff specialist, the labeler. The labeler has a stack of peelable (removable) gummed stickers. These stickers are imprinted, in order, with the variables of the parameter list appearing on the funnel of the procedure. As the boxes pass by the labeler, he slaps a sticker on each, covering up the original inscription on the box (Figure 6-26).

When the last window box has been labeled, the chamber is sealed so

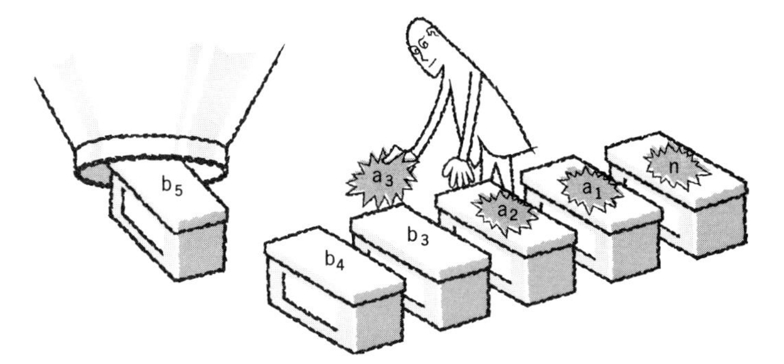

Figure 6-26 The labeler at work inside the chamber.

Figure 6-27 Interior of the procedure after execution is called for.

that there is no further contact with the main flow chart. The interior of the procedure at this stage is as in Figure 6-27, where we are assuming the value of m to be 11.

Now the procedure is executed exactly as it appears in the procedure flow chart. The assigner and the reader operate, using the variables on the stickers, without knowing what the original variables on the boxes were. The initial values in these boxes are, of course, those they brought with them from the main program.

When the execution of the procedure has been completed and we come to the return box, what then? At this point, the door of the chute opens and all the boxes with the gummed stickers are dumped out. Here, another specialist, the unlabeler, peels off the gummed stickers and the boxes return to the main program bearing their original inscriptions (Figure 6-28).

We can summarize the net effect of the procedure this way. A certain well-defined list of main flow-chart variables has "fallen under the sway" of the reference flow chart and some, or all, of these variables may have had their values changed in the process.

An example of a main flow chart that uses the SORT procedure is given in Figure 6-29. In this flow chart a number is input and assigned to k. Then 2k numbers are input and assigned to $b_1, b_2, \ldots, b_k, c_1, c_2, \ldots, c_k$. The first time the sort procedure is used, the variables $k, b_1, b_2, \ldots, b_k$ are substituted for $n, a_1, a_2, \ldots, a_n$ in the definition of the procedure. Then the steps in the procedure itself are carried out. After the return to the main flow chart, the value of k will be unchanged,

Figure 6-28 The unlabeler at work outside the chamber.

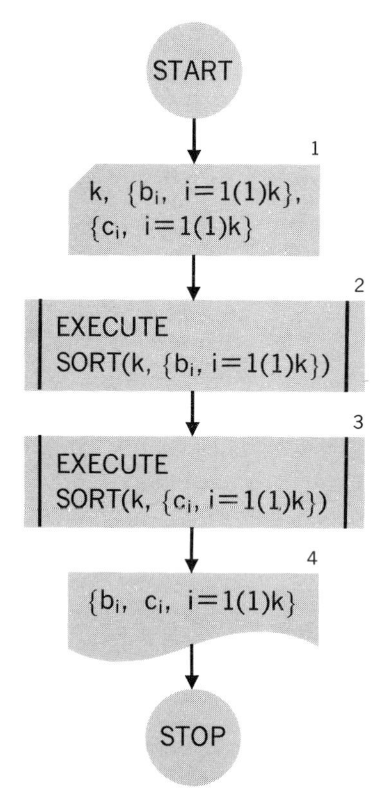

Figure 6-29 Execute boxes in a flow chart.

but the values of $b_1, \ldots, b_k$ will have been rearranged into nondecreasing order.

The second use of SORT will cause the c's to be rearranged.

Finally, the b's and c's are output, the smallest b followed by the smallest c, then the next smallest b, followed by the next smallest c, and so on.

EXERCISES 6-4, SET A

1. Rewrite the flow chart of function ABSOL(X) from Problem 4, Exercises 6-1, to make ABSOL(X) into a procedure.

2. (a) For complex numbers of the form a + bi, prepare a reference flow chart for procedure cxadd(a1, b1, a2, b2, a, b) that accepts the real parts a1 and a2, and the imaginary parts b1 and b2, of two complex numbers and returns their sum (a,b).

(b) Similarly, prepare a reference flow chart for procedure cxsubt that computes the difference of two complex numbers: (a1 + b1i) − (a2 + b2i).

(c) Prepare a procedure flow chart for cxmult that yields the product of two complex numbers.

(d) The quotient of two complex numbers is to be given by procedure cxdiv. Prepare the reference flow chart.

(e) Prepare a flow chart that inputs two complex numbers and an index oper whose value indicates the operation (1 for add, 2 for subtract, 3 for multiplication, and 4 for division) to be performed on them. The output is to be an echo check of input followed by the result of the computation printed in the form a "+" b "i". Then a new set of data should be read.

3. Prepare the reference flow chart for a procedure called SORT2. The parameter list is to be $(K,\{A_i,i=1(1)K\}, \{B_i,i=1(1)K\})$. $\{A_i\}$ is a vector whose values are to be arranged in nondecreasing order, and $\{B_i\}$ is a vector to be rearranged in the same way as $\{A_i\}$, so that B_J remains associated with A_J.

4. (a) Prepare a reference flow chart for a procedure that receives a given integer N and returns COUNTFAC, the count of integer factors that N has. (*Hint.* You may wish to adapt Figure 4-20.) Could this procedure have been written as a function?

(b) Prepare a flow chart that uses COUNTFAC to output a list of all prime numbers up through 1000. Of course, a prime number is an integer having only two factors, 1 and the number itself. Explain why this is a very inefficient method for making a list of primes.

[6]**5.** (a) Prepare a flow chart for a procedure aliquot(number,PARTS,n) which takes a given integer number, less than 10^3, and returns its aliquot parts in the first n elements of vector PARTS. The aliquot parts of a number may be thought of as being all its factors except the number itself; e.g., the aliquot parts of 12 are 1, 2, 3, 4, 6.

(b) A "perfect" number was considered by the Greeks to be a number having a value equal to the sum of its aliquot parts; e.g., for 6, 1 + 2 + 3 = 6. Prepare a flow chart for finding all perfect numbers up through 500. (See Problem 3 of Exercises 4-2, Set B).

(c) 220 and 284 are referred to as "friendly" numbers, since the aliquot parts of 220 total 284, and the aliquot parts of 284 total 220. Prepare a flow chart for finding all friendly numbers up through 500. *Hint.* Start from the flow chart you developed above in Part *b*.

[6] *Note.* An extremely interesting article on perfect numbers appeared in the Mathematical Games section of the *Scientific American,* Vol. 218, No. 3, pp. 121–126 (March 1968).

EXERCISES 6-4, SET B

1. Draw a function reference flow chart (LEAST) to find the algebraically smallest element of the vector A with components $A_1, A_2, \ldots, A_N$.

2. Draw a functional reference flow chart (SUBLEAST) to find the subscript of the smallest element of A.

3. Draw a reference flow chart for a procedure called MARKS to find both the smallest element of A and its subscript. Can a single functional reference flow chart be used instead?

EXERCISES 6-4, SET C

Students in a computer programming class were recently given an interesting flow-charting assignment which is given below together with one student solution. Your job is to study the problem and the solution carefully and point out what corrections are needed, if any, and to explain what these corrections accomplish.

Here is the problem.

Draw the flow chart for a procedure called DELETE that deletes duplicate values from a sorted list of k values, $\{b_i,\ i=1(1)k\}$.

Let the list of parameters for the procedure be

$$k,\ \{b_i,\ i=1(1)k\},\ m$$

In executing DELETE, the parameter m is to be assigned a value equal to the number of duplicates that have been found and removed.

After deleting the m duplicates, the length of the list, recorded as the value of k, should be decreased by m from its original value. That is, there are to be no gaps in the list after the deletions. For example, if the given sorted list of k = 8 values is:

b_1	b_2	b_3	b_4	b_5	b_6	b_7	b_8
1	2	2	3	9	9	9	10

then after execution of DELETE, 3 duplicates will have been removed, leaving 5 elements on the list, i.e.,

b_1	b_2	b_3	b_4	b_5
1	2	3	9	10

Moreover, the value 3 will have been assigned to m and the length k will have been reduced to 5.

The student's solution is given in Figure 6-30.

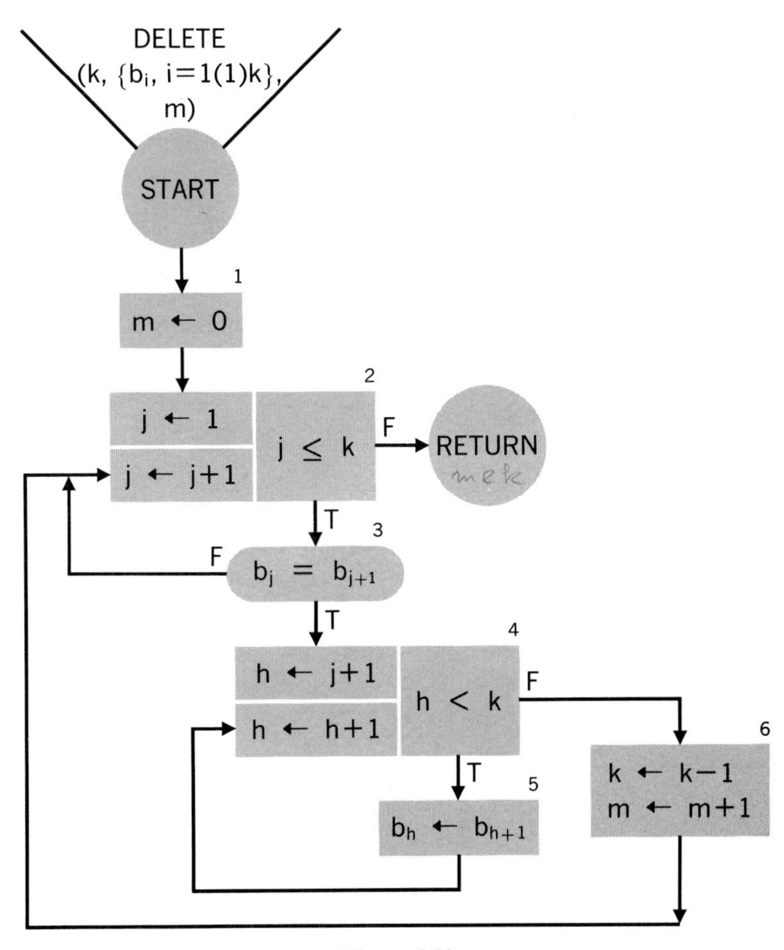

Figure 6-30

PROBLEMS 6-4

1. Recall Problem 8 Exercises 3-6, Set A, to determine the actual degree of a polynomial, given n and the set of coefficients $\{a_i,\ i=0(1)n\}$. For this problem, assume that the coefficients are integers and draw the flow chart for a *procedure* called DEGREE that accomplishes the same thing as Problem 8. That is, another program can call on DEGREE by supplying it with the polynomial data n, $\{a_i,\ i = 0(1)n\}$ as arguments. DEGREE returns control to the calling program when it has revised (or "put its stamp of approval on") the value of n.

2. Draw the flow chart for a procedure, SIMPLIFY, for taking a polynomial of degree n with integer coefficients, represented by n, $\{a_i,\ i=0(1)n\}$, and replacing it by the polynomial obtained when one divides each coefficient by the greatest common factor of the coefficients. (*Hint.* Use the GCD function reference flow chart.)

3. If a(x) and b(x) $\neq 0$ are polynomials with integer coefficients, then there exist a nonzero constant, c, and polynomials q(x) and r(x) with integer coefficients and with degree r(x) < degree b(x) so that

$$c \cdot a(x) = q(x) \cdot b(x) + r(x)$$

That is, some multiple c of a(x) is divisible by b(x). This is called the *remainder theorem for polynomials*. The process of finding r(x) is referred to as reducing a(x) mod b(x).

Draw the flow chart for a procedure called REDUCEMOD that:

(a) Takes two integer polynomials a(x) and b(x), represented by n, $\{a_i, i=0(1)n\}$ and m, $\{b_i, i=0(1)m\}$, where b(x) is known to have *actual* degree m and to be already simplified as in Problem 2.

(b) Computes r(x) as in the above formula, simplifies r(x) as in Problem 2, and replaces a(x) by r(x). Be sure that no fractions occur in the computation so that there will be no round-off error.

(*Hint.* Use the procedures DEGREE, SIMPLIFY, and GCD.)

4. Draw a flow chart for finding the *greatest common divisor in simplest form* of two polynomials with integer coefficients. By a greatest common divisor of two polynomials, we mean a polynomial of highest possible degree which is a divisor of both the given polynomials, the quotients being permitted to have fractional coefficients. Repeating the derivation of the Euclidean algorithm in Section 3-3, we find that this greatest common divisor is unique except for multiplication by any nonzero rational number. By "simplest form" we mean that the coefficients must be integers having no common factor. It is quite evident that multiplying the given polynomials by nonzero integers will not alter this simplest greatest common divisor. (*Hint.* Use the procedures DEGREE, SIMPLIFY, and REDUCEMOD.)

6-5 EXTENSIONS OF REFERENCE FLOW CHARTS

Alternate Exits

Frequently, there are situations in which we wish to use a procedure to indicate (perhaps in addition to a calculated result) which of two or more paths the main flow chart should follow. In some reference flow charts, we wish to pursue alternate paths when unusual or error situations arise. In other reference flow charts, the selection of alternate paths may be the principal purpose of the procedure.

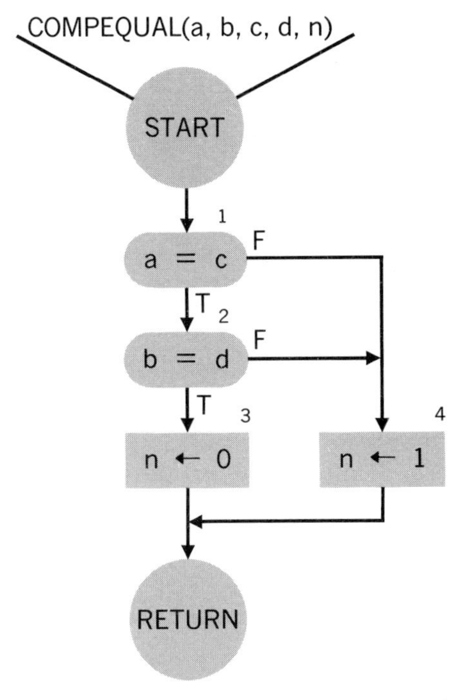

Figure 6-31 Test for equality of complex numbers.

One technique for choosing alternate paths is to include an output variable whose value will tell the main flow chart which path to take. This technique is illustrated in Figure 6-31 for a procedure whose purpose is to determine whether two complex numbers a + bi and c + di are equal.

The only effect of the procedure is to assign a value of zero or one to the variable n, depending on whether the complex numbers are or are not equal. Since n is the output variable, it appears in the parameter list. (Could this flow chart have been prepared as a functional reference instead of a procedure?)

Figure 6-32 shows how COMPEQUAL may be referenced in a main flow chart to decide whether or not the complex numbers x + yi and u + vi are equal.

A second way of using a procedure to choose alternate paths actually combines the EXECUTE box with the decision box. In flow chart language, this can be pictured as in Figure 6-33.

The parameter list of COMPEQU contains, in addition to variables for the real and imaginary parts of the numbers to be compared, the

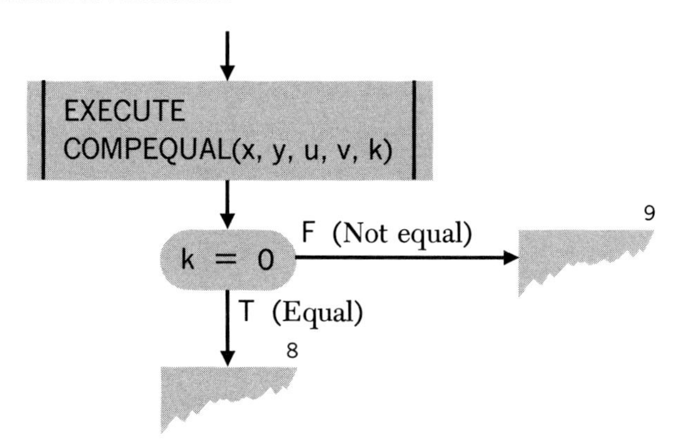

Figure 6-32 Are x + yi and u + vi equal?

flow-chart box number identifying the start of an alternate path in the flow chart.

In Figure 6-33 the *normal* return leads to box 8, while an alternate return leads to box 9. A reference flow chart for this procedure is shown in Figure 6-34.

Compared with Figure 6-31, we see that boxes 3 and 4 of that figure have been eliminated. A new terminal (we always use circles for the terminals of our flow charts) appears with the direction "GO TO boxz". This is an alternate exit from the procedure.

We now have three distinctly different ways of ending a reference flow chart, each represented by a distinct box as shown in Figure 6-35. Form *a* is used only in functional reference flow charts to indicate that the value of a local variable x is returned to the calling program. Form *b* is used in reference flow charts to indicate that a procedure has been completed and the next flow-chart box in normal sequence is to be used.

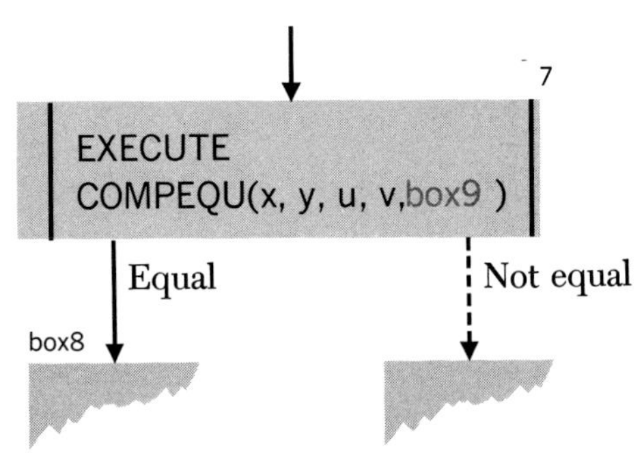

Figure 6-33 Choosing alternate paths.

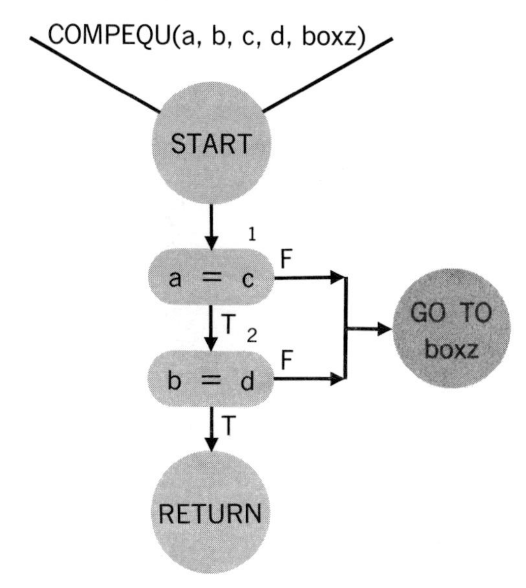

Figure 6-34 A procedure to make a choice.

Form *c* is used in reference flow charts to indicate that the procedure has been completed and that the next flow chart box to be used is the one that corresponds to boxz.

The window-box model of our procedure needs a new feature to reflect the GO TO terminal box. It is pictured in Figure 6-36.

When the master computer wants to use COMPEQU, he sends in the window boxes inscribed with x, y, u, and v and, in addition, a slip of paper on which is written box9 (the label of the alternate next flow-chart box). Four boxes and the slip of paper are dropped in the funnel in the proper order. Gummed labels (a,b,c,d) are stuck on the four boxes in order, and the slip of paper is assigned to the local window box boxz. Now the busy crew inside the sealed chamber gets to work and finally the four boxes slide out of the chute. If the crew determines that the alternate

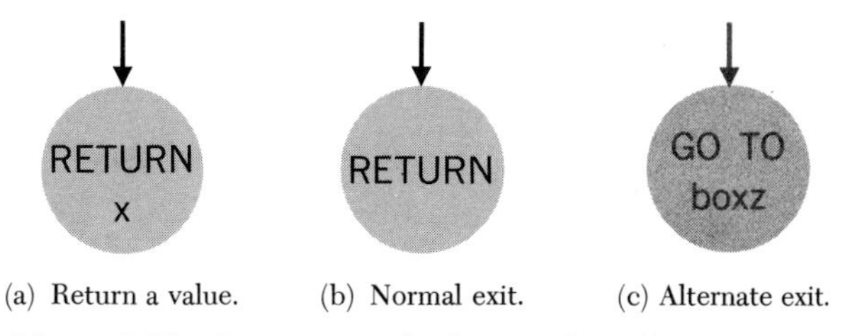

(a) Return a value. (b) Normal exit. (c) Alternate exit.

Figure 6-35 Comparison of reference flow chart endings.

Figure 6-36 A choice procedure.

exit is to be used, they shove window box boxz up against the GO TO window. In collecting these boxes, the reader and his crew now check the GO TO window to see whether it is empty or contains the label of a flow-chart box. The reader makes a note of whatever is in the window and returns it to the master computer, who now knows which flow-chart box is next.

Function Name Arguments

It will be very useful to be able to use the name of a reference flow chart (either a functional reference or a procedure) as an argument of a procedure. Suppose, for example, that we want a procedure to compare the values of functions f(x) and g(x) for a given value of x. Figure 6-37 shows how such a procedure can be flowcharted.

In Figure 6-37*b*, dummy names for two functions, ff and gg, appear as "formal parameters" in the reference flow chart defining FUNCOMP. When FUNCOMP is actively used in the EXECUTE box of Figure 6-37*a*, the corresponding "actual parameters" (in this example, the function names SINE and COSINE) appear in the parameter list. In addition, FUNCOMP has two alternate exits (the formal parameters boxn and boxm corresponding to the actual parameters box14 and box15). When FUNCOMP is called upon for execution, the actual parameters are associated with the formal parameters of the reference flow chart. That is,

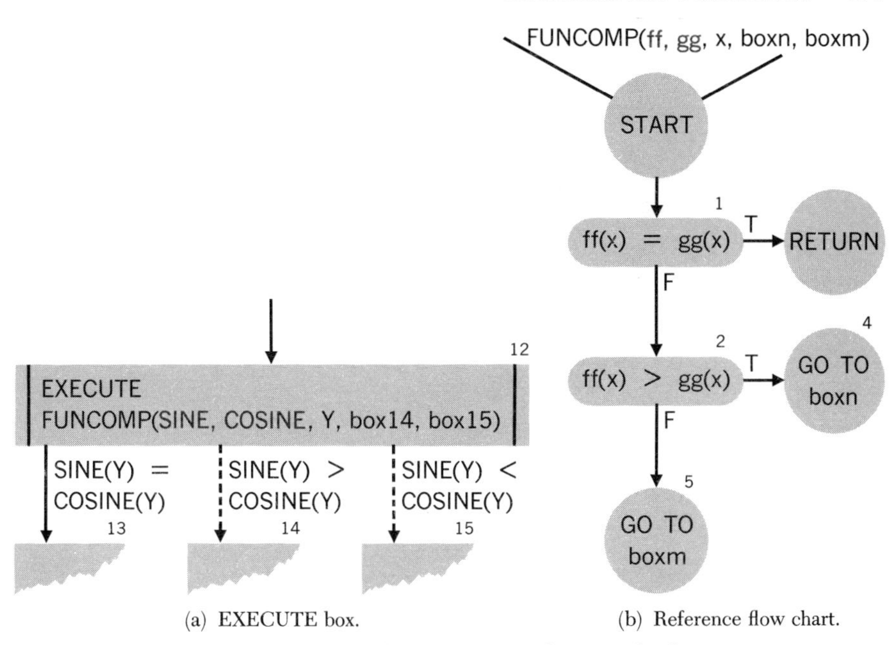

(a) EXECUTE box. (b) Reference flow chart.

Figure 6-37 Procedure to compare functional values.

FUNCOMP is instructed that, for this execution, ff is to be considered the SINE function and gg, the COSINE function.

We are sure that the reader will think of ways to extend the window-box model so that function names can be used inside a sealed chamber for a procedure. We will leave this final extension of the model up to your imagination.

EXERCISES 6-5

1. Figure 6-6 is a reference flow chart for Newton's algorithm. Prepare an improved version in which the value of ϵ used in box 4 is given by the calling program, and provide an alternate exit if the argument is negative.

2. Draw a flow chart of a procedure for solving two equations in two unknowns. Prepare an alternate exit for the special case when the two equations correspond to parallel or concurrent lines.

3. (a) Draw a reference flow chart for a procedure to find the real roots of any quadratic equation of the form $ax^2 + bx + c = 0$. Your flow chart is to use alternate exits to distinguish finding of no roots, one root, two real roots, or complex roots.

(b) Draw a flow chart that will use the reference flow chart of part *a* and will print the roots found with an appropriate message.

(c) Draw a flow chart to do the same job as the flow chart of part *a* but without using alternate exits. You must provide a variable that will carry back to the main flow chart the information as to which of the four possible cases has occurred.

(d) Draw a flow chart that will use the reference flow chart of part *c* and print out the roots found with messages, as in *b*.

4. Refer to Problem 1, Section 6-3, Set A. Suppose the function f were redefined as

$$f(x,y) = \frac{(x^3 + y)^2 + 5}{x - 2}$$

This function is not defined at $x = 2$.

Draw two procedures for computing values of f, one using an alternate exit, the other using a variable to carry the information about the exceptional case back to the main flow chart. In each case, show a flow-chart fragment that calls for f and computes

$$Z = f(r,s) + 6 \times W$$

5. It is desired to sum up the values of a function at a number of equally spaced points in an interval starting with the left endpoint. Draw a flow chart for a procedure that will carry this out for any function, any interval, and any spacing (or increment). Provide an error exit for when the increment is negative or the number given as the right endpoint of the interval is to the left of the left endpoint.

6-6 CHARACTER STRINGS

In this section we will develop several special procedures for handling character strings. This subject is met again in later chapters that study problems in symbol manipulation. We begin by considering a string of characters denoted by $s_1, s_2, \ldots, s_n$. These characters can be numerals, but we will think of them generally as alphabetic characters. We include punctuation marks, spaces, and digits, as well as the letters of the alphabet.

Therefore, a string might represent a sentence such as: The quick brown fox jumped over the lazy dog. In this case, s_1 is T, s_2 is h, s_3 is e, s_4 is a space, s_5 is q, and so on. A string could also represent the digits and decimal point of a number such as 3.14159. In this case, s_1 is 3, s_2 is the decimal point, s_3 is 1, and so on. A string could even represent a mathematical expression such as r+q(t+u(v+w)). Here s_1 would be r, s_2 the plus sign, etc.

To handle strings, we need a notation that will allow us to refer to strings, individual elements of strings, and substrings. We choose to use subscripted lowercase letters to identify individual elements of strings, as in the last few paragraphs, and to refer to a string (or a substring) by the familiar-looking notation $\{s_i, i=1(1)n\}$, which is read as "the set of elements s_i, with i varying from 1 to n in steps of 1." This kind of notation is particularly convenient in referring to substrings. For example, $\{s_i, i=3(1)8\}$ refers to the third through eighth (inclusive) elements of a string. On the other hand, such explicit notation seems unnecessarily cumbersome when handling *complete* strings so we will sometimes shorten it and call a complete string of length n merely $\bar{S}$ (a capital letter with a bar—or string—over it).

You may be wondering if there is a difference between a string and a vector. We usually think of the components of a vector as having numeric values and the elements of a string as being characters, but this is not the basic difference. The real difference is that operations on vectors do not normally change the number of components, whereas operations on strings frequently do change the number of elements.

In problems concerned with strings, some basic procedures are needed. One of the simplest is a procedure that searches a string to determine whether or not a particular character, such as a decimal point or a right parenthesis, is present. Just such a procedure, defining ischp (for "*is* *ch*aracter *p*resent"), is shown in Figure 6-38 together with a flow chart using ischp.

Sometimes it is important to find out not only *whether* a certain character is present but also *how often* it occurs in a string. To do this we must transform procedure ischp slightly, adding one more input variable, m, the subscript of the first element to be examined. Then it should be possible to use and reuse the new procedure, chekch (for "*check* *ch*aracter"), employing the output variable p to tell us when to increase a tally. While the flow chart in Figure 6-39*b* shows a reference flow chart for procedure chekch, Figure 6-39*a* counts and prints out how often the character value of x occurs in a string $\bar{T}$ of length ℓ.

Instead of searching a string for a single character, we next consider the problem of searching a string for a specified *substring*. Suppose our original given string is a sentence: The quick brown fox jumped over

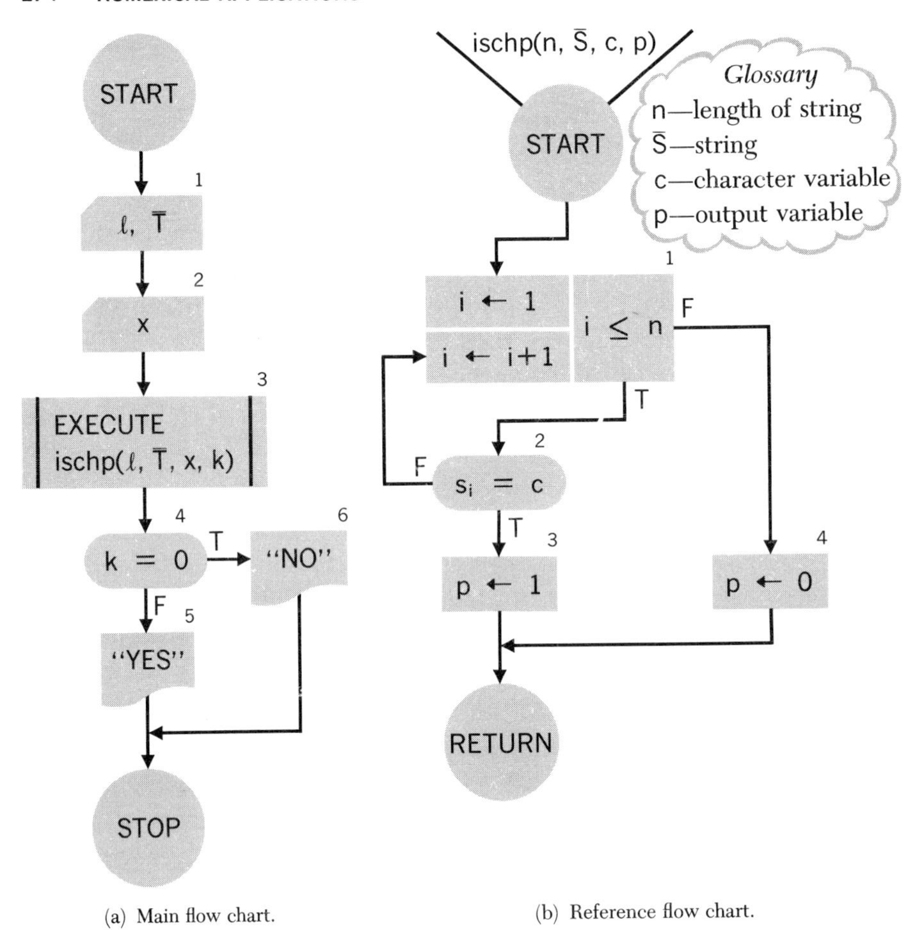

(a) Main flow chart. (b) Reference flow chart.

Figure 6-38 Searching for a character.

the lazy dog. We need a procedure very little different from chekch to count the occurrences of the substring consisting of the letters t h e.

This procedure, chekst (for *checkst*ring), is given in Figure 6-40. The variables are exactly the same as in the preceding figure except that the variable c is now replaced by the *length* k of the specified substring, followed by the name $\bar{C}$ of the substring itself. If p is not set equal to zero, then $s_p, s_{p+1}, \ldots, s_{p+k-1}$ is the first occurrence of the substring in which $p \geq m$.

On entry to the procedure, the variable ℓ is given the value of the starting point m. Of course, there is no point in looking for the first appearance of c_1, beginning with s_ℓ, if this starting point is too far along the

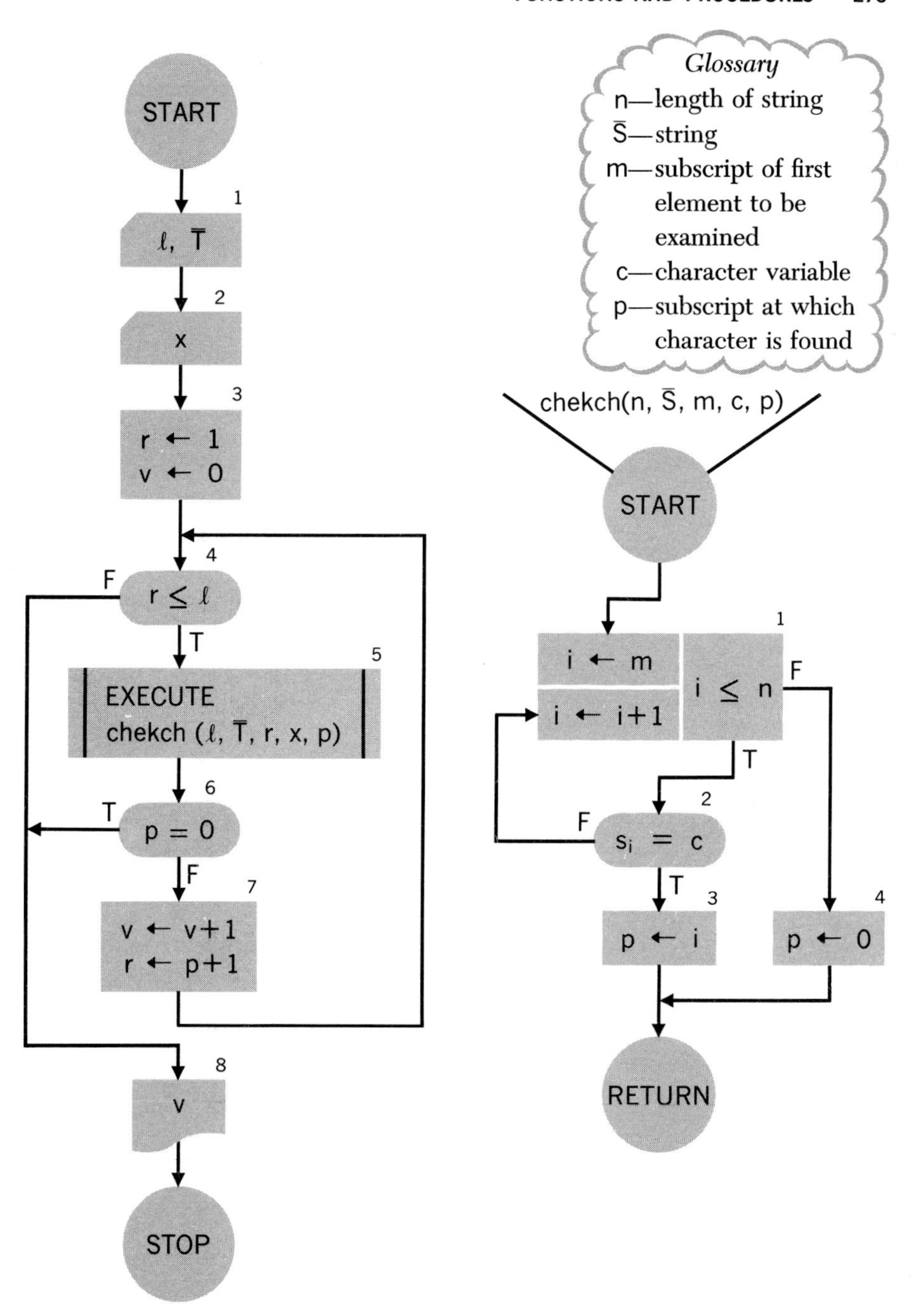

(a) Main flow chart

(b) Reference flow chart

Figure 6-39 Character search.

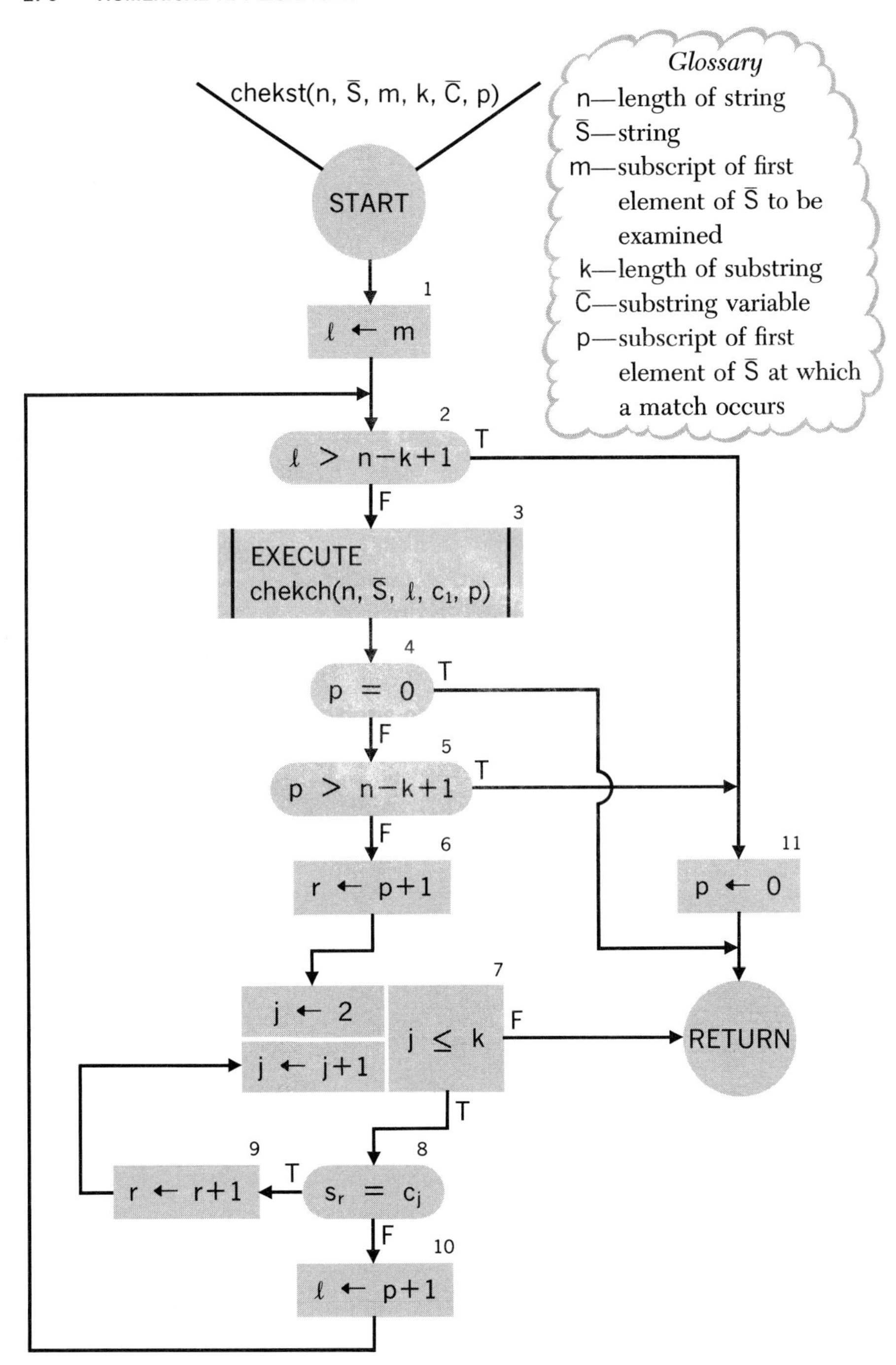

Figure 6-40 Searching for a string.

string, i.e., if $\ell > n-k+1$. If $\ell \leq n-k+1$, the procedure chekch is used to find the first occurrence of c_1, beginning the search at s_ℓ.

Then, if there is no occurrence at all, p is set equal to zero, and there is nothing to do but return. If there is an occurrence, but the value of p at which it occurs is too large, then p must be set equal to zero before returning.

If there still has been no return from the procedure, the next $k - 1$ characters, $s_{p+1}, s_{p+2}, \ldots, s_{p+k-1}$, must be compared with $c_2, c_3, \ldots, c_k$. If there is agreement, the procedure returns, and the value of p is correct as it stands. But if any pairs do *not* agree, the entire process must be started over again, this time with the new starting point at s_{p+1}. Accordingly, ℓ is assigned the value $p+1$, and all steps are repeated, except, of course, for the initial assignment to ℓ.

Figure 6-40 is an example of one procedure being used by another, as discussed in the preceding section. In many cases up to now, we have drawn flow charts that were thought of as "main flow charts." Now we can consider such flow charts as being procedures themselves. In this way, we see how more and more complicated building blocks can be constructed.

EXERCISES 6-6

1. Construct a *procedure*, to be called contch, for counting the total number of occurrences of a specified character in a given string. The parameter list should be $(n, \bar{S}, c, count)$.

2. In an arithmetic expression, parentheses must "match up." That is, every left parenthesis must have a corresponding right parenthesis. Suppose that during the scan of a string representing an arithmetic expression, a counter is kept that starts at zero, adds one for each left parenthesis encountered, and subtracts one for each right parenthesis encountered. Then, if the expression is correctly written (with respect to parentheses), the counter must never have a negative value and must have a zero value at the end of the scan. Prepare a procedure flow chart (called parenchek) to determine if an arithmetic expression is properly parenthesized.

3. Construct a procedure, called contst, for finding the total number of occurrences of a specified substring in a given string. The parameter list should be $(n, \bar{S}, k, \bar{C}, count)$.

4. A teacher has the daily grades for his class for an entire term in a string $\bar{A}$.

The grades are grouped by student; i.e., $a_1, \ldots, a_i$ are for the first student, $a_{i+1}, \ldots, a_j$ are for the second student, etc.

(a) Flowchart a function called aver that will average elements m through n of string $\bar{A}$. Assume all grades are numerical.

(b) Write a program using aver that inputs a string $\bar{A}$, inputs the first and last subscripts, m and n, of the grades for a single student, outputs these subscripts together with the student's average, and then returns for data on the next student.

(c) Consider ways to alter the flow chart for aver if recorded grades are only letter grades.

CHAPTER 7

SOME MATHEMATICAL APPLICATIONS

In this chapter and in the next, we present several fundamental types of calculation problems that occur repeatedly in many fields of study. For each type of problem, we develop one or more methods of solution and present flow charts for their implementation. More powerful methods than the ones given in these two chapters are available. However, the methods presented here are applicable to a surprisingly large proportion of the problems in numerical calculation for which computers are used.

7-1 ROOTS OF EQUATIONS

In your algebra courses a considerable portion of your energies were devoted to finding solutions of equations like

$$7x + 5 = 4x + 3$$

or

$$x^2 = 3x + 5$$

By a solution of this kind of equation, we mean a value, which, when assigned to x, makes the equation true. Thus, $-2/3$ is the only solution of the first equation above, while the second equation has two solutions, given by the quadratic formula. These are:

$$\frac{3 + \sqrt{29}}{2} \quad \text{and} \quad \frac{3 - \sqrt{29}}{2}$$

As we advance to a consideration of more complicated equations such as

$$3x^3 = 7x + 2$$

or

$$5 \sin x = x + 2$$

or

$$x^5 = x^4 - 3x^2 + 1$$

we find that explicit formulas for the solutions are either so complicated as to be practically useless or else such formulas do not exist at all. When numerical answers to such problems are needed, we are forced to resort to approximation. In practical applications we will generally be satisfied if a method is available that approximates the solution to whatever degree of accuracy is required.

Methods for making such approximations are in abundant supply. The one to be presented in this chapter is certainly the simplest and, for actual computer implementation, generally the best.

Before launching into the development of this method, we make a minor reformulation of the problem. An equation such as

$$3x^3 = 7x + 2$$

can always be rewritten so that the expression on the right side of the "equals" symbol is zero:

$$3x^3 - 7x - 2 = 0$$

The problem is now reformulated as follows. Consider the function defined by

$$f(x) = 3x^3 - 7x - 2 = 0$$

and find the values of x for which

$$f(x) = 0$$

In general, values of x for which

$$f(x) = 0$$

are called *roots* or *zeros* of the function f. Thus the solutions of the equation

$$3x^3 = 7x + 2$$

are the roots of the function f defined by

$$f(x) = 3x^3 - 7x - 2$$

It is also common practice to use the terminology "roots of an equation" in place of "solutions of an equation."

Locating a Root by Graphing

Graphical methods are perhaps the simplest of the many methods that have been proposed for finding the roots of equations. If the equation is written in the form $f(x) = 0$, then you have only to calculate $f(x)$ for a suitable set of values of x and plot the graph of $y = f(x)$. Wherever this graph crosses the x-axis, there will be a root of the equation. Of course, you can get only an approximate result by such a graphical procedure because of the limitations of your ability to draw a graph very accurately. You also may have difficulty in finding the right domain of the values of x to use in plotting the graph.

Suppose that you want to obtain approximations for the roots of the equation

$$3x^3 - 7x - 2 = 0$$

Draw the graph of $y = 3x^3 - 7x - 2$. To do this, first calculate a small table of values.

x	−3	−2	−1	0	1	2	3
y	−62	−12	2	−2	−6	8	58

The graph is shown in Figure 7-1. Three roots are seen to be between −2 and −1, between −1 and 0, and between 1 and 2.

An alternative method is to write the equation to be solved in the form $f_1(x) = f_2(x)$ and plot the graphs of $y = f_1(x)$ and $y = f_2(x)$. The x-coordinates of the points where these graphs intersect will give you the roots of the equation.

For example, suppose you want to obtain approximations for the roots of the equation $x = \cot x$. Draw the graphs of $y = x$ and $y = \cot x$ (Figure 7-2). The x-coordinates of the points where these curves intersect give the roots of the equation.

You can see that there are infinitely many roots, the smallest ones being near $\pm\pi/4$. The other roots lie near to $\pm k\pi$, $k = 1, 2, 3, \ldots$.

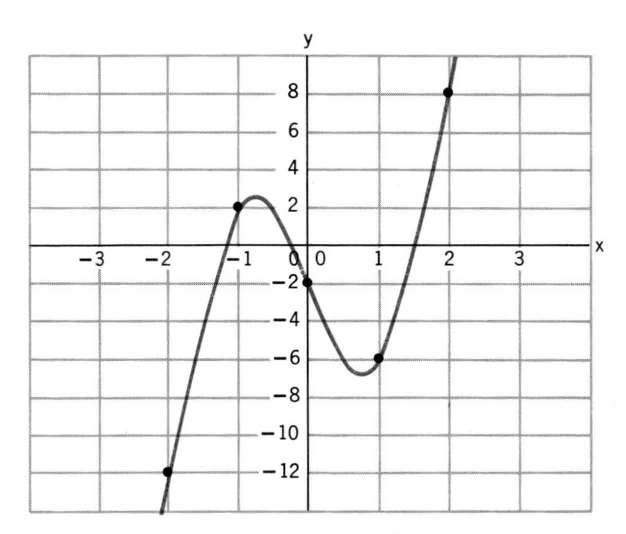

Figure 7-1 Graph of $y = 3x^3 - 7x - 2$.

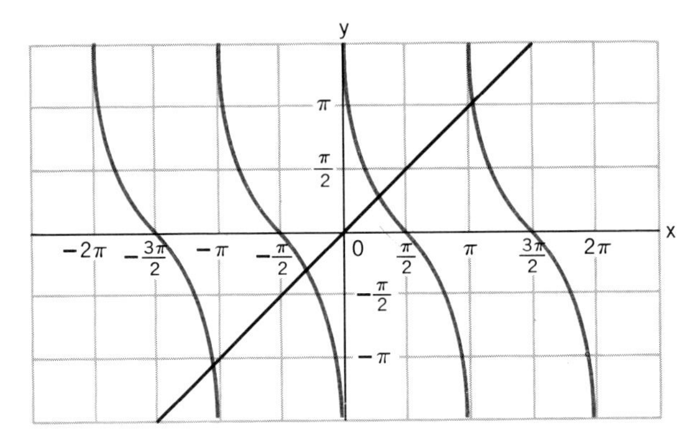

Figure 7-2 Graphs of $y = x$ and $y = \cot x$.

EXERCISES 7-1, SET A

1. For each of the following two equations, plot the graph of $y = f(x)$, where $f(x)$ denotes the left-hand side. Obtain approximate roots for each equation.

   (a) $x^3 - 2x - 5 = 0$ (b) $x^2 - 3x - 4 \sin^2 x = 0$

2. By plotting the graphs of $y = f_1(x)$ and $y = f_2(x)$ for suitably chosen $f_1(x)$ and $f_2(x)$, obtain approximations for the roots of the following equations.

   (a) $x = \tan x$ (b) $5 - x = 5 \sin x$

3. By plotting the graph of

$$b^4 - 13.2 \times b^3 - 60.96 \times b^2 + 60.96 \times 13.2 \times b - 60.96 \times 6.6 \times 6.6 = y$$

find an approximate root.

The Method of Successive Bisection

Either of the graphical methods just described will give us an approximation to a root of the equation. Once we have an idea of where the root lies, we can improve the accuracy of the root.

Many of the methods that are used with computers for solving such problems amount to methods of search. Because a computer calculates rapidly, we do not hesitate to have it evaluate a function more often than we would ask a person to do so. At the same time, of course, the methods should be systematic and efficient so that we are not penalized with unnecessary functional evaluations.

The general strategy in methods of search is to establish that the target (in this case, a root of an equation) is to be found in some interval of a variable, and then use some test or criterion to reduce this interval. The method of successive bisection is a relatively simple technique for repeatedly reducing the size of the interval in which a root of an equation will be found. The method is designed for use when the function is known in advance to be continuous (that is, no breaks in the graph) and to have just one root in the given interval. We consider it incidental that the method will also produce one of the roots in the case that the function has an odd number of roots in the interval. If the number of roots in the interval is even, the method is inapplicable.

Suppose we seek a root of the equation $f(x) = 0$ where $f(x)$ is a function of x. Suppose further that $f(x_1) < 0$ and $f(x_2) > 0$, i.e., the graph of $y = f(x)$ is below the x-axis at $x = x_1$ and above the x-axis at $x = x_2$. This situation is illustrated in Figure 7-3*a*. If the graph of $y = f(x)$ has no gaps or jumps between $x = x_1$ and $x = x_2$, then it must cross the x-axis between x_1 and x_2 and, hence, there must be a root of $f(x) = 0$ between x_1 and x_2.

We now bisect the interval (x_1,x_2) and denote the midpoint by x_M so that we have

$$x_M = \frac{(x_1 + x_2)}{2}$$

If $f(x_M) = 0$, then we have a root. However, if $f(x_M) > 0$, as in Figure 7-3*a*, then there is a root between x_1 and x_M. This is the criterion for reducing the size of the interval of interest. So, to prepare for the next step, we assign the value of x_M to the variable x_2. Thus, we can denote once more the interval in which the root lies by (x_1,x_2), but the length of our new interval is half that of the original interval, as shown in Figure 7-3*b*.

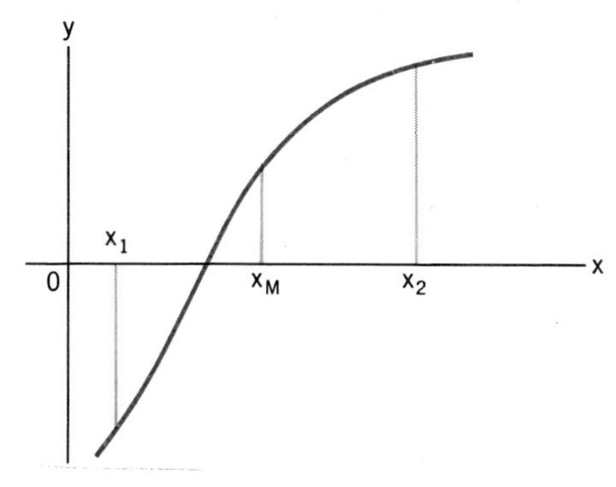

Figure 7-3*a* Graph of some $f(x)$ with a root between x_1 and x_2.

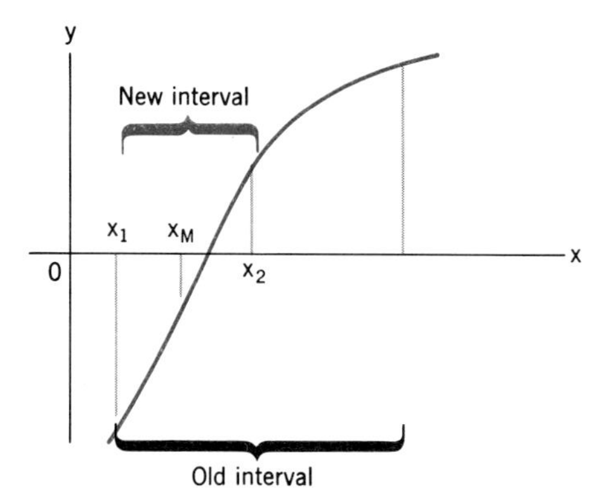

Figure 7-3*b* New interval after one bisection.

Again, calculate the value of the function at the midpoint x_M of the new interval. This time $f(x_M) < 0$, as shown in Figure 7-3*b*, and therefore the root is between x_M and x_2. Again we have isolated the root in an interval half the length of the previous interval. If we now assign the value of x_M to the variable x_1, we can again denote the current interval containing the root by (x_1,x_2).

By repeating this bisection process, we can come as close to the root as we please because at each step we halve the length of the interval in which the root lies. Thus, 10 steps will reduce the length of the interval by a factor of 2^{10} or roughly 1000, while 20 steps will reduce it by a factor of 2^{20} or roughly 1,000,000.

Example. We again consider the equation

$$3x^3 - 7x - 2 = 0$$

The corresponding graph is drawn in Figure 7-1. If we let $f(x) = 3x^3 - 7x - 2$, we see that

$$f(1) < 0 \qquad \text{and} \qquad f(2) > 0$$

and so we know there is a root of the equation between 1 and 2.

We now bisect this interval. The midpoint is $x_M = 3/2$. We easily find by substitution

$$f(\tfrac{3}{2}) = -19/8 \qquad \text{so} \qquad f(\tfrac{3}{2}) < 0$$

Thus the root lies in the interval (3/2,2). The midpoint of this interval is $x_M = 7/4$. But

$$f(\tfrac{7}{4}) = 117/64 \qquad \text{so} \qquad f(\tfrac{7}{4}) > 0$$

Hence, the root lies in the interval (3/2,7/4).

We can continue this process, halving the interval as many times as we wish, each time finding in which half interval the root lies.

EXERCISES 7-1, SET B

Use the method of bisection to find approximate values of the indicated roots of the following equations. In each case, start with the indicated interval, which is known to contain a root, and use the indicated number of bisection steps.

1. $x^3 - 2x - 5 = 0$	(2,3)	4 steps
2. $x = \tan x$	(3,5)	4 steps

Compare your results with the results found graphically in Exercises 7-1A.

Now we will develop a flow chart based on the successive bisection method for approximating a root (or "zero") of a given function F in a given interval. In passing to the flow-chart stage, we will use X1, X2, and XM instead of x_1, x_2, and x_M.

The basic operation of the bisection process is the replacement of the interval (X1,X2), in which a root of F is known to lie, by a subinterval of half its length in which the root is known to lie. If we assume that the initial values of X1 and X2 are such that F(X1) and F(X2) have opposite signs, then the partial flow chart of Figure 7-4 describes the steps of this operation. In box 5 the midpoint XM is calculated. In box 7 we see the easiest way of deciding whether F(X1) and F(XM) have the same or opposite signs. They have the same or opposite signs according to whether their product is positive or negative. If their product is zero, then F(XM) must be zero, since we are assuming that F(X1) is already known to be

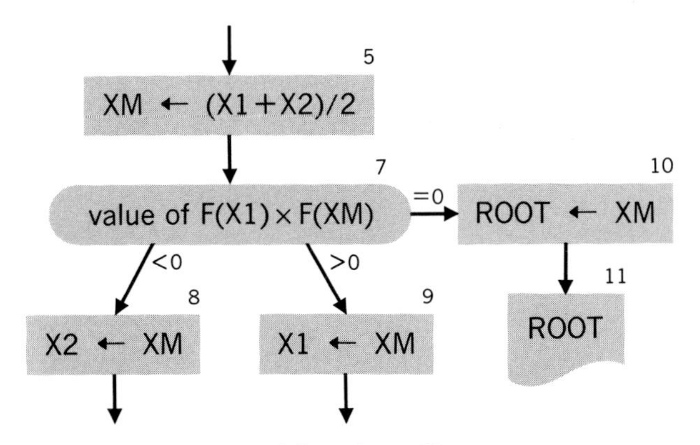

Figure 7-4 Partial flow chart of bisection process.

different from zero. Even though it seems very unlikely that an endpoint of one interval would exactly coincide with a root, we will be prepared should it happen.

At each stage, before we decide to replace the interval (X1,X2) by an interval half as long, we need to check the length of the interval, that is, the absolute value of the difference, X1 − X2. If it is sufficiently small (say smaller than a given value ϵ), we accept the value XM at the midpoint of the interval as the root of the equation. Otherwise, we repeat the operations of the flow chart of Figure 7-4.

We are now ready to draw a complete flow chart for finding a root by the bisection method. (See Figure 7-5.) We assume the equation is given in the form F(X) = 0. We are given two numbers, the initial values of

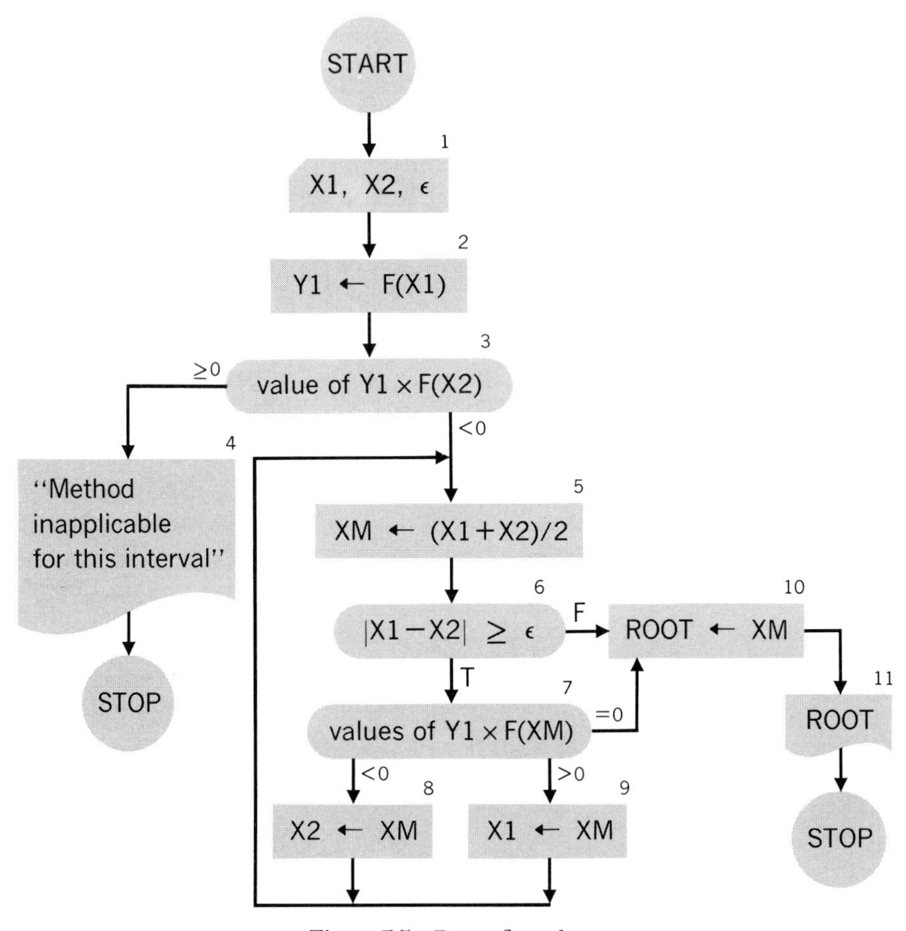

Figure 7-5 Bisect flow chart.

X1 and X2, between which a root is supposed to lie. We also assume that a tolerance ϵ is given and that we are supposed to calculate the root with an error less than ϵ. More precisely, the true root is to lie within an interval of length ϵ centered on the calculated root. Values of X1, X2, and ϵ are read in box 1 of Figure 7-5.

In box 2 the value of F(X1) is assigned to an auxiliary variable Y1. This is based on the principle that if you are going to use a particular value of an expression several times, you assign that value to an auxiliary variable to avoid repeating the identical computation. The fragment of Figure 7-4 is repeated in boxes 5, 7, 8, 9, 10, and 11 of Figure 7-5. Box 3 is a test to determine whether the initial values of F(X1) and F(X2) have the same or opposite signs. If they have opposite signs, then Y1 · F(X2) is negative, so we go to box 5 and start the bisection process. If F(X1) and F(X2) do not have opposite signs, then Y1 · F(X2) is nonnegative and the method is inapplicable. This is indicated in box 4.

One little trick remains to be explained. We see that only one assignment has been made to the variable Y1 so that its value never changes; its value is always F at the initial value of X1. We want, in box 7, to determine whether F(X1) and F(XM) have the same or different signs. Only if the signs are the same do we assign XM to X1. But then the new F(X1) and the old one will have the same sign. In other words, the sign F(X1) never changes. The test of sign in box 7 can thus be made using the initial value of F(X1) as well as with the latest value.

EXERCISES 7-1, SET C

Step through the flow chart of Figure 7-5 with the indicated functions, the indicated intervals, and the indicated values of ϵ. Determine whether there are an odd number of roots in the interval and, if there are, determine the value of ROOT. Slide-rule accuracy is adequate. Tables may be used in Problems 2 and 3.

1. $x^3 - x - 1 = 0$	[0,2]	$\epsilon = 0.1$
2. $x + \ln x = 0$	[.1,1]	$\epsilon = 0.15$
3. $5 - x = 5 \sin x$	[0,2]	$\epsilon = 0.4$
4. $x^3 - 3x - 2 = 0$	[0,2]	$\epsilon = 0.1$
5. $x^3 - 2x^2 - 13x - 10 = 0$	[0,4]	$\epsilon = 0.1$

The following example should be used as a guide.

Problem. $3x^4 - 2x^3 + 7x - 4 = 0 \quad [0,1] \quad \epsilon = 0.4$

Solution. An odd number of roots. For $\epsilon = 0.4$ the root is 0.625:

$$f(x) = 3x^4 - 2x^3 + 7x - 4 = 0$$

Step	X1	Sign of F(X1)	X2	Sign of F(X2)	XM	Sign of F(XM)	|X1−X2|
	0	−	1	+	0.5	−	1
1	0.5	−	1	+	0.75	+	0.5
2	0.5	−	0.75	+	0.625	+	0.25

Bisection as a Procedure

After you have traced through the details of Bisect in Figure 7-5 and made sure it is in good working order, we are ready to proceed with converting it into a procedure. Bisect always operates on a function F.

We will let one of the parameters be a dummy function name so that the procedure will be able to find roots of functions having a variety of actual names. If we don't add a dummy function name (F) to the parameter list, we will be able to search only for a root of functions named F in the calling program and we would be unable to have one main flow chart call on the procedure to find a root of more than one function. Clearly, a function name should be an element of the parameter list when we convert Bisect to a procedure.

Since Figure 7-5 has an alternate exit, it also seems natural to include a label (box number) in the parameter list. Calling the bisect procedure ZERO, we show the funnel as it would replace the START and box 1 of

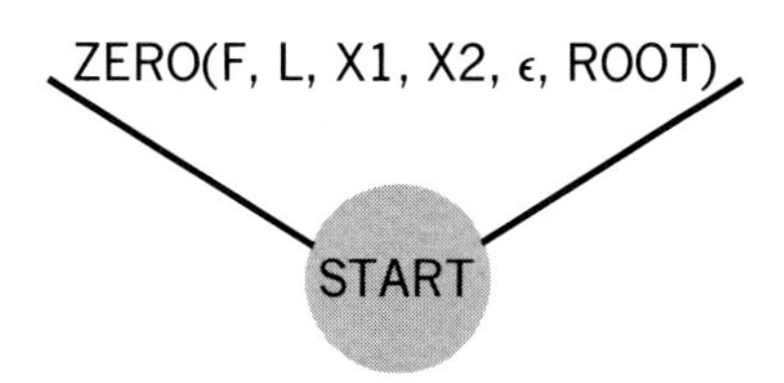

Figure 7-5. Here the F is a placeholder for a function reference that will be supplied by the main flow chart. The parameter L is a placeholder for a statement label, as described in Section 6-5.

Figure 7-6 shows the complete flow chart for our new procedure, ZERO.

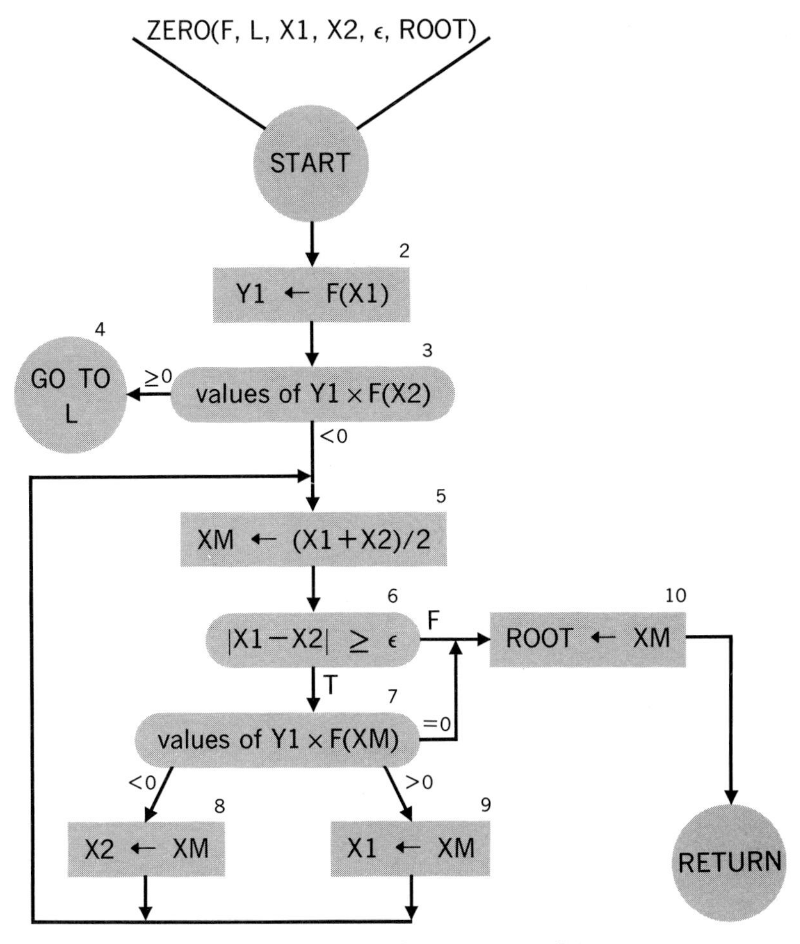

Figure 7-6 ZERO: bisection procedure.

Recall from Section 6-5 that variables in the funnel of a procedure can be thought of as either slips of paper or window boxes coming into the hopper of the brick chamber. In this procedure *some* variables are to be treated in one of these ways and *some* in the other.

Let us concentrate our attention on the variables X1 and X2 in the funnel. X1 and X2 start as the ends of our original interval. Recall that our procedure has as its only purpose the locating of a root. The procedure should not make any capricious alterations in the values of the main flow-chart variables. Looking at boxes 8 and 9, we see that assignment is made to X1 and X2. Therefore, if the values of X1 and X2 are brought to the procedure in their window boxes, these boxes will be returned to the main flow chart with changed values. This will throw a monkey wrench into the main flow chart if original values of these variables are needed later on. We insist, therefore, that the initial values to be assigned to X1 and X2 should be brought to the hopper on slips of paper.

We are indifferent to which of the two treatments is to be used for the variable ϵ. On the other hand, the sole purpose of the output variable, ROOT, is to hold the result going back to the main flow chart. Clearly, there must be a window box to carry this information back, so a window box belonging to a main flow-chart variable is anticipated and, when received by ZERO, will be relabeled ROOT.

If you are only a user of the ZERO procedure, rather than its author, you may not care how the variables are treated internally as long as you are assured that the only variable that can be changed inside the procedure is ROOT. On the other hand, if you have to design and flowchart a procedure, recognizing and understanding the ways of treating the variables can be essential.

Before leaving this subject, we want to point out that the danger of mistreating variables X1 and X2 might have been avoided in another way. The top of the flow chart of Figure 7-6 could have been altered to use X1 and X2 as auxiliary variables, as shown in Figure 7-7. Handled this way, it is immaterial how A and B come into the hopper.

Now that we have completed our examination of the symbols in the funnel of ZERO, we will briefly indicate the way in which this procedure is used.

First, we must be aware that there are three flow charts implicit in the preceding discussion. Besides the flow chart for the procedure ZERO,

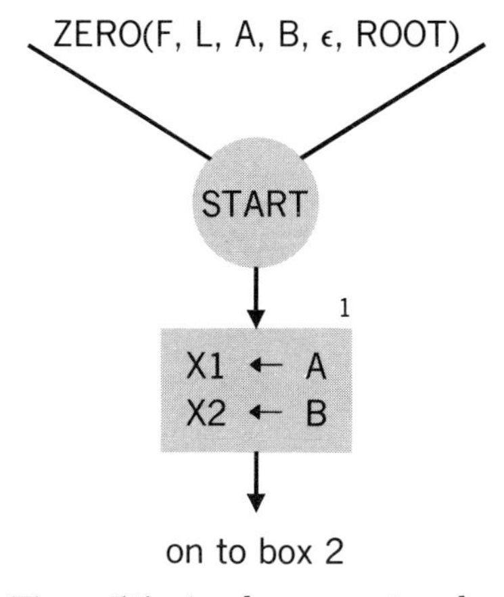

Figure 7-7 Another protection plan.

there must be a main flow chart that calls for the execution of ZERO and at least one function reference flow chart for the function to which ZERO is to be applied. We illustrate in Figure 7-8 a simple case study. For this purpose we have created functions FUNCT and G defined by

$$\text{FUNCT}(X)=X^3-5X-1$$

and

$$G(X)=X^3+3X^2+4X$$

A main flow chart will usually do something more interesting with the roots than just print their values, but Figure 7-8 will serve our purpose. The main flow chart, *a*, reads values for a, b, and epsi. It then calls upon the ZERO procedure, giving the values of the variables read and the name of a function (FUNCT). Then the ZERO procedure takes charge, using the flow chart for FUNCT(X) for each functional evaluation in boxes 2, 3, and 7, and iterating until a value is found for ROOT. This value is returned to the main flow chart where it is called R and is printed.

Starting in box 5 of the main flow chart, the same process is repeated except that the variables have different names and the use of a different function, G(X), is specified. Notice that to be able to use the same procedure to find roots of various functions, the function name must be changeable and so it should be an input to the procedure.

EXERCISES 7-1, SET D

1. By graphing, it becomes clear that each of the two equations $\sin x = \frac{2}{3}x$ and $\tan x = 10x$ has a solution in the interval $[.1, \pi/2]$. Prepare all the necessary flow charts for determining which of these roots is the greater. The ZERO procedure is understood to be available already in flow-chart form.

2. By a certain theorem, the function $H(x) = 6x^5 + 5x^4 - 4x^3 - 2x - 1$ has exactly one positive root. Since $H(0) = -1 < 0$ and $H(1) = 4 > 0$, this function has at least one root in the interval (0,1). Draw the necessary flow charts which, when used together with ZERO, will print out the value, R, of this root and G(R) where $G(x) = x^6 + x^5 - x^4 - x^2 - x - 1$ and five values of G(x) and H(x) separated by .01 in x on both sides of R.

3. Draw the flow charts which, used together with ZERO, will print out the root of $\ln x = -x$. In this problem the reference flow chart for the natural logarithm function, ln, does not have to be drawn.

4. Suppose a satellite is in a circular orbit. Let the radius be 1, centered

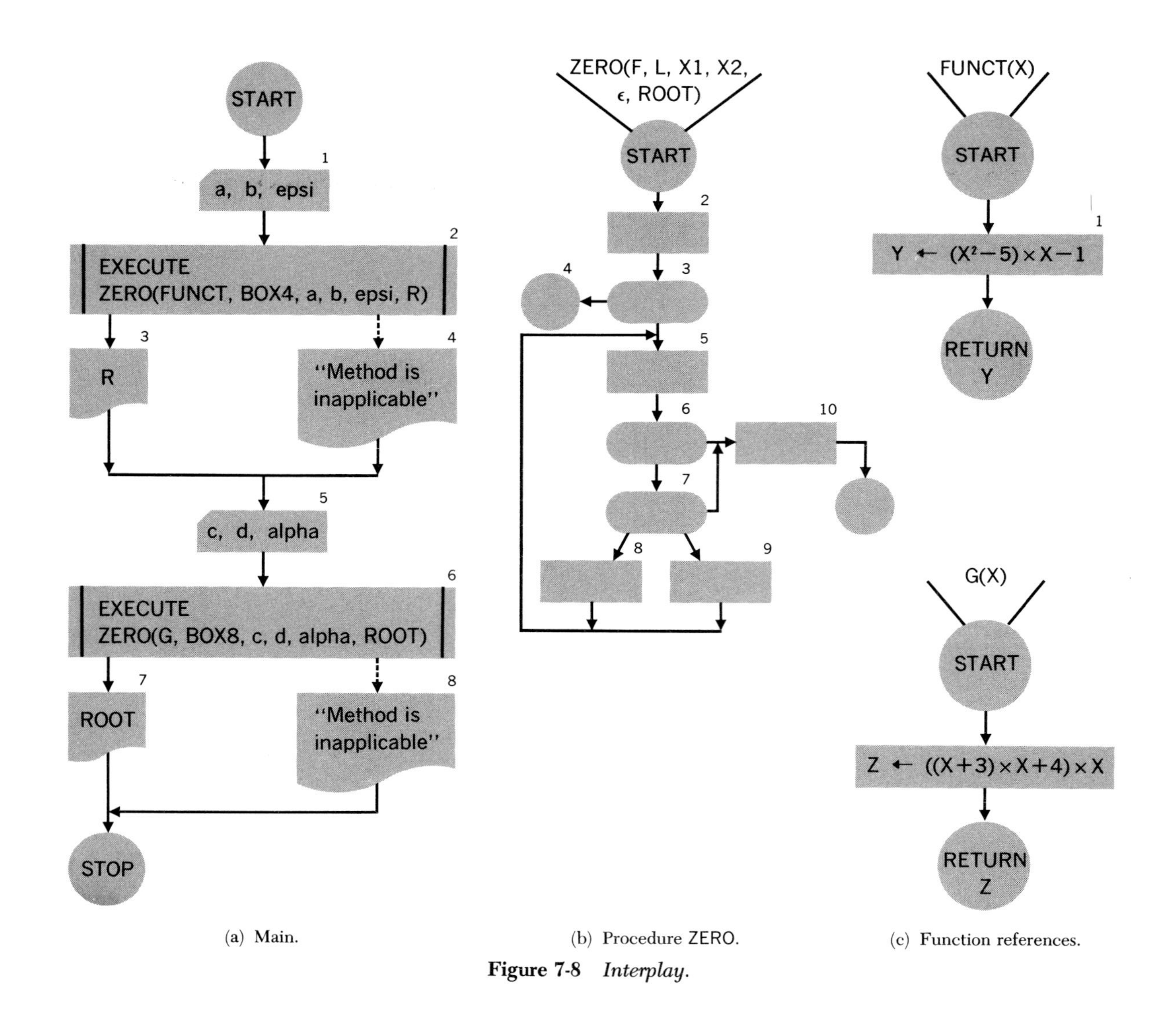

(a) Main. (b) Procedure ZERO. (c) Function references.

Figure 7-8 *Interplay.*

at the origin. Draw the necessary flow charts to be used in conjunction with ZERO for finding the intersections of the orbit with the following trajectories.

(a) $xy = \frac{1}{4}$ for $0 \leq x \leq \frac{1}{2}$

(b) $y = x^n$ where $n = 1, 2, 3, 4, 5$
for $0 \leq x \leq 1$

*5. A variety of algorithms can be devised for finding roots of functions by choosing the new point between x_1 and x_2 in various ways. One simple way of choosing that new point, instead of taking x_M as in bisection, would be to

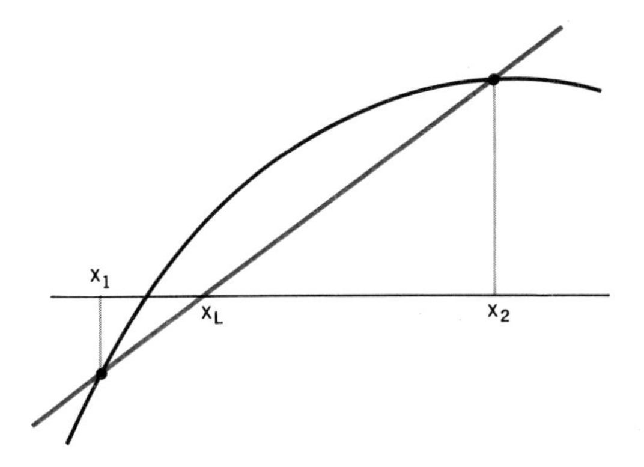

choose x_L, the point at which a straight line drawn from $(x_1, f(x_1))$ to $(x_2, f(x_2))$ intersects the x-axis. The point x_L is given by

$$x_L = x_1 - \frac{f(x_1)}{m}$$

where m is the slope of the straight line. Complete the algorithm for this method, prepare a flow chart, and comment on its advantages as compared to bisection.

7-2 LOCATING MAXIMA AND MINIMA

A function, f(x), is said to have a *maximum* in an interval (a,b) if there is a point, x_{max}, for which $f(x_{max})$ is larger than any other value of the function in the interval. The meaning of the *maximum* and *minimum* of a function[1] is pictured in Figure 7-9. The function has a minimum if there

[1] You may already know that the maximum or minimum of a function occurs at the point at which the straight-line tangent to the graph of the function becomes horizontal. If so, you may think the task of finding a maximum is solved—but our problem is to find a way to *tell a computer* to find a maximum. Besides, look at Problem 3 in Exercises 7-2, Set C, for an example of a function for which there is no horizontal line properly tangent to the graph.

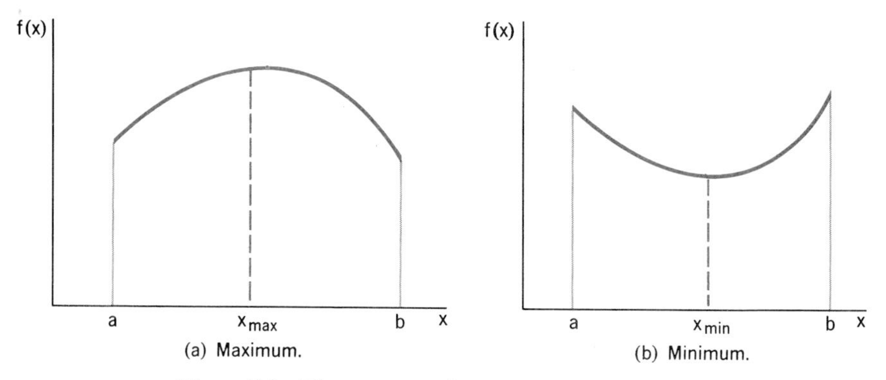

Figure 7-9 The meaning of maximum and minimum.

is a point, x_{min}, for which $f(x_{min})$ is smaller than any other value of the function in the interval. The collective term for maxima and minima is *extrema.*

Suppose you have to make the largest possible box out of a sheet of cardboard 20 inches long and 10 inches wide. A way to make this box by cutting squares out of corners, folding up the tabs, and taping the corners together is shown in Figure 7-10. Of course, the volume of the box is the product of its final length by its final width by its final height. What size should the cut-out squares be so that the volume is a maximum? The length of the box will be $(20 - 2x) = 2(10 - x)$, the width will be $(10 - 2x) = 2(5 - x)$, and its height will be x. Therefore, the volume to maximize is

$$V = 4(10 - x)(5 - x)x$$

A natural first step is to plot values of V against x. From the statement of the problem, x must be greater than zero or else there is no box—and no volume. Besides, x has to be less than 5 inches since that is half the

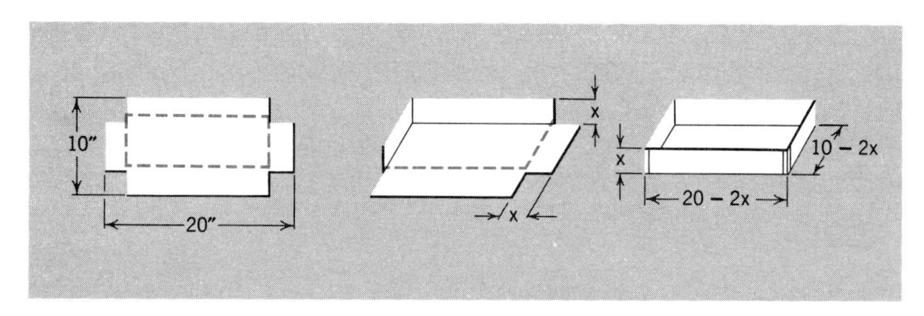

Figure 7-10 A cardboard box.

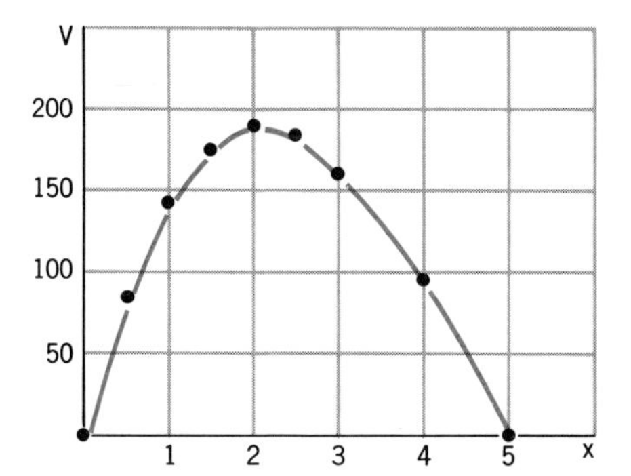

Figure 7-11 The volume of a box.

width of the cardboard. So we plot V for $0 \leq x \leq 5$ as shown in Figure 7-11, and we see that the maximum volume occurs somewhere around $x = 2$ inches.

Our purpose here is to discover and flowchart an algorithm for locating the maximum (or minimum) of a function that has this general appearance. Throughout, we will assume that:

(a) The function f(x) is known to have a single maximum in the interval (a,b).

(b) Moving from left to right, the graph of f(x) increases steadily to the maximum (without intervals of temporary decrease such as would form troughs).

(c) Moving further to the right, f(x) decreases steadily from the maximum (without intervals of temporary increase such as would form troughs).

In other words, we assume f(x) looks generally like Figure 7-9*a* or Figure 7-11.

To search for the maximum of f(x), it is reasonable to evaluate the function at some point, x_1, within (a,b). Let's do that and call the value $f(x_1)$. What can we learn from $f(x_1)$? As shown in Figure 7-12, we can always find functions having their maximum on either side of x_1, and we know no better than before where to look for the maximum.

Evaluate the function at some second point, x_2, in (x_1,b). If $f(x_2)$ turns out to be larger than $f(x_1)$, the situation is as shown in Figure 7-13. Now, if the maximum were between a and x_1, the function would have to increase from f(a) to its maximum, temporarily decrease to $f(x_1)$, increase again to $f(x_2)$, and finally decrease to f(b). Then there would have to be

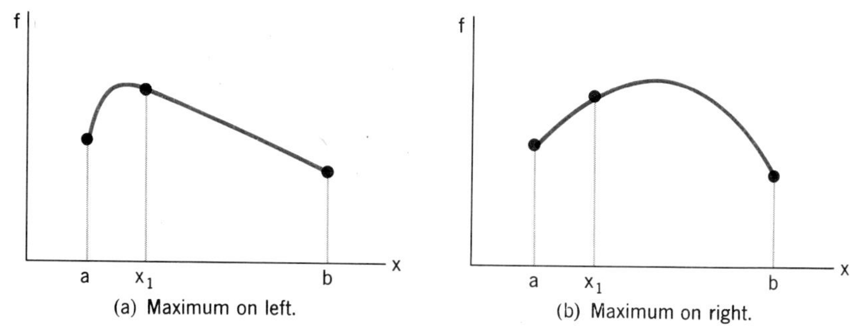

Figure 7-12 One division point doesn't help.

troughs in the graph such as we have already assumed would not exist. Therefore, if $f(x_1) < f(x_2)$, the maximum cannot be in (a,x_1) so it must be in (x_1,b). Figure 7-13 shows two examples of possible functions without troughs.

If $f(x_2)$ turns out to be smaller than (or equal to) $f(x_1)$, the situation is as shown in Figure 7-14. Now, if the maximum were in the interval (x_2,b), the graph would have to have a trough such as we have outlawed. Therefore, if $f(x_1) \geq f(x_2)$, the maximum cannot be in (x_2,b), so it must be in (a,x_2). Figure 7-14 shows two examples of possible functions without troughs.

What we have learned, now, is that if we split (a,b) into three parts in any arbitrary way, one or the other end part can be disposed of by comparing the functional values at the division points, x_1 and x_2. Some ways of splitting the interval will most likely be better than others. For example, if we choose x_1 and x_2 close together near the midpoint of (a,b), almost half the interval can be excluded each time the interval is subdivided. A second plausible way to subdivide (a,b) is into three equal parts.

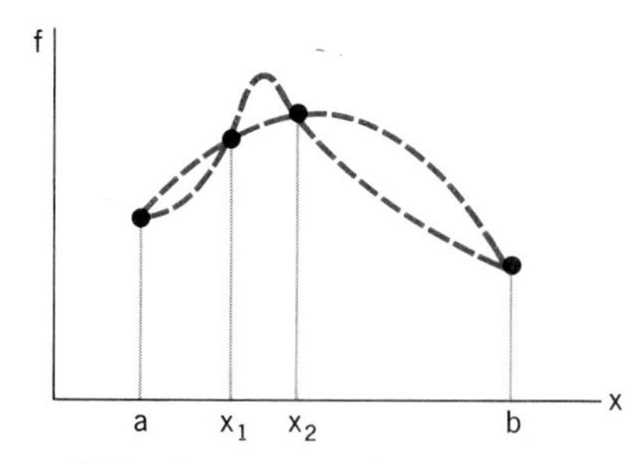

Figure 7-13 First case with two division points.

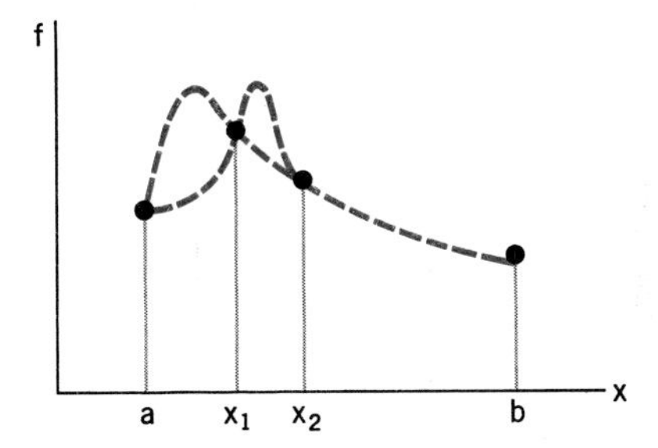

Figure 7-14 Second case with two division points.

EXERCISE 7-2, SET A

Find the maximum of

$$V = 4(10 - x)(5 - x)x$$

by subdividing, starting with the interval (0,5) and continuing until x_{max} is found to an accuracy of two digits following the decimal point. You may choose the subdivisions any way you want. It is suggested you arrange your work according to the following table.

a	b	x_1	x_2	$\frac{1}{4}V(x_1)$	$\frac{1}{4}V(x_2)$	excluded interval	new x
0	5	1.5	2.5	44.625	46.875	0–1.5	2
1.5	5	2.0	2.5	etc.			

The Method of Trisection

Trisection is the maximizing technique in which the interval is divided into thirds. We will examine this technique with two purposes; to flow-chart a simple algorithm for maximizing and to try to discover reasons for choosing other subdivision techniques. The flow chart shown in Figure 7-15 describes trisection and the comparison of functional values leading to the exclusion of one of the end subintervals.

As we begin Figure 7-15, the maximum is known to be in the interval (a,b) which, in box 3, is trisected. Two functional evaluations are performed there. In box 4 the two functional values are compared and, depending on the result, one of the endpoints is assigned a new value (that of the closer trisecting point). When we complete Figure 7-15, the maximum is in a *new* interval (a,b) which is 2/3 the length of the old and defined by the calculated values of A and B. We should be able to

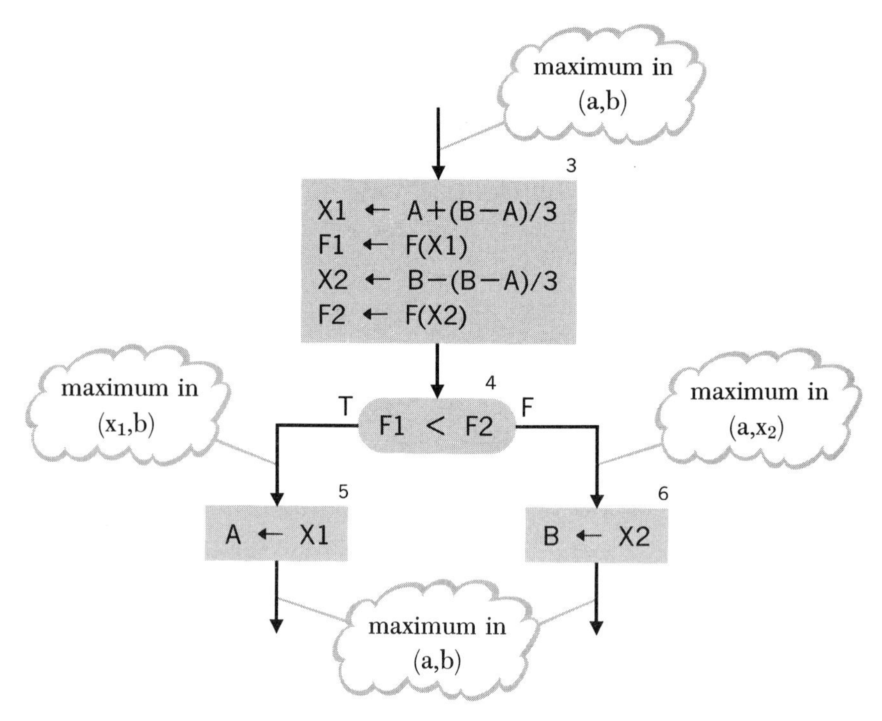

Figure 7-15 Segment of a flow chart for trisection.

repeat Figure 7-15 until the interval becomes small enough that we are satisfied with any point (say, the midpoint) in (a,b) as an approximation to x_{max}. The flow chart showing this repetition is given in Figure 7-16.

Every time we repeat the flow chart in Figure 7-16, we must find two new points for trisection and evaluate the function at both of these points. If the function is at all complicated, the two evaluations in box 3 may take more time than all the other assignments and tests in the figure. This leads us to ask if there is some systematic way to choose the points of subdivision so that one of the old points remains usable, and we need only one new functional evaluation per iteration.

EXERCISE 7-2, SET B

1. Prepare a flow chart similar to Figure 7-16 for trisection applied to minimization.

2. Find the maximum of $V = 4(10 - x)(5 - x)x$ by tracing the flow chart of Figure 7-16. Start with the interval (1.6,2.5). Produce a table of A, X1, F1, X2, F2, B for four iterations.

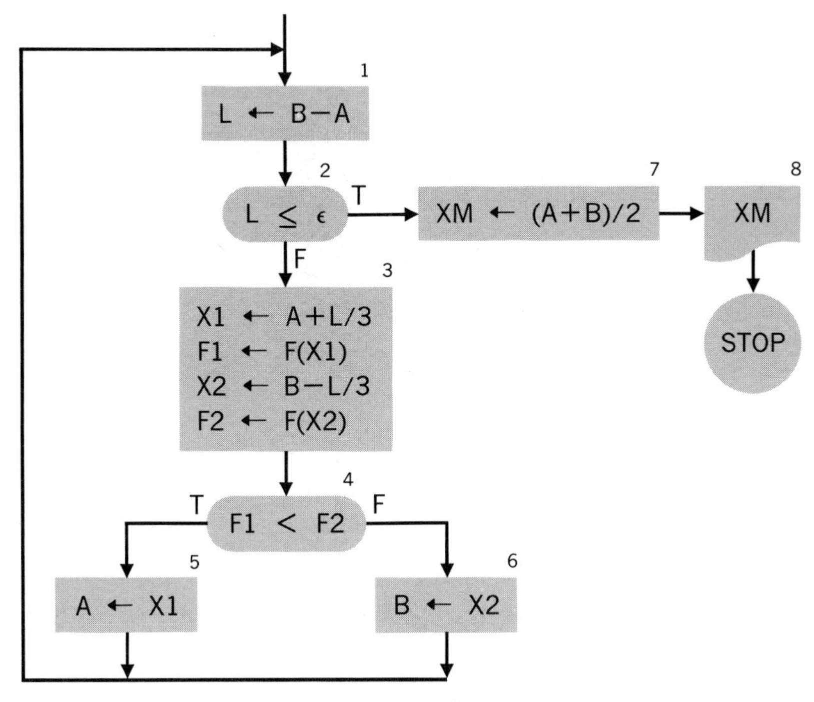

Figure 7-16 Trisection for maximization.

Other Search Methods

How can we go about subdividing an interval containing a single extremum so that, no matter which end of the interval is excluded, one of the old points of subdivision (and its functional value) will remain usable? Since we don't know ahead of time where the extremum may be, we will subdivide *symmetrically* so that no matter which end interval is excluded, the resulting length will be the same.

For simplicity, suppose the original interval is one unit long and is subdivided symmetrically at the points $1-x$ and x, as shown in Figure 7-17. As a result of the first iteration, one of the end subintervals will be excluded (see Figure 7-18). In either case, the length of the remaining interval is x. As is shown in the figure, a new point is chosen each time to subdivide the remaining interval symmetrically.

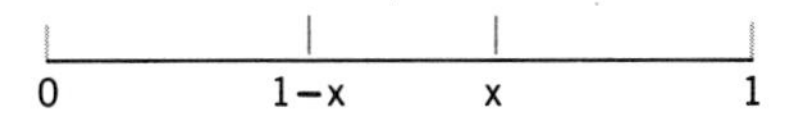

Figure 7-17 Symmetric subdivision.

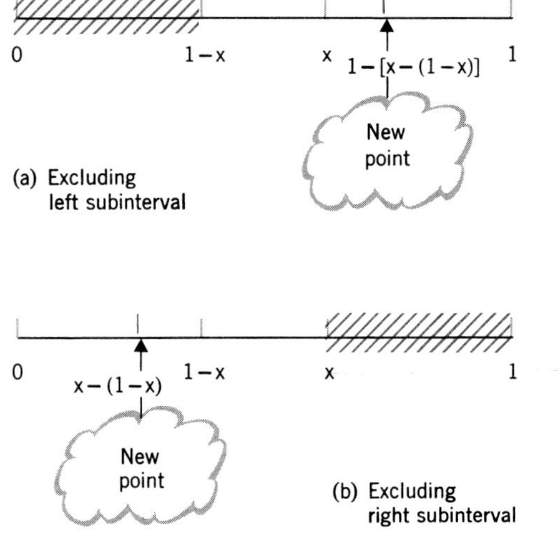

Figure 7-18 Successive subdivisions.

Let us focus our attention on the ratio, r, of the length of the interval *after* an iteration to the length of the interval *before* the iteration. This is the same as the ratio of the middle interval plus one end interval to the total. Starting with an interval of unit length, this ratio would be assigned the value x:

$$r \leftarrow x$$

In a second iteration, which excludes one of the new end subintervals (unshaded) in Figure 7-18, the new value of the ratio will be $(1 - x)/x$. The ratio r can be assigned this new value from the old by

$$r \leftarrow \frac{1 - r}{r}$$

Let's look at a third iteration. Suppose that right-end subintervals have been excluded the first two times. Then the remaining interval looks like Figure 7-19. A new point is chosen to subdivide $(0, 1 - x)$ symmetrically

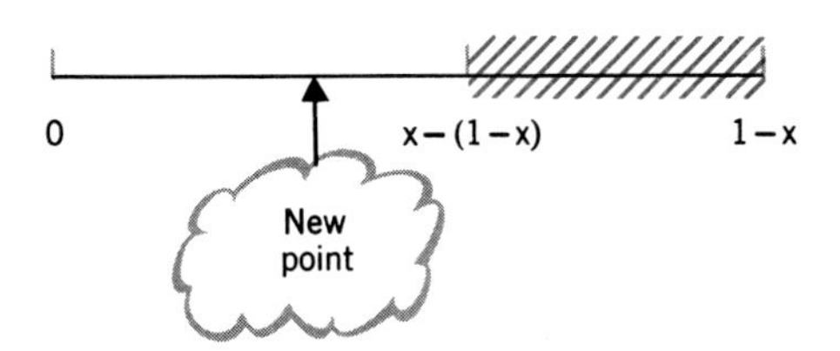

Figure 7-19 A third iteration.

and functional values are compared. When one of the end subintervals is excluded (remember, they are both the same length), r becomes

$$r \leftarrow \frac{x - (1 - x)}{1 - x} = \frac{1 - \left(\frac{1 - x}{x}\right)}{\frac{1 - x}{x}} = \frac{1 - r}{r}$$

That is, the preceding value of r is used to calculate $(1 - r)/r$ and that value is assigned to r. Clearly, in successive iterations, the same assignment will continue to calculate r, the ratio of the new to the old interval.

To decide how to choose the original value x, consider how we would like to have the intervals related after a sufficiently large number of iterations. Suppose that as a result of the final subdivision we ask that the subdividing points fall on top of each other. As can be seen in Figure 7-20, the points of subdivision would divide the final interval in two, providing a single value for the coordinate of the extremum being sought.

Let the final value of the ratio r be y. Then the preceding value of r is given by solving

$$y = \frac{1 - r}{r}$$

which gives

$$r = \frac{1}{1 + y}$$

At each stage, r is the ratio of the distance from the left end of the interval to the right point of subdivision, to the length of the whole interval. If the final value of r, from Figure 7-20, is

$$y = \frac{1}{2}$$

then in the next to the last iteration

$$r = \frac{1}{1 + \frac{1}{2}} = \frac{2}{3}$$

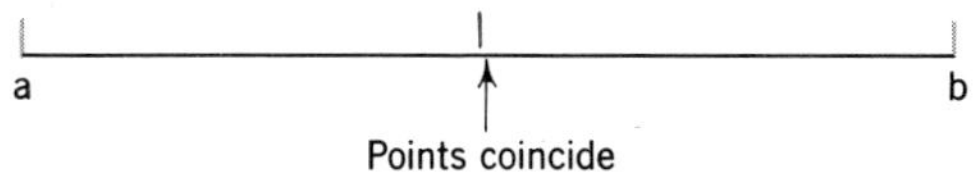

a b

Points coincide

Figure 7-20 The last subdivision.

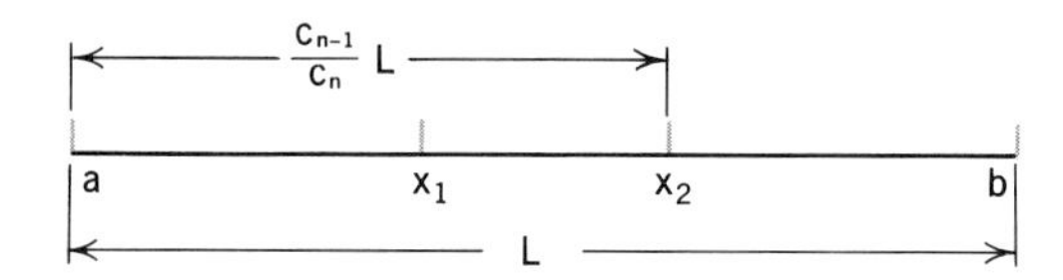

Figure 7-21 Subdivision by Fibonacci.

and in the next earlier iteration

$$r = \frac{1}{1 + \frac{2}{3}} = \frac{3}{5}$$

and in the iteration before that

$$r = \frac{1}{1 + \frac{3}{5}} = \frac{5}{8}$$

Continuing to look at earlier iterations, we find r taking on the series of values

$$\tfrac{1}{2}, \tfrac{2}{3}, \tfrac{3}{5}, \tfrac{5}{8}, \tfrac{8}{13}, \tfrac{13}{21}, \tfrac{21}{34}, \tfrac{34}{55}, \text{ etc.}$$

Do you see anything familiar about these numbers? Do you recognize them as ratios of successive terms of the Fibonacci sequence? (See Chapter 1, Section 2.)

The interpretation of this result is that if we start out by subdividing the original interval of length L according to two successive Fibonacci terms, c_{n-1} and c_n, the ratio r for all of the following symmetric subdivisions will be ratios of Fibonacci terms—and these ratios are nearly constant (Figure 7-21).

Now we can draw a flow chart for the Fibonacci search for a maximum. The initial subdivision of the interval [a,b] according to Fibonacci terms is shown in Figure 7-22, where R is the ratio of two successive and sufficiently large terms of the Fibonacci sequence. The basis of the process is the exclusion of an end subinterval and the selection of a new point of subdivision that maintains symmetry, as shown in Figure 7-23. We

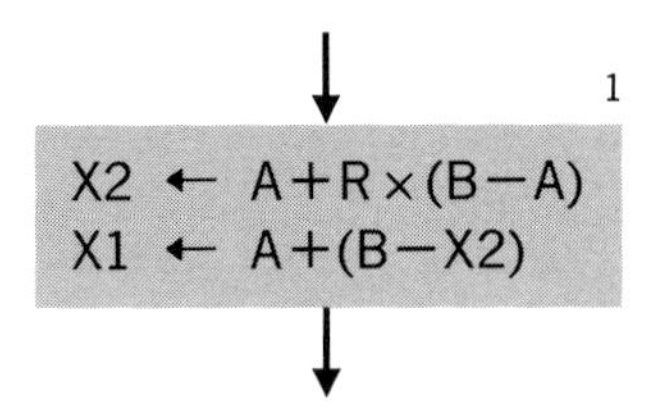

Figure 7-22 Initial subdivision of the interval [a,b].

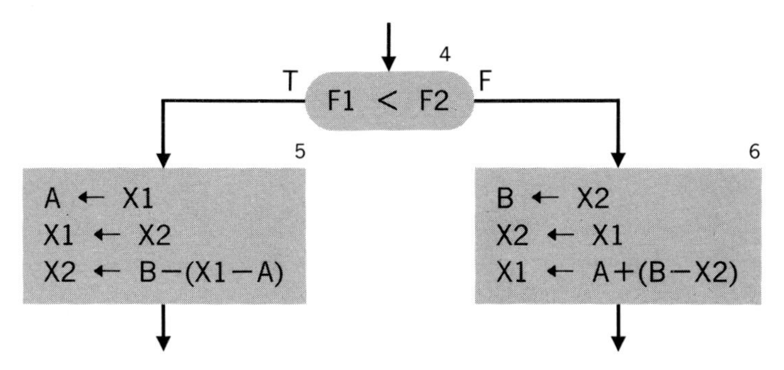

Figure 7-23 Symmetric subdivision flow chart for getting a maximum.

know that the process is finished when X1 and X2 coincide. The test for this coincidence is shown in Figure 7-24 where coincidence is required only within some ϵ to allow for rounding error in the subdivision process.

We assemble these flow chart pieces in Figure 7-25 and include functional evaluations where necessary.

Finally, let's compare the effectiveness of the flow charts in Figure 7-16 (trisection) and Figure 7-25 (Fibonacci search) in finding the maximum of a function. We have been led to discover the Fibonacci search strategy through our desire to limit the number of functional evaluations to one per iteration. Sure enough, each time around the loop in Figure 7-25, the function is evaluated at only one point (the last line in either box 5 or box 6). We have already pointed out that trisection requires two functional evaluations per iteration.

In the case of trisection, one third of the interval is excluded in each iteration so that the ratio r is

$$r(\text{trisection}) = \frac{2}{3}$$

For Fibonacci search, r is not constant but is nearly so, except for the last two or three iterations. Its value is approximately

$$r(\text{Fibonacci}) = .61805$$

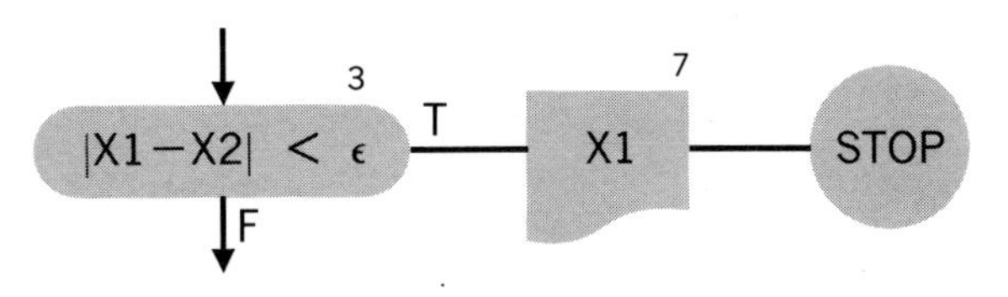

Figure 7-24 When to stop.

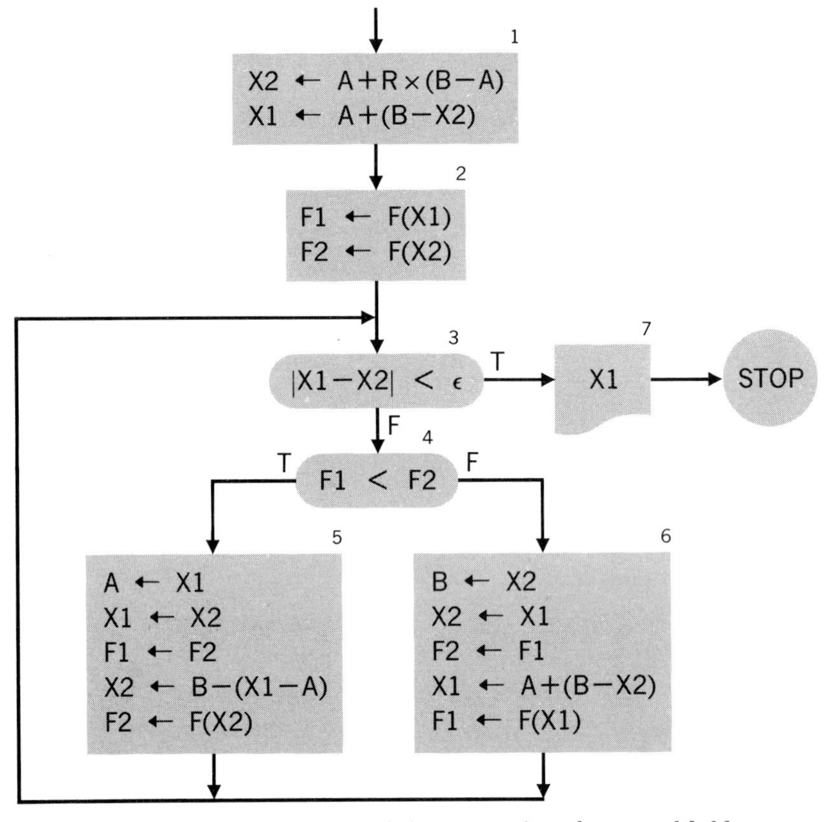

Figure 7-25 Fibonacci search (maximizing) on the interval [a,b].

A more thorough comparison than is appropriate here shows that to achieve the same accuracy in finding an extremum, the Fibonacci search will have to evaluate the function only about 40% as many times as will the trisection method.

To conclude this section, we provide in Figure 7-26 a procedural reference flow chart for the Fibonacci search for a maximum, to be called MAXIM.

EXERCISES 7-2, SET C

1. Prepare a flow chart for a Fibonacci search for the minimum of a function.
2. Suppose we were to require that the ratio r remain constant. Then

$$r = \frac{1 - r}{r}$$

gives

$$r^2 + r - 1 = 0$$

or

$$r = \frac{-1 + \sqrt{5}}{2}$$

Make a table of the lengths of symmetric subintervals and their sum to five digits based on this value of r for four iterations, assuming an initial interval of unit length.

3. By tracing through Figure 7-25, prepare a complete table of A, X1, F1,

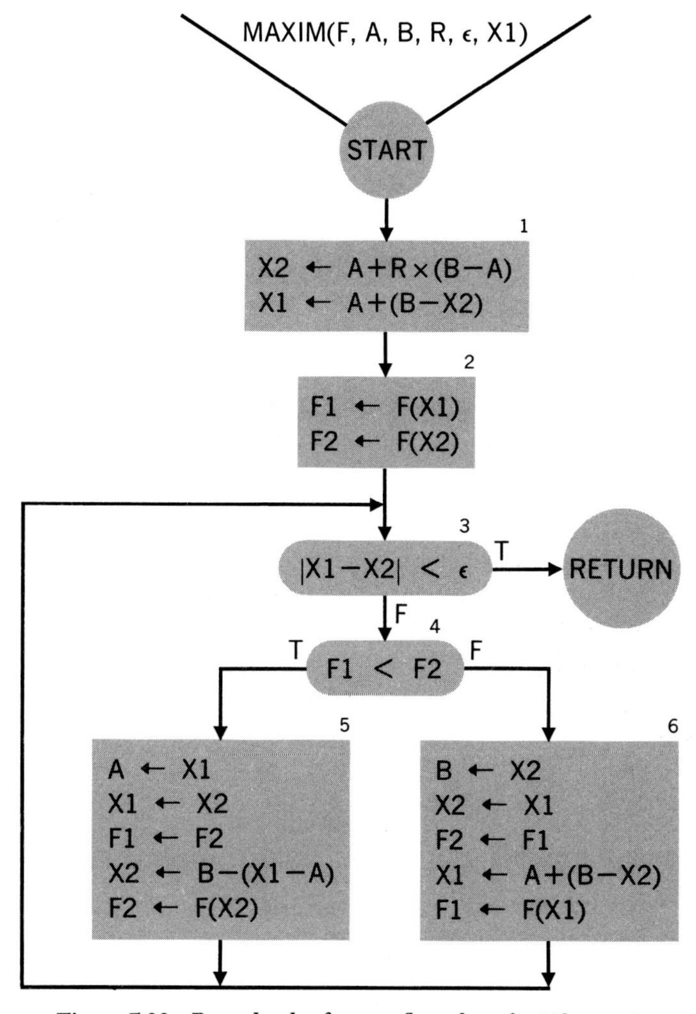

Figure 7-26 Procedural reference flow chart for Fibonacci.

X2, F2, B, |X1 − X2|, starting with A = 0, B = 34, and R = 21/34. The function is defined as

$$
\begin{aligned}
f(x) &= x & 0 \le x \le 20 \\
f(x) &= 40 - x & 20 \le x \le 34
\end{aligned}
$$

*4. Many other strategies are possible in searching for extrema. One such strategy is to subdivide into four equal subintervals by choosing x_1, x_2, and x_3. Two of the four subintervals can be excluded for each pair of comparisons (i.e., $f(x_1):f(x_2)$ and $f(x_2):f(x_3)$). Prepare a flow chart describing this method. Compare its effectiveness with the Fibonacci search by considering the rate at which the interval is reduced and the average number of functional evaluations per iteration.

7-3 COMPUTING AREAS

An important part of theoretical and applied mathematics deals with problems involving areas of regions with curved boundaries. These problems, especially that of finding the area of a circle, have been of interest to mathematicians since the dawn of history. About 2300 years ago, the Greek mathematician, Archimedes, severely handicapped by the poor notation available in those days for representing numbers, was still able to prove mathematically that the area of a circle of radius 1 (the number known as π) is less than $3\frac{1}{7}$ and more than $3\frac{10}{71}$. This has always been considered an outstanding mathematical achievement.

Expressing Archimedes' estimates in decimal form, we find that

$$3.140845 < \pi < 3.142857$$

Taking the average of these two estimates yields

$$3.141851$$

as an approximation for π with a maximum error of .001006 (Figure 7-27). Today, routine methods are available for calculating such areas to any desired degree of accuracy. We know that the value of π correct to eight decimal digits is 3.1415926. Some people have made a hobby of calculating π to a great many decimal places. In fact, the value of π is known to hundreds of thousands of decimal places. A little technique would enable you to program a computer to make such computations if anyone were willing to supply the computer time for such frivolous activities.

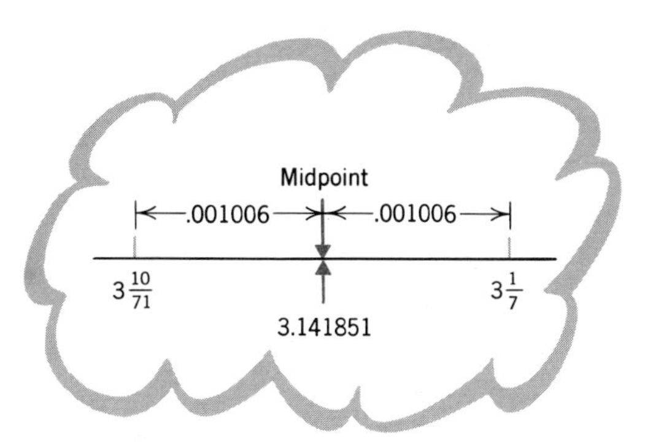

Figure 7-27

To study *area* we need to make a few basic assumptions—all very simple and, we hope, intuitively obvious. These are as follows.

1. For every region that can be outlined in a plane, there is an associated nonnegative number called the area of the region.
2. If a region R is contained in a region S, then the area of R is less than or equal to the area of S. This is exemplified in Figure 7-28, where R is the region enclosed by the inner curve and S is the entire region enclosed by the outer curve.
3. If a region is subdivided into a number of nonoverlapping parts, then the area of the entire region is the sum of the areas of the parts. Thus, the area of the entire region R in Figure 7-29 is the sum of the areas of the regions labeled 1, 2, and 3.
4. Congruent regions have equal areas. Thus, the two circles of the same radius have the same area and, similarly, the two congruent triangles have the same area (Figure 7-30).
5. The area of a rectangle is the product of the length and width (Figure 7-31).

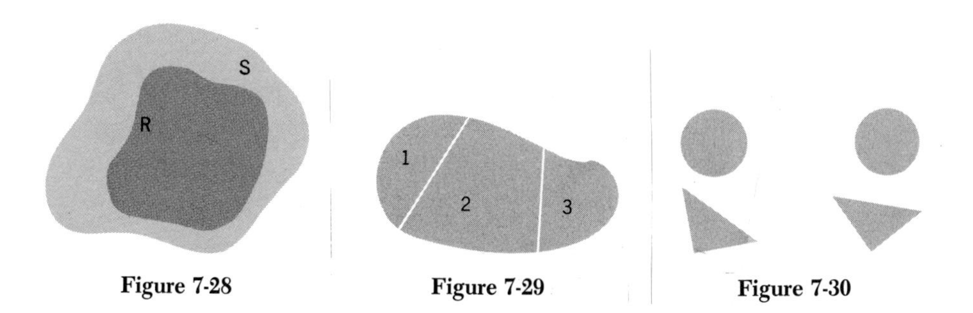

Figure 7-28 Figure 7-29 Figure 7-30

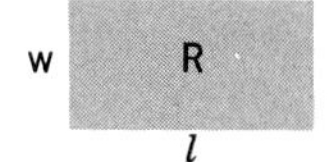

Figure 7-31

On the basis of these five statements, we are prepared to approximate areas of regions with curved boundaries to any desired degree of accuracy.

The established mathematical approach to area is to consider the areas of regions bounded on the bottom by the x-axis, on the sides by vertical lines, and on the top by a curve—the graph of a function. This is seen in Figure 7-32.

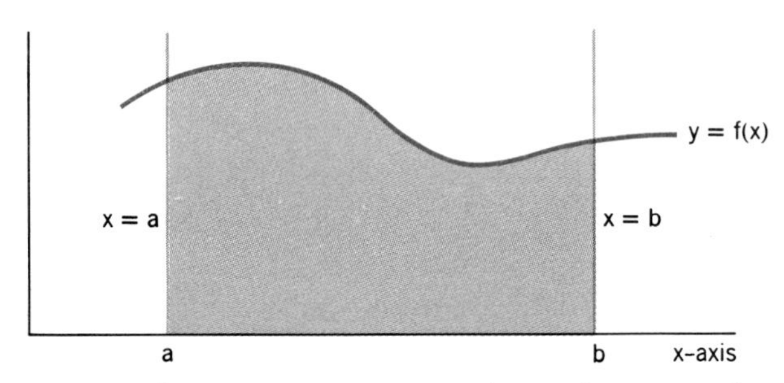

Figure 7-32 Graph of f(x) showing the region under the function in the interval [a,b].

This is not the specialization that it might appear, since we will be able to find the areas of regions, such as are depicted in Figure 7-33, as differences of areas of regions of the standard type. We see how in Figure 7-34. (You should see how property 3 of area is called into use here.)

Let us consider for the moment a rather crude attack on the problem of finding the area under the graph of

$$f(x) = \frac{1}{x} \quad \text{between} \quad x = 1 \quad \text{and} \quad x = 2$$

Figure 7-33

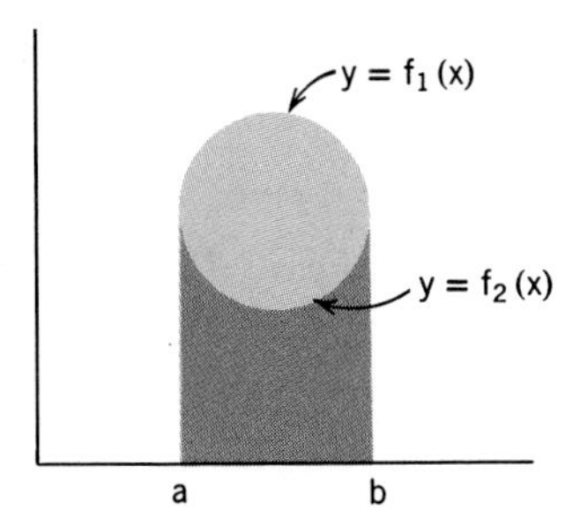

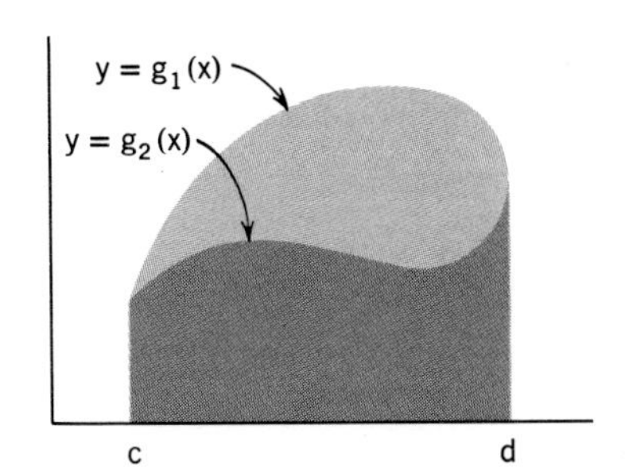

Figure 7-34 Suggesting ways to compute the area of a region by taking differences of areas.

Figure 7-35 shows three reproductions of this graph as it would appear on a sheet of graph paper with five squares between x = 1 and x = 2.

Since the region S is contained in the region R, which is in turn contained in V, we have, by property 2 of area, the inequalities

$$\text{area (S)} \leq \text{area (R)} \leq \text{area (V)}$$

Since S is composed of 13 little squares, each having (by property 5) the area $\frac{1}{5} \times \frac{1}{5} = \frac{1}{25}$, we see by property 3 that the area of S is $13 \times \frac{1}{25}$ and, similarly, the area of V is $21 \times \frac{1}{25}$. Thus we have firm upper and lower estimates for the area of R:

$$.52 = 13 \times \tfrac{1}{25} \leq \text{area (R)} \leq 21 \times \tfrac{1}{25} = .84$$

This method can be refined by drawing a larger picture, say, 10 divisions between 1 and 2 or 100 divisions. But we could hardly manage to estimate the area with accuracy to more than three decimal places (which would require counting almost a million little squares). In addition to being tedious, this method is not very instructive, relying as it

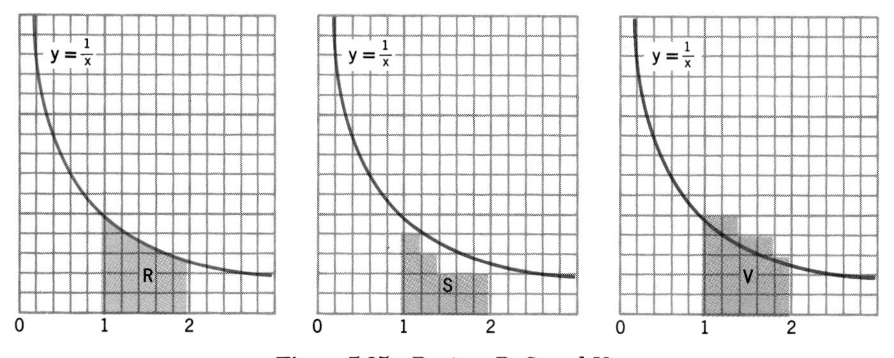

Figure 7-35 Regions R, S, and V.

does on accurate drawing, etc. Still, it serves as an introduction to the fundamental method we present next.

Using the same example, the area under the graph of $f(x) = 1/x$ between $x = 1$ and $x = 2$, we see in Figure 7-36 three pictures of the region under discussion.

In Figure 7-36*b* we see that a staircase-shaped region S has been inscribed in R, while in 7-36*c* we see R inscribed in another such staircase-shaped region. As before, application of property 2 shows that

$$\text{area (S)} \leq \text{area (R)} \leq \text{area (V)}$$

and application of properties 3 and 5 shows that the areas of S and V are each the sum of the areas of four rectangles given respectively by

$$\begin{aligned}
\text{area (S)} &= \tfrac{1}{4} \times f(\tfrac{5}{4}) + \tfrac{1}{4} \times f(\tfrac{3}{2}) + \tfrac{1}{4}f(\tfrac{7}{4}) + \tfrac{1}{4}f(2) \\
&= \tfrac{1}{4} \times (f(\tfrac{5}{4}) + f(\tfrac{3}{2}) + f(\tfrac{7}{4}) + f(2)) \\
&= \tfrac{1}{4} \times (\tfrac{4}{5} + \tfrac{2}{3} + \tfrac{4}{7} + \tfrac{1}{2}) \cong .634523 \\
\text{area (V)} &= \tfrac{1}{4} \times f(1) + \tfrac{1}{4} \times f(\tfrac{5}{4}) + \tfrac{1}{4} \times f(\tfrac{3}{4}) + \tfrac{1}{4} \times f(\tfrac{7}{4}) \\
&= \tfrac{1}{4} \times (f(1) + f(\tfrac{5}{4}) + f(\tfrac{3}{2}) + f(\tfrac{7}{4})) \\
&= \tfrac{1}{4} \times (1 + \tfrac{4}{5} + \tfrac{2}{3} + \tfrac{4}{7}) \cong .759523
\end{aligned}$$

Thus we have

$$.634523 \leq \text{area (R)} \leq .759523$$

Using the average of these upper and lower estimates as an approximation for the area (Figure 7-37), we have

$$|\text{area (R)} - .697023| \leq .0625$$

That is, when we use .697023 as an approximation for the area of R, the error cannot exceed $.0625 = 1/16$. (Actually, the error turns out to

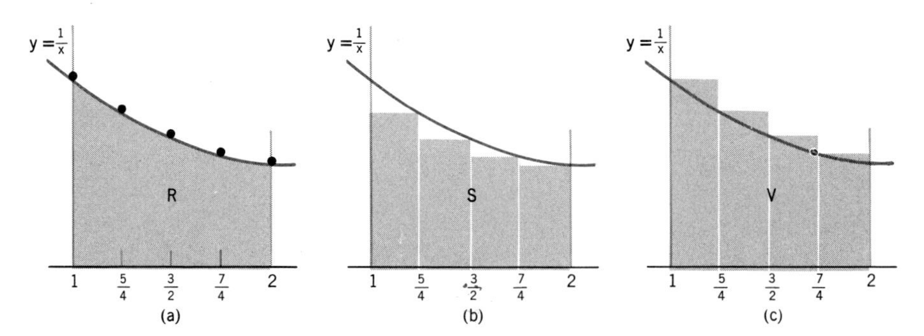

Figure 7-36 Regions R, S, and V revisited.

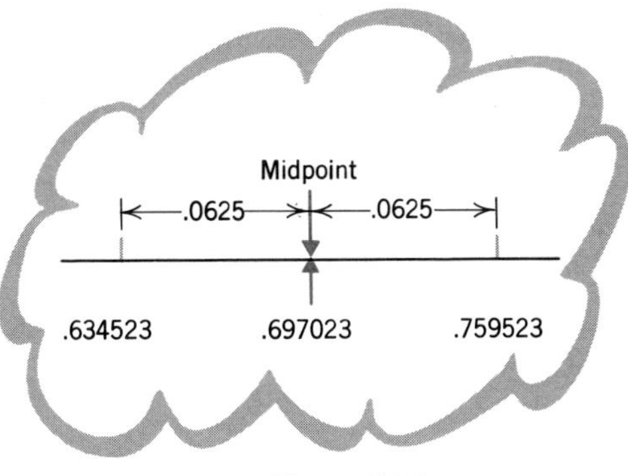

Figure 7-37

be about .0042. We will have something to say later on about why the error is so small.) If we divide the interval [1,2] into a large number of parts instead of just four, the error becomes much smaller.

The only property of the function $f(x) = 1/x$ that has been used in this presentation is the property that the functional values change monotonically as x increases. Our analysis then applies as well to any decreasing function with any interval [a,b] replacing [1,2].

In Figure 7-38 we see a decreasing function f over an interval [a,b] which is partitioned into four subintervals. The width of the subintervals, denoted by w, is $(b - a)/4$. The shaded areas in Figures 7-38*a* and 7-38*b* represent the upper and lower sums, U and L, which may be calculated as

$$U = w \times f(a) + w \times f(a + w) + w \times f(a + 2w) + w \times f(a + 3w)$$
$$L = w \times f(a + w) + w \times f(a + 2w) + w \times f(a + 3w) + w \times f(b)$$

and now

$$L \leq \text{area } (R) \leq U$$

The shaded area in Figure 7-38*c* represents the difference between U and L. It is because the function is decreasing that the rectangles in this figure can be "slid" horizontally without overlapping so as to just fit in a rectangle of width w and height $f(a) - f(b)$. That is,

$$U - L = w \times (f(a) - f(b))$$

If the average, T, of U and L,

$$T = \frac{U + L}{2}$$

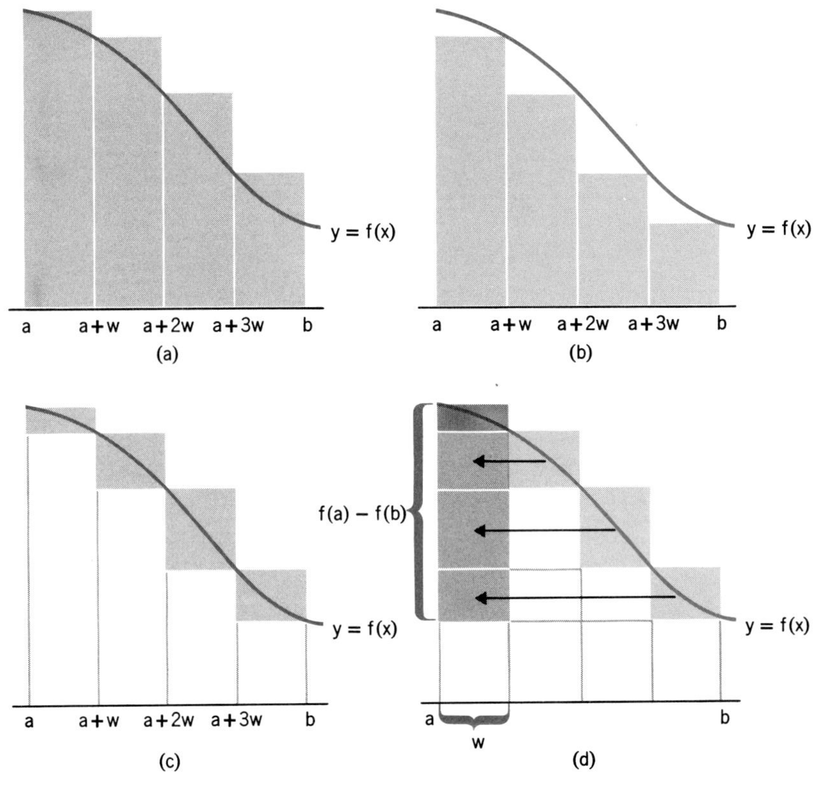

Figure 7-38 Four views of a decreasing function f(x) on the interval [a,b].

is used as an approximation to the area under f between a and b (Figure 7-39), then

$$|T - \text{area (R)}| \leq \frac{U - L}{2}$$

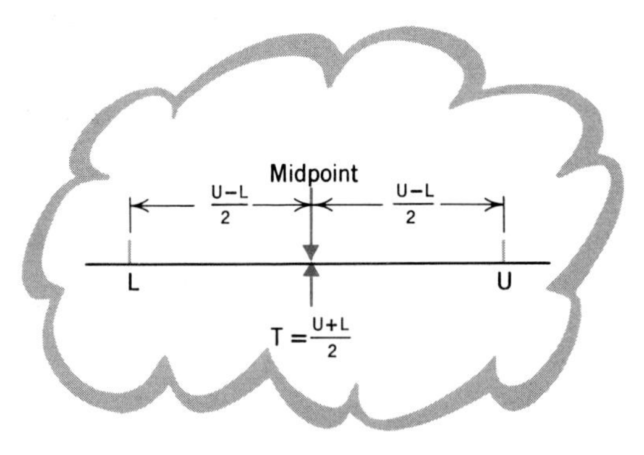

Figure 7-39

That is, the error in using $(U + L)/2$ as an approximation for the area under the curve cannot exceed $(U - L)/2 = w\times(f(a) - f(b))/2$.

Expressing the average $T = (U + L)/2$ in the form

$$T = \frac{U+L}{2} = w \times \frac{f(a) + f(a+w)}{2} + w \times \frac{f(a+w) + f(a+2w)}{2}$$

$$+ w \times \frac{f(a+2w) + f(a+3w)}{2} + w \times \frac{f(a+3w) + f(b)}{2}$$

we see that $(U + L)/2$ can be represented as the sum of the area of four trapezoids, as shown in Figure 7-40. For this reason, the method we have just developed for estimating areas is called the *trapezoid rule*.

We can see now that the error in using the area of the trapezoidal region is very small, much smaller than half the difference of U and L, the bound for the error calculated above and depicted in the preceding figure. A "tighter" bound for the error will be established in the next section.

For actual computing purposes, the calculation of the average $T = (U + L)/2$ is made in the following form:

$$\begin{array}{rl} U = & w \times [f(a) + f(a+w) + f(a+2w) + f(a+3w)] \\ L = & w \times [f(a+w) + f(a+2w) + f(a+3w) + f(b)] \\ \hline U + L = & w \times [f(a) + 2f(a+w) + 2f(a+2w) + 2f(a+3w) + f(b)] \end{array}$$

$$T = \frac{U+L}{2}$$

$$= w \times \left[\frac{f(a) + f(b)}{2} + f(a+w) + f(a+2w) + f(a+3w)\right]$$

$$= w \times \left[\frac{f(a) + f(b)}{2} + \sum_{k=1}^{3} f(a + k\times w)\right]$$

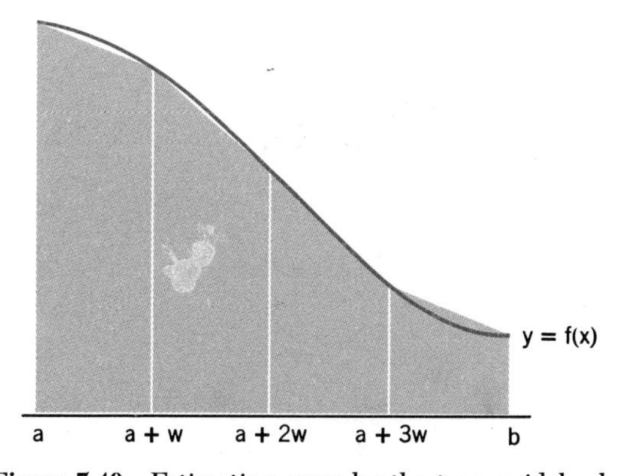

Figure 7-40 Estimating areas by the trapezoidal rule.

All this was done for four partitions of the interval [a,b]. If, say, n partitions of the interval are used, then the calculations must be modified to take the form

$$T = \frac{U + L}{2} = w \times \left[\frac{f(a) + f(b)}{2} + \sum_{k=1}^{n-1} f(a + k \times w)\right]$$

where

$$w = \frac{b - a}{n}$$

and the bound for the error is

$$|T - \text{area }(R)| \leq \frac{U - L}{2} = w \times \frac{|f(a) - f(b)|}{2}$$

Taking the absolute value of f(a) − f(b) makes the error estimate valid for increasing functions as well as for decreasing functions, as the reader may easily verify.

Flowcharting the Algorithm

We are given a *monotone* (that is, either increasing or decreasing) function, f, two "endpoints," a and b, and an error tolerance, EPS. We are to construct a flow chart for computing an approximation with error guaranteed to be less than EPS. The necessary formulas have all been developed in the preceding discussion. Recalling the basic formula for the area calculation,

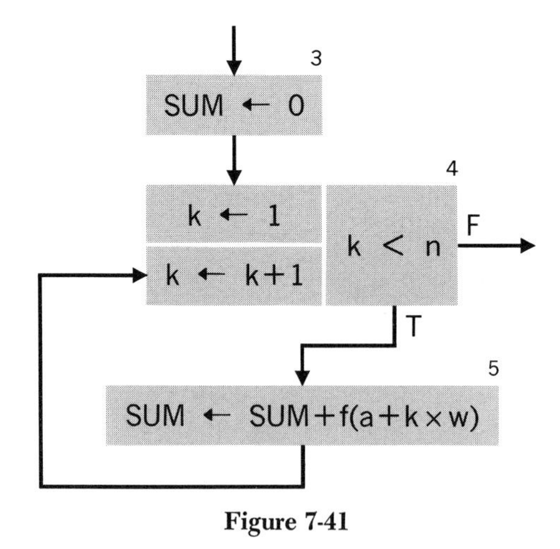

Figure 7-41

$$T = w \times \left[\frac{f(a)+f(b)}{2} + \sum_{k=1}^{n-1} f(a+k \times w)\right]$$

we can easily single out the iterative computation that forms the heart of our calculation:

$$\sum_{k=1}^{n-1} f(a+k \times w)$$

Flowcharting such a sum is by now a familiar process for us. The flowchart fragment is seen in Figure 7-41. The complete computation of the area approximation, which we will call TRAP, for trapezoid rule requires only one more box (Figure 7-42). The preliminary assignment of values to the variables n and w will essentially complete our task. Recalling the formulas for interval width and error bound

$$w = \frac{b-a}{n} \quad \text{and} \quad w \times \frac{|f(b)-f(a)|}{2} < EPS$$

we combine them to find

$$\frac{b-a}{n} \times \frac{|f(b)-f(a)|}{2} < EPS$$

or

$$n > \frac{(b-a) \times |f(b)-f(a)|}{2 \times EPS}$$

Since n must be an integer, we use the CHOP function and make the

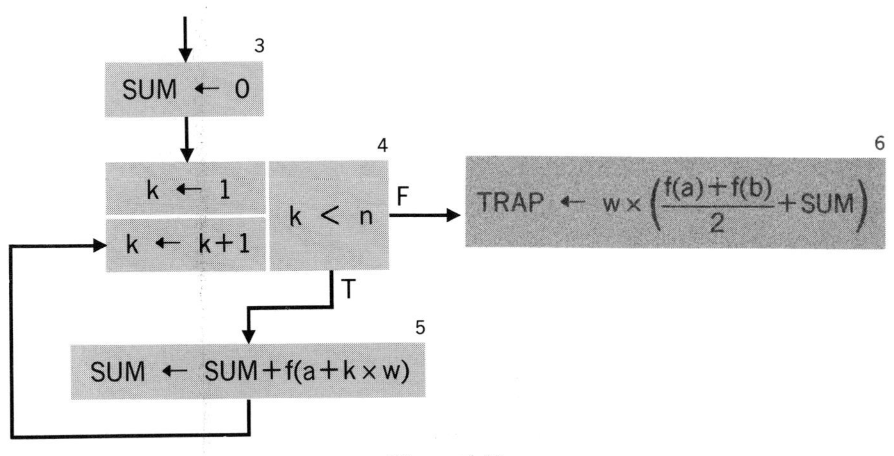

Figure 7-42

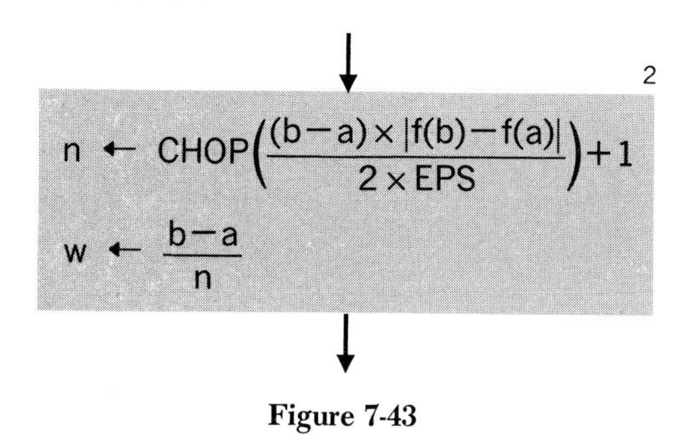

Figure 7-43

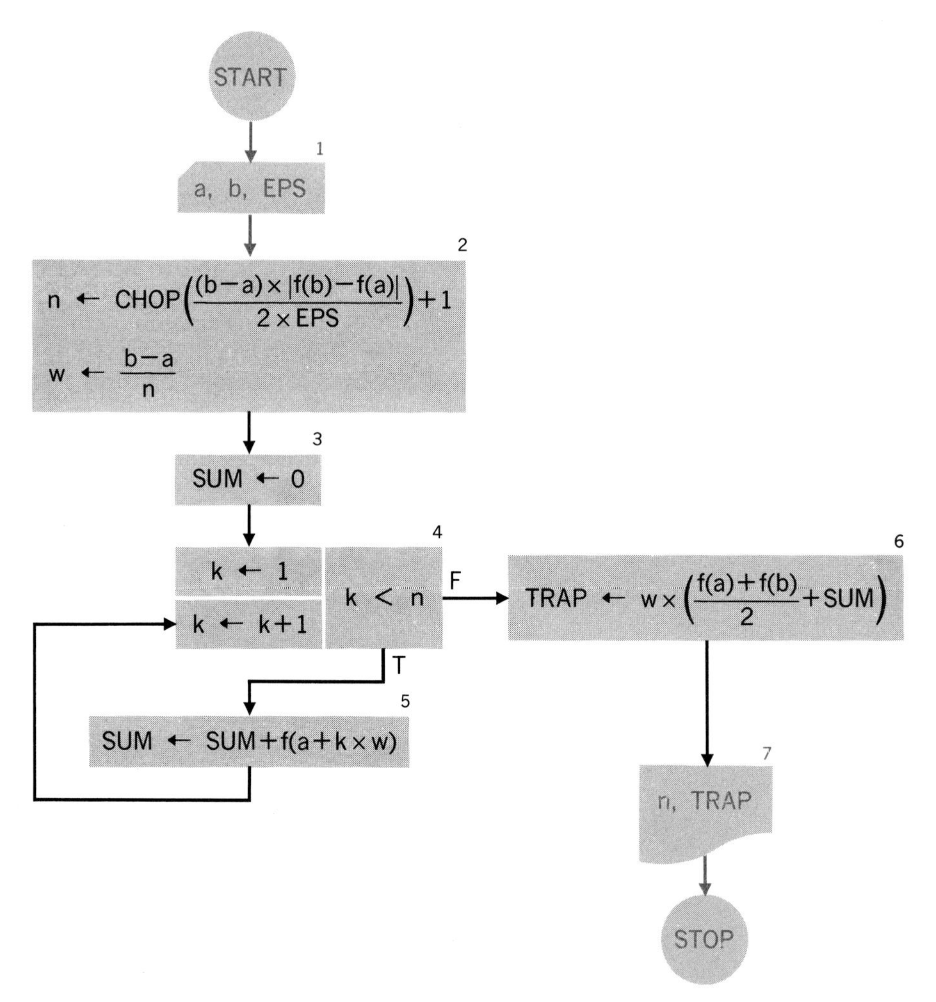

Figure 7-44 Using the trapezoid rule to approximate area under a monotone function on the interval [a,b].

assignments (Figure 7-43). Only input and output remain; our completed flow chart is shown in Figure 7-44.

As with all important algorithms, no sooner do we construct them than we search for improvements and embellishments. Now our plan is to construct a flow chart that will compute the trapezoidal area approximations with 1, 2, 4, 8, 16, . . . etc. subintervals, stopping when our calculated error bound is less than an input value EPS. This flow chart, shown in Figure 7-45, contains a number of subtleties. You should try to study it and see why it works. The portions shown in rust are the main points of difference from Figure 7-44. Try to explain them all. If you have difficulties, the problems at the end of this section may be helpful. Which of the two algorithms do you think is better? Why?

EXERCISES 7-3

1. For the areas described below, calculate approximations following the steps of the flow chart of Figure 7-45.

   (a) Below $y = x^2$, above the x-axis, between $x = 2$ and $x = 4$. Use $\epsilon = 1.0$. (True area is 56/3.)
   (b) Below $y = x^3$, above $y = x^2$, between $x = 1$ and $x = 4$. Use $\epsilon = 10$. (True area is 171/4.)

2. Modify Figure 7-45 to approximate the value of π to four decimal places.

3. The number x, for which $\ln x = 1$, is a very important mathematical constant on a par with π. This constant is designated by the letter e. It is interesting that we now have a method at our disposal (although not the best one) for computing the value of e. This method is based on the fact that e is the root of

$$\ln x - 1 = 0$$

Thus, if we can prepare a flow chart that will compute the values of $\ln x - 1$ to, say, six decimal places, we can then apply the procedure ZERO to find this root. Use the fact that the area under the curve $y = 1/x$ for the interval $(1, x)$ is $\ln x$.

Make the necessary revisions in the flow chart of Figure 7-45 to convert it into a functional reference flow chart for $f(x) = \ln x - 1$. You will have to decide what to do about a, b, ϵ, and f occurring in Figure 7-45. The main flow chart, which calls on ZERO, will involve the use of some preliminary estimates of the interval in which the root lies.

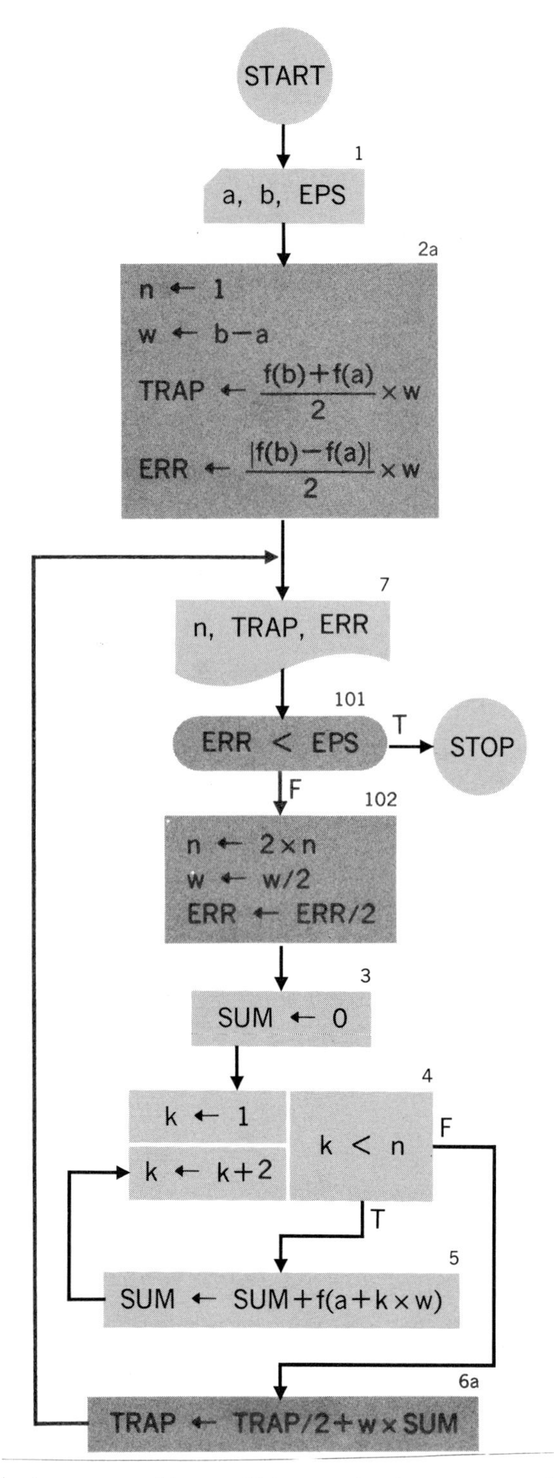

Figure 7-45 A sequence of trapezoidal approximations to area under a curve.

PROBLEM 7-3

One potential weakness of the algorithm in Figure 7-45 should be observed. If EPS is made very small for the purpose of gaining a very accurate result, there is a corresponding increase in the number of terms that must be added to the sum (in box 5). If the number of terms to be added is very large, the resulting round-off error of the kind described in Section 5-4 may reduce rather than increase the accuracy of the result. Your job in this problem is to improve the Figure 7-45 flow chart by applying the batch-adding technique described in Figure 5-4.

7-4 CONVEX FUNCTIONS, THE MIDPOINT RULE, AND REDUCTION OF ERROR ESTIMATES FOR COMPUTED AREAS

A function is said to be *convex* provided that whenever we choose two points on its graph and draw the chord joining them, then, between these two points the graph of the function lies below the chord. The function is said to be *concave* if the graph always lies above the chord. We see these ideas illustrated in Figure 7-46.

We will deal here with convex functions although our final conclusions will hold for concave functions as well.

For functions where graphs are unbroken curves, it is adequate to prove that for every chord, at the midpoint of the chord, the graph lies below the chord (Figure 7-47). In other words, it suffices for convexity to show that for every choice of a and b we have

$$f\left(\frac{a + b}{2}\right) \leq \frac{f(a) + f(b)}{2}$$

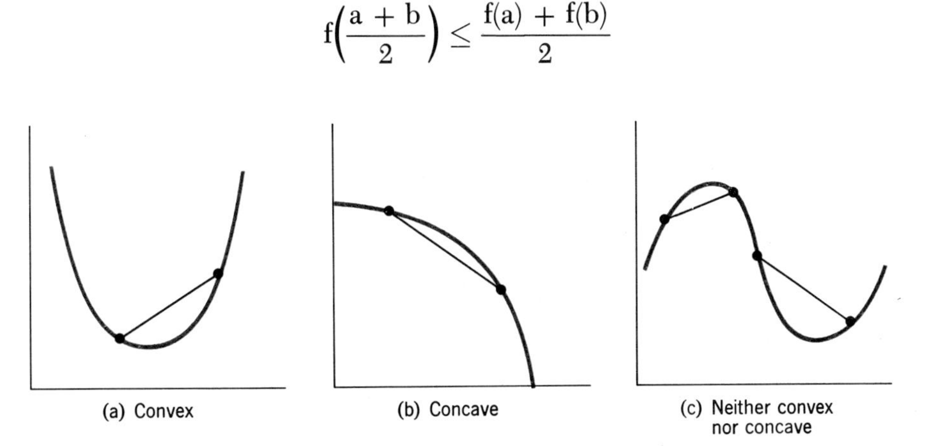

Figure 7-46 Three types of functions.

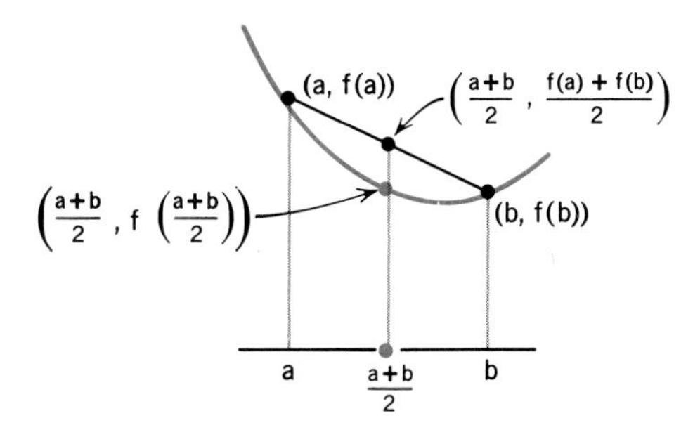

Figure 7-47 Midpoint of the function lies below the chord.

To put it still another way, we can say that the function is convex if the process of first averaging a and b and then applying the function produces smaller results than first applying the function to a and b and then averaging.

Using this criterion to establish convexity is usually quite tricky. (Calculus provides much more routine methods.) We illustrate with one example.

Example. Show that the function

$$f(x) = \frac{1}{x} \qquad x > 0$$

is convex.

Solution. We need to show that for all positive numbers a and b

$$\frac{1}{\frac{a+b}{2}} \leq \frac{\frac{1}{a} + \frac{1}{b}}{2}$$

or, equivalently, that

$$\frac{\frac{1}{a} + \frac{1}{b}}{2} - \frac{1}{\frac{a+b}{2}} \geq 0$$

We start out with the usual algebraic steps involved in simplifying the expression on the left. Thus,

$$\frac{\frac{1}{a}+\frac{1}{b}}{2} - \frac{1}{\frac{a+b}{2}} = \frac{\frac{b+a}{ab}}{2} - \frac{2}{a+b}$$

$$= \frac{b+a}{2ab} - \frac{2}{a+b}$$

$$= \frac{(a+b)^2 - 4ab}{2ab(a+b)}$$

$$= \frac{a^2 + 2ab + b^2 - 4ab}{2ab(a+b)}$$

$$= \frac{a^2 - 2ab + b^2}{2ab(a+b)}$$

$$= \frac{(a-b)^2}{2ab(a+b)}$$

$$\geq 0 \quad \text{as desired}$$

The reason for the final conclusion is that the denominator is positive, since a and b are both > 0, while the numerator (being a square) is non-negative. In fact, we can assert that the *in*equality holds here unless $a = b$.

For many curves the convexity may be difficult to establish in this way although it is geometrically quite obvious.

Returning to the area under a curve, we now present another method of approximation called the "midpoint rule."

In using this method we (1) subdivide the interval as before and (2) construct over each subinterval a rectangle whose height is the functional value at the midpoint of the subinterval. In the case shown in Figure 7-48, the sum of the areas of the rectangles can be expressed as

$$M = w \times f(a + \tfrac{1}{2}w) + w \times f(a + \tfrac{3}{2}w) + w \times f(a + \tfrac{5}{2}w)$$

$$= w \times \sum_{k=1}^{3} f(a + (k - \tfrac{1}{2}) \times w)$$

In general, this formula will take the form

$$M = w \times \sum_{k=1}^{n} f(a + (k - \tfrac{1}{2}) \times w)$$

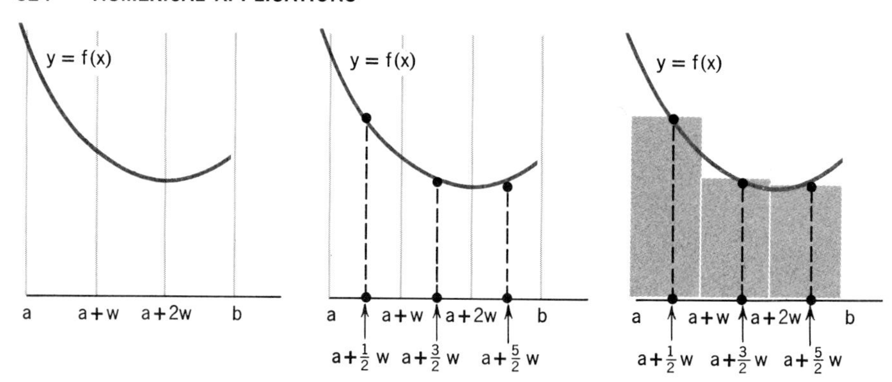

Figure 7-48 Constructing rectangles over each subinterval.

where n is the number of subintervals and

$$w = \frac{b - a}{n}$$

is the common width of the subintervals.

Let us now focus our attention on one of these midpoint rectangles. We can see that if we pivot the top edge of the rectangle about its center, the rectangle is replaced by a trapezoid having the same area as the rectangle. (We can see in Figure 7-49*b*, using congruent triangles, that the area "lost" on the left is exactly balanced by the area "gained" on the right.) And in Figure 7-49*c* we see the top edge pivoted so as to lie entirely below the graph of the function. (This is always possible for *convex functions,* although we will not attempt to prove it here.)

Now we can see, as illustrated in Figure 7-50, that for a convex function, f, the midpoint rule gives approximations that are *less* than the actual area under the curve, while the trapezoid rule gives approximation *greater* than the area under the curve. Thus, we find that, in the case

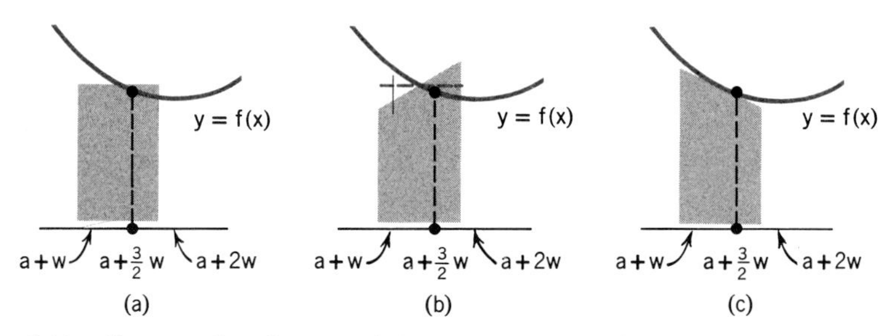

Figure 7-49 Showing that the area of the rectangle is less than the area under the curve.

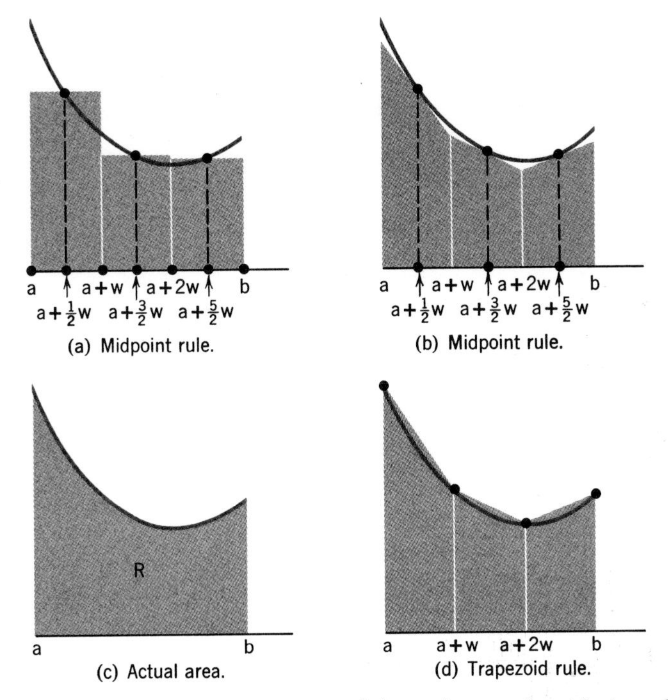

Figure 7-50 Comparing the approximations of the midpoint rule with that of the trapezoidal rule.

of convex functions,

$$M \leq \text{area}(R) \leq T$$

where M and T represent the *m*idpoint and *t*rapezoidal areas respectively. In the case of concave functions, we would have

$$T \leq \text{area}(R) \leq M$$

In either case, using $(M + T)/2$ as an approximation for the area of R, the error will be less than $|T - M|/2$. As we saw in Section 7-3,

$$\left|\text{area}(R) - \frac{M + T}{2}\right| \leq \frac{|T - M|}{2}$$

None of this analysis requires that the function f be strictly increasing or decreasing over the interval [a,b].

To see how much better the $|T - M|/2$ estimates of error are than the $|U - L|/2$ estimates of Section 7-3, we may compare them graphically for the example, $f(x) = \dfrac{1}{x}$ on the interval (1,2). (Figure 7-51).

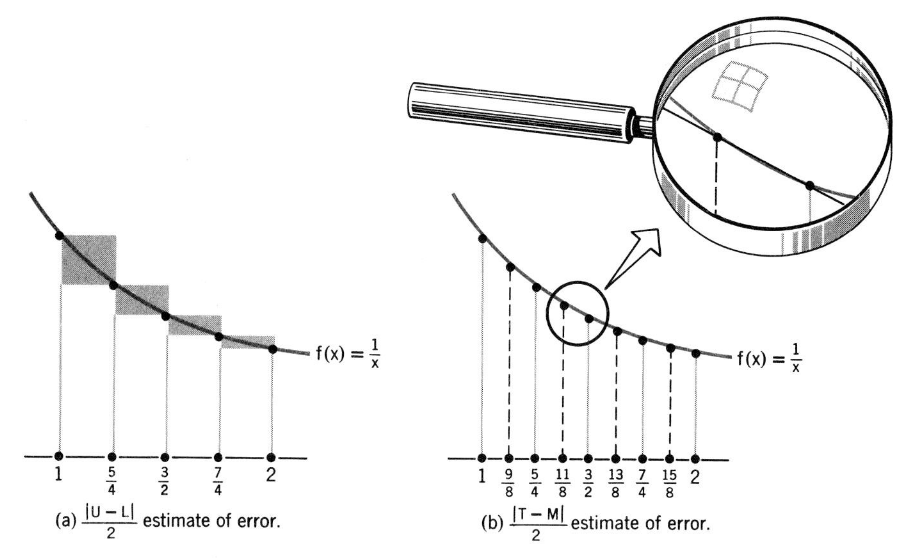

Figure 7-51 Comparing methods for estimating error in computed area.

The error bound for the trapezoid formula calculated in the preceding section was half the shaded area in Figure 7-51*a*. The error bound as calculated in this section is represented by half the shaded area in Figure 7-51*b*, which lies so close to the curve as to be hardly discernible by eye.

Calculating these approximations and estimates by hand, we find that

$$T = \frac{1}{4} \times \left(\frac{f(1) + f(2)}{2} + f\left(\frac{5}{4}\right) + f\left(\frac{3}{2}\right) + f\left(\frac{7}{4}\right)\right)$$

$$= \frac{1}{4} \times \left(\frac{1 + \frac{1}{2}}{2} + \frac{4}{5} + \frac{2}{3} + \frac{4}{7}\right) \cong .697024$$

$$M = \frac{1}{4} \times \left(f\left(\frac{9}{8}\right) + f\left(\frac{11}{8}\right) + f\left(\frac{13}{8}\right) + f\left(\frac{15}{8}\right)\right)$$

$$= \frac{1}{4} \times \left(\frac{8}{9} + \frac{8}{11} + \frac{8}{13} + \frac{8}{15}\right) \cong .691220$$

$$\frac{M + T}{2} \cong .694122$$

Now we calculate and compare two error bounds: the error bound from the preceding section,

$$\left|\text{area (R)} - \left(\frac{U + L}{2}\right)\right| \leq \frac{w}{2} \times |f(a) - f(b)| = \frac{1}{16} = .0625$$

and the error bound from this section,

$$\left|\text{area (R)} - \left(\frac{T + M}{2}\right)\right| \leq \frac{|T - M|}{2} \cong \frac{.697024 - .691220}{2} = .002922$$

The comparison becomes even more striking when very fine schemes of subdivision of the intervals are used.

We remark but will not attempt to justify that the weighted average of M and T

$$\tfrac{2}{3}M + \tfrac{1}{3}T$$

gives remarkably better results than the ordinary average

$$\tfrac{1}{2}M + \tfrac{1}{2}T$$

which we have used here. This two-third, one-third rule for approximating areas is called "Simpson's rule." In the above example, Simpson's rule gives .693189 as the approximate area, as compared with the actual value .693147 . . . , and so gives an error $< .00005$.

The reader can verify that the average $(M + T)/2$ is exactly the result of the trapezoid formula with twice as many partition points. Thus, the error estimate $|T - M|/2$ becomes an error estimate for the trapezoid rule with twice as many partition points. These observations are reflected in the flow chart of Figure 7-52.

This flow chart computes approximations for the area under the graph by TRAPezoid, MIDpoint, and SIMPson rules and calculates the ERRor bound established above for the trapezoid rule. The computation is performed for $n = 1, 2, 4, 8, \ldots$, etc. The process stops when the value of ERR is less than the input value of EPS. No further explanation is given, except for the following. The value assigned to ERR in box 2 is arbitrarily chosen to allow us to pass safely through box 8. The subsequent assignments to ERR in box 9 are genuine error bounds calculated according to the preceding analysis. Now you should be able to study and understand it on the basis of the discussion in this section.

In the case that our functions are not convex or concave over the entire interval, the error analysis given above will not apply. However, the interval can, in general, be divided into subintervals of convexity and concavity (Figure 7-53) so that the approximations yielded by these methods almost always will be very good even though we are not able (without the aid of calculus) to give bonafide bounds for our error.

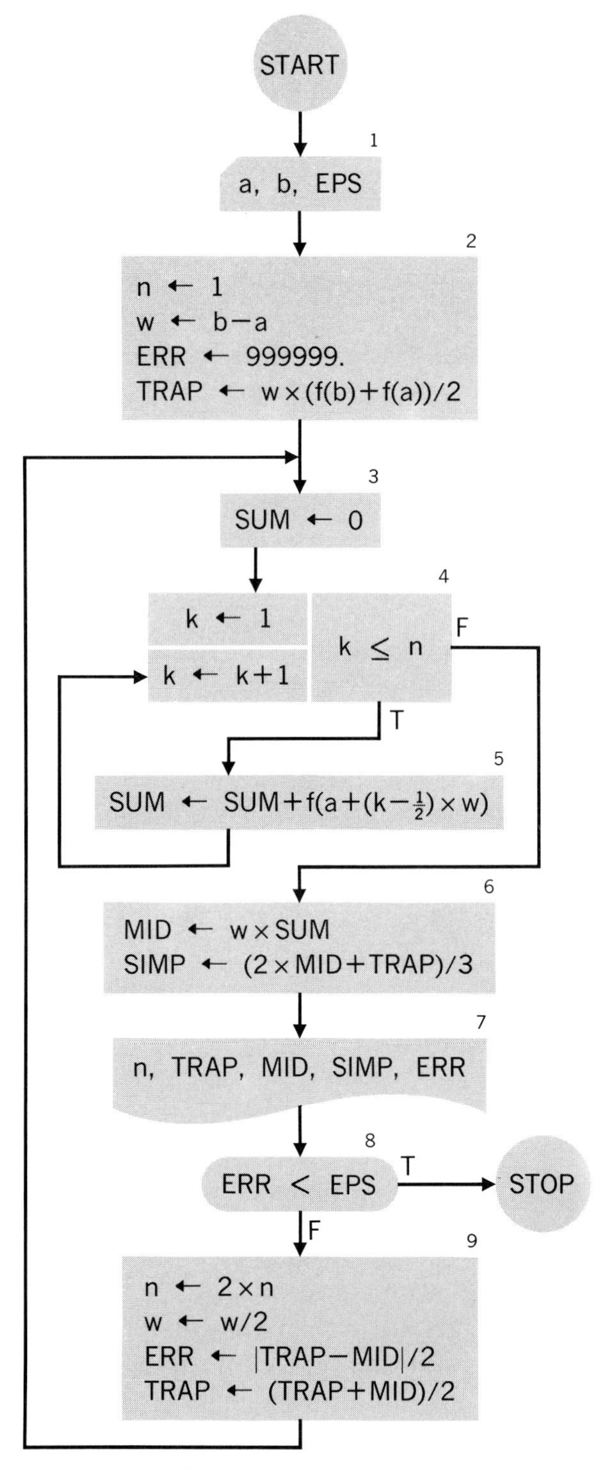

Figure 7-52 Approximations of area using the trapezoid, midpoint, and Simpson rules, by means of successive bisection of the interval [a,b].

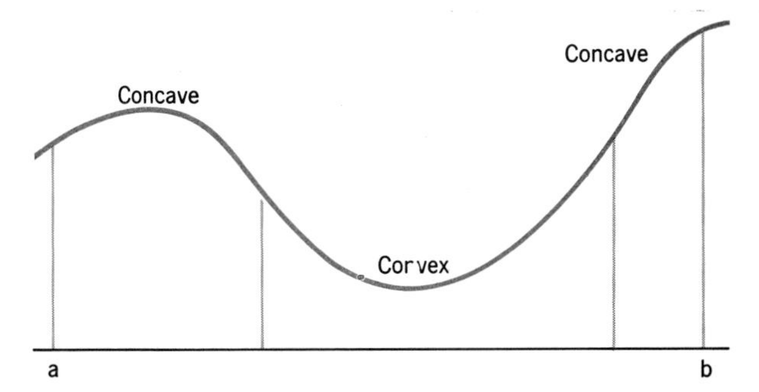

Figure 7-53 Showing how to subdivide an interval into concave and convex subintervals.

EXERCISES 7-4

1. Prove that $f(x) = x^2$ is convex.
2. Prove that $f(x) = x^3$ is:

   (a) Convex for $x \geq 0$.
   (b) Concave for $x \leq 0$.

3. Letting T_n and M_n represent the trapezoidal and midpoint approximations for the area under a curve where the interval [a,b] is partitioned into n subintervals:

   (a) Give an illustrative example of the formula

$$T_{2n} = \frac{T_n + M_n}{2}$$

   for a specific function, f, and a particular interval [a,b] of your choosing.
   (b) Prove this formula for the specific evample chosen.

4. In the flow chart of Figure 7-52:

   (a) Explain the role of the variable SUM occurring in boxes 3, 5, and 6.
   (b) Explain the assignments in box 9.

5. Write a computer program for the flow chart of Figure 7-52 and run it with $f(x) = 1/x$ and:

   (a) [a,b] = [1,2]
   (b) [a,b] = [2,4]
   (c) [a,b] = [5,10]

Compare the output from these calculations. Does this motivate you to a guess or conjecture of some mathematical fact? Can you explain the phenomenon which occurs? In all cases, use an EPS in the range .0001 to .0000001 depending on the word length of your computer.

6. Obtain an approximation of π by an application of the algorithm in Figure 7-52. Choose an appropriate function and an interval as suggested by the circle arc illustrated here.

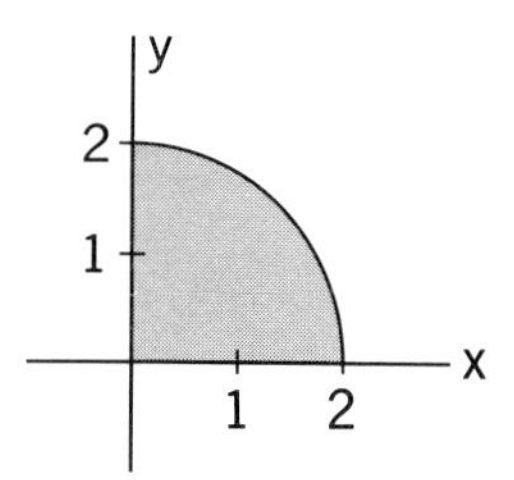

7. The function $f(x) = 4/(1 + x^2)$ is neither convex nor concave over the entire interval [0,1]. Thus, our error estimates don't work. Nevertheless, the errors are very small. Use your program for the flow chart of Figure 7-52 to compute the area under this curve between 0 and 1. On the basis of your output, make a guess as to the exact value of this area.

CHAPTER 8

MORE MATHEMATICAL APPLICATIONS

8-1 SIMULTANEOUS LINEAR EQUATIONS

Introduction: Solution by Graphing

You have often solved systems of two equations. You may have also solved systems of three or even four simultaneous linear equations. In many problems of science, engineering, business, politics, etc., it is necessary to solve systems of simultaneous linear equations involving very large numbers of variables and equations, perhaps as many as 10,000 equations involving 10,000 variables. It is therefore important to study the problem of solving systems of linear equations and to devise efficient methods for solving such systems.

You will recall that the problem of solving two simultaneous linear equations in x and y can be interpreted geometrically. Thus, an equation such as

$$3x - 4y = 12$$

represents a straight line that can be plotted on a set of xy-axes. Another equation such as

$$4x + 12y + 23 = 0$$

also represents a straight line. If we are asked to solve these equations simultaneously, then we are seeking values of x and y which satisfy both equations at the same time. Geometrically, this means that the point whose coordinates are these values of x and y lies on both lines and, hence, is their intersection. The graphs of these two lines are shown in Figure 8-1. We see that the lines intersect in the point $(1, -9/4)$ and thus $x = 1$, $y = -9/4$ is the solution of this pair of equations.

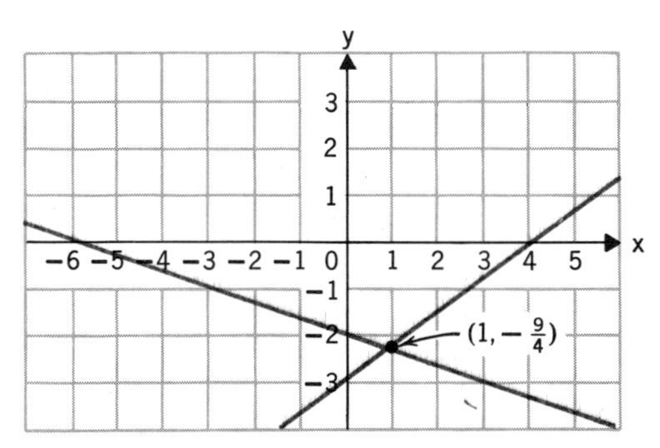

Figure 8-1 Graphs of $3x - 4y = 12$ and $4x + 12y + 23 = 0$.

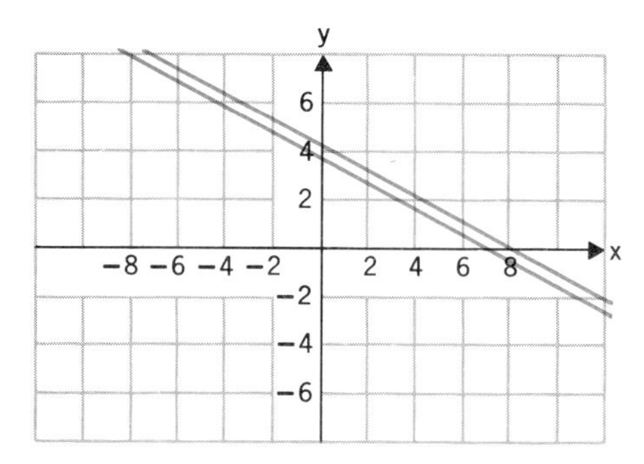

Figure 8-2 Graphs of $x + 2y = 7$ and $x + 2y = 8$.

We know that two lines always intersect in exactly one point unless they are parallel or are really the same line. Thus, two simultaneous linear equations also have exactly one solution unless they represent parallel lines or the same line. If the lines are parallel, there is no solution. For example, the equations

$$\begin{aligned} x + 2y &= 7 \\ x + 2y &= 8 \end{aligned}$$

represent parallel lines and, hence, have no solution. This situation is shown in Figure 8-2.

On the other hand, the equations

$$\begin{aligned} x + 2y &= 7 \\ 2x + 4y &= 14 \end{aligned}$$

have infinitely many solutions since they are really the same line, namely, the lower line of Figure 8-2.

In other words, multiplying every term of a linear equation by the same constant (not zero) does not change the graph of that equation.

We next discuss a principle that provides the basis for our method of solution of systems of equations. Suppose we start with a system of equations representing the two intersecting lines given in Figure 8-1:

$$\begin{aligned} \ell_1: &\quad 3x - 4y = 12 \\ \ell_2: &\quad 4x + 12y = -23 \end{aligned}$$

Next, suppose we multiply the first equation through by -3 and the second by 2 and add, as displayed on the top of the next page.

$$
① \left[\begin{array}{r|rcl} -3 & 3x - 4y & = & 12 \\ 2 & 4x + 12y & = & -23 \\ \hline \ell_3: & -x + 36y & = & -82 \end{array} \right.
$$

In this way, we obtain the equation of a third line, ℓ_3. What relationship, if any, does this line have to the original lines ℓ_1 and ℓ_2? It turns out that this line also passes through the point of intersection of ℓ_1 and ℓ_2, as shown in Figure 8-3.

We can show that ℓ_3 passes through the point of intersection of ℓ_1 and ℓ_2 by performing the operations in ① in a slightly different way.

$$
② \left[\begin{array}{r|l} -3 & 3x - 4y = 12 \\ 2 & 4x + 12y = -23 \\ \hline \multicolumn{2}{l}{-3 \times (3x - 4y) + 2 \times (4x + 12y) = -3 \times 12 + 2 \times (-23)} \end{array} \right.
$$

(After simplification, this latter equation reduces to the one obtained above for ℓ_3.) Now suppose that the coordinates of the point of intersection of ℓ_1 and ℓ_2 are substituted into the left-hand side of the equation that results from the operations in ②. Since this point lies on ℓ_1, we see that the value of the first expression in parentheses will be 12, and since this point lies on ℓ_2, the value of the second expression in parentheses will be -23. Thus, when the coordinates of the point of intersection of ℓ_1 and ℓ_2 are substituted in the left-hand side of the equation developed in ②, that expression has the value

$$
-3 \times 12 + 2 \times (-23)
$$

In other words, the equation developed in ② is satisfied by the point of intersection of ℓ_1 and ℓ_2.

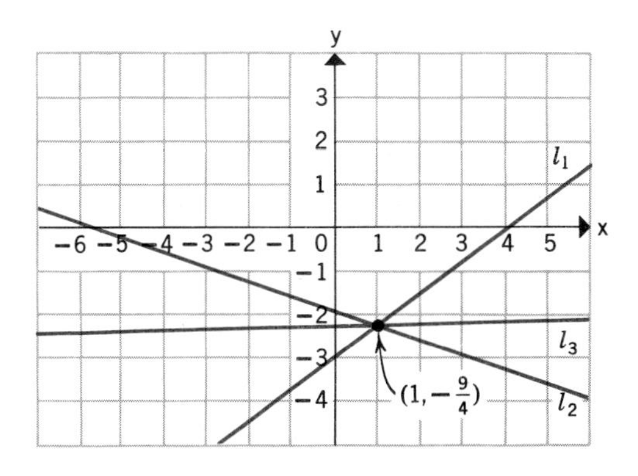

Figure 8-3 ℓ_3 also passes through the point of intersection of ℓ_1 and ℓ_2.

This means then that the pair of equations (that is, one of the original equations and the new equation)

$$\begin{aligned} \ell_1: &\quad 3x - 4y = 12 \\ \ell_3: &\quad -x + 36y = -82 \end{aligned}$$

has the same solution as the original pair

$$\begin{aligned} \ell_1: &\quad 3x - 4y = 12 \\ \ell_2: &\quad 4x + 12y = -23 \end{aligned}$$

We express this fact by saying that these two pairs of equations are *equivalent.* Of course, there was nothing special about the multipliers -3 and $+2$. The same conclusions hold for any pair of multipliers (so long as the multiplier of the equation we *replace* is not zero).

When the multipliers are chosen appropriately, the resulting pair of equivalent equations can be brought into a form particularly easy to solve. Thus,

$$\begin{array}{r|l} -\frac{4}{3} & 3x - 4y = 12 \\ 1 & 4x + 12y = -23 \\ \hline & 0 \cdot x + 17\frac{1}{3}y = -39 \end{array}$$

so that the original pair of equations may be replaced by

$$\begin{aligned} 3x - 4y &= 12 \\ 17\tfrac{1}{3}y &= -39 \end{aligned}$$

This pair of equations may be solved by first solving the second for y,

$$y = -\tfrac{9}{4}$$

and then substituting this value for y in the first equation and solving this for x,

$$\begin{aligned} 3x - 4 \cdot (-\tfrac{9}{4}) &= 12 \\ x &= 1 \end{aligned}$$

so that the solution of the given system of equations is

$$(1, -\tfrac{9}{4})$$

The secret of our success here lies in bringing our system of equations into "triangular" form:

$$\begin{aligned} 3x - 4y &= 12 \\ 4x + 12y &= -23 \end{aligned} \quad \Rightarrow \quad \begin{aligned} 3x - 4y &= 12 \\ 17\tfrac{1}{3}y &= -39 \end{aligned}$$

The same method can be applied to systems of three equations in three unknowns where we start with a system like the one on the left below and work toward an equivalent system having the triangular form seen on the right.

$$\begin{aligned} 3x + 2y + 7z &= 4 \\ 2x + 3y + z &= 5 \\ 3x + 4y + z &= 7 \end{aligned} \quad \Rightarrow \quad \begin{aligned} c_1x + c_2y + c_3z &= d_1 \\ c_4y + c_5z &= d_2 \\ c_6z &= d_3 \end{aligned}$$

The steps are shown below.

STEP-BY-STEP ANALYSIS OF GAUSS ELIMINATION PROCESS

Step 1. To the second equation, add $-\frac{2}{3}$ times the first equation.

$$-\tfrac{2}{3} \quad \begin{aligned} 3x + 2y + 7z &= 4 \\ 2x + 3y + z &= 5 \\ 3x + 4y + z &= 7 \end{aligned}$$

Step 2. To the third equation, add $-\frac{3}{3}$ $(= -1)$ times the first equation.

$$-1 \quad \begin{aligned} 3x + 2y + 7z &= 4 \\ 0x + \tfrac{5}{3}y - \tfrac{11}{3}z &= \tfrac{7}{3} \\ 3x + 4y + z &= 7 \end{aligned}$$

Step 3. To the third equation, add $-\dfrac{2}{\frac{5}{3}} \left(= -\dfrac{6}{5}\right)$ times the second equation.

$$-\tfrac{6}{5} \quad \begin{aligned} 3x + 2y + 7z &= 4 \\ 0x + \tfrac{5}{3}y - \tfrac{11}{3}z &= \tfrac{7}{3} \\ 0x + 2y - 6z &= 3 \end{aligned}$$

$$\begin{aligned} 3x + 2y + 7z &= 4 \\ 0x + \tfrac{5}{3}y - \tfrac{11}{3}z &= \tfrac{7}{3} \\ 0x + 0y - \tfrac{8}{5}z &= \tfrac{1}{5} \end{aligned}$$

Finally, we perform the "back solution":

$$\begin{aligned} -\tfrac{8}{5}z = \tfrac{1}{5} &\Rightarrow z = -\tfrac{5}{8}(\tfrac{1}{5}) = -\tfrac{1}{8} \\ \tfrac{5}{3}y - \tfrac{11}{3}z = \tfrac{7}{3} &\Rightarrow y = \tfrac{3}{5}(\tfrac{7}{3} + \tfrac{11}{3}z) = \tfrac{3}{5}(\tfrac{7}{3} + \tfrac{11}{3}(-\tfrac{1}{8})) = \tfrac{9}{8} \\ 3x + 2y + 7z = 4 &\Rightarrow x = \tfrac{1}{3}(4 - 2y - 7z) \\ &\qquad = \tfrac{1}{3}(4 - 2(\tfrac{9}{8}) - 7(-\tfrac{1}{8})) = \tfrac{7}{8} \end{aligned}$$

Flowcharting the Solution

We can see that the process just performed involves repetitions of the same kinds of steps and, thus, it should be possible to flowchart it. First, we write the general system of three equations in three unknowns in the form:

$$a_{11}x_1 + a_{12}x_2 + a_{13}x_3 = b_1$$
$$a_{21}x_1 + a_{22}x_2 + a_{23}x_3 = b_2$$
$$a_{31}x_1 + a_{32}x_2 + a_{33}x_3 = b_3$$

It is convenient to denote the variables in the equations as x_1, x_2, and x_3, instead of x, y, and z, in order that we can employ looping in the "back solution."

This system provides an especially profitable use of double subscripts. The first subscript on any a_{ij} denotes the equation in which the coeffi-

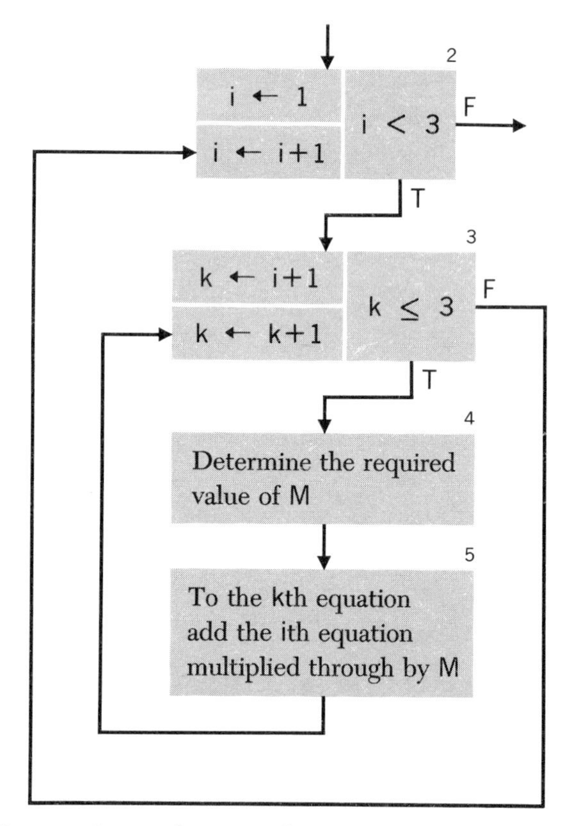

Figure 8-4 Schematic showing how to reduce the set of three equations to triangular form.

cient appears, and the second subscript identifies its position in the equation. The subscripted variable a_{ij} will be used to denote the coefficients of our x_i's throughout the computing process, but the value of an entry will often change from step to step.

In order to start building this flow chart we summarize Steps 1, 2, and 3.

Step 1. (a) Determine the required value of the multiplier M.
(b) To the second equation, add the first equation multiplied through by M.

Step 2. (a) Determine the required value of the multiplier M.
(b) To the third equation, add the first equation multiplied through by M.

Step 3. (a) Determine the required value of the multiplier M.
(b) To the third equation, add the second equation multiplied through by M.

The instructions *a* and *b* need be written only once if we introduce the nested loop shown in Figure 8-4.

In fact, we can make a schematic flow chart for our entire solution process, as shown in Figure 8-5.

It remains only to break down boxes 4, 5, 8, and 13 of this schematic flow chart into their arithmetic components.

Let's start with box 5, "to the kth equation add the ith equation, multiplied through by M. This can be thought of as reassigning values to the coefficients in the kth equation, as follows:

$$a_{k1} \leftarrow a_{k1} + M \cdot a_{i1}$$
$$a_{k2} \leftarrow a_{k2} + M \cdot a_{i2}$$
$$a_{k3} \leftarrow a_{k3} + M \cdot a_{i3}$$
$$b_k \leftarrow b_k + M \cdot b_i$$

These assignments (for a suitable value of M) can be condensed as shown in Figure 8-6.

And how are these suitable values of M to be determined? Well, when to equation 2 we added equation 1 multiplied through by M, the purpose was to assign zero as the new value of a_{21}, etc. A tabulation of these "purposes" is in Table 8-1. In short, when we added M times equation i to equation k, the purpose was to assign 0 as the new value of a_{ki} in the assignment

$$a_{ki} \leftarrow a_{ki} + M \cdot a_{ii}$$

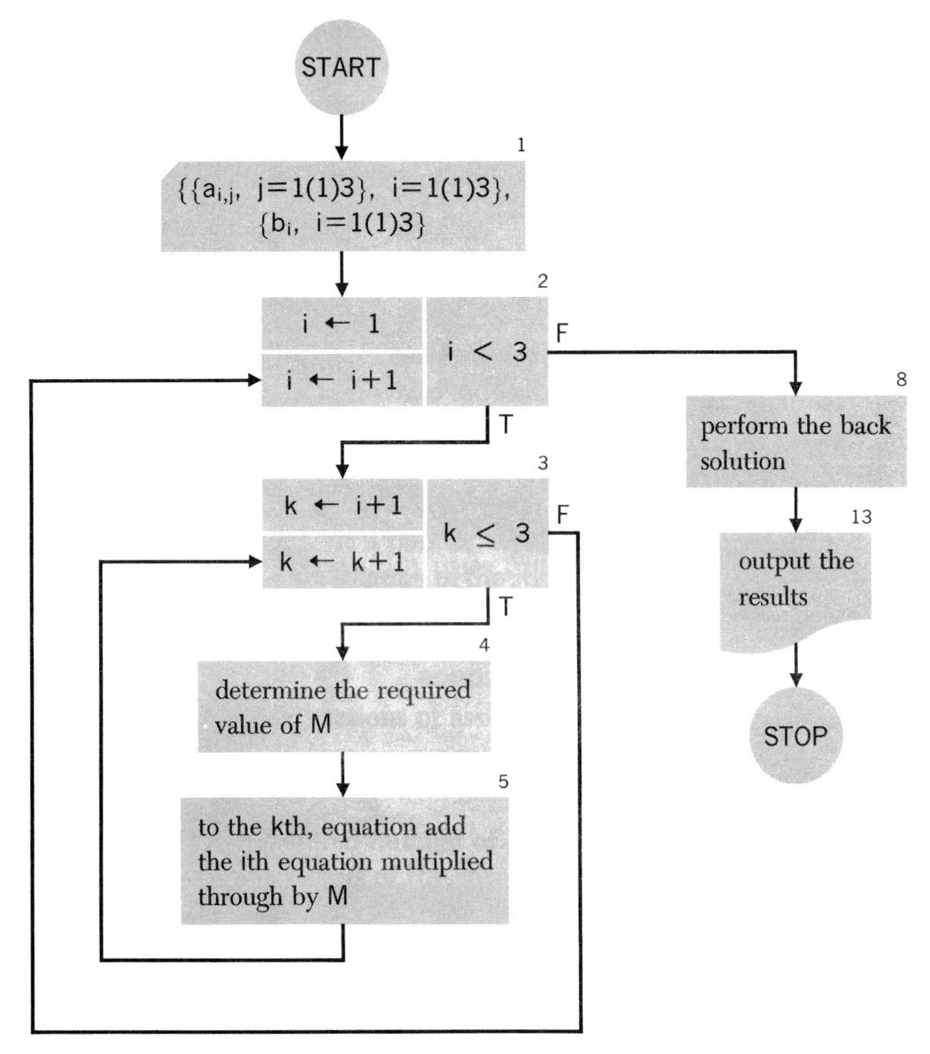

Figure 8-5 Schematic flow chart for Gauss elimination.

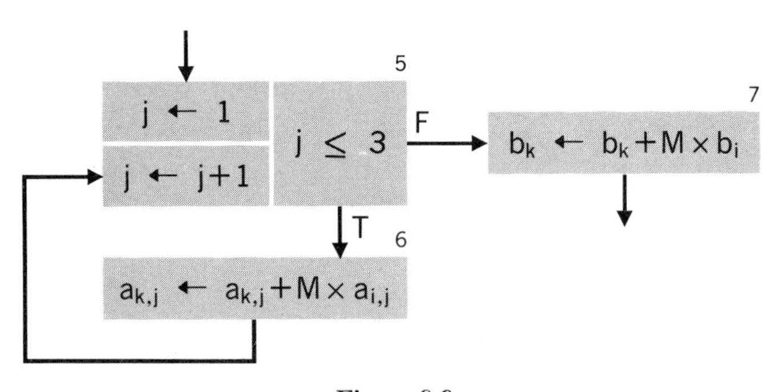

Figure 8-6

TABLE 8-1

When to equation	We add M times equation	The purpose is to assign zero as the new value of
2	1	a_{21}
3	1	a_{31}
3	2	a_{32}

Hence, we want to determine M so that

$$a_{ki} + M \cdot a_{ii} = 0$$

or

$$M = -a_{ki}/a_{ii}$$

Box 4, in the flow chart of Figure 8-5, is reduced to the detail shown in Figure 8-7.

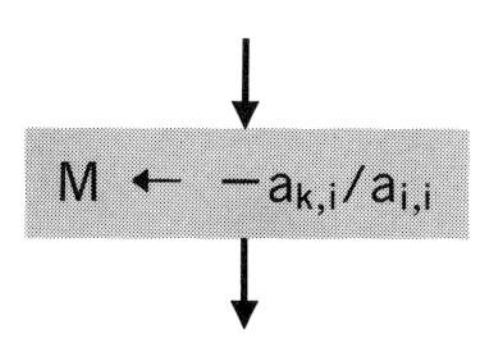

Figure 8-7 Implementation of box 4 of schematic flow chart.

THE BACK SOLUTION

Once the system has been brought into the form

$$a_{11}x_1 + a_{12}x_2 + a_{13}x_3 = b_1$$
$$a_{21}x_1 + a_{22}x_2 + a_{23}x_3 = b_2$$
$$a_{31}x_1 + a_{32}x_2 + a_{33}x_3 = b_3$$

have value zero (a_{21}, a_{31}, a_{32})

then the back solution can be obtained iteratively by the successive assignments

$$x_3 \leftarrow b_3/a_{33}$$
$$x_2 \leftarrow (b_2 - a_{23}x_3)/a_{22}$$
$$x_1 \leftarrow (b_1 - a_{13}x_3 - a_{12}x_2)/a_{11}$$

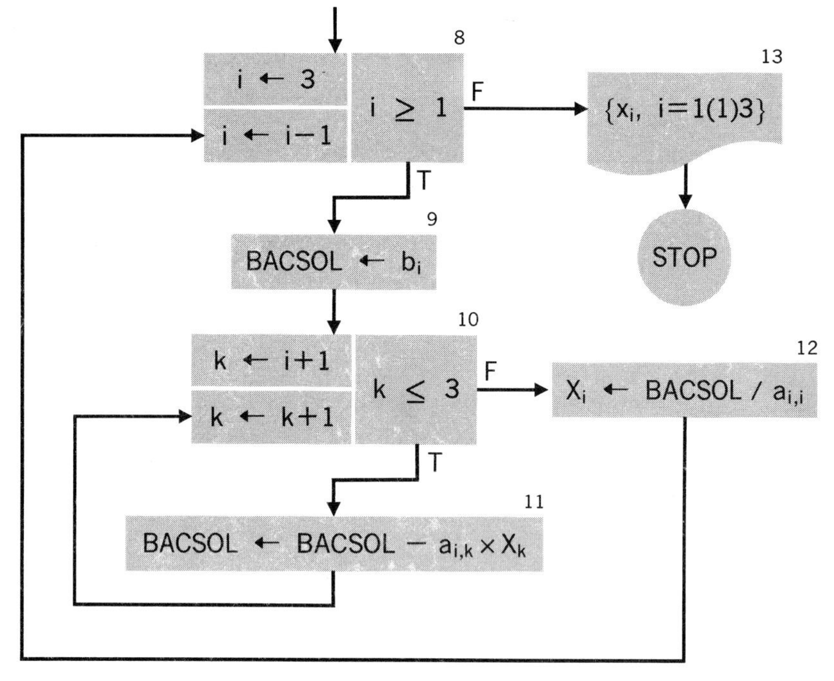

Figure 8-8 The back solution.

These computations can be represented as in Figure 8-8, where we note that the values of the variables x_i are indeed computed in reverse order (see box 8).

The entire flow chart for the Gauss algorithm is assembled from Figures 8-5 to 8-8 in Figure 8-9.

It should be noted that in order to modify the algorithm to solve n equations in n unknowns, it is only necessary to replace each occurrence of "3" by "n" and to add the box

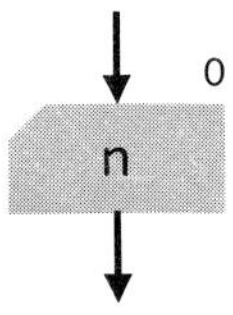

at the beginning.

A Minor Improvement in the Algorithm

It should be noted that all the values assigned to the $a_{k,j}$ in box 6 are zero when $j \leq i$. This, of course, is our objective—reducing the system to triangular form. Since the values of such matrix entries are not used subsequently, no real purpose is served by making these assignments. Thus, in the initialization portion of flow-chart box 5, we may replace

$$j \leftarrow 1 \quad \text{by} \quad j \leftarrow i+1$$

One can test his understanding of an algorithm by making or at least following through a trace of it. We strongly advise that you study care-

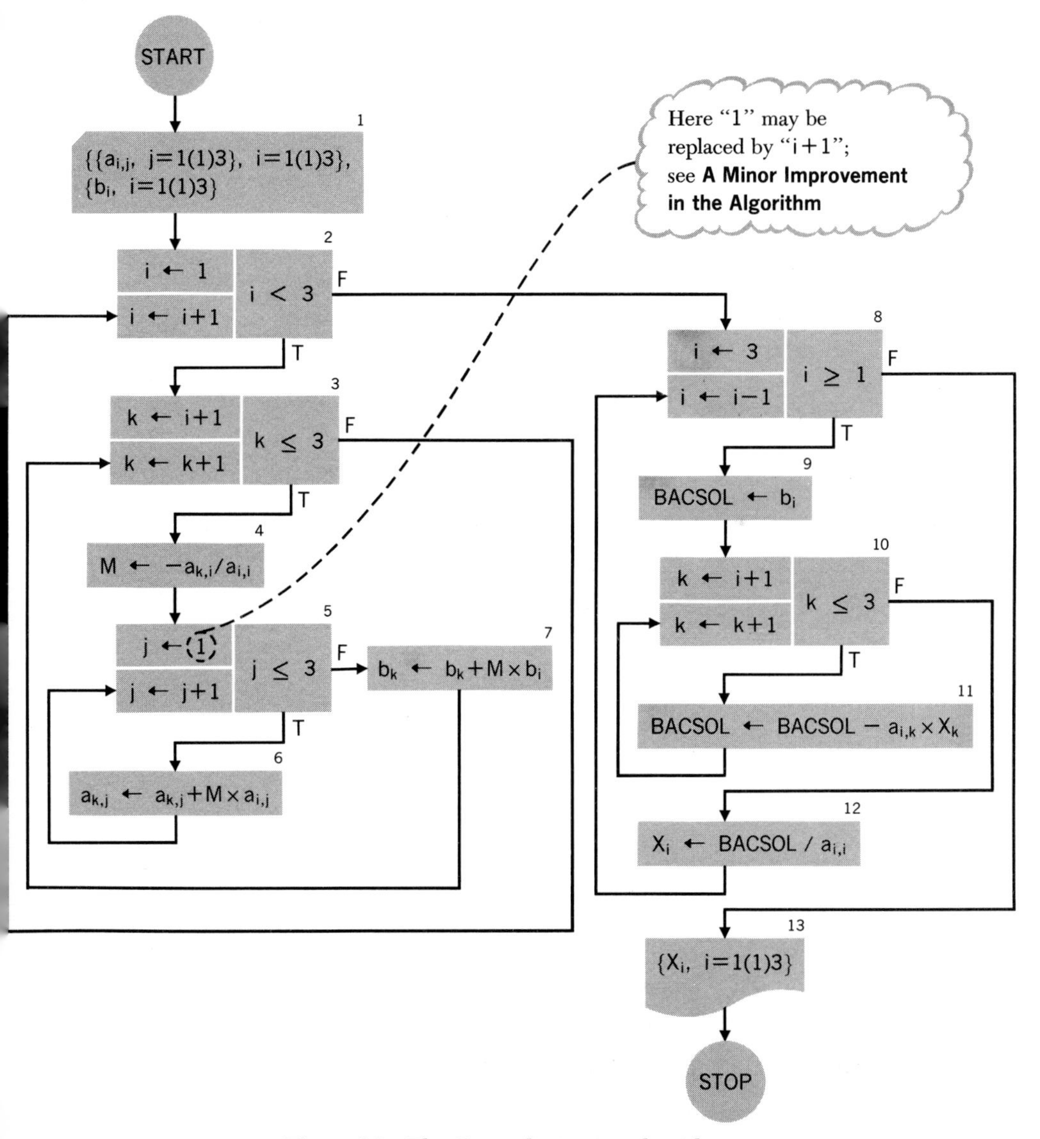

Figure 8-9 The Gauss elimination algorithm.

TABLE 8-2

Step	Box	Values of Variables																				Test	T or F	Go To Box
		i	j	k	a_{11}	a_{12}	a_{13}	a_{21}	a_{22}	a_{23}	a_{31}	a_{32}	a_{33}	b_1	b_2	b_3	M	BAC SOL	x_1	x_2	x_3			
1	1	—	—	—	3	2	7	2	3	1	3	4	1	4	5	7	—	—	—	—	—			
2	2	1																				$1 < 3$	T	3
3	3			2																		$2 \le 3$	T	4
4	4																−2/3							5
5	5		2																			$2 \le 3$	T	6
6	6								5/3															5
7	5		3																			$3 \le 3$	T	6
8	6									−11/3														5
9	5		4																			$4 \le 3$	F	7
10	7														7/3									3
11	3			3																		$3 \le 3$	T	4
12	4																−1							5
13	5		2																			$2 \le 3$	T	6
14	6											2												5
15	5		3																			$3 \le 3$	T	6
16	6												−6											5
17	5		4																			$4 \le 3$	F	7
18	7															3								3
19	3			4																		$4 \le 3$	F	2
20	2	2																				$2 < 3$	T	3
21	3			3																		$3 \le 3$	T	4
22	4																−6/5							5
23	5		3																			$3 \le 3$	T	6
24	6												−8/5											5
25	5		4																			$4 \le 3$	F	7
26	7															1/5								3
27	3			4																		$4 \le 3$	F	2
28	2	3																				$3 < 3$	F	8
29	8	3																				$3 \ge 1$	T	9
30	9																	1/5						10
31	10			4																		$4 \le 3$	F	12
32	12																				−1/8			8
33	8	2																				$2 \ge 1$	T	9
34	9																	7/3						10
35	10			3																		$3 \le 3$	T	11
36	11																	15/8						10
37	10			4																		$4 \le 3$	F	12
38	12																			9/8				8
39	8	1																				$1 \ge 1$	T	9
40	9																	4						10
41	10			2																		$2 \le 3$	T	11
42	11																	7/4						10
43	10			3																		$3 \le 3$	T	11
44	11																	21/8						10
45	10			4																		$4 \le 3$	F	12
46	12																		7/8					8
47	8	0																				$0 \ge 1$	F	13
48	13														Output			→	7/8	9/8	−1/8			STOP

fully the trace given in Table 8-2 for the problem we have been considering, using this system of equations:

$$\begin{aligned} 3x_1 + 2x_2 + 7x_3 &= 4 \\ 2x_1 + 3x_2 + 1x_3 &= 5 \\ 3x_1 + 4x_2 + 1x_3 &= 7 \end{aligned}$$

Correcting an Omission and Making a Substantial Improvement

Rather than juggle too many balls at one time, we have quietly passed over a possibility that could completely nullify our algorithm.

In box 4 of Figure 8-9 we see

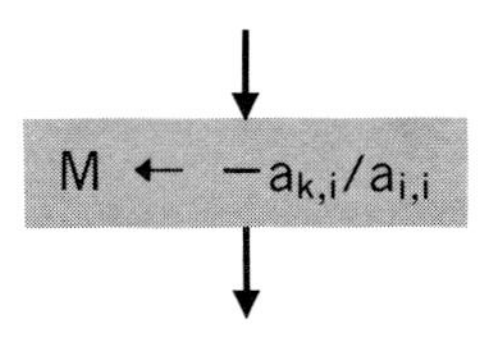

Now, what if the value of $a_{i,i}$ is zero? Clearly something must be done about such a catastrophe. To see what *can* be done, let us examine the execution of the algorithm in mid-process with a system of five equations in five unknowns. Suppose we have reached the point in the algorithm suggested by Figure 8-10*a*. (In this figure we merely display the coefficients and drop out the x_i's for easier readability and conservation of space.)

At this stage, we have already reduced the coefficients below the rust line to zero and are about to use the value of a_{33} (called the *pivot element*) to bring to zero the values of the coefficients situated directly below a_{33}, with the aim of arriving at the condition illustrated in Figure 8-10*b*. Suppose, however, it turns out that $a_{33} = 0$. What can we do? It is reasonably clear that we can interchange the order of writ-

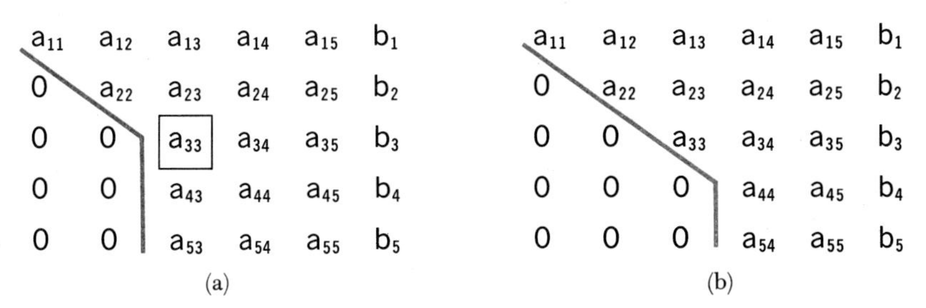

Figure 8-10

ing down the equations, bringing the 4th or 5th equation to the third position, so that the value in the pivot position will no longer be zero.

This would imply looking down the third column from the third position onward in search of a nonzero element, then interchanging the equation in which this element is found with the third equation. Of course, rearranging the order in which our equations are written will not change the mathematical solution of the problem.

Before plunging into this task, let us reflect a little more on the problem. Suppose that our pivot element a_{33}, while not exactly equal to zero, is very nearly zero. In this case we will divide by a small quantity to obtain a relatively large result, and we may very well magnify any errors that are creeping into the solution. An example of the potentially disastrous effect of division by small pivotal elements has already been presented in Section 5-5. The danger is not restricted to machines with sharply limited arithmetic accuracy (as in the three-digit example of Chapter 5), but can become serious for machines with eight digit, or even greater precision, as the number of equations in the system to be solved increases.

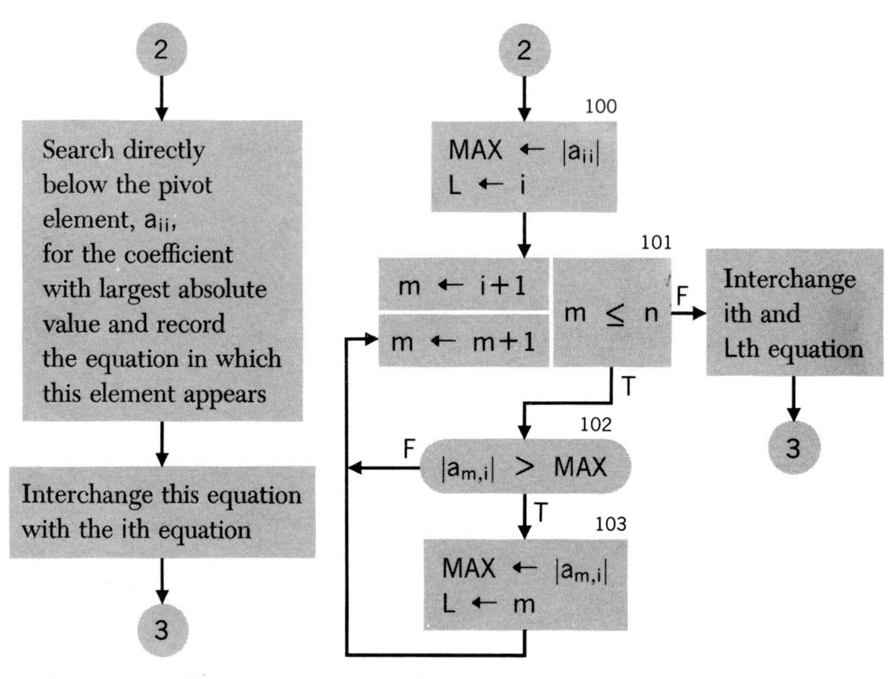

(a) Schematic partial pivoting.

(b) Pivoting mechanism partially arithmetized.

Figure 8-11

Remember that the dangers are not restricted to systems in which diagonal elements of the original system of equations are obviously small (as in the Chapter 5 example). In reality, all the pivotal elements except the first are the result of computation and their magnitude can not be easily predicted from the appearance of the original system.

We discovered in Chapter 5 that improved results were obtained by ordering the equations so that the pivotal elements had the largest possible absolute value. The same thing holds true in the Gauss algorithm; at each stage in the process we should scan the coefficients directly below the pivot element in a search of the coefficient with the largest possible absolute value and then interchange equations to bring this largest coefficient into the pivot position. This produces a loop to be squeezed between box 2 and box 3 of the Gauss algorithm of Figure 8-9. This loop is presented, first schematically and then arithmetically in Figure 8-11.

Before interchanging the equations we should:

1. Test whether MAX $= 0$

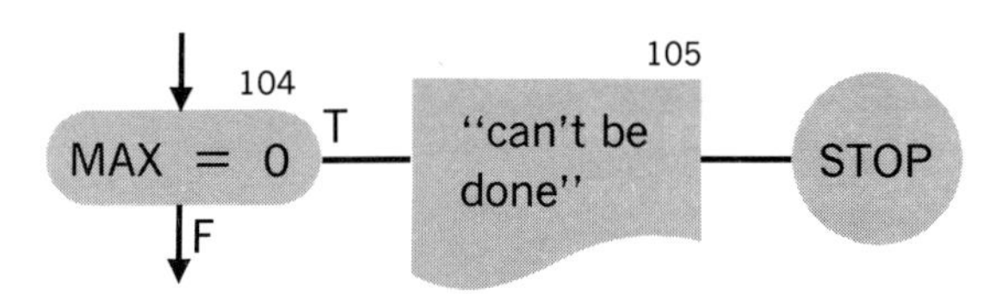

2. Check whether L is, in fact, equal to i. If it is, no row interchange is needed.

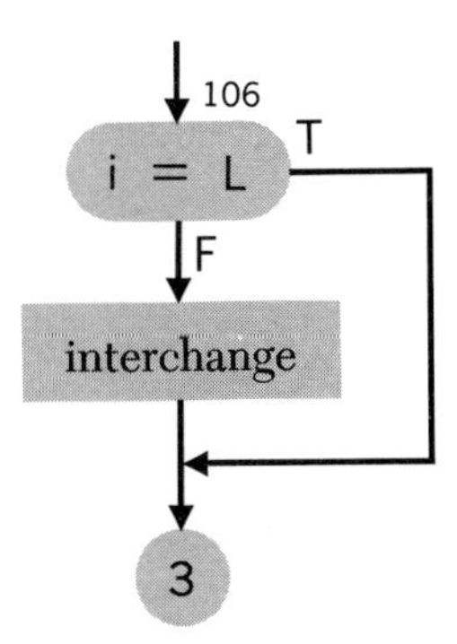

The equation interchange itself is accomplished by interchange of the corresponding coefficients (Figure 8-12). Now, at last, we assemble the whole algorithm as shown in Figure 8-13.

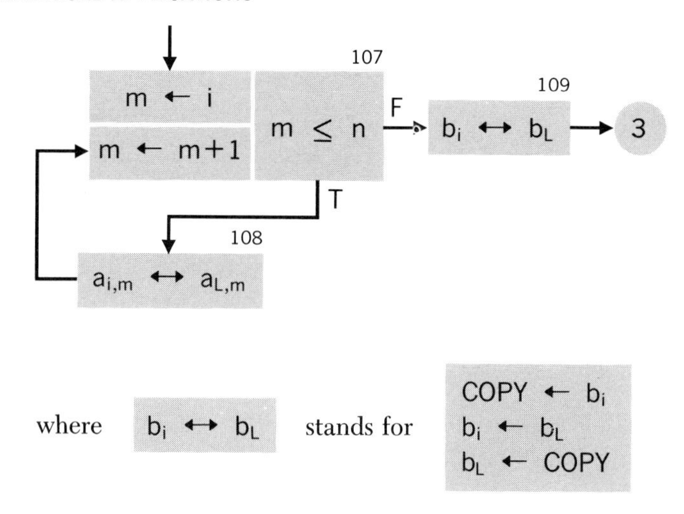

Figure 8-12

EXERCISE 8-1

If you have access to a computer, program the Gauss Algorithm of Figure 8-13 *with* and *without* partial pivoting. Use both programs to solve the following set of five linear equations and compare your results.

$$\begin{aligned}
1.2345x_1 + 2.3456x_2 + 3.4567x_3 + 4.5678x_4 + 5.6789x_5 &= 17.2835 \\
3.2168x_1 - 4.1234x_2 - 1.9876x_3 + 2.3456x_4 + 1.8321x_5 &= 1.2835 \\
4.4513x_1 - 1.7778x_2 + 1.4691x_3 + 6.1298x_4 - 2.6110x_5 &= 7.6614 \\
3.1286x_1 + 4.3124x_2 - 5.2899x_3 + 6.2189x_4 + 2.1610x_5 &= 10.5310 \\
-1.0101x_1 + 3.9886x_2 + 2.4141x_3 - 6.1298x_4 + 4.0001x_5 &= 3.2629
\end{aligned}$$

8-2 AVERAGES AND DEVIATION FROM THE AVERAGE

One of the principal activities in statistics is that of calculating averages and measuring deviations from the average. We can easily illustrate this method with a set of examination scores. For the purpose of avoiding tedious calculations, we will choose a small class of eight students. The grades on an examination (with 25 points possible) were:

$$25, 23, 22, 21, 17, 9, 6, 5$$

If you were asked to calculate the average grade, you would probably add up all the grades and divide by the number of students taking the exam, thus obtaining

$$\frac{25 + 23 + 22 + 21 + 17 + 9 + 6 + 5}{8} = 16$$

This is called the *arithmetic mean* of the test scores.

To measure the deviation (or dispersal or scattering) of the test scores from the mean, it is natural to calculate how much each score differs from the mean and then average these differences. (Here we mean the absolute differences—without regard to sign.) The calculations are tabu-

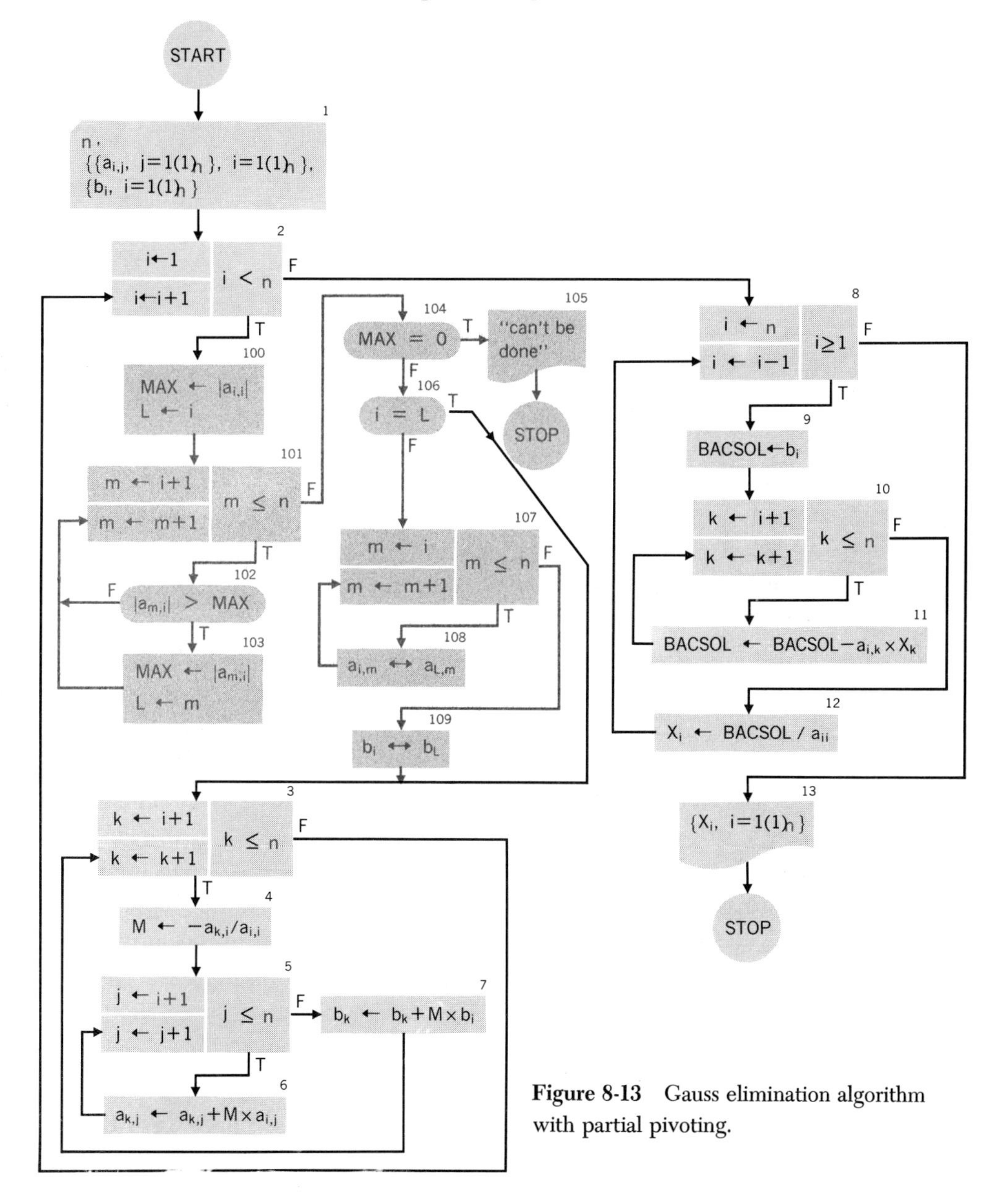

Figure 8-13 Gauss elimination algorithm with partial pivoting.

lated below. Here, then, the average amount by which the test scores deviate from the mean is seven points.

									Total	Arithmetic Mean
Test Score	25	23	22	21	17	9	6	5	128	16
Deviation from mean	9	7	6	5	1	7	10	11	56	7

It is interesting to note that the arithmetic mean is *not* necessarily the grade from which the test scores deviate the least. In this case, for example, the deviation from the grade of 18 is calculated below. Here, then, we see that on the average the test scores deviate from the grade of 18 by less than they deviate from the arithmetic mean of 16.

									Total	Arithmetic Mean
Test Score	25	23	22	21	17	9	6	5	128	16
Deviation from 18	7	5	4	3	1	9	12	13	54	6.75

It is interesting to consider taking as our "average" score, instead of the arithmetic mean, that score yielding the smallest average deviation (or, what is the same thing, that score yielding the smallest total deviation). We then want to find the number x so that the sum of the deviations from x is a minimum.

That is, we want

$$|25 - x| + |23 - x| + |22 - x| + |21 - x| + |17 - x| + |9 - x| + |6 - x| + |5 - x|$$

to be a minimum.

The problem is much easier to solve than one might think. The method of solution involves considering the deviations in pairs. First of all, consider the sum of the deviations of the highest and lowest scores

$$|25 - x| + |5 - x|$$

We can see geometrically that when x is taken between 5 and 25 then $|5 - x| + |25 - x|$ is the length of the interval from 5 to 25 or 25 −

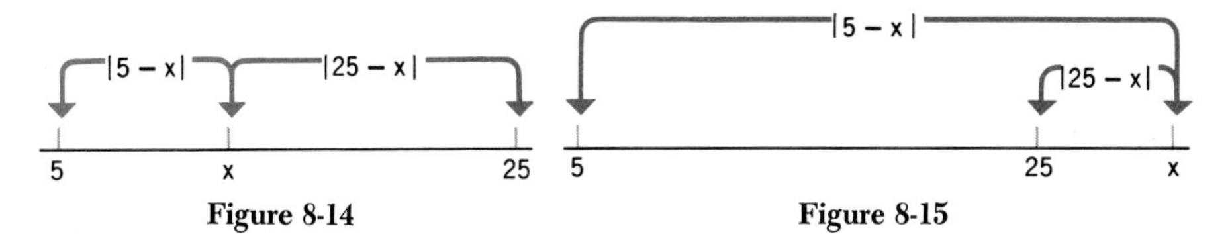

Figure 8-14 Figure 8-15

$5 = 20$ (Figure 8-14). However, when x is outside the interval [5,25], then the sum $|5 - x| + |25 - x|$ will exceed the length of the interval [5,25] (Figure 8-15). If we pair in the same way, the second highest and second lowest test scores, etc., we find that

$$\begin{aligned} |25 - x| + |5 - x| &\geq 20 \\ |23 - x| + |6 - x| &\geq 17 \\ |22 - x| + |9 - x| &\geq 13 \\ |21 - x| + |17 - x| &\geq 4 \end{aligned}$$

Each of these inequalities becomes an equality if the number x lies between the innermost pair, 17 and 21 (Figure 8-16). Hence we find that the total deviation from x,

$$\begin{aligned} &|25 - x| + |23 - x| + |22 - x| + |21 - x| + |17 - x| + |9 - x| \\ &\qquad + |6 - x| + |5 - x| \geq 20 + 17 + 13 + 4 = 54 \end{aligned}$$

The minimum value of 54 is actually achieved if

$$17 \leq x \leq 21$$

Any such value of x is called a *median* grade.

This method of averaging does not always give a unique answer, but it is clear that there will be as many scores above the median as there are below. (In case several papers share the median score, this last sentence will have to be slightly reworded.)

The method of finding the median can be described as follows. Arrange the tests in order of descending scores and count down half way. If the number of tests is odd, the middle paper has the median

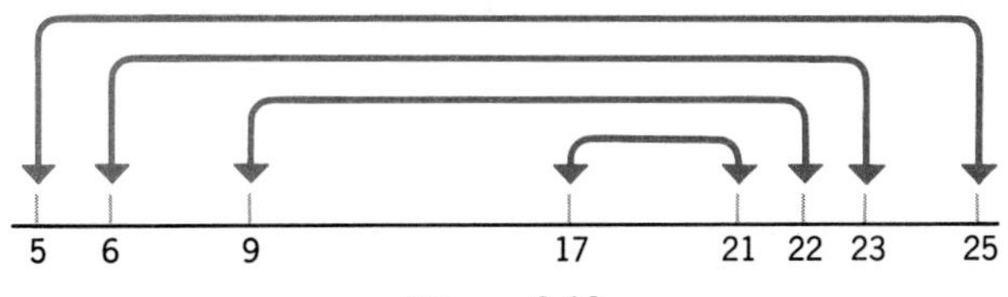

Figure 8-16

score. If the number of papers is even, then medians are numbers between the lowest score in the top half and the highest score in the bottom half.

EXERCISES 8-2

1. Show that the average deviation from the median is given by

$$\frac{(\text{Sum of top half scores}) - (\text{Sum of bottom half scores})}{\text{Number of tests}}$$

2. A large number of students (20 to 30 thousand) are taking a college entrance test. The number is sufficiently large that computer sorting of the test scores would use considerable time and a lot of memory. Devise a flow chart for computing the arithmetic mean, the median, and the average deviation from each. Test scores are whole numbers between 0 and 100.

3. A large school district has on the order of 4000 teachers with salaries ranging between $5000 and $18,000 per year. Compare the methods of finding the median salary with and without sorting:

   (a) In the case that the answer must be exact to the nearest penny.
   (b) In the case that an error of no more than $5 will be tolerated.

8-3 Root-Mean-Square Deviation

The general practice in statistics is to calculate average deviation in a way quite different from that used in the preceding section. To see how it is done, let us return to the test scores in the sample in Section 8-2. We will show how the average deviation from a test score of 18 (for example) would be calculated. The method consists of four steps.

Test score	25	23	22	21	17	9	6	5

Step 1. Calculate the deviation from 18 for each score as before.

Test score	25	23	22	21	17	9	6	5
Deviation from 18	7	5	4	3	1	9	12	13

Step 2. Calculate the squares of the deviations.

Test scores	25	23	22	21	17	9	6	5
Deviation from 18	7	5	4	3	1	9	12	13
Squares of deviations	49	25	15	9	1	81	144	169

Step 3. Find the arithmetic mean of these squares:

$$\frac{49 + 25 + 16 + 9 + 1 + 81 + 144 + 169}{8} = \frac{494}{8} = 61.25$$

Step 4. Take the square root of the arithmetic mean:

$$\sqrt{61.25} = 7.826$$

This is the number used in statistics as the average deviation from the test score of 18. We can see that it is not the same as the average deviation computed by the method of Section 8-2, which was 6.75. From the above steps we can see that this new method of computing average deviation can be described as "the square *root* of the arithmetic *mean* of the *squares* of the *deviations.*" The italicized words reveal the rationale for the name "root-mean-square deviation" which furnishes the title for this section.

It should be noted that virtually all methods of "averaging" used in mathematics are of this general type: we first subject the numbers to be averaged to some treatment (squaring, in this case), take the arithmetic mean of the treated numbers, and finally reverse the treatment (square root) on this arithmetic mean.

As in the preceding section, we would like to find the test score, $\bar{x}$, from which our data deviates the least. That is, so that

$$\sqrt{\frac{\sum_{i=1}^{8}(x_i - \bar{x})^2}{8}}$$

is as small as possible. It is clear that the value of $\bar{x}$ which makes this deviation the smallest will be the value of $\bar{x}$ which makes

$$\sum_{i=1}^{8}(x_i - \bar{x})^2$$

the smallest.

For the test data in our example, this means finding $\bar{x}$ so that

$$(5 - \bar{x})^2 + (6 - \bar{x})^2 + (9 - \bar{x})^2 + (17 - \bar{x})^2 + (21 - \bar{x})^2 + (22 - \bar{x})^2 + (23 - \bar{x})^2 + (25 - \bar{x})^2$$

is as small as possible. To solve this problem we expand each of the above squares and add them, as shown below:

$$\begin{array}{rrr}
\bar{x}^2 - & 10\bar{x} + & 25 \\
\bar{x}^2 - & 12\bar{x} + & 36 \\
\bar{x}^2 - & 18\bar{x} + & 81 \\
\bar{x}^2 - & 34\bar{x} + & 289 \\
\bar{x}^2 - & 42\bar{x} + & 441 \\
\bar{x}^2 - & 44\bar{x} + & 484 \\
\bar{x}^2 - & 46\bar{x} + & 529 \\
\bar{x}^2 - & 50\bar{x} + & 625 \\
\hline
8\bar{x}^2 - & 256\bar{x} + & 2510
\end{array}$$

Next, we resort to the method of completing the square.

$$\begin{aligned}
8\bar{x}^2 - 256\bar{x} + 2510 &= 8(\bar{x}^2 - 32\bar{x}) + 2510 \\
&= 8(\bar{x}^2 - 32\bar{x} + (16)^2) - 8(16)^2 + 2510 \\
&= 8(\bar{x} - 16)^2 - 2048 + 2510 \\
&= 8(\bar{x} - 16)^2 + 462
\end{aligned}$$

Since $8(\bar{x} - 16)^2$ is always ≥ 0, we see that whatever value is taken for $\bar{x}$,

$$8(\bar{x} - 16)^2 + 462 \geq 462$$

with equality only when $\bar{x}$ has the value 16. Thus the minimum value of

$$\sum_{i=1}^{8} (x_i - \bar{x})^2$$

is 462, so that the minimum value of the root-mean-square deviation

$$\sqrt{\frac{\sum_{i=1}^{8} (x_i - \bar{x})^2}{8}} \quad \text{is} \quad \sqrt{\frac{462}{8}} = \sqrt{57.75} \cong 7.60$$

In this case we see that the number, 16, from which the test scores had the least root-mean-square deviation turns out to be the arithmetic mean of the test scores. It is natural to wonder whether this is the case in general; it *is*, and it is not difficult to prove. In fact, it is largely a repetition of the above calculations in general form. Here is a demonstration of this.

Recall that, in general, the root-mean-square deviation from the number $\bar{x}$ is given by

$$\sqrt{\frac{\sum_{k=1}^{N}(x_k - \bar{x})^2}{N}}$$

To minimize this deviation, we minimize

$$\sum_{k=1}^{N}(x_k - \bar{x})^2$$

To do this, we first expand out the squared expression, simplify, and complete the square:

$$\sum_{k=1}^{N}(x_k - \bar{x})^2 = \sum_{k=1}^{N}(\bar{x}^2 - 2x_k\bar{x} + x_k{}^2)$$

$$= \sum_{k=1}^{N}\bar{x}^2 - 2\sum_{k=1}^{N}x_k\bar{x} + \sum_{k=1}^{N}x_k{}^2$$

In this latest expression, notice that $\bar{x}$ and $\bar{x}^2$ do not depend on the value of k. Thus, when we add N constants, each of which has the value $\bar{x}^2$, we are simply calculating $N\bar{x}^2$. Similarly, since $\bar{x}$ does not depend on the value of k, it is a constant in every term of the second summation and so can be factored out of the sum. These facts lead us to restate the expression as follows:

$$\sum_{k=1}^{N}(x_k - \bar{x})^2 = N\bar{x}^2 - 2\bar{x}\sum_{k=1}^{N}x_k + \sum_{k=1}^{N}x_k{}^2$$

$$= N\left(\bar{x}^2 - 2\bar{x}\frac{\sum_{k=1}^{N}x_k}{N}\right) + \sum_{k=1}^{N}x_k{}^2$$

Before the step of completing the square, we note that this last expression can be simplified to

$$N(\bar{x}^2 - 2A\bar{x}) + S$$

where

$$A = \frac{\sum_{k=1}^{N}x_k}{N}$$

is the arithmetic mean of the data values and where

$$S = \sum_{k=1}^{N} x_k{}^2$$

the sum of the squares of the data values. Now

$$\begin{aligned}\sum_{k=1}^{N} (x_k - \bar{x})^2 &= N(\bar{x}^2 - 2A\bar{x}) + S \\ &= N(\bar{x}^2 - 2A\bar{x} + A^2) - NA^2 + S \\ &= N(\bar{x} - A)^2 - NA^2 + S\end{aligned}$$

As before, this expression has its minimum value when $\bar{x} = A$ and this minimum value is $-NA^2 + S$.

And the root-mean-square deviation can now be calculated as

$$\sqrt{\frac{\sum_{k=1}^{N} (x_k - A)^2}{N}} = \sqrt{\frac{S - NA^2}{N}} = \sqrt{\frac{S}{N} - A^2}$$

Since S/N is the average of the squares of the data values, we see that the expression $S/N - A^2$ inside the square root can be described as the average of the squares minus the square of the average.

The root-mean-square deviation computed in this way is called the *standard deviation.*

In the next section we will meet this problem: we have a lot of numbers

$$z_1, z_2, z_3, \ldots, z_n$$

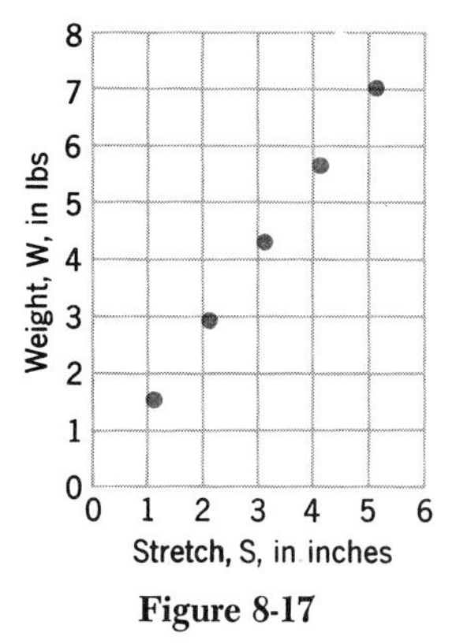

Figure 8-17

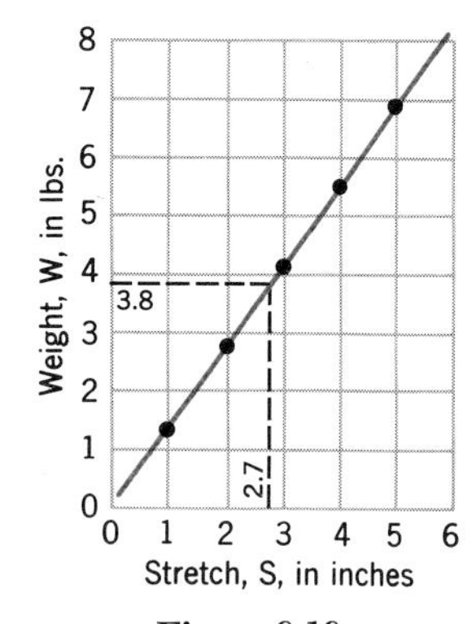

Figure 8-18

and we want to find the value of B so that

$$\sum_{k=1}^{n} (z_k - B)^2$$

will be as small as possible. We can see that this is the same problem as the one solved above but with letters changed. The desired value of B is given by

$$B = \bar{z} = \frac{\sum_{k=1}^{n} z_k}{n}$$

EXERCISE 8-3

Draw a flow chart for reading a set of data values and calculating the arithmetic mean and standard deviation.

8-4 THE MATHEMATICS OF PREDICTION

One of the basic problems in statistics is that of prediction or, more specifically, predicting the value of one variable on the basis of the value of another variable.

In order to illustrate our meaning, suppose that we have a spring and a set of weights and that we perform an experiment to see how much weight is necessary to stretch the spring 1 inch, 2 inches, 3 inches, 4 inches, and 5 inches. The results of this experiment for a particular spring are tabulated below and graphed in Figure 8-17.

Amount of stretch (S) in inches	1	2	3	4	5
Weight (W) in lbs	1.4	2.8	4.1	5.5	6.9

We can see that all the points on this graph seem to lie on a straight line. In Figure 8-18 we see the line drawn through these five data points.

Suppose an object of unknown weight is hung on the spring, giving a stretch of 2.8 inches. We can use our graph and "predict" that the object will prove to weigh 3.8 lbs. [Such an experiment was first performed about 300 years ago by the physicist, Robert Hooke. On the basis of his experiments, he announced "Hooke's Law" for the stretching of springs, namely, that the amount of stretch is proportional to the weight causing the stretch,

$$W = K \times S$$

Here, the "spring constant," K, depends on the dimensions of the spring metal used in its construction. Hooke's Law of stretching provides the basis for meat scales in use today.]

In the above example, we have seen how we can predict the value of the variable W from the value of the variable S. In this case, it turned out to be particularly simple because the variables were related by the formula

$$W = K \times S$$

However, the same method can be used even when the variables are not "functionally related" in this way, as we will see in our next example.

Example. Recently, data were collected to study the relationship between heights of fathers and the heights of their sons. One hundred men with grown sons were selected, and their heights were recorded together with those of their oldest sons at maturity. The results are shown on the graph of Figure 8-19.

Here, for each point plotted, the abscissa represents the height of a father while the ordinate represents the height of his eldest son (at maturity).

A glance at the graph will suffice to establish that the situation here is quite different from that of the stretched spring. On the basis of knowing the height of the father, we are not going to be able to make a reliable prediction of the height of the son. Evidently, some factors other than the heights of the fathers are involved.

And yet, there is a definite tendency for taller fathers to produce taller sons. The task we are setting for ourselves is the quantitative measurement of this tendency. As in the case of the stretched spring, we will try to place on this graph the line that best fits this data, the line that will best predict heights of sons from heights of fathers "on the average."

In this case, we cannot locate this line by eye as in the previous example. In fact, we require a definition of what we mean by the best

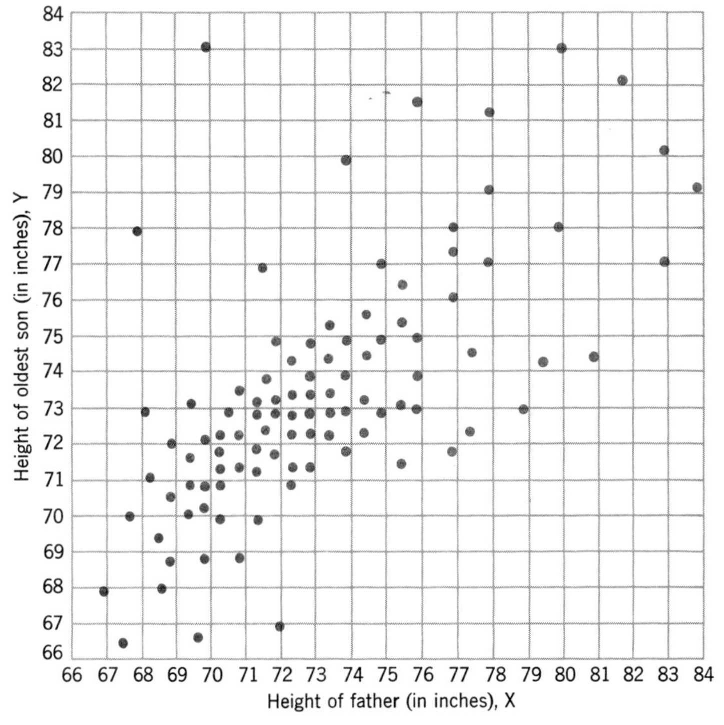

Figure 8-19

fitting line. The line we want is the one that shows *an average deviation* of sons' actual heights from the heights predicted by the line *that is as small as possible.*

This definition will not be complete until we specify the method to be used in averaging the deviations. The two methods for averaging deviations in the preceding sections were as follows.

1. The arithmetic mean of the absolute values of the deviations.
2. The root-mean-square of the deviations.

In this case, the first method is very cumbersome to work with. Furthermore, advanced study of statistics yields strong theoretical support of the second method. For these reasons, we will adopt the root-mean-square method of averaging our deviations. The best fitting line in this sense is called the "line of regression" of sons' heights on fathers' heights. It is defined as follows.

Definition. The *line of regression* of sons' heights on fathers' heights is the line producing the smallest possible root-mean-square deviation of the sons' actual heights from those predicted by the line.

In order to solve this problem, we must first investigate how these root-mean-square deviations are calculated. It will be convenient to use an example having fewer data pairs than in Figure 8-19. In Figure 8-20 we see five data points and a line

$$y = Mx + B$$

In Figure 8-21 we see depicted the deviations, d_1, d_2, d_3, d_4, d_5 of the actual values of y from those predicted by the line. The root-mean-square deviation of the sons' actual heights from the predicted values is

$$\bar{d} = \sqrt{\frac{d_1^2 + d_2^2 + d_3^2 + d_4^2 + d_5^2}{5}} = \sqrt{\frac{\sum_{i=1}^{5} d_i^2}{5}} \qquad (1)$$

Noting that when the father's height is x_1, the son's height predicted from $y = Mx + B$ is

$$Mx_1 + B$$

we see that

$$d_1 = y_1 - (Mx_1 + B)$$

etc., so that the root-mean-square deviation in Equation 1 can be expressed in the form

$$\bar{d} = \sqrt{\frac{\sum_{i=1}^{5}(y_i - Mx_i - B)^2}{5}}$$

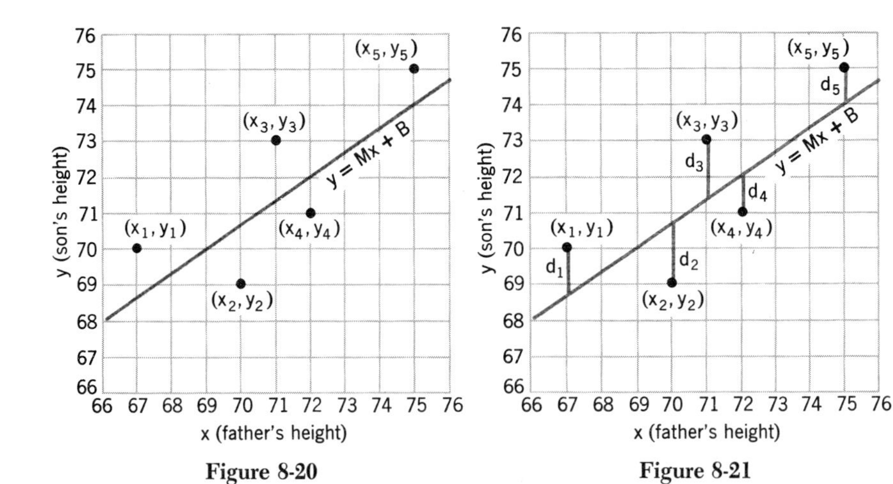

Figure 8-20 Figure 8-21

In the general case, with N data points, this, of course, takes the form

$$\bar{d} = \sqrt{\frac{\sum_{i=1}^{N} (y_i - Mx_i - B)^2}{N}}$$

The problem now is to find values of M and B that make this deviation as small as possible. As in a similar situation in the preceding section, we see that these will be the values of M and B which make

$$N\bar{d}^2 = \sum_{i=1}^{N} (y_i - Mx_i - B)^2$$

as small as possible.

Your understanding of the method to be used will be helped by this analogy.

If we want to find the youngest college freshman in the U.S., we can first find the youngest college freshman in each state and then pick the youngest from among these state-wide winners.

Similarly, if we want to find the line among all lines for which the expression

$$\sum_{i=1}^{N} (y_i - Mx_i - B)^2$$

is smallest, we can regard the problem as a sort of contest in two stages. First, for each value of the slope, M, we find the line with that slope for which

$$\sum_{i=1}^{N} (y_i - Mx_i - B)^2$$

is a minimum. Then, only the winners of each of these contests will compete in the grand finale, the determination of the line, among all the lines, for which

$$\sum_{i=1}^{N} (y_i - Mx_i - B)^2$$

is smallest.

Theorem. Among all lines with a given, fixed slope M, the one for which

$$N\bar{d}^2 = \sum_{i=1}^{N} (y_i - Mx_i - B)^2$$

is a minimum is the line passing through the point $(\bar{x},\bar{y})$.

$$\left[\text{Here, } \bar{x} \text{ denotes } \frac{1}{N} \times \sum_{i=1}^{N} x_i \text{ and } \bar{y} = \frac{1}{N} \times \sum_{i=1}^{N} y_i.\right]$$

Recalling that lines having the same slope are parallel and, conversely, the theorem tells us (as illustrated in Figure 8-22) that among a family of parallel lines, the one for which

$$\sum_{i=1}^{N} (y_i - Mx_i - B)^2$$

is a minimum is the one passing through the point $(\bar{x},\bar{y})$. This point is called the *centroid* of the data points (x_1,y_1), (x_2,y_2), etc. (The result stated in the theorem is rather surprising in that this point, the centroid, does not depend in any way on the value of M.)

Proof of the theorem. We introduce the notation

$$z_i = y_i - Mx_i \tag{2}$$

so that

$$\sum_{i=1}^{N} (y_i - Mx_i - B)^2 \qquad \text{becomes} \qquad \sum_{i=1}^{N} (z_i - B)^2$$

Since M is given and fixed, each of the z_i's can be calculated as a numerical constant. The minimization problem becomes that of finding the value of B for which

$$\sum_{i=1}^{N} (z_i - B)^2$$

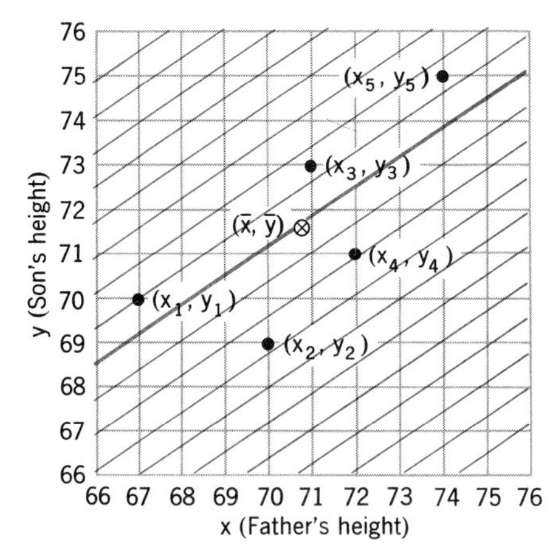

Figure 8-22 (All lines have same slope M).

takes on a minimum value. But this problem was solved in the preceding section where we found the value of B to be given by the arithmetic mean of the z_i's,

$$B = \bar{z} = \frac{\sum_{i=1}^{N} z_i}{N}$$

Using Equation 2, we may write

$$\begin{aligned} B = \bar{z} = \frac{\sum_{i=1}^{N} z_i}{N} &= \frac{1}{N} \sum_{i=1}^{N} (y_i - Mx_i) \\ &= \frac{1}{N} \sum_{i=1}^{N} y_i - M \cdot \frac{1}{N} \sum_{i=1}^{N} x_i \qquad (2a) \\ &= \bar{y} - M\bar{x} \end{aligned}$$

Substituting this value of B in the equation $y = Mx + B$, yields us the equation of the minimizing line of that family,

$$y = Mx + \bar{y} - M\bar{x}$$

which can be rewritten as

$$y = \bar{y} + M(x - \bar{x}) \qquad \text{or} \qquad y - \bar{y} = M(x - \bar{x}) \qquad (3)$$

which is the equation of the line with slope M passing through the point $(\bar{x},\bar{y})$.

Thus we see that in the competition for that line among all lines that makes the expression

$$\sum_{i=1}^{N} (y_i - Mx_i - B)^2$$

the smallest, only those lines through the centroid need compete. As we saw in Equation 2a, the value of B for these lines through the centroid is given by $B = \bar{y} - M\bar{x}$ (Figure 8-23) whence, by substitution, we obtain

$$N\bar{d}^2 = \sum_{i=1}^{N} (y_i - Mx_i - B)^2 = \sum_{i=1}^{N} [y_i - \bar{y} - M(x_i - \bar{x})]^2$$

Hence, we seek the value of M which makes this latter expression a minimum. A summary of the steps in the solution is as follows.

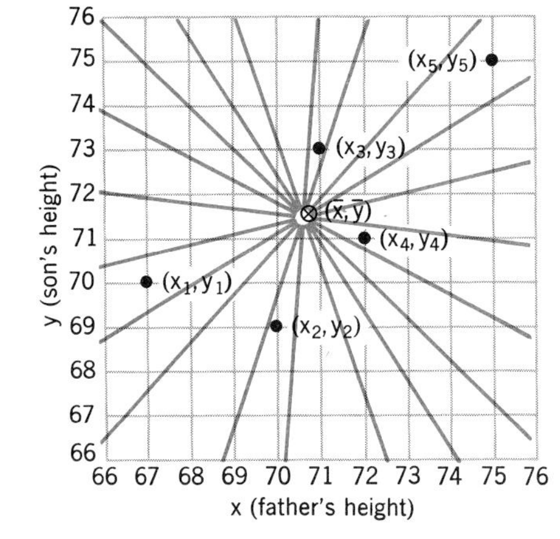

Figure 8-23

Step 1. Expand the square in the expression

$$\sum_{i=1}^{N} [y_i - \bar{y} - M(x_i - \bar{x})]^2$$

Step 2. Change the order of adding to add first "vertically" and then "horizontally."

Step 3. Obtain a quadratic expression in M.

Step 4. Minimize by "completing the square."

We show what this means with N = 5:

$$5 \times (\bar{d})^2 = \sum_{i=1}^{5} [(y_i - \bar{y}) - M(x_i - \bar{x})]^2$$

$$= \sum_{i=1}^{5} [M^2(x_i - \bar{x})^2 - 2M(x_i - \bar{x})(y_i - \bar{y}) + (y_i - \bar{y})^2]$$

$$\begin{aligned} = \quad & M^2 (x_1 - \bar{x})^2 - 2M (x_1 - \bar{x})(y_1 - \bar{y}) + (y_1 - \bar{y})^2 \\ + & M^2 (x_2 - \bar{x})^2 - 2M (x_2 - \bar{x})(y_2 - \bar{y}) + (y_2 - \bar{y})^2 \\ + & M^2 (x_3 - \bar{x})^2 - 2M (x_3 - \bar{x})(y_3 - \bar{y}) + (y_3 - \bar{y})^2 \\ + & M^2 (x_4 - \bar{x})^2 - 2M (x_4 - \bar{x})(y_4 - \bar{y}) + (y_4 - \bar{y})^2 \\ + & M^2 (x_5 - \bar{x})^2 - 2M (x_5 - \bar{x})(y_5 - \bar{y}) + (y_5 - \bar{y})^2 \end{aligned}$$

$$= M^2 \sum_{i=1}^{5} (x_i - \bar{x})^2 - 2M \sum_{i=1}^{5} (x_i - \bar{x})(y_i - \bar{y}) + \sum_{i=1}^{5} (y_i - \bar{y})^2$$

This carries us through Step 3. We now simplify the expression by introducing the notation,

$$a = \sum_{i=1}^{5}(x_i - \bar{x})^2, \quad b = \sum_{i=1}^{5}(x_i - \bar{x})(y_i - \bar{y}), \quad c = \sum_{i=1}^{5}(y_i - \bar{y})^2$$

Now, the familiar square-completing process takes the form,

$$\begin{aligned} 5 \times (\bar{d})^2 &= \sum_{i=1}^{5}[(y_i - \bar{y}) - M(x_i - \bar{x})]^2 \\ &= aM^2 - 2bM + c \\ &= a\left(M^2 - \frac{2b}{a}M\right) + c \\ &= a\left(M^2 - \frac{2b}{a}M + \left(\frac{b}{a}\right)^2\right) - \frac{b^2}{a} + c \\ &= a\left(M - \frac{b}{a}\right)^2 + \frac{ac - b^2}{a} \end{aligned}$$

Since the first term in this expression cannot be less than zero, the whole expression takes on its minimum value when the first term is zero, that is, when

$$M = \frac{b}{a} = \frac{\sum_{i=1}^{5}(x_i - \bar{x})(y_i - \bar{y})}{\sum_{i=1}^{5}(x_i - \bar{x})^2} \tag{4}$$

and the minimum value is

$$\begin{aligned} 5 \times \bar{d}^2 &= \frac{ac - b^2}{a} \\ &= \frac{\left(\sum_{i=1}^{5}(x_i - \bar{x})^2\right)\cdot\left(\sum_{i=1}^{5}(y_i - \bar{y})^2\right) - \left(\sum_{i=1}^{5}(x_i - \bar{x})(y_i - \bar{y})\right)^2}{\sum_{i=1}^{5}(x_i - \bar{x})^2} \end{aligned} \tag{5}$$

The value obtained by solving for $\bar{d}$ is called the *standard error*.

In the general case with N data points, these formulas are only modified by replacing "5" by "N."

Example. We will run through these computations for the data graphed in Figure 8-20 (Table 8-3).

Equations 4, 3, and 5 give for the slope of the line of regression,

$$M = \frac{18.6}{26.8} \cong .6933$$

TABLE 8-3

i	x_i	y_i	$x_i - \bar{x}$	$y_i - \bar{y}$	$(x_i - \bar{x})^2$	$(y_i - \bar{y})^2$	$(x_i - \bar{x})(y_i - \bar{y})$
1	67	70	−3.8	−1.6	14.44	2.56	6.08
2	70	69	−0.8	−2.6	0.64	6.76	2.08
3	71	73	0.2	1.4	0.04	1.96	0.28
4	72	71	1.2	−0.6	1.44	0.36	−0.72
5	74	75	3.2	3.4	10.24	11.56	10.88
SUM	354	358	0	0	26.80	23.20	18.60
arithmetic mean of sum	70.8	71.6					
	$\bar{x}$ ↗	$\bar{y}$ ↗					

for the equation of the line of regression,

$$y = .6933(x - 70.8) + 71.6$$

and for the standard error

$$\bar{d} = \sqrt{\frac{26.8 \times 23.2 - (18.6)^2}{5 \times 26.8}} \cong 1.450$$

When N is very large, this is clearly the sort of calculation we would like a computer to do for us. One method of flowcharting these calculations is seen in Figure 8-24.

The calculations in this flow chart divide into five parts which should be self-explanatory.

1. Reading in the data (box 1).
2. Calculating the mean of the variables x and y (boxes 3–5).
3. Calculating $\sum_{i=1}^{N} (x_i - \bar{x})^2$, $\sum_{i=1}^{N} (y_i - \bar{y})^2$,

and $\sum_{i=1}^{N} (x_i - \bar{x})(y_i - \bar{y})$ (boxes 6–8).

4. Calculating the slope of the regression line and the standard error (box 9).
5. Outputting the results (box 10).

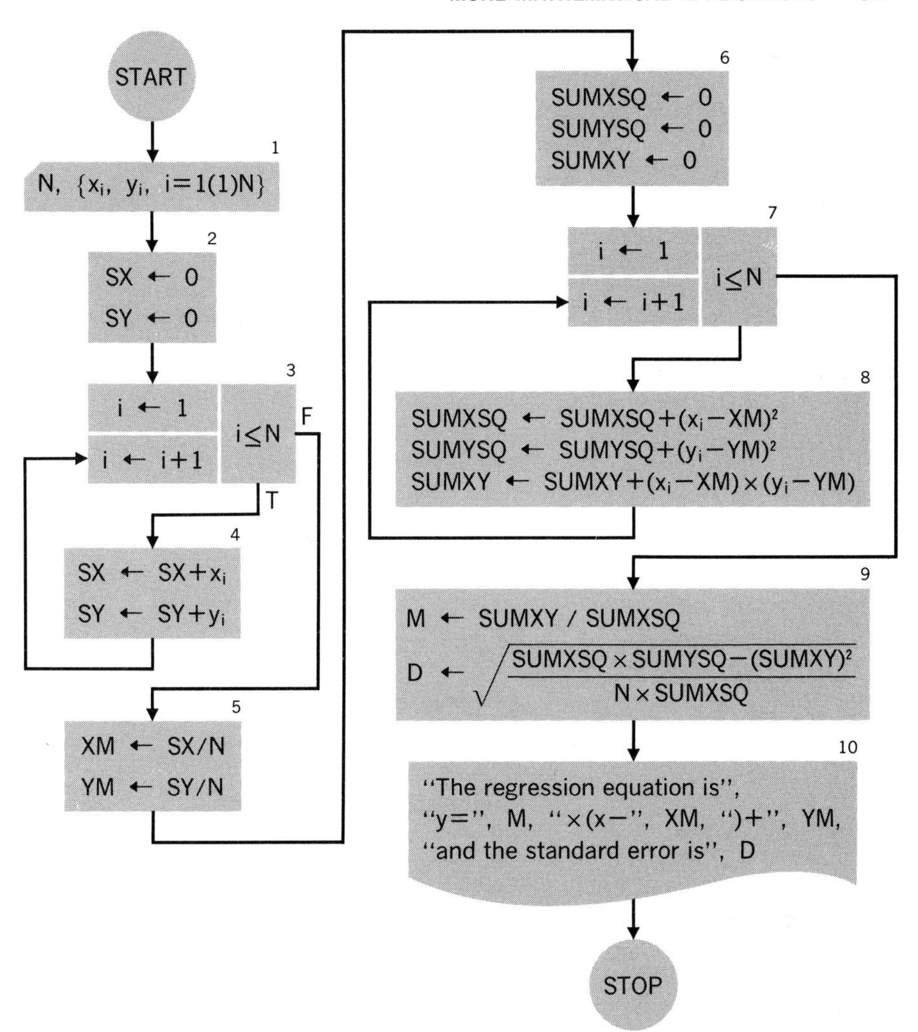

Figure 8-24 First regression flow chart.

This flow chart contains a gross inefficiency. We see that in box 1 we have stored the data over which we make two "passes," in box 4 and box 8. This is wasteful of both time and space, but it seems to be required by the necessity of knowing the values of XM and YM before beginning the next loop of computations which require the variables x_i and y_i to be "adjusted to their means," XM and YM. Rather surprisingly, this difficulty can be overcome by use of the formulas derived below in which we remember that

$$\bar{x} = \frac{1}{N} \sum_{i=1}^{N} x_i \qquad \text{or} \qquad \sum_{i=1}^{N} x_i = N\bar{x}$$

and

$$\bar{y} = \frac{1}{N} \sum_{i=1}^{N} y_i \qquad \text{or} \qquad \sum_{i=1}^{N} y_i = N\bar{y}$$

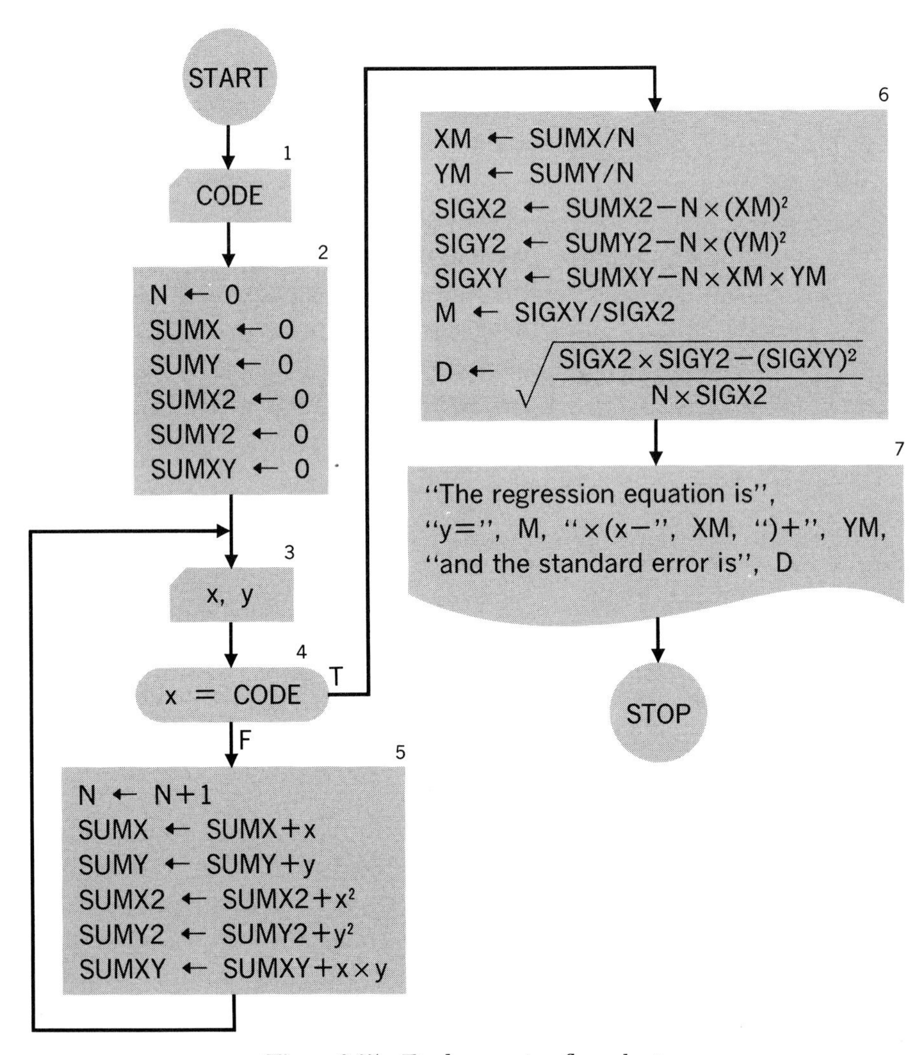

Figure 8-25 Final regression flow chart.

And now

$$\sum_{i=1}^{N} (x_i - \bar{x})^2 = \sum_{i=1}^{N} (x_i^2 - 2\bar{x}x_i + \bar{x}^2)$$

$$= \sum_{i=1}^{N} x_i^2 - 2\bar{x} \sum_{i=1}^{N} x_i + N\bar{x}^2$$

$$= \sum_{i=1}^{N} x_i^2 - 2\bar{x}N\bar{x} + N\bar{x}^2$$

$$= \sum_{i=1}^{N} x_i^2 - N\bar{x}^2$$

Similarly,

$$\sum_{i=1}^{N} (x_i - \bar{x})(y_i - \bar{y}) = \sum_{i=1}^{N} (x_iy_i - \bar{x}y_i - \bar{y}x_i + \bar{x}\bar{y})$$

$$= \sum_{i=1}^{N} x_iy_i - \bar{x} \sum_{i=1}^{N} y_i - \bar{y} \sum_{i=1}^{N} x_i + N\bar{x}\bar{y}$$

$$= \sum_{i=1}^{N} x_iy_i - \bar{x}N\bar{y} - \bar{y}N\bar{x} + N\bar{x}\bar{y}$$

$$= \sum_{i=1}^{N} x_iy_i - N\bar{x}\bar{y}$$

These formulas show us that we may build up the sums

$$\sum_{i=1}^{N} x_i^2, \qquad \sum_{i=1}^{N} y_i^2 \qquad \text{and} \qquad \sum_{i=1}^{N} x_iy_i$$

as the data is read and then make a single correction (subtracting $N\bar{x}^2$, $N\bar{y}^2$, $N\bar{x}\bar{y}$, respectively) after $\bar{x}$ and $\bar{y}$ have been computed. This modification also eliminates the necessity for subscripted variables. We provide, instead, for a CODE card to signal the end of our data. The flow chart is seen in Figure 8-25.

PART III

NONNUMERICAL APPLICATIONS

CHAPTER 9

TREES

9-1 INTRODUCTION

The use of flow charts to represent algorithms has helped us to recognize their underlying "structure." Furthermore, attention paid to the structure of an algorithm usually results in a better understanding of the computational process, and often results in our recognizing alternatives and potential improvements to the original design. Similar rewards result from attention paid to the structural relationships among the components of a set of data.

There is, in fact, a close connection between the steps we need to express an algorithm and the way we choose to think about or *represent* the data that is to be transformed by that algorithm. Experience in constructing algorithms leads to an increased appreciation of this interdependence. You are about to gain some of this experience by studying the chapters in Part III. Your ability to think about the structure of a set of data and to consider how its alternative representations can affect the nature of the algorithms that deal with such data will doubtless improve. Some structural forms of data that have already been considered are vectors and arrays. Another type of structure is called the *tree* (Figure 9-1). Tree structures are important in representing certain types of data and, oddly enough, the steps themselves of a number of algorithms exhibit a treelike structure.

First, we will give four simple examples of processes whose strategy of execution (algorithms) or whose data are pictured as a tree. Later, we will tackle three fascinating problems, the first one at the end of this chapter and the other two in Chapter 11. When we are finished studying these, we shall deserve the title *tree expert.*

Let us agree now, before we get too far along, that all trees in this chapter will henceforth be drawn upside-down (Figure 9-2). We do this only because we find it convenient. You have to be willing to think of a tree growing toward the earth, its trunk "hanging" from the sky.

Example 1. Tree-like algorithms

Our first example shows how we can represent the 16 conclusions to the well-known eight-coin problem as a "decision tree." The problem is this. You are given eight coins, a, b, c, d, e, f, g, and h, and are told that they are all of uniform weight except one, which is either heavier or lighter than the others. You are given an equal arm balance, but you may only

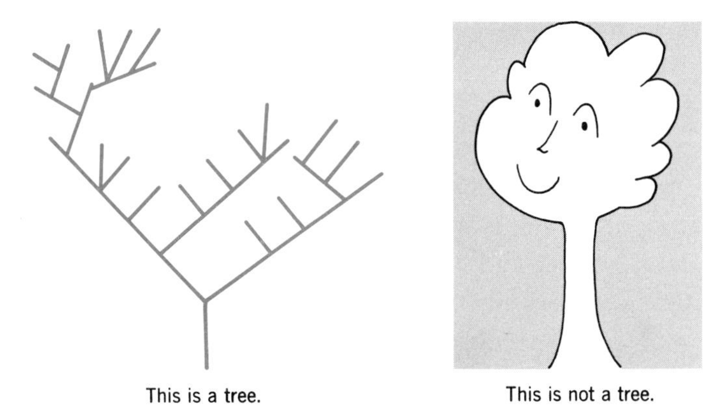

This is a tree.

This is not a tree.

Figure 9-1

use it three times for comparing coins or groups of coins. Your job is to determine the maverick coin and identify it as being either lighter or heavier than the rest.

Here is the strategy to use (see Figure 9-3) for all possible cases.

1. Compare the weights of two subsets of equal numbers of coins, and consider the significance of the *three* possible outcomes. If the weights of the two subsets are equal, the coin in which we are interested cannot be in either subset compared.

2. Once we have isolated a pair containing the "odd" coin and we want to know if one of them is heavy or light, we weigh one of the two candidates against any other which is known to be "standard."

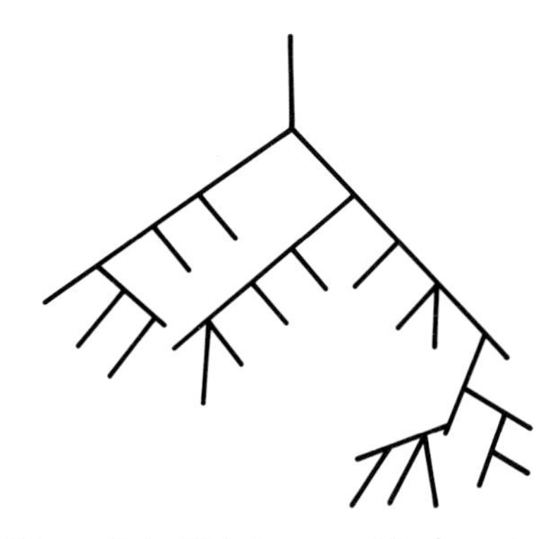

Figure 9-2 This is an upside-down tree.

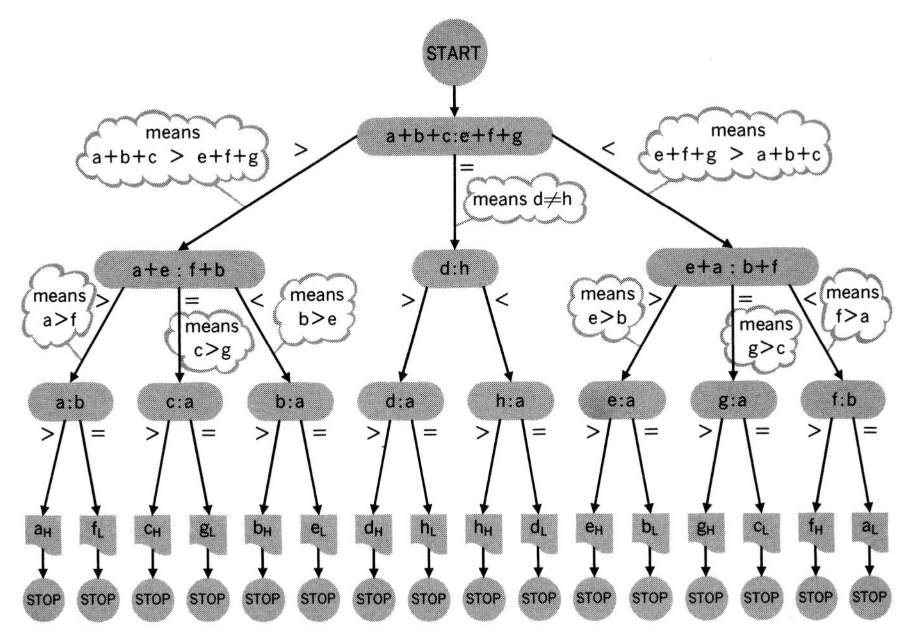

Figure 9-3 Tree diagram of a strategy for identifying the odd coin. Conclusions are subscripted: subscript H means *heavy;* subscript L means *light.*

There are 16 possible cases, each of which may occur, given the eight labeled coins. The algorithm given in Figure 9-3 has a treelike structure. Conclusions are reached by following a unique path (a sequence of three weighings) from the top or *root* of the tree diagram to one of the terminal boxes or *leaves* at the bottom.

EXERCISES 9-1, SET A

1. Suppose you are given twelve seemingly identical balls and are told that one ball is *heavier* than the others, which are the same weight. Draw the tree diagram algorithm to identify the heavy ball in three weighings.

2. Suppose you are given twelve seemingly identical balls and are told that one ball is *different* in weight (either heavier or lighter). Draw a tree diagram algorithm to identify the odd ball and to determine if it is heavier or lighter in three weighings.

3. Are all decision sequences trees? Consider the following three flow charts. Which are trees? Try to formulate a definition for a tree structure.

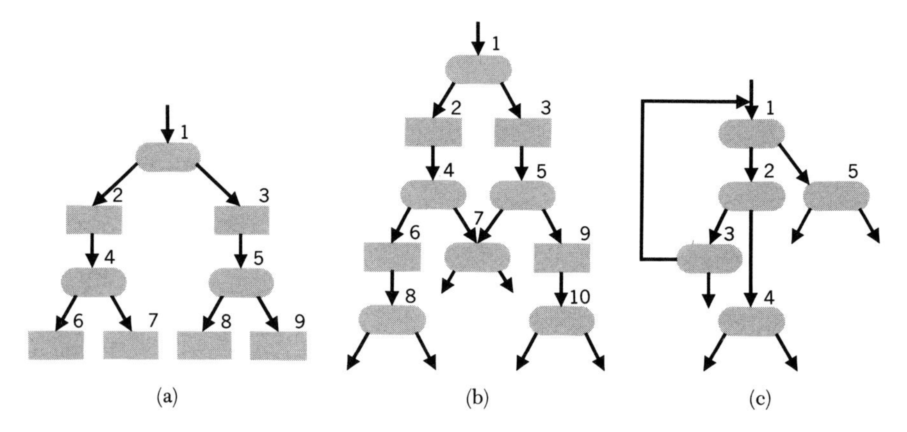

Example 2. Game trees

A more interesting type of decision tree, frequently referred to as a *game tree,* shows the moves made by the players. Each time a player makes a move, he selects among the available choices of "legal" moves. Each line segment of the tree represents one choice by one player during the playing of one game. Figure 9-4 is a tree for the game of "Eight." This two-player game is so trivial you may not enjoy playing it. Its tree is simple enough, however, that we can study it easily, and it serves as a good illustration of similar but far more complicated games.

The rules of "Eight." Each player takes a turn at picking a number from one to three, adding this number to a running sum that is initially set at zero. The first player has a free choice of numbers 1, 2, and 3. The choice in each play thereafter is restricted. A player may not choose the opponent's preceding selection. The player who brings the running sum to a total of exactly eight wins the game; a player exceeding eight loses. There is no draw possible.

When we study the game tree, we can observe that a complete game from start to finish is represented by one path (e.g., the rust line) from the beginning or *root* of the tree down to an end or terminal point. Thus, on the rust line, A chooses 1 from among his three initial choices. Then B chooses 3, then A chooses 1, etc., until at the last move for A the running sum is 7, and his choices are 1 and 3. So he chooses 1 to make the sum 8 and wins. Triangular shaped endpoints denote a win for A. Square shaped endpoints denote a win for B.

Each time a player makes a move, you can imagine he looks at three choices, 1, 2, and 3. He rules out one of these as the game rules demand,

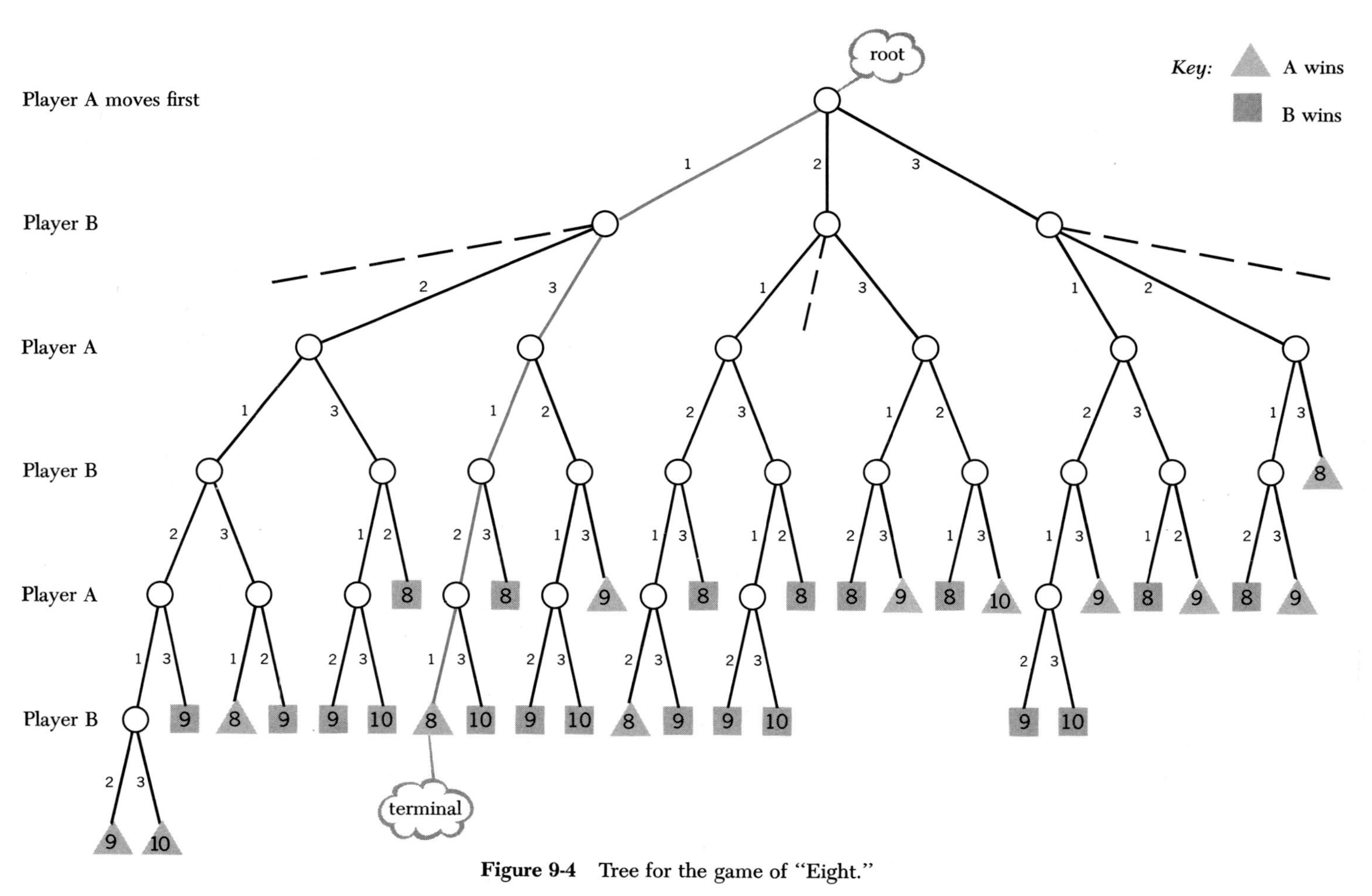

Figure 9-4 Tree for the game of "Eight."

after the very first play. Such *inadmissible* moves would not ordinarily appear in the tree because they tend to clutter the diagram. We have shown them as dashed lines for B's first move only as a reminder.

EXERCISES 9-1, SET B

1. (a) How many distinct games of "Eight" are there?

Imagine the game of Eight is played by tots at the local kindergarten in the following way. Player A twirls the arrow of a three-part spinner, to select

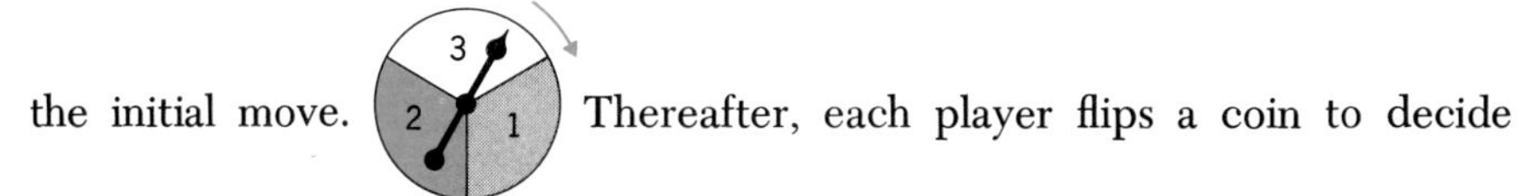

the initial move. Thereafter, each player flips a coin to decide among the two admissible choices. (Heads the smaller, tails the larger.)

(b) What percentage of games played will follow the rust-colored path in Figure 9-4?

(c) What are A's chances of winning? Express this result as number of games won for every 100 games played.

* (d) If each player chooses each move as shrewdly as possible, what do you think are A's chances of winning? A plays first. *Hint.* The answer is 0 times out of 100. See if you can develop a proof of this assertion. In Chapter 11 we will take another look at this problem.

In each of the next two exercises, you are given the rules of a simple, two-player game. Your job in each case is to show part or all of the game tree with at least four complete games displayed in the part of the tree that you manage to complete.

2. The game of *Hex* (or Hexapawn) uses a 3 by 3 checkerboard. Each player begins the game with three pieces in his base line, as shown in Figure 9-5. Play alternates between rust and gray. The rules of the game are as follows.

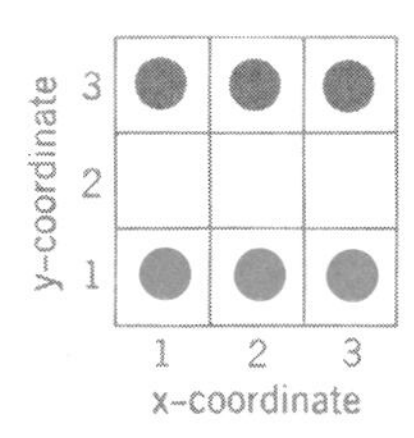

Figure 9-5 Board position at the beginning of the game of Hex.

1. Either rust or black, in his turn, can move forward one space to an unoccupied space.
2. Or he can move diagonally one space to capture an opponent. A captured piece is removed from the board.
3. The game is won by reaching the opponent's base line.
4. Or by leaving the opponent without a move.
5. Or by capturing all opponent pieces.

Hint. Each segment of the tree should be labeled to indicate the move it represents. One way would be to show the *before* and *after* x,y coordinates of the piece that is moved. For example, on rust's first play he has three choices: (1,1) → (1,2), or (2,1) → (2,2), or (3,1) → (3,2). Each of these moves can be further abbreviated to four-digit numbers without loss of information, that is, 1112, 2122, and 3132, respectively.

3. *The game of "31."* Take a die and roll it. The side that turns up gives the running sum's initial value. Thereafter, each player moves by tilting the die over on its side (one of four possible sides, of course—remember that opposite faces, 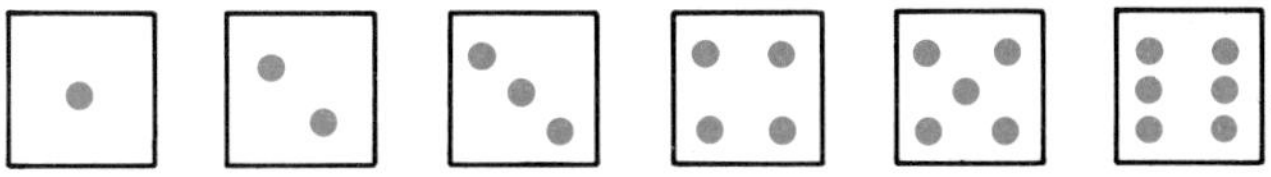 , always add to seven). The side that turns up after the tilt-over is then added to the running sum. The game proceeds tilt after tilt. A player whose tilt brings the total to exactly 31 wins the game; a player exceeding 31 loses. There are no draws.

Data Trees

Flow charts of algorithms often have the characteristic tree-like structure, but it is also interesting that *data* can be arranged in a tree-like structure. We now give two such examples.

Example 3. Monotone subsequences

Here we shall revisit the problem of finding longest monotone subsequences studied in Section 4-5.

Suppose you are told to look at the sequence

$$5, 0, 9, 6, 1, 12, 3, 7, 2$$

and are then asked, "What do you see?" The natural reply would be, "I see a string of nine integers." True enough, but now suppose you are commanded, "Picture in your mind's eye all the possible monotone decreasing subsequences of this string." "A hopeless task," you say? Not if you think in terms of trees! See the answer in Figure 9-6.

A most revealing discovery! We have taken a string of numbers, imposed a particular problem, and discovered that the problem's answer lies in inspecting a related tree. Notice that every monotone decreasing subsequence in S can be represented as a path running from the root S to one of the terminal squares. From now on, we'll call these circles and squares *nodes*.

The longest of such subsequences is easy for the eye to pick out once the tree is drawn. It is the one whose terminal node is found at a level of the tree farthest from the root node. In this example, only one path reaches to level 4, so there is only one longest monotone decreasing subsequence.

If a computer is to be used, we must have an algorithm that, in effect, systematically scans the entire tree. This is the interesting part, which will be taken up starting with the next section.

EXERCISE 9-1, SET C

1. Construct a tree that displays all monotone *increasing* subsequences of the same sequence given in Figure 9-6.

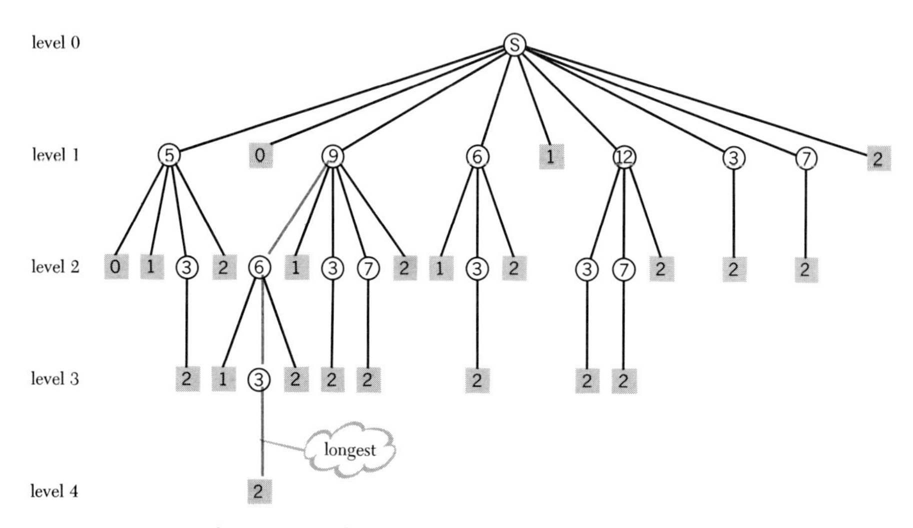

Figure 9-6 Tree of monotone *decreasing* subsequences for the string S = 5, 0, 9, 6, 1, 12, 3, 7, 2.

2. Imagine you are a student registering at a university who has decided to enroll in a particular group of five courses. The five courses, together with the available sections and the times each will be taught, are listed in Figure 9-7. We presume these data are extracted from the official class schedule. Notice that the time periods are letter-coded for convenience.

Course	Open Sections		
ENG 132	D	(9–10	MWF)
	F	(11–12	MWF)
	E	(10–11	MWF)
FRE 141	F	(11–12	MWF)
	H	(1–2	MWF)
	Q	(10–11:30	TTH)
HIS 231	F	(11–12	MWF)
	H	(1–2	MWF)
MTH 172	D	(9–10	MWF)
	F	(11–12	MWF)
	Q	(10–11:30	TTH)
CSC 131	F	(11–12	MWF)
	H	(1–2	MWF)

Time Table

Course	Letter Codes for Possible Set				
	#1	#2	#3	#4	#5
ENG 132					
FRE 141					
HIS 231					
MTH 172					
CSC 131					

Figure 9-7 Data extracted from the printed class schedule.

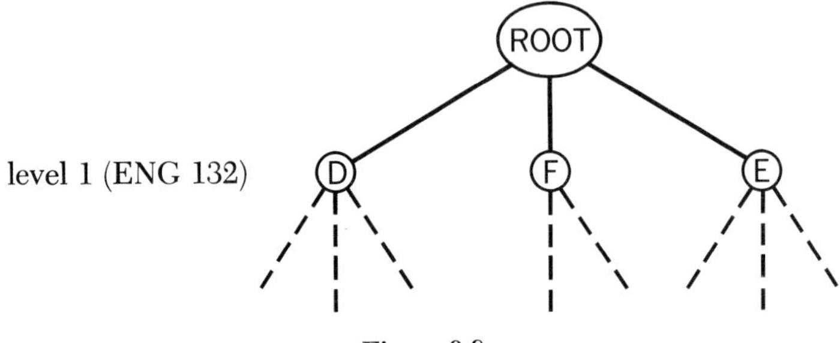

Figure 9-8

Does a possible set of sections for the five courses exist, that is, is it possible to select a set with no time conflicts? If so, how many distinct feasible sets can be selected? To be distinct, a set need differ in no more than one section from other possible sets. Complete a column of the time table shown in Figure 9-7 for each feasible set.

Hint. This problem, and others like it, can be solved systematically by constructing a tree of labeled nodes. The structure for the tree might be such that the set of nodes along any path emanating from the root would represent a set of nonconflicting course sections. For example, labeled nodes at level 1 could represent the various available sections of ENG 132 (Figure 9-8). Nodes at level 2 could correspond to various sections of FRE 141, etc. Any path running from the root to level 5 that has no two nodes with the same label would represent a feasible set of courses.

Example 4. Tree representation of expressions

Suppose we are given:

$$((a \times w + b) \times w) \uparrow 2/(d \times y)$$

It seems obvious that whoever first wrote this string of characters intended that it have a mathematical meaning. By now, you are quite expert at interpreting such strings. This interpretation, remember, involved the application of a relatively complicated set of rules (Tables 2-1 and 2-3). Figure 9-9 shows how we can represent the same string as a tree and give it the same interpretations. We shall quickly discover that the rules for evaluating an expression represented as a tree are much simpler to state because *part of the interpretation is inherent in the structure of the tree.*

Before proceeding with this line of thought, it will be helpful to summarize and supplement the tree terminology developed thus far. This is done with the aid of Figure 9-10.

We see that every tree has a *root node* from which extend *segments*

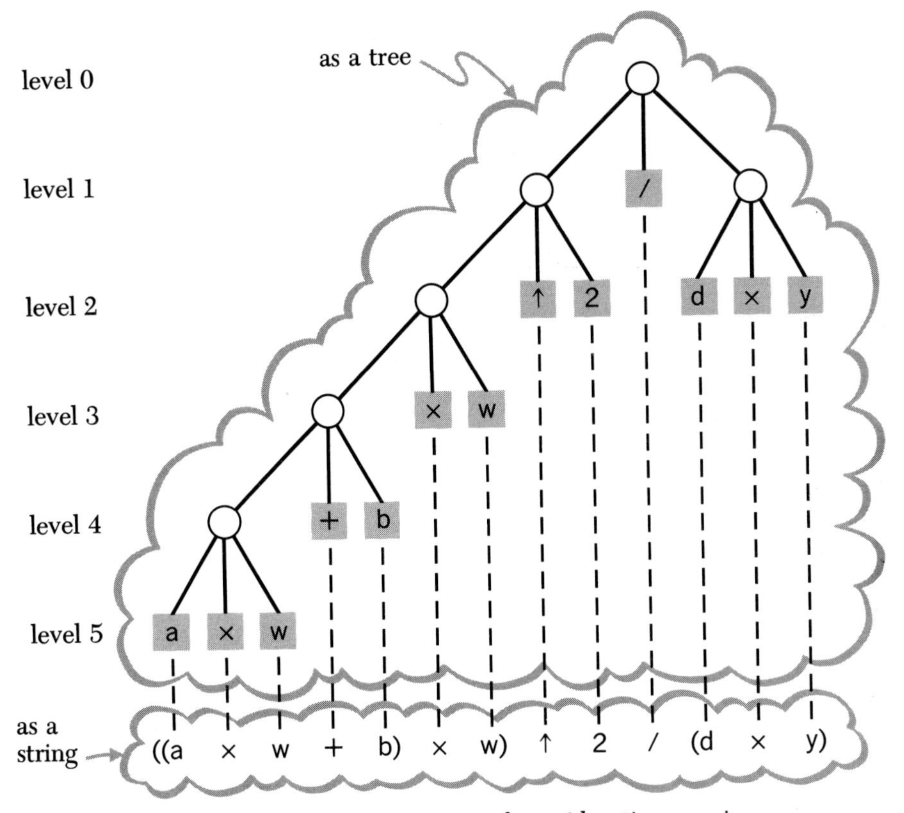

Figure 9-9 A tree representation of an arithmetic expression.

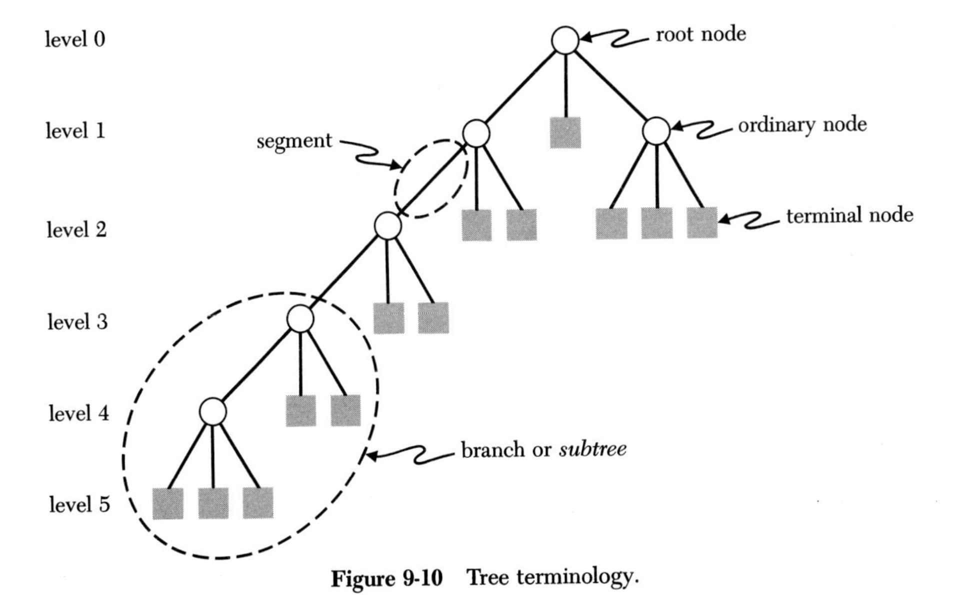

Figure 9-10 Tree terminology.

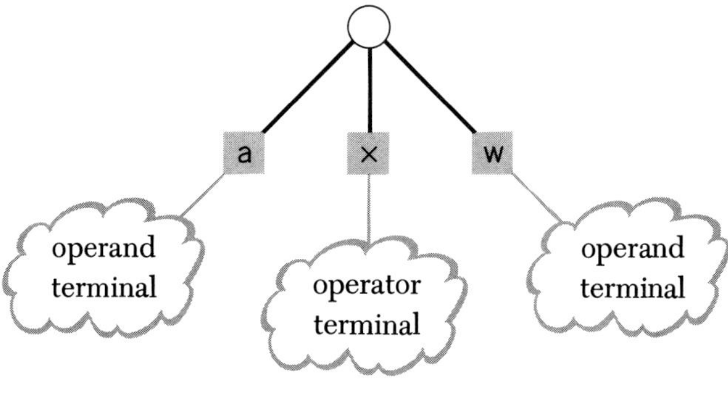

Figure 9-11

(two or more, in general) to other nodes, which in turn branch to others, eventually ending at a *terminal node.* Every *branch* can be thought of as a subtree[1] and, hence, has its own beginning node. A branch includes everything that hangs from the beginning node. Nodes can be located (identified) by *level,* which is a node count along a *path* from the root (level 0) to a terminal.

The *expression tree,* by its very structure, provides the key to evaluating the expression that is represented. For example, suppose values for the variables of our expression are

a	w	b	d	y
3	2	2	−1	7

Notice that a tree branch of the form shown in Figure 9-11 can be taken to mean:

Look up the values of a and w, and compute a × w = 3 × 2 = 6. Now replace the branch by the terminal node 6.

Correspondingly, the branch

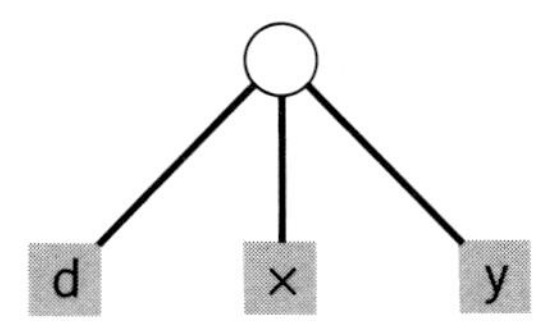

is interpreted as:

[1] Occasionally, we will want to use the term *subtree* as distinct from branch. A subtree is a more general concept. It refers to *any* tree you can get from the original tree by "pruning," i.e., cutting off some of its branches.

Compute $d \times y = -1 \times 7 = -7$, and replace the branch by the terminal node -7.

Figure 9-12 represents a sequence of meaningful substitutions which, when carried out, will ultimately lead to the replacement of the whole tree, root node and all, by a single terminal, which represents the value of the expression.

Proper evaluation is guaranteed if we follow one simple *replacement rule* which says:

Whenever you find a branch consisting of a node leading to three terminals (an operator and two operands), you can replace that branch by a single terminal value.

Thus, the replacement sequence in Figure 9-13, though different from that of Figure 9-12, leads us irrevocably to the same value, $\boxed{\frac{-256}{7}}$. If a computer were performing these steps for us, we would get the same approximation of $\boxed{\frac{-256}{7}}$, notwithstanding the fact that computer operations are nonassociative. Another point to note is that the tree-like representation of a complicated arithmetic expression allows us to see all the meaningful subexpressions (all the branches) at a glance.

Once we represent an expression as a tree, then evaluations of the expression hinge only on the ability to repeatedly search and find branches that are subject to the replacement rule. At any given time, an expression tree, if it is not already fully evaluated, will exhibit at least one such branch.

EXERCISES 9-1, SET D

1. Draw a tree representation for the expression

$$B \uparrow 2 - 4 \times A \times C$$

2. The following are two proposed tree representations for the expression

$$I - N \times A \uparrow N / D + \emptyset \times U - T$$

Which, if either, of these trees, if evaluated by the branch replacement rule, will yield a result computationally equivalent to the result we get when following the evaluation rules laid down in Chapter 2, Tables 2-1 and 2-3? If the

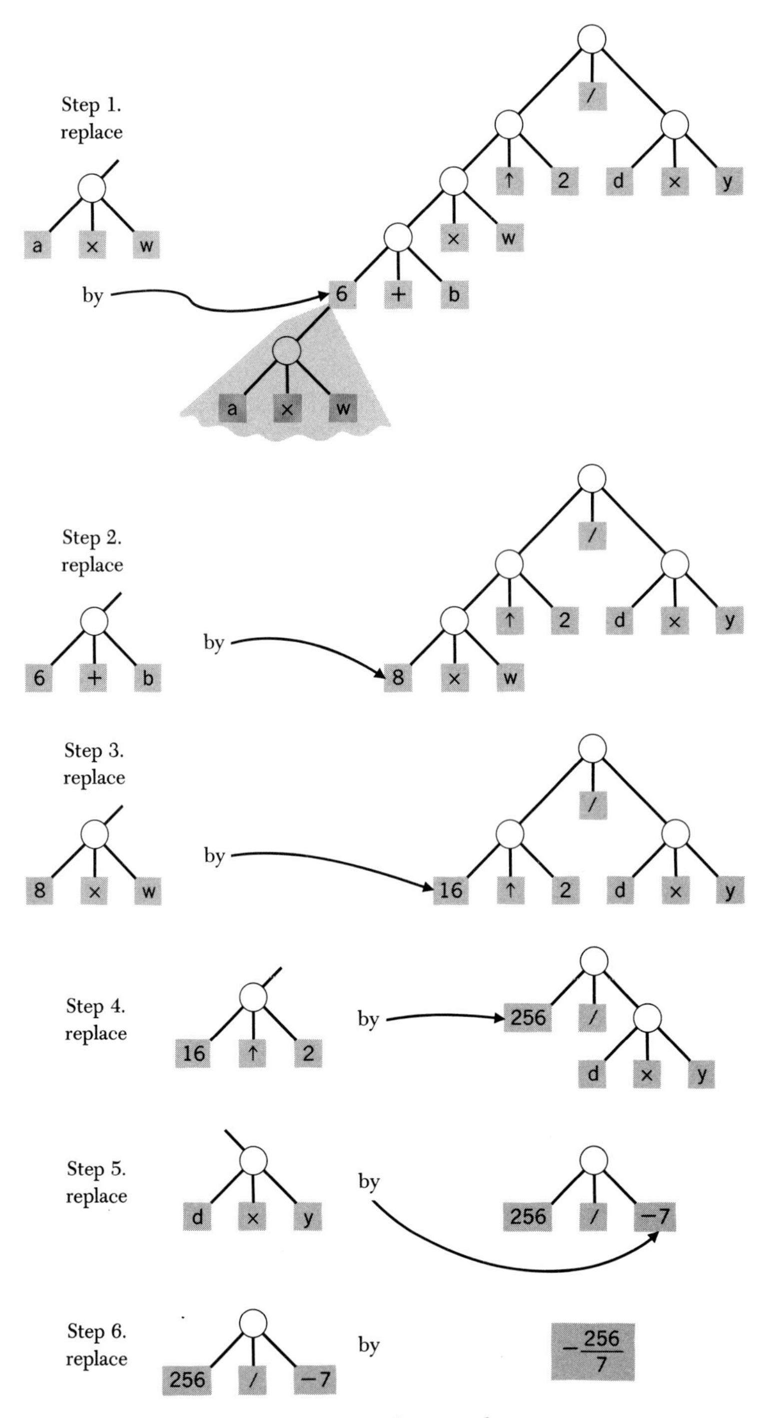

Figure 9-12 A stepwise evaluation of a tree expression.

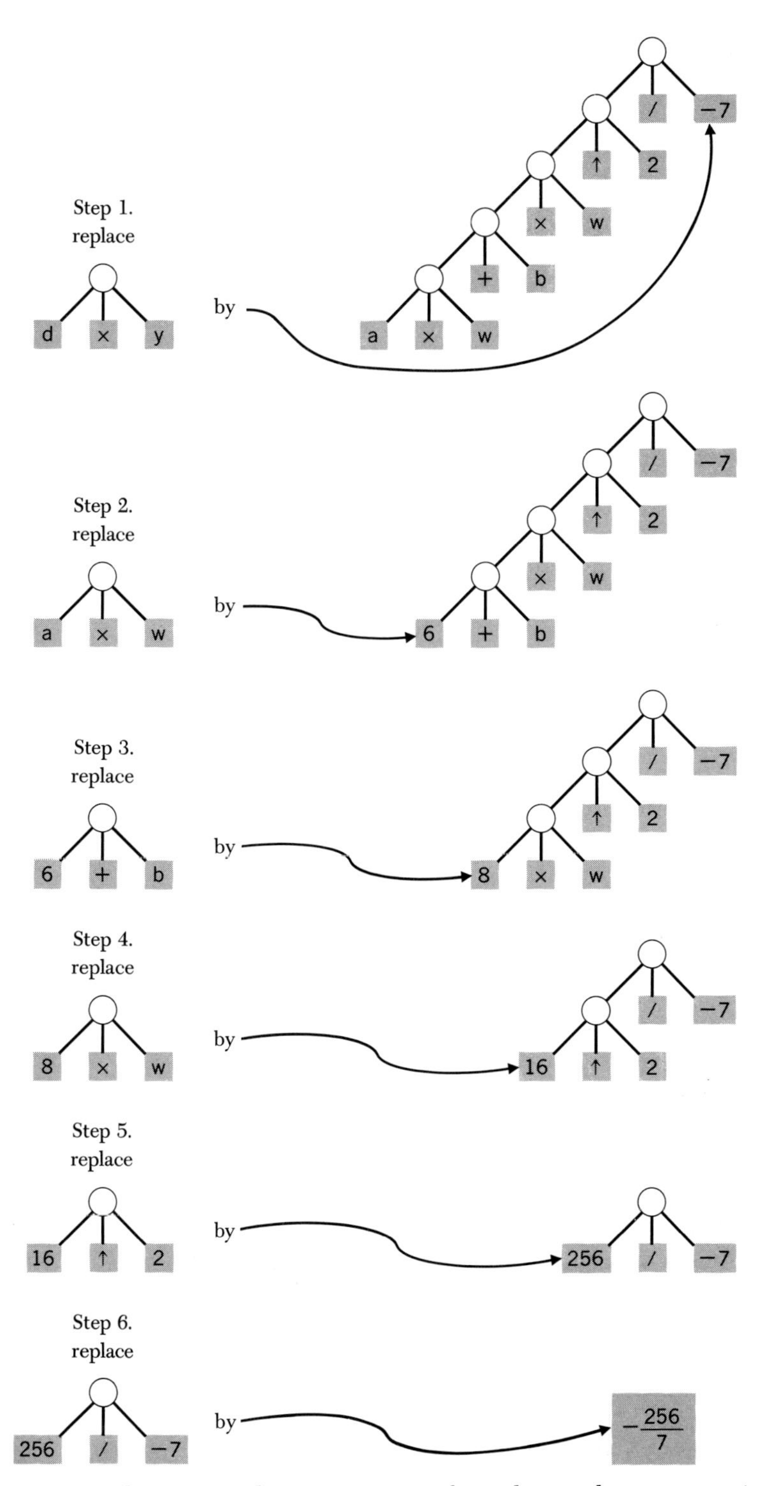

Figure 9-13 Alternative replacement sequence for evaluating the tree expression.

evaluation of either one of the trees is not compatible with these rules, describe the discrepancy.

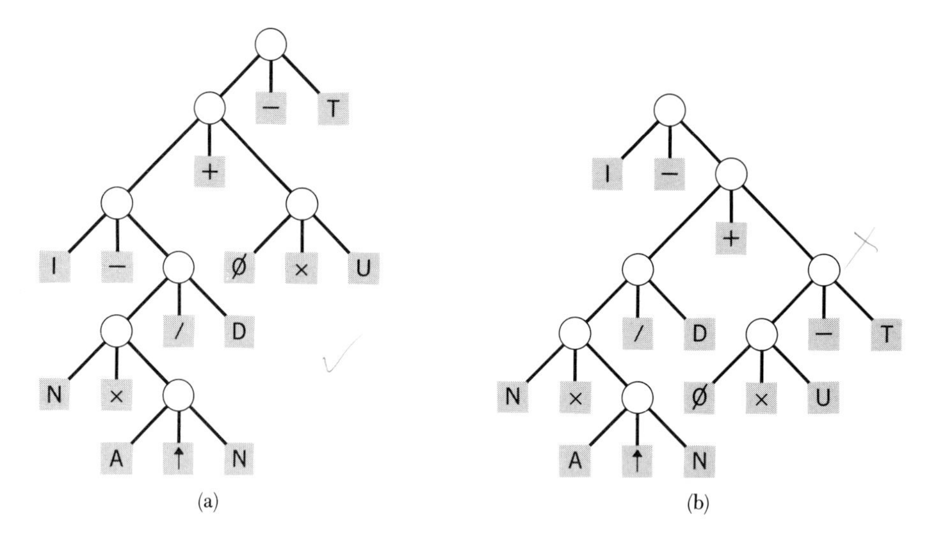

(a) (b)

In each of the following exercises, draw a tree representation for the given expression.

3. $(a - b) \times (c - d)/(e \times (f + g))$

4. $A + \sqrt{Z}$ (*Suggestion.* One way to express $\sqrt{x}$ in tree form is as an operator with one operand. This means that some nodes of the tree need have only *two* branches.)

[2]**5.** $\cos(x^2 + y^2)$

[2]**6.** $\sqrt{\frac{1}{2}(1 + q / \sqrt{p^2 + q^2})}$

9-2 TREE SEARCHES

We have now seen enough of trees to have noted their main *structural* characteristics: segments of each branch always connect to new nodes that form a continuation of the same branch; there is no looping back to nodes closer to the root; and there is no crossing or crisscrossing between branches.

There are many ways one can construct and store a tree structure in memory. One particular way will be developed in Chapter 11. Depending on what use is to be made of the tree, some representations (we will

[2] The suggestion given in Problem 4 will help you here, too.

call these *storage structures*) are better than others. Trees are searched for one reason or another, either to gain specific information, to reach a conclusion, or to modify the tree in a certain way. A tree search lies at the heart of a number of mathematical problems and a great number of games.

Natural Order Tree Search

There is a systematic way, which is of particular interest, to scan all nodes of a tree. It's a good way to search in a number of problems where a systematic approach is needed. We call it *natural order* searching. Although a squirrel has better ways of finding nuts in a tree, it will help us to understand natural order search if we imagine a nut-seeking squirrel willing to follow these rules.

1. Start at the trunk (root) and don't stop (unless you find a nut, of course) until you get to a leaf (terminal node).
2. Upon reaching a terminal, back up to the node you just passed, i.e., to the *parent* node of this terminal.
3. Now move forward again along any remaining untried segment toward another leaf node.
4. If there are no untried segments, crawl backward to the predecessor (parent) node and repeat the process of trying to reach another leaf node.
5. If you ever find yourself back to the root having already tried all segments from the root, you've finished searching the entire tree in natural order.

Figure 9-14 shows a natural order search of a tree. The numbers beside the nodes indicate the sequence in which they are first encountered (that is, as the squirrel sees them in its forward progress). We picture one of these nodes as a nut. It is the 23rd node encountered. Notice the systematic, left-to-right selection of segments at each node.

Algorithm for Natural Tree Search

We are now ready to present, in Figure 9-15, a systematic procedure, i.e., an algorithm, for conducting a natural order tree search. In a specific application, some of the boxes in this flow chart (especially box 5) may be broken down into a number of flow-chart components.

The details of box 4 may very well be crucial to the success of the search. As many segments as possible that are inadmissible (undesirable

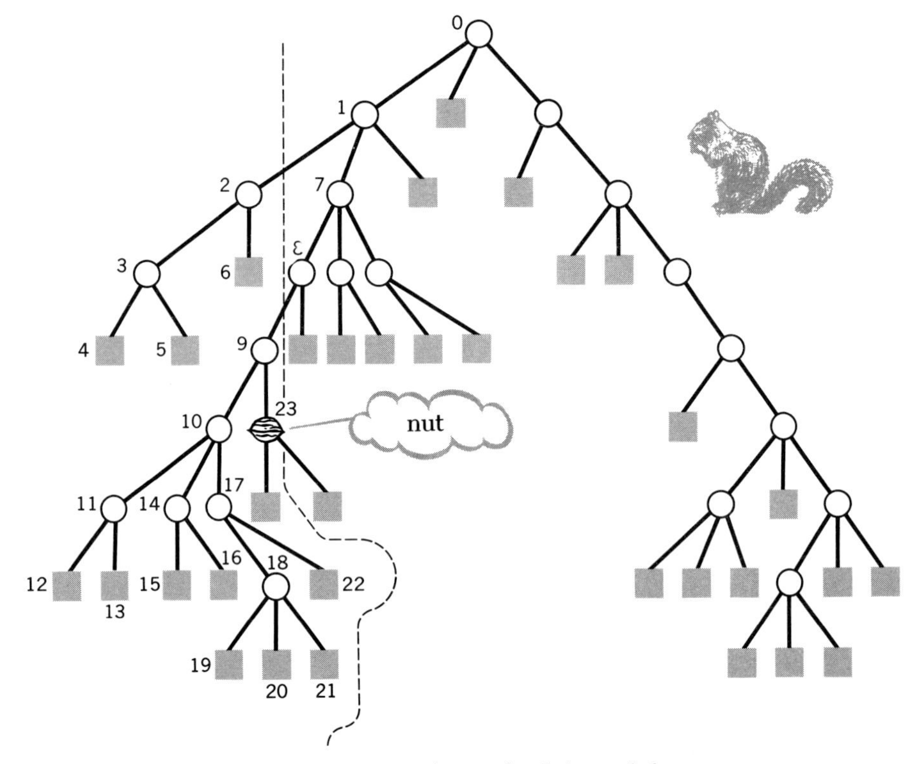

Figure 9-14 Systematic (*natural order*) search for a nut.

or illegal) must be ruled out at each stage. For example, the squirrel should recognize each dead limb and not search it. Otherwise, the proportion of useless paths will grow rapidly, meaning that the efficiency of the search method will plummet toward zero.

Next, we will examine two interesting problems that employ this type of search in their algorithmic solution.

9-3 THE FOUR-COLOR PROBLEM

Maps are colored to make it easy to see at a glance the extent of each country. It is clearly necessary that neighboring countries (that is, countries with a common boundary line) be assigned different colors. Does the map maker then need more than four colors to do his job? He doesn't care, but we *do*.

This problem is one of the most celebrated challenges in mathematics.

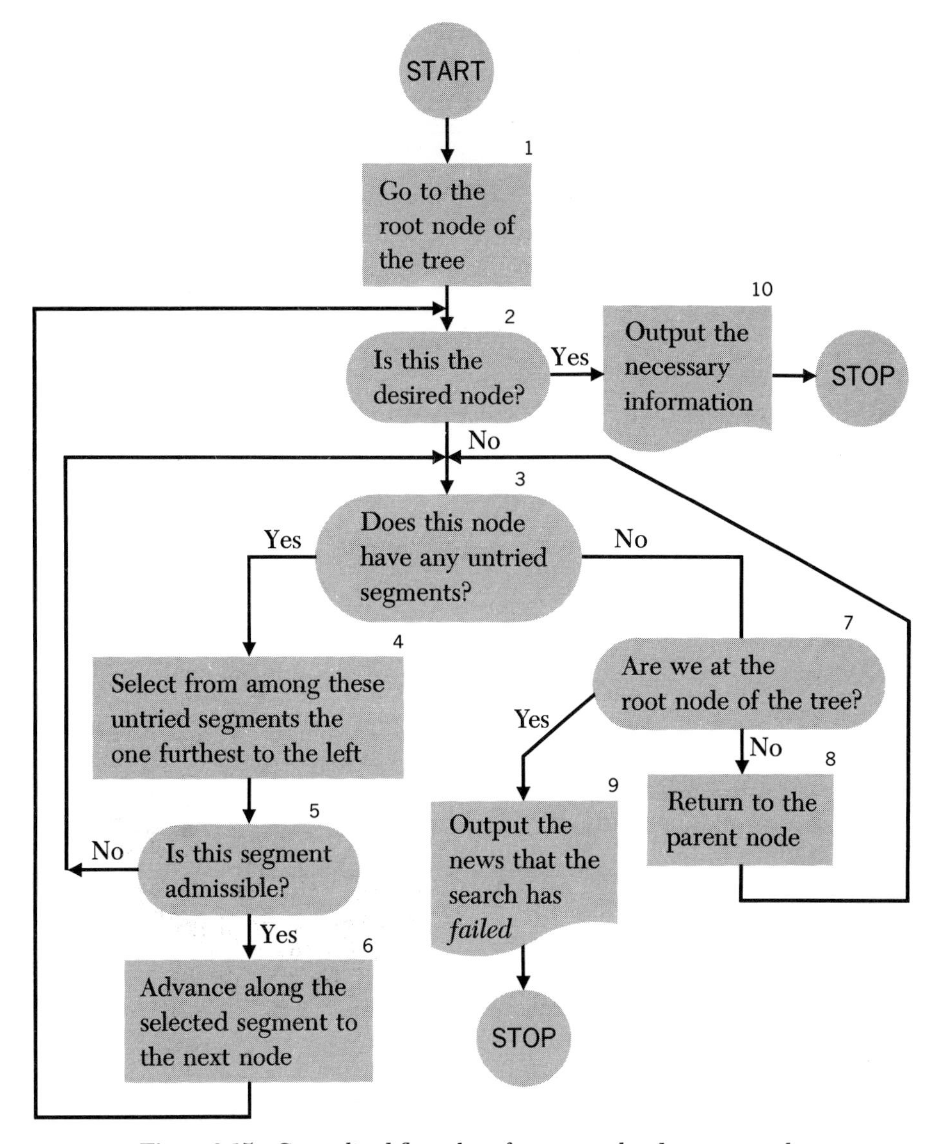

Figure 9-15 Generalized flow chart for a natural order tree search.

It is of great intellectual interest and has intrigued many people from all paths of life. Its solution has little or nothing whatsoever to do with making maps. A map maker is and always will be able to print maps using as many different colors as he needs.

A checkerboard is an example of a map that can be colored with only two colors. The four-country map shown in Figure 9-16 requires *four*

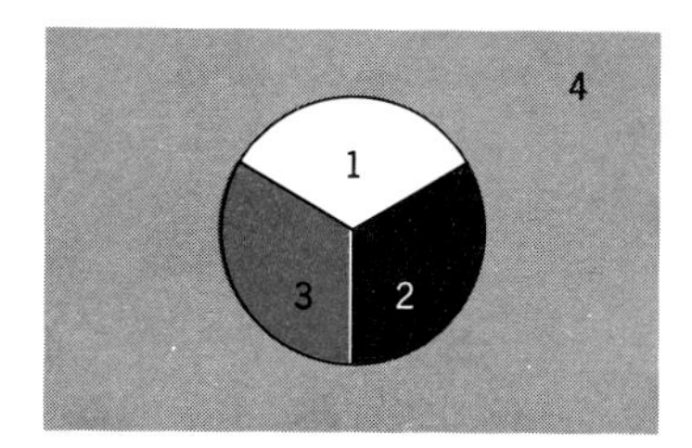

Figure 9-16

colors. The reason for this is that, each pair of countries being adjacent, no two can have the same color.

It didn't take us long to find a map requiring four colors. Yet, in over a hundred years of searching, no one has succeeded in finding a map requiring five! It is natural to conjecture that every possible map can be colored with four colors, and many mathematicians have racked their brains trying to prove this conjecture. The best they have been able to do so far is to show that every map can be colored using no more than five colors.[3]

We are about to see how computer methods can be applied to the four-color problem. We will not use the computer to show that the four-color conjecture is *true*. Indeed, it is entirely possible that no computer can ever prove this. However, true or false, we can use the computer to determine whether a particular map can be colored in only four colors. This is the task for which we want to construct an algorithm.

Before getting started on this algorithm, a few remarks concerning the coloring of maps may be helpful.

A *minimal five-color map* is a map requiring five colors, such that every other map requiring five colors has at least as many countries. Of course, no minimal five-color map has ever been found. But, mathematicians have shown that if such maps exist at all, then some of them satisfy these two conditions.

1. No point is a boundary point of more than three countries.
2. Each country is a neighbor of at least five others.

Moreover, it can also be shown that *every* minimal map, if any exist, must satisfy the second condition.

It is therefore customary to consider as candidates for counter-examples to the four-color conjecture only maps fulfilling these conditions.

[3] A very simple proof of the five-color theorem exists. It may be found, for example, in *What is Mathematics?* by Courant and Robbins.

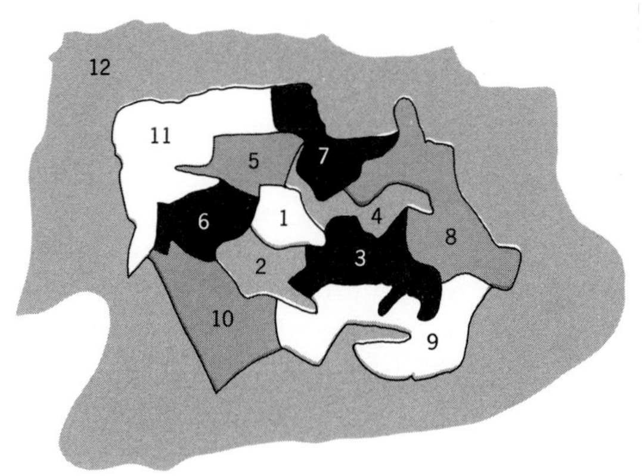

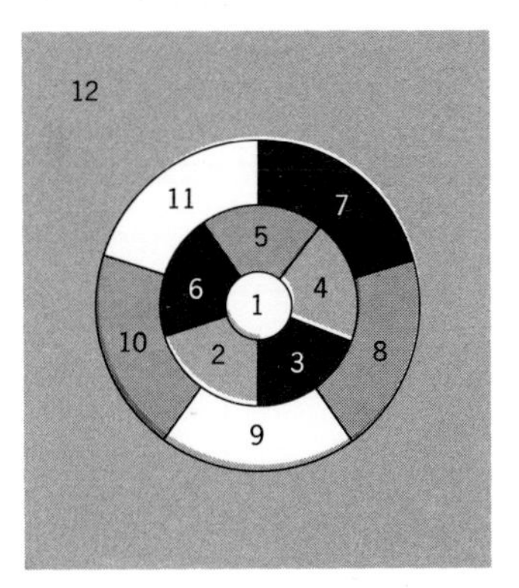

Figure 9-17

Four-Coloring as a Tree Search

We can model the problem of four-coloring a given map, say, the one pictured in Figure 9-17, as one of traveling along a path through a tree like that shown in Figure 9-18. Each segment represents a decision to color a country, with colors 1, 2, 3, or 4. The ith segment in a path from the root corresponds to the coloring of the ith country of the map.

We can always choose three countries which are neighbors of one another and begin by coloring these countries. Since each of these countries must then be of a different color and it is immaterial which colors we assign to them, we choose colors 1, 2, and 3. That is why our tree (Figure 9-18) shows only one segment coming from each of the first three nodes.

In coloring all the remaining countries, it's convenient to imagine that for each there are up to four choices possible. Most of the time, however,

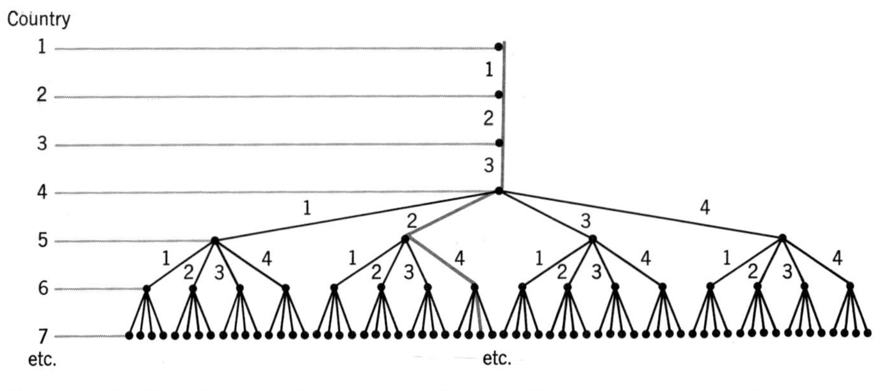

Figure 9-18 Showing the coloring tree and one path representing the coloring of the first six countries (colored line).

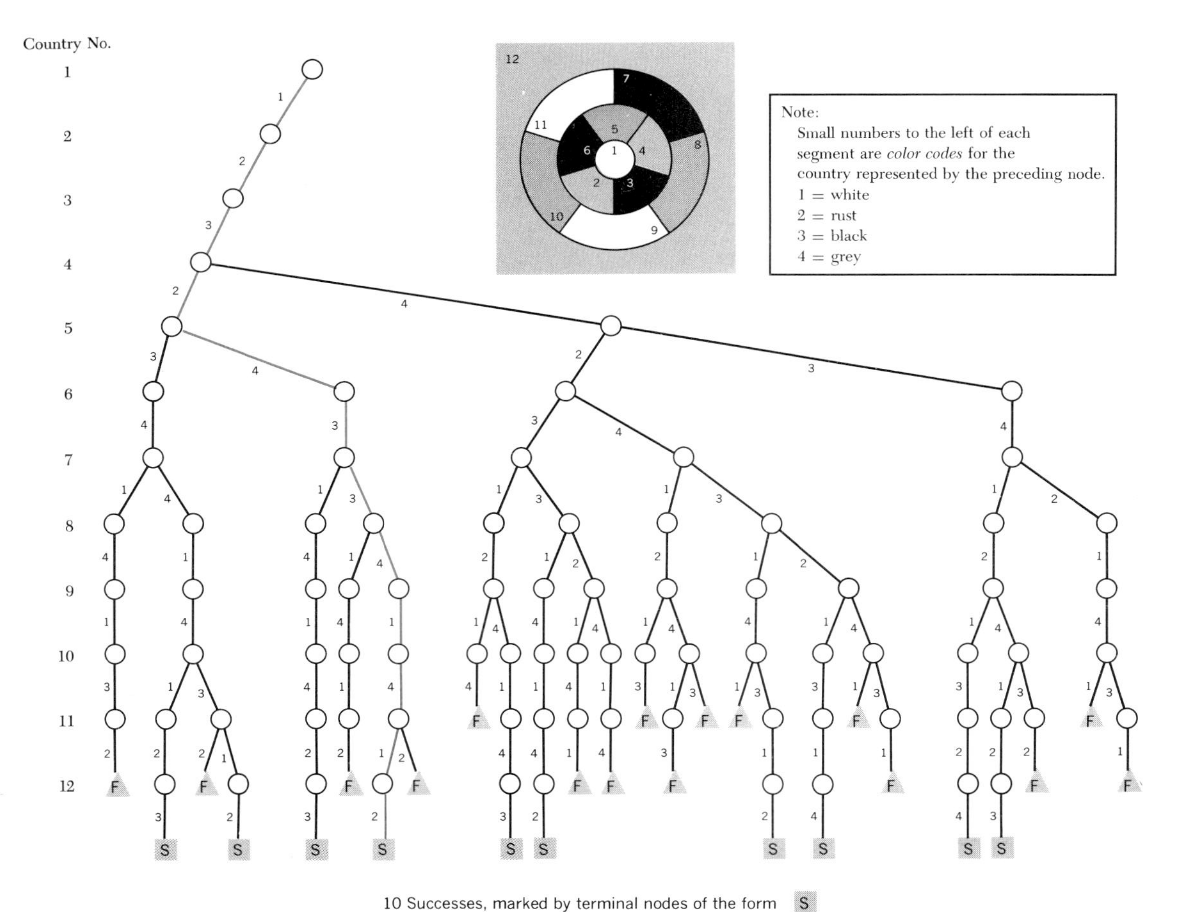

Figure 9-19 Entire coloring tree showing all ways to four-color the map of Figure 9-17.

as can be seen in Figure 9-19, only one, two, or three of these choices will be admissible. Sometimes even all four choices will be inadmissible, as exemplified by terminal nodes marked F in Figure 9-19. Only ten paths lead to S (success) terminals.

EXERCISES 9-3

1. Compute the theoretical maximum number of possible terminal nodes for the coloring tree of the 12-country map in Figure 9-17. *Hint.* Use Figure 9-18 as a guide.

2. Assume that it takes only 1 microsecond to check another path to a terminal, and that the search of half of these paths is required before the desired terminal is reached. How long would the computer chug away before it found what it was looking for in a 39-country map? Assume all segments to be admissible. Express your answer in units of *years*.

3. By renumbering the countries in the map of Figure 9-17, show that a coloring tree can have nodes with three and even four permissible segments emanating from them.

Problem Statement

Study the material in the next few paragraphs and develop a detailed flow-chart algorithm for four-coloring any n-country map, using the guidelines of the generalized algorithm for the tree search given in Figure 9-15.

Auxiliary Information

In following the ensuing discussion use the map provided in Figure 9-20 as an example. The first step in preparing for the algorithm is the numbering or indexing of the countries. As you see, this has already been done.

The efficiency of the algorithm will be greatly improved if each country borders on the one with the next lower number and on at least one *other* country with a lower number. We do not absolutely insist on this but, if you have done Problem 3 of Exercise 9-3, you will appreciate why we recommend this approach.

We do, however, require that the first three countries all be neighbors of each other.

How do we represent the map in computer memory? One way is to construct a "connection table," listing after each country all of its

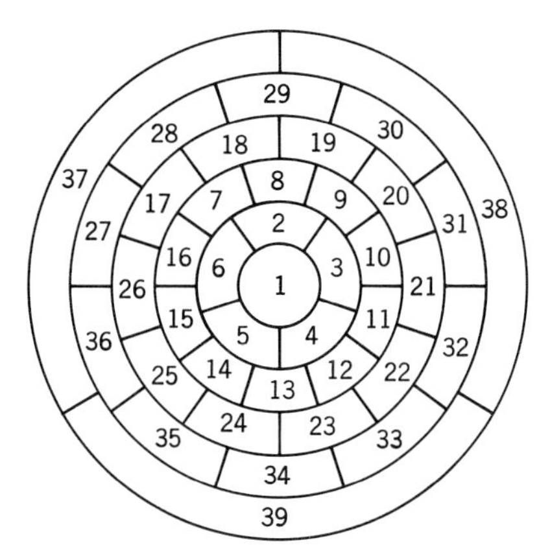

Figure 9-20 Example of map to be four-colored by a computer algorithm.

neighbors in increasing order. This is shown for our example in Table 9-1.

Our algorithm can consult this table when deciding how to color a particular country. For example, if we were coloring country 15, we could see in row 15 that countries 5, 6, and 14 are neighbors that have

TABLE 9-1 The Connection Table for the Map in Figure 9-20

Country	Neighbors						Country	Neighbors						
1.	2	3	4	5	6		21.	10	11	20	22	31	32	
2.	1	3	6	7	8	9	22.	11	12	21	23	32	33	
3.	1	2	4	9	10	11	23.	12	13	22	24	33	34	
4.	1	3	5	11	12	13	24.	13	14	23	25	34	35	
5.	1	4	6	13	14	15	25.	14	15	24	26	35	36	
6.	1	2	5	7	15	16	26.	15	16	17	25	27	36	
7.	2	6	8	16	17	18	27.	17	26	28	36	37		
8.	2	7	9	18	19		28.	17	18	27	29	37		
9.	2	3	8	10	19	20	29.	18	19	28	30	37	38	
10.	3	9	11	20	21		30.	19	20	29	31	38		
11.	3	4	10	12	21	22	31.	20	21	30	32	38		
12.	4	11	13	22	23		32.	21	22	31	33	38	39	
13.	4	5	12	14	23	24	33.	22	23	32	34	39		
14.	5	13	15	24	25		34.	23	24	33	35	39		
15.	5	6	14	16	25	26	35.	24	25	34	36	39		
16.	6	7	15	17	26		36.	25	26	27	35	37	39	
17.	7	16	18	26	27	28	37.	27	28	29	36	38	39	
18.	7	8	17	19	28	29	38.	29	30	31	32	37	39	
19.	8	9	18	20	29	30	39.	32	33	34	35	36	37	38
20.	9	10	19	21	30	31								

been colored already. Our choice of colors for 15, then, depends solely on the currently chosen colors for 5, 6, and 14.

Knowing that country 15 also has neighbors numbered 16, 25, and 26 appears to be superfluous to our needs. This leads us to the idea of a shaved-down table, which we shall call the "*reduced* connection table." It is constructed by striking out of each row in the table all numbers greater than the number of the row itself. The reduced connection table for our example is seen in Table 9-2 and can be thought of in this case as a 39 row by 7 column array called CONN. The number of nonnull elements in each row is given by elements of an associated vector W. Thus, the algorithm can search the first w_i elements in the ith row of CONN to determine which neighbors have already been colored.

At all times during the search, we should maintain a record of the *current* color path, that is, the one that runs from the root node through the country last colored. A COLOR vector can be used to hold this informa-

TABLE 9-2 Reduced Connection Table for the Map in Figure 9-20

Country i	Neighbors $CONN_{ij}$	Width w_i	Country i	Neighbors $CONN_{ij}$	Width w_i
1		0	21	10 11 20	3
2	1	1	22	11 12 21	3
3	1 2	2	23	12 13 22	3
4	1 3	2	24	13 14 23	3
5	1 4	2	25	14 15 24	3
6	1 2 5	3	26	15 16 17 25	4
7	2 6	2	27	17 26	2
8	2 7	2	28	17 18 27	3
9	2 3 8	3	29	18 19 28	3
10	3 9	2	30	19 20 29	3
11	3 4 10	3	31	20 21 30	3
12	4 11	2	32	21 22 31	3
13	4 5 12	3	33	22 23 32	3
14	5 13	2	34	23 24 33	3
15	5 6 14	3	35	24 25 34	3
16	6 7 15	3	36	25 26 27 35	4
17	7 16	2	37	27 28 29 36	4
18	7 8 17	3	38	29 30 31 32 37	5
19	8 9 18	3	39	32 33 34 35 36 37 38	7
20	9 10 19	3			

tion, the element $COLOR_i$ holding the color code chosen for country i. As we travel around the tree during natural search, the COLOR vector must be changed accordingly. (In the interest of clarity and efficiency, use a nonsubscripted variable TRYCOLOR to hold successive tentative color choices for each country. Assign TRYCOLOR to $COLOR_i$ only when its value has been found to be currently admissible.) When we reach and have successfully coded the last country, the four-coloring scheme can be displayed by printing the components of this vector.

Finally, notice that Table 9-2 gives all the input data required for the algorithm. You've now been given enough help, you're on your own.

CHAPTER 10

COMPILING

10-1 POLISH STRINGS

When a procedural language program (like FORTRAN or ALGOL) is read into a computer, quite a lot of activity takes place before the machine actually begins to execute the program. First of all, the program is stored in the computer's memory so that the computer can scan the FORTRAN program, character by character, and generate a list of machine language instructions.

For example, if the machine were SAMOS, then the procedural language statement

$$A \leftarrow A+B\times C$$

would be converted into machine language instructions somewhat as follows. (We assume that A, B and C have been given the storage locations 1001, 1002, and 1003.)

±	OPER		ADDRESS	REMARKS
1	2 3 4	5 6 7	8 9 10 11	
	L D A		1 0 0 2	Put B in accumulator
	M P Y		1 0 0 3	Multiply accumulator by C
	A D D		1 0 0 1	Add A to accumulator
	S T Ø		1 0 0 1	Assign value in accumulator to A

The process of converting procedural programs into machine language instructions is called *compiling*. In this chapter we will study some facets of the compiling process. In Chapter 13 we will return to complete the discussion of compiling. Even with the improvements made in Section 2-3, it is awkward to convert our customary notation for arithmetic expressions into machine language instructions. We will show you why this is so.

Consider the arithmetic expression

$$\frac{B+\sqrt{B^2-4\times A\times C}}{2\times A}$$

which represents the *negative* of one of the roots of the equation

$$A\times X^2+B\times X+C = 0$$

(We have omitted the minus sign in front of the first B above to avoid the complication of a *unary* minus at this point.)

Adopting the modifications of Section 2-3, the above expression takes the form

(B+(B↑2−4×A×C)↑.5)/(2×A)

Now, let's number the operations in this expression in the order in which the operations are performed in the evaluation process. This is the order in which they will appear in our list of machine language instructions.

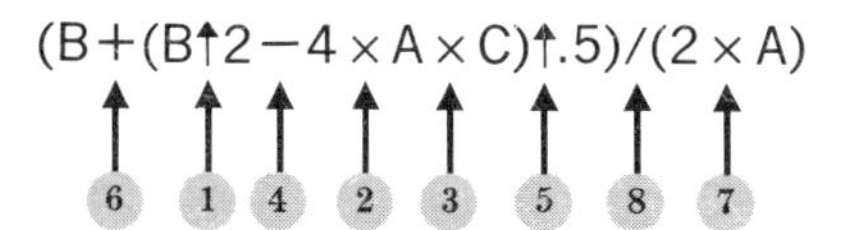

Now we see the difficulty. The machine must engage in a great deal of back-and-forth scanning of the expression to find the next operation to be performed.

To eliminate this difficulty, the machine makes a preliminary translation of arithmetic expressions into *Polish string notation* (so called after the Polish mathematician, Lukasiewicz, who originated this kind of notation). This notation has the advantage that operations appear in the order in which they are actually performed in the evaluation.

The basic idea behind Polish string notation is that operators are written at the end of the expression rather than in the middle. Thus, A+B would be written as AB+. In this new form, the operator + is viewed as a command to add the values of the two variables immediately preceding it.

In computing we have permitted a variable to be a string of characters, and this permissiveness introduces the risk of a certain confusion in the use of Polish notation unless we are alert to the problem. For example, the expression

AA/AAA

if converted into Polish notation, will be

AAAAA/

Unfortunately, the same form will result when AAA/AA, A/AAAA, AAAA/A, etc. are expressed in Polish notation. Thus, unless we have suitable protection, an expression in the form of Polish string notation can be unclear in that we may not be able to identify it uniquely with an expression in the *usual* notation.

To avoid this ambiguity we will need to insist that every variable be delimited, that is, its beginning and end identified. In the usual notation we partially depend on the operators to delimit the variables, but in Polish notation this no longer works. There are a number of ways of delimiting variables; one is to insist that a variable can consist of only one character, another is to insert some distinguishing mark, say, the blank (□) after (or before) each variable when the expression is being converted into Polish notation. Then the expression

AA/AAA

can be converted, without fear of ambiguity, into

AA AAA /

All present-day compilers *preedit* input expressions using something equivalent to the above approaches. Each multicharacter variable, constant, or operator is replaced by a uniquely coded symbol which is frequently of fixed length. (Sometimes, special delimiting codes are used to indicate the end of the symbol.) In Chapter 12 we will return to the discussion of some of the techniques used in preediting.

In the comparatively simple examples that follow, it will be convenient to use only expressions having single-character variables. This will save us the trouble of inserting marks between the elements of an expression when it is displayed in Polish notation.

Here is an example of how this *postfix* (or operators-at-the-end) notation replaces the customary *infix* (or operators-in-the-middle) notation in a more complicated expression.

Infix	Postfix
(A+B)×(C−D)	(AB+)(CD−)×

In the postfix form, the operator × is viewed as a command to multiply the values of the two expressions (AB+) and (CD−) immediately preceding it.

How can we devise general rules for translating from infix to postfix? Well, if we represent our infix expression as a tree, then, to make this translation, we merely go through the tree and bend the branches at each node, so that the operator branch is brought to the right. See, for example, Figure 10-1. As another example, consider the infix expressions A+(B×C) and (A+B)×C (Figure 10-2).

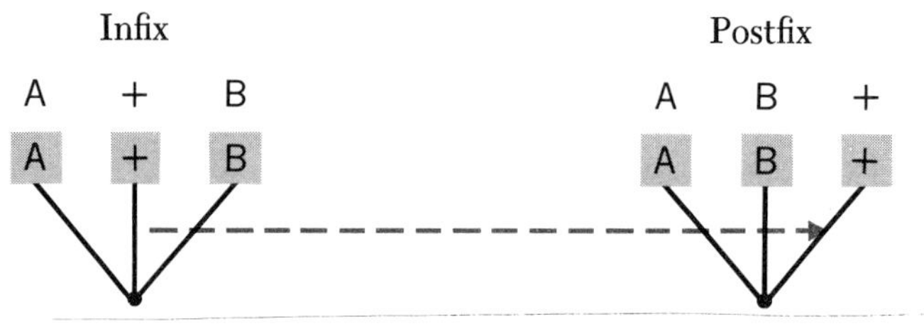

Figure 10-1

Here, the original infix expressions

$$A+(B\times C) \qquad \text{and} \qquad (A+B)\times C$$

differed in appearance only in the way in which the parentheses were inserted. But this is not the case with their postfix translations

$$A(BC\times)+ \qquad \text{and} \qquad (AB+)C\times$$

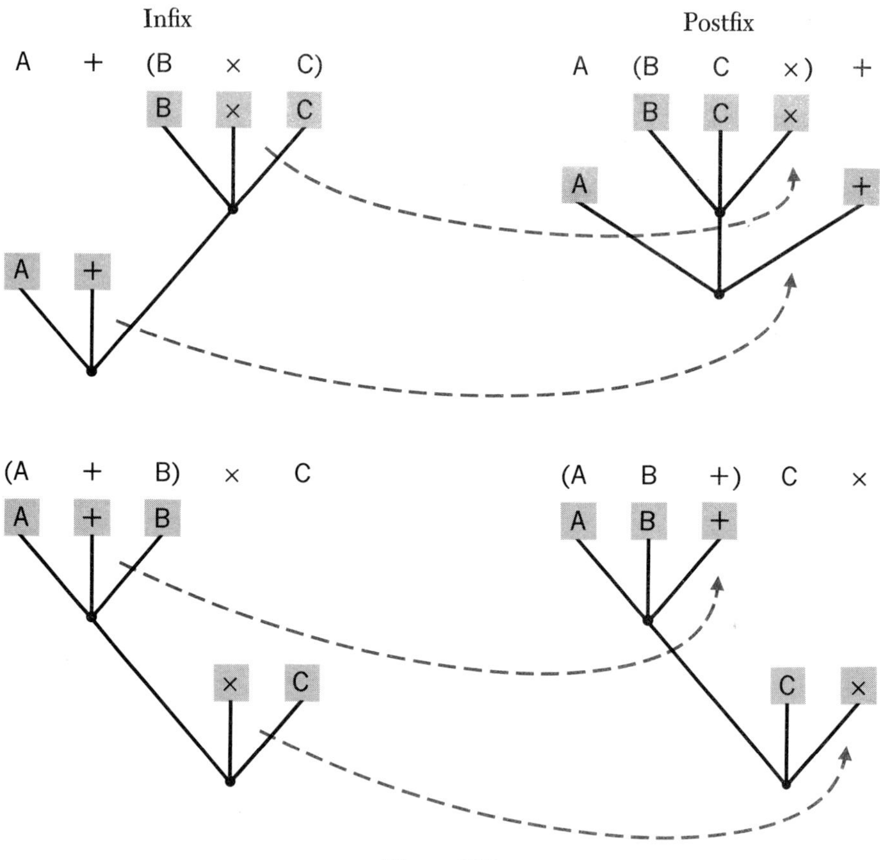

Figure 10-2

Here we see that the operators occur in different positions in the two expressions. The locations of these operators alone are sufficient to indicate the intended operations—the parentheses are not necessary. We may thus write

$$ABC\times+ \qquad \text{and} \qquad AB+C\times$$

in place of the above expressions and no confusion can arise. No "precedence rules" are necessary for the operations.

Another way of saying this is that in any Polish string expression, there is only one way in which to insert parentheses so as to obtain a meaningful result. That is, there is only one way to insert parentheses so that the entire expression and each subexpression will have the form

expression1 expression2 operator

You should satisfy yourself that this is the case in the above examples.

To understand the meaning of a Polish string, you must be able to identify the subexpressions on which each operator is operating. We will show how this is done for the quadratic formula expression discussed at the beginning of the section. After the initial editing, replacing 2 by the symbol T, 4 by F and .5 by H, for example, this has the infix form

$$(B+(B\uparrow T-F\times A\times C)\uparrow H)/(T\times A)$$

The translation of this expression to a Polish string (which you will be asked to make, using tree manipulation) has the form

$$BBT\uparrow FA\times C\times -H\uparrow +TA\times /$$

Using brackets, we identify the subexpressions and the operators acting on them according to these rules.

1. Variables are subexpressions; put a bracket under each variable.
2. Each time we come to an operator, we place a bracket under that operator together with the two immediately preceding subexpressions, forming a new subexpression.

The work starts out like this:

B B T ↑ F A × C × − H ↑ + T A × /

and the finished job appears as

B B T ↑ F A × C × − H ↑ + T A × /

ORDER IN WHICH OPERATIONS ARE PERFORMED	
Infix	Postfix
(B+(B↑T−F×A×C)↑H)/(T×A) ↑ ↑ ↑ ↑ ↑ ↑ ↑ ↑ ⑥ ① ④ ② ③ ⑤ ⑧ ⑦	BBT↑FA×C×−H↑+TA×/ ↑ ↑ ↑ ↑ ↑ ↑ ↑ ↑ ① ② ③④ ⑤⑥ ⑦⑧

Figure 10-3 The sequence of evaluation of the quadratic expression.

The secret of the success of Polish string notation is revealed here—each operator is the terminal symbol in exactly one subexpression.

We can see that the order in which the variables occur is the same for the infix and postfix expressions, but the order in which the operators occur is radically different. We compare in Figure 10-3 the order in which the operations are performed in the infix and postfix expressions.

The fact that operations are performed in exactly the order in which they occur in postfix notation shows the importance of this notation in computing. No back-and-forth scanning is necessary.

EXERCISES 10-1

1. Translate the expression for the solution of the quadratic equation, that is,

$$(B+(B\uparrow T-F\times A\times C)\uparrow H)/(T\times A)$$

to Polish form. Show the translation as a series of trees, each differing from the preceding one by the bending of one branch. For each tree in the series, give the corresponding expression.

2. Translate the expression

$$A/B/C\times D\times C/B\times A$$

to Polish form. In the translated expression, identify all subexpressions and verify that each is terminated by an operator.

3. The sum of the first n terms of an arithmetic progression is given by

$$(n/2)\times(2\times a+(n-1)\times d)$$

where a is the first term and d is the common difference between terms of the progression. Rewrite the expression in Polish notation.

4. The sum of the first n terms of a geometric progression is given by

$$a \times (1-r \uparrow n)/(1-r)$$

where a is the first term and r is the common ratio of terms of the progression. Rewrite the expression in Polish notation.

10-2 EVALUATING POLISH STRINGS

To understand Polish string expressions properly and appreciate their efficiency, we will inspect the simple single-scan method of evaluating them.

The method works like this. As we scan the expression, we construct a list of numbers called the "stack." This list is so constructed that whenever we come to an operator, the numbers on which that operator is to act are the two values most recently entered in the list.

The rules for constructing this list are as follows.

1. When a *variable* is scanned, its value is entered at the open end of the stack.
2. When an *operator* is scanned:

   (a) The last two numbers are removed from the stack.
   (b) The indicated operation is performed on these values.
   (c) The result computed in *b* is entered at the open end of the stack.

We show how this works with our old standby, the quadratic formula expression in Polish notation

$$BBT\uparrow FA \times C \times -H\uparrow +TA \times /$$

with the values of the variables being

A	B	C	F	H	T
3	7	−20	4	.5	2

(Remember that the value of this expression will be the *negative* of a root of the equation $3x^2 + 7x - 20 = 0$.)

To show the construction of the stack, we have written in Figure 10-4 the expression vertically at the left. On the right, we show the condition of the stack after the character in the left column is scanned.

Single Scan Evaluation of BBT↑FA × C × −H↑+TA × / With Values Given Above		
Character Scanned	Computation (if any)	Condition of Stack (open end at the right)
B		7
B		7 7
T		7 7 2
↑	$7 \uparrow 2 = 49$	7 7 2 49
F		7 7 2 49 4
A		7 7 2 49 4 3
×	$4 \times 3 = 12$	7 7 2 49 4 3 12
C		7 7 2 49 4 3 12 −20
×	$12 \times (-20) = -240$	7 7 2 49 4 3 12 −20 −240
−	$49 - (-240) = 289$	7 7 2 49 4 3 12 −20 −240 289
H		7 7 2 49 4 3 12 −20 −240 289 .5
↑	$289 \uparrow .5 = 17$	7 7 2 49 4 3 12 −20 −240 289 .5 17
+	$7 + 17 = 24$	7 7 2 49 4 3 12 −20 −240 289 .5 17 24
T		7 7 2 49 4 3 12 −20 −240 289 .5 17 24 2
A		7 7 2 49 4 3 12 −20 −240 289 .5 17 24 2 3
×	$2 \times 3 = 6$	7 7 2 49 4 3 12 −20 −240 289 .5 17 24 2 3 6
/	$24/6 = 4$	7 7 2 49 4 3 12 −20 −240 289 .5 17 24 2 3 6 4

Figure 10-4 Detailed scan of a quadratic expression.

B	B	T	↑	F	A	×	C	×	−	H	↑	+	T	A	×	/
7	7	2	49	4	3	12	−20	−240	289	.5	17	24	2	3	6	4

Figure 10-5 A shorthand way of following the condition of the stack.

The purpose of Figure 10-4 is to show the condition of the stack at all stages of the process. In applying the method, you would not make all these copies of the stack; your final work would look like Figure 10-5.

At the end (for a correctly written postfix expression), everything should be crossed out except the value appearing under the last operator, which is the value of the expression.

The reason for the use of the word "stack" is now apparent, since the stack works very much like a stack of plates in a cafeteria. During the

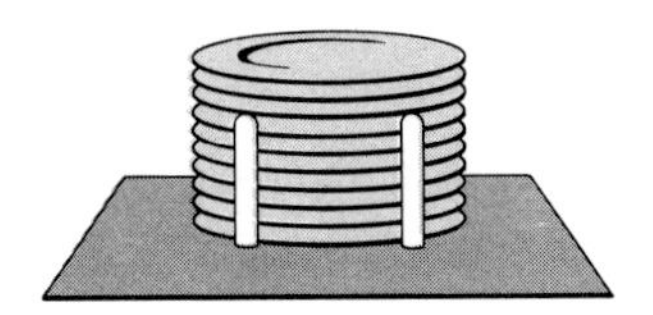

lunch hour, customers are lifting plates off and employees are adding plates on to the stack. Removals and additions are made at the same end of the stack so that the most recent plate added is the first to be removed. And so it is with the stacks used in evaluating arithmetic expressions.

EXERCISES 10-2

1. In Problem 3, Exercises 10-1, you were supplied with the formula for summing an arithmetic progression. Apply this formula to evaluate the first eight terms of the progression

$$3, 7, 11, 15, \ldots$$

by using an evaluation scheme similar to the one shown in Figure 10-4.

2. In Problem 4, Exercises 10-1, you were supplied with the formula for summing a geometric progression. Apply this formula to evaluate the first eight terms of the progression

$$2, 4, 8, 16, \ldots$$

using an evaluation scheme similar to Figure 10-5.

10-3 TRANSLATING FROM INFIX TO POSTFIX

We have examined one method of translating from infix to postfix, namely, by manipulating the branches of a tree. However, this method is complicated and time-consuming. We must try for a method based on a single scan of the infix expression.

Let's look at an infix expression and its postfix translation.

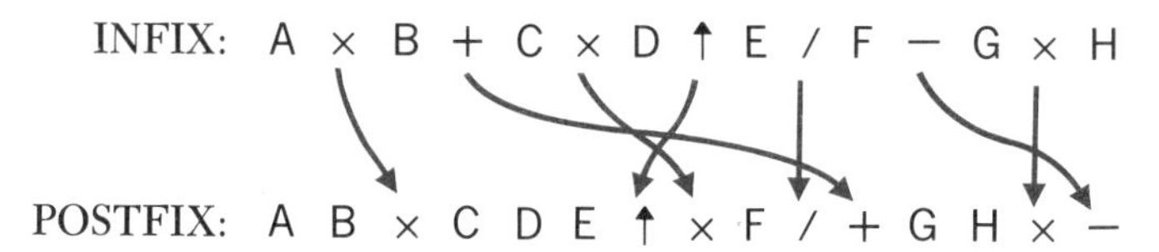

As we have seen before, the variables occur in the same order in the two expressions, but the operators are radically rearranged. How do we know where to put the operators? How do we know, for example, when we are ready to write the + in the above postfix expression?

The answer lies in the following consideration. In infix notation, each operator lies between the two subexpressions on which it acts.

Left-hand Sub-expr. + Right-hand Sub-expr.

In the translation to postfix notation, this operator will occur immediately to the right of the translation of the right-hand subexpression.

Transl. of L.H. Sub-expr. Transl. of R.H. Sub-expr. +

In the above example, the left and right expressions operated on by the + in the infix expression are as indicated below.

A × B + C × D ↑ E / F − G × H

But how do we know where the end of the right-hand expression is? Is there anything special about the letter "F" which gives us this information? No! The answer lies in the symbol "−". The reason that the minus is not included in the bracket is that it is an operator whose precedence level is not higher than that of "+". That is the reason that the "−" signals the end of the right-hand subexpression acted on by the "+".

This principle can be implemented in the translation process by using the notion of a stack which was introduced in the preceding section. Here is how it works in scanning the infix expression.

1. When the element scanned is a variable, it is immediately placed at the right end of the postfix expression being created.
2. When the element scanned is an operator, it is placed at the open end of a stack.
3. *But*, before the operator is placed at the end of the stack, the operator presently at the end of the stack is inspected. It is transferred to the right end of the postfix expression if its precedence level is equal to or higher than that of the new operator to be added to the stack. The next operator so uncovered in the stack is likewise inspected *until* the stack is empty or the operator at the end of the stack has a lower precedence level than that of the operator being added to the stack.

In Figure 10-6 we show how all this works in the case of the foregoing expression.

Character Scanned	Stack	Postfix Expression
A		A
×	×	A
B	×	AB
+	× +	AB ×
C	+	AB × C
×	+ ×	AB × C
D	+ ×	AB × CD
↑	+ × ↑	AB × CD
E	+ × ↑	AB × CDE
/	+ × ↑ /	AB × CDE ↑ ×
F	+ /	AB × CDE ↑ × F
−	+ / −	AB × CDE ↑ × F / +
G	−	AB × CDE ↑ × F / + G
×	− ×	AB × CDE ↑ × F / + G
H	− ×	AB × CDE ↑ × F / + GH
□	− ×	AB × CDE ↑ × F / + GH × −

Figure 10-6 Translating from infix to postfix.

The handling of parentheses is still to be discussed. The rules are simple and should be self-explanatory.

1. When a left parenthesis is scanned, it is placed directly in the stack. Nothing is removed from the stack.
2. When a right parenthesis is scanned, operators are transferred one at a time from the end of the stack to the postfix expression until a left parenthesis is reached.
3. At this point, this parenthesis pair is discarded and no longer appears anywhere either in the stack or in the postfix expression.

Figure 10-7 demonstrates this process, using our favorite (quadratic formula) expression:

(B+(B↑T−F×A×C)↑H)/(T×A)

The reader must satisfy himself that the rules given above do, in fact, accomplish the desired translation. And, also, he must be sure he sees why operators are removed from the stack in the first-in-last-out order. Figure 10-7 should be studied carefully, as well as the exercises that follow.

The stack has been treated somewhat differently here than in the preceding section. Instead of leaving the crossed-out entries in the list, they have disappeared entirely. In working examples, the student may find it convenient to continue to cross out the deleted entries.

EXERCISES 10-3

Use the stack technique described in this section to translate the following infix expressions to postfix form. *Hint.* Use the format of Figure 10-7 as a guide.

1. (n/2)×(2×a+(n−1)×d)
2. a×(1−r↑n)/(1−r)
3. 2×π×((a↑2+b↑2)/2)↑.5
   (circumference of an ellipse with semiaxes a and b)
4. ((u−x)↑2+(v−y)↑2)↑.5
   (distance between points (x,y) and (u,v))
5. p×(1+i/q)↑(n×q)
   (value of principal p at interest i compounded q times per year after n years)

Character Scanned	Stack	Postfix Expression
(	(	
B	(	B
+	(+	B
(	(+(	B
B	(+(	BB
↑	(+(↑	BB
T	(+(↑	BBT
−	(+(↑−	BBT↑
F	(+(−	BBT↑F
×	(+(−×	BBT↑F
A	(+(−×	BBT↑FA
×	(+(−××	BBT↑FA×
C	(+(−×	BBT↑FA×C
)	(+(−×	BBT↑FA×C×−
↑	(+↑	BBT↑FA×C×−
H	(+↑	BBT↑FA×C×−H
)	(+↑	BBT↑FA×C×−H↑+
/	/	BBT↑FA×C×−H↑+
(	/(	BBT↑FA×C×−H↑+
T	/(	BBT↑FA×C×−H↑+T
×	/(×	BBT↑FA×C×−H↑+T
A	/(×	BBT↑FA×C×−H↑+TA
)	/(×	BBT↑FA×C×−H↑+TA×
□	/	BBT↑FA×C×−H↑+TA×/

Figure 10-7 Translation of an expression with parentheses.

10-4 FLOWCHARTING THE TRANSLATION PROCESS

The translation process described in the preceding section can easily be flowcharted. To those who have studied Chapter 6, it should be evident that we will wish to view the process as a procedure, TRANSL, which accepts as input a character string, $\overline{\text{INFIX}}$, and returns a character string, $\overline{\text{POST}}$. Within this section we will purposely overlook the usefulness of expressing the flow chart as a procedure, assuming that this can be readily done after study of Chapter 6. Also, we will simplify matters by assuming that there is no initial or intermediate blank character in $\overline{\text{INFIX}}$ and that there is at least one blank character at the right end.

To construct the flow chart we will need:

1. A vector or subscripted variable S, representing the stack.
2. Three indices or pointers, namely:
   (a) n, giving the position of the latest entry in the stack, S.
   (b) i, giving the position being scanned in the infix expression.
   (c) k, giving the position of the most recent entry in the postfix expression.

3. A function LEV which, when applied to a character being scanned, will indicate a precedence level identifying the type of symbol.

The values of this function LEV are obtained by expanding the precedence table in Section 2-3 to apply to characters (CHAR) other than operators. The complete tabulation of values of LEV is given in Table 10-1. Note that we associate the highest value of LEV with the *highest* precedence level.

By placing the assignment operator ($\leftarrow$) and the relations ($<$, $>$, $\leq$, $\geq$, $=$, $\neq$) in our list of characters, we give our flow chart the capability of translating complete assignment statements and not just arithmetic expressions.

Explanation of the Translation Flow Chart

A decision box (box 2) in Figure 10-8 inspects the infix expression, character by character, until a blank space "□" signals the end of the expression.

TABLE 10-1

CHAR	LEV (CHAR)
a variable or constant	6
$\uparrow$	5
$\times$, /	4
+, −	3
$<$, $>$, $\leq$, $\geq$, $=$, $\neq$	2
(, $\leftarrow$	1
)	0

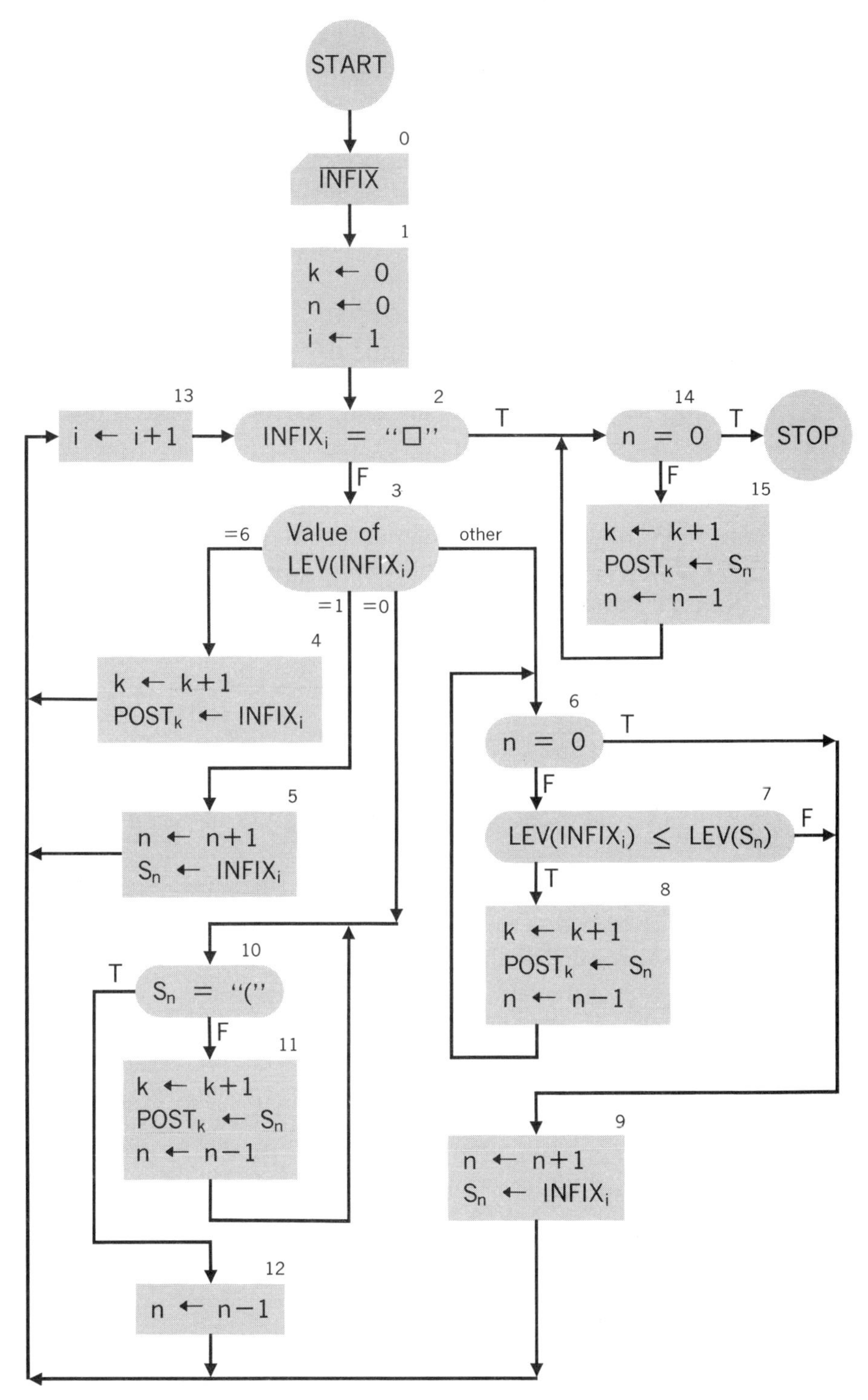

Figure 10-8 Flow chart for translating infix to postfix.

The test in box 3 identifies the type of character being scanned. If this character is:

1. A variable (exit 6 from box 3), then we place it at the end of the postfix string (box 4).

2. "(" or "←" (exit 1 from box 3), then we place it at the end of the stack (box 5).

3. ")" (exit 0 from box 3), then we transmit characters from the end of the stack to the end of the postfix expression (box 11) until a "(" is reached (box 10) which we cause to disappear (box 12).

4. An arithmetic operator or a relation ("Other" exit from box 2), then we:

(a) Transmit from the end of the stack to the postfix expression (in last-in-first-out order) any characters with greater level numbers than the scanned characters (boxes 6, 7, and 8).

(b) Place the scanned character at the end of the stack (box 9).

When the end of the expression is reached (T exit from box 2), everything left in the stack is transmitted in last-in-first-out order to the postfix expression (boxes 14 and 15).

EXERCISES 10-4

1. Assume preediting has placed a blank between each two characters of the infix expression. Show the changes that would be required to the flow chart in Figure 10-8 to accommodate this new infix form.

2. Assume a blank character is to be inserted *after* each character of the postfix form. Show the changes that would be required in Figure 10-8.

3. Suppose preediting has placed a blank in between each two elements of the infix expression, but assume these elements are *not of fixed length.* Show the changes that would be necessary in the Figure 10-8 flow chart to accommodate this infix form.

CHAPTER 11

MORE ON TREE SEARCH AND STORAGE CONCEPTS

11-1 INTRODUCTION

Having studied Chapter 9, you are well on the way to becoming a tree expert. Tackling the two more advanced problems in this chapter will substantially increase your ability to produce algorithmic solutions to difficult problems. With the first problem, we will consider alternate ways of performing a tree search and see how each approach suits the needs of the problem. We will also introduce several new concepts in the storing of arrays and data trees and in the retrieval of information from these structures.

Level-by-Level Tree Search

Is *natural* order tree searching, as we described it in Chapter 9, the *only* systematic way to search a tree? Figure 11-1 suggests what we will call the *level-by-level* tree search which can be thought of as a companion piece to Figure 9-14.

It may be difficult to imagine a nut-hunting squirrel using this search strategy, but we will explain the search in "squirrel context" anyway. In this approach the squirrel searches all the *nearest* nodes first (at level 1). This means that the squirrel moves from node to node at the same level. If he fails to find a nut at level 1, he jumps to the next level (level 2), looks at all the nodes there, and so on, until he does find a nut.

Algorithms for level-by-level search, depending on the particular application, may halt after the first *desired* node is located or they may continue, completing the search of the current level for more such nodes, if any, and then stop. Or they may continue the search, level-by-level, until the entire tree has been scanned. In the next section where we will study the second type of search we will see that there are penalties involved in making a level-by-level search as compared with a natural order search. However, the ensuing rewards can often far overbalance these penalties.

11-2 THE BORDER-CROSSING PROBLEM

To set the stage for this problem, we offer the following bit of computer science fiction. It is entitled "Traveling Overland in the United States of Europe.":

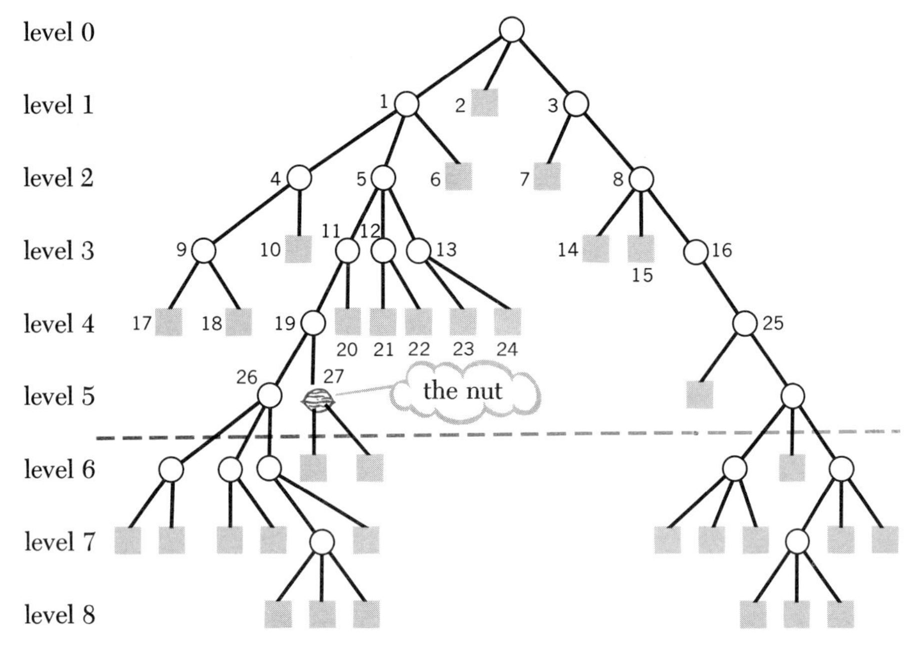

Figure 11-1 Search in level-by-level order.

In 1984 the twenty-six countries shown on the map (of Figure 11-2) agreed to form a federal Union. For the first 10 years of the Union, they further agreed to continue the practice of maintaining customs at the various borders between their states (mainly because the customs agents of the individual countries formed their own union and strenuously objected to this form of politically generated unemployment).

The first few years of the Union proved to be somewhat unstable. Individual states squabbled. Borders between neighboring states were sometimes closed for several hours (days, or even months) while the governors of the disputing states fought out bitter political battles, mostly shortlived.

By 1988 the frequency of these state versus state disputes became so high that the Federal Government's Bureau of Public Roads began offering a computer service to assist in the solution of the routing problems of interstate trucking firms.

If a client phoned in giving his source (state) and destination (state), the computer would reply (almost instantly) giving:

a. The route with the minimum number of OK border crossings (custom inspections), avoiding all border crossings currently closed.
b. All the routes (if more than one) that involve this minimum number of border crossings.

The trucker could then select among the choices reported by the computer, if any. In some (unfortunate) cases, the computer would phone this message. "You can't get there from here. Suggest you ship by air freight."

It will be interesting to see if we can develop an algorithm that provides essentially the same service as the one given by the USOE's Bureau of Public Roads. Any algorithm we develop should be general enough so that it would be applicable to any federation of contiguous states.

The Tree Search That Is Involved

Even if we know nothing about computers, we can sense that some kind of tree search is involved here. For example, suppose we want to travel from Spain (ES for España) to Holland (H) using a best path

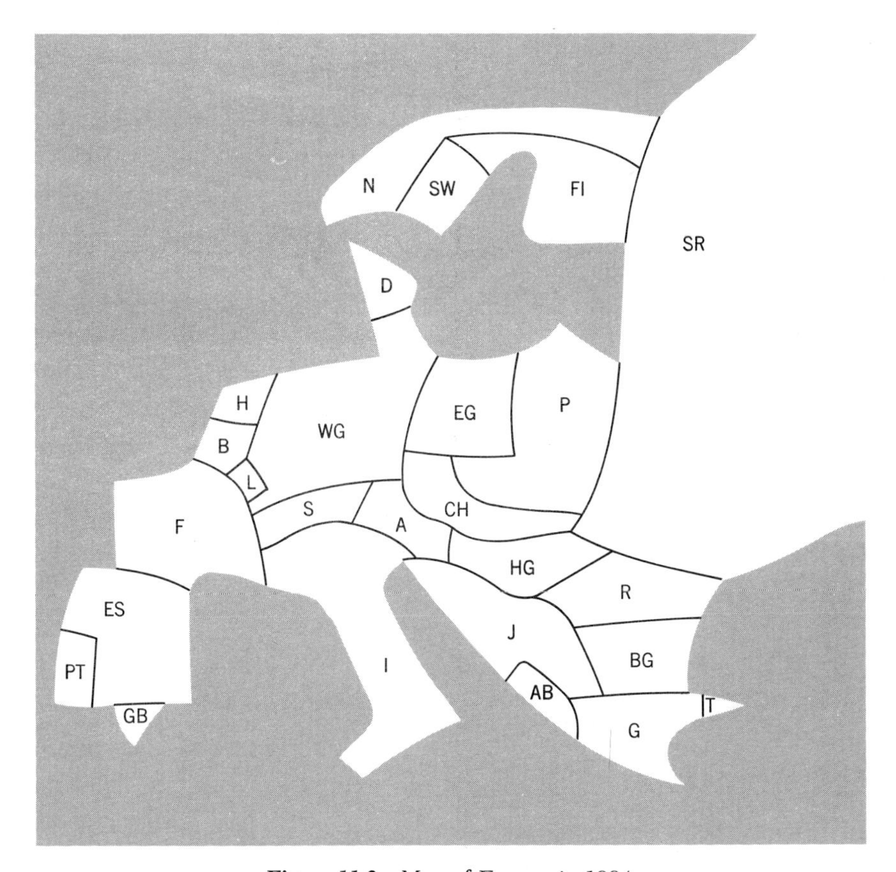

Figure 11-2 Map of Europe in 1984.

(minimum number of borders crossed). First, we consider Spain's neighbors (at level 1), which are Portugal (PT), Gibralter (GB), and France (F). Then we ask where we can go from each of these countries (level 2), moving on in this way from level to level (of the tree) until we reach a level that contains among its countries the one we call our destination. This tree is sketched in Figure 11-3.

There are two conclusions we can deduce from the tree.

1. A minimum of three border crossings is required to get from Spain to Holland.
2. The two colored paths that reach terminals marked H show that there are, in this case, two best paths.

There are also several things to keep in mind about the actual *construction* of the tree.

1. It is best to build the tree from the root node *one level at a time* in left-to-right-order.
2. Certain uninteresting terminals can be encountered at any level. Thus, at level 1, GB has only one neighbor, ES. The same is true for PT. Hence, the path from ES through GB cannot continue (except, of course, to return to ES, which we do not allow).
3. A segment emanating from the node for country P at level n is *inadmissible* if it leads to another country Q, and Q has already appeared *somewhere* in the tree at a level equal to or lower than n. For example,

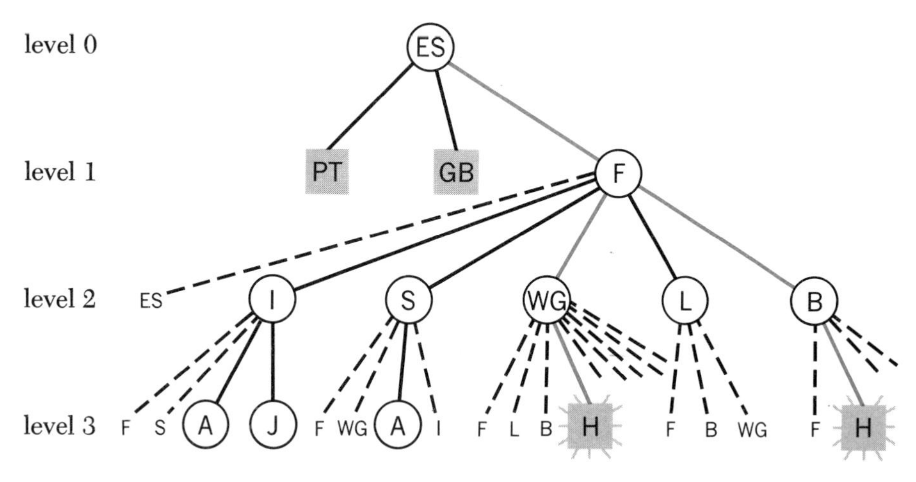

Figure 11-3 Traveling from Spain to Holland along best paths (colored lines).

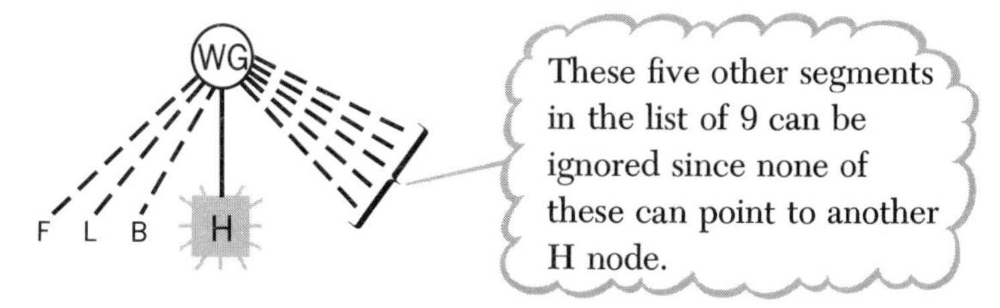
WG
F
L
B
H
These five other segments in the list of 9 can be ignored since none of these can point to another H node.

Figure 11-4

at level 2 the node for Italy has four possible segments emanating from it, but only two are admissible. Segments to F and S are both inadmissible because each appears as a node at level 2 or less.

4. When considering the segments emanating from a node, if any one is discovered leading to the destination node, there is no need to consider any more segments *from that node.* This is suggested by the way we draw the segments emanating from WG (Figure 11-4, for example).

5. After finding our destination via a segment from one node at a certain level, it is still necessary to look for other possible occurrences of the destination by "expanding" the remaining nodes at this level (in left-to-right order). Thus, at level 2, even though we found that H could be reached from WG, we complete the expansion of nodes L and B, the other nodes on this level. In this way we find the second occurrence of H at level 3.

6. Finally, there is absolutely no point in looking for an H node at a level higher than level 3. Any such nodes will represent tree paths *exceeding* the minimum "length."

Generalized Algorithm for Level-by-Level Tree Search

To summarize, we see that the level-by-level search goes hand in hand with the construction of the tree, drawing on whatever data is needed. Figure 11-5 displays a generalized algorithm for such a search.

Data Structures Required for Level-by-Level Tree Search

We are now ready to consider what input data are required in the computer algorithm of the border-crossing problem and what storage arrangement will be appropriate. We must also think about the tree data that will be *generated* by the algorithm and its appropriate storage structure.

It may be well to digress momentarily to compare storage requirements of this problem with that of the four-color problem of Chapter 9. In the

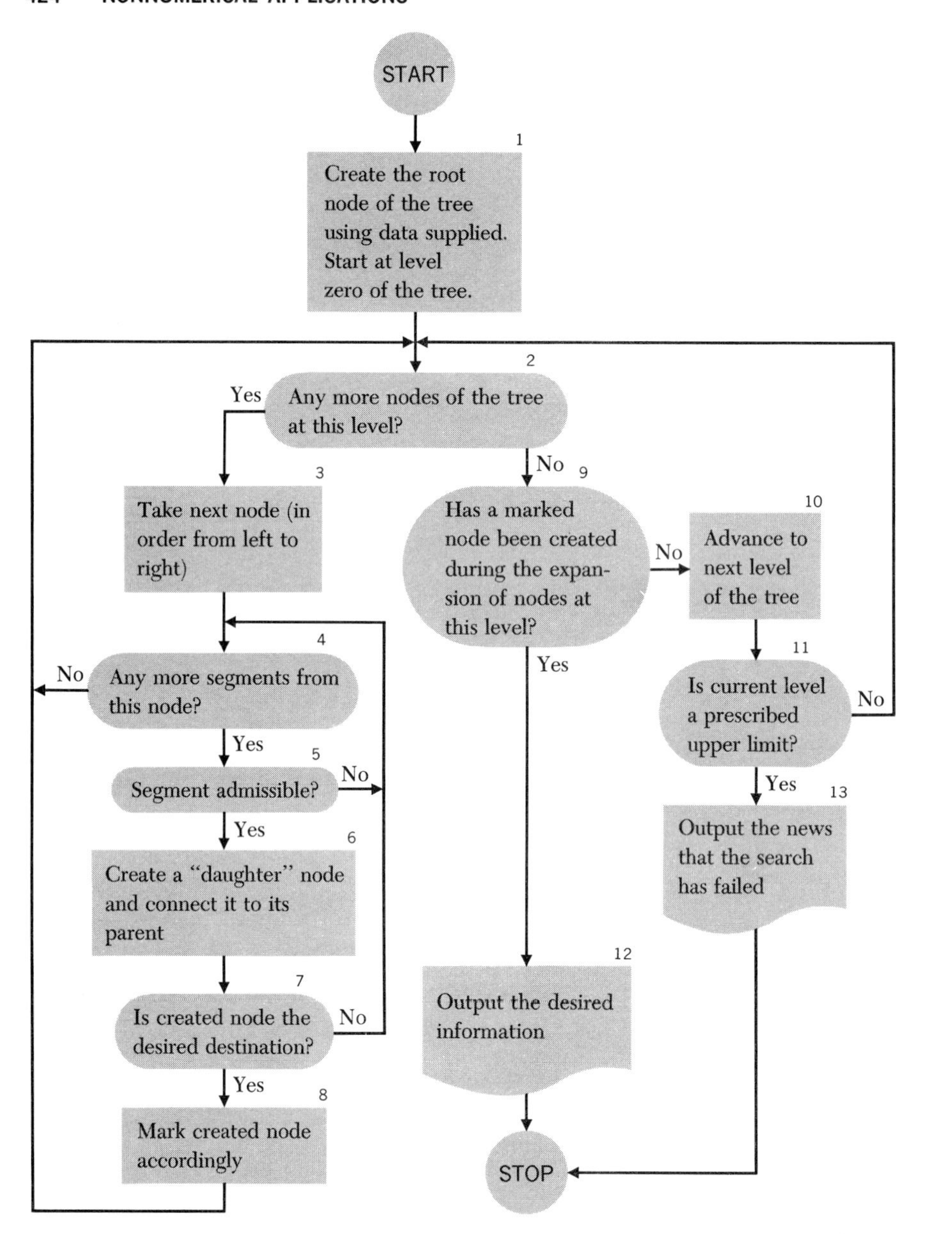

Figure 11-5 Generalized algorithm for the level-by-level tree search (with concurrent tree construction, as needed).

latter case, only one path of the coloring tree was of interest to us at any one time. This was the path from the root to the node currently being looked at (in the natural order search). We suggested that a record of this path be kept in the form of the COLOR vector. If the current node ever turned out to be a terminal node marked [S] (Success), then COLOR's contents could be output, and that was that. But in this problem we must somehow keep a record of the *entire tree so far traversed* (for example, the solid lines of Figure 11-3). The reason is that any one (or several) of these paths may prove to be the one(s) containing the destination terminal. In the example of Figure 11-3, for instance, when the scan of level 3 is completed, the algorithm must be able to recover and print out the nodes along the two (or, in general, several) best paths that were found. The easiest way to do this is to keep a record of the tree itself.

Representation of Map of Europe

Having studied the four-color problem, you would be correct in assuming that the connection table approach (Table 9-1) is an eminently suitable method for the digital coding of maps. However, as you can see in Table 11-1, we will be adding a new twist. Table 11-1 shows the connection table having 26 variable-length rows. The integer code for each country is displayed along with the letter code that was used in the actual map (Figure 11-2). We will use only the integer codes in our computer algorithm.

Closed borders. The table entries that are encircled by clouds refer to closed borders. If, for example, we are told that the border between France and West Germany is closed, we have to remove it or specially mark it (for example, with a cloud). See the WG entry on row F and the F entry on row WG. Also shown is another closed border between Norway and Finland. We sense that the closing of this border will not greatly complicate the problem of finding best paths, so we will temporarily forget about this part of the problem.

The Concept of an Access Vector

The column headed "Access Vector, BCL" in Table 11-1 is something new. It has special value in case one wants to conserve storage for "jagged" arrays like this map of Europe. That is, if you consider the map as a 26-row array, it would require nine columns to contain the row with the most elements. Other rows would be wasteful of space. If memory space is at a premium, other ways to store such a table should be considered.

The space-saving method we suggest here is to imagine the whole table stored as a single *vector,* which we will call MAP. For n countries

TABLE 11-1 Map of Europe

Country Number	Country Name	Access Vector, BCL	Neighbors 1	2	3	4	5	6	7	8	9
1	GB	1	3 ES								
2	PT	2	3 ES								
3	ES	3	2 PT	1 GB	5 F						
4	L	6	5 F	6 B	8 WG						
5	F	9	3 ES	10 I	9 S	8 WG	4 L	6 B			
6	B	15	5 F	7 H	8 WG	4 L					
7	H	19	8 WG	6 B							
8	WG	21	5 F	4 L	6 B	7 H	11 D	25 EG	18 CH	19 A	9 S
9	S	30	5 F	8 WG	19 A	10 I					
10	I	34	5 F	9 S	19 A	20 J					
11	D	38	8 WG								
12	N	39	13 SW	14 FI	15 SR						
13	SW	42	12 N	14 FI							
14	FI	44	13 SW	12 N	15 SR						
15	SR	47	26 R	17 HG	18 CH	16 P	14 FI	12 N			
16	P	53	25 EG	15 SR	18 CH						
17	HG	56	15 SR	26 R	20 J	19 A	18 CH				
18	CH	61	15 SR	17 HG	19 A	8 WG	25 EG	16 P			
19	A	67	10 I	9 S	8 WG	18 CH	17 HG	20 J			
20	J	73	10 I	19 A	17 HG	26 R	23 BG	22 G	21 AB		
21	AB	80	20 J	22 G							
22	G	82	21 AB	20 J	23 BG	24 T					
23	BG	86	22 G	20 J	26 R						
24	T	89	22 G								
25	EG	90	16 P	18 CH	8 WG						
26	R	93	15 SR	23 BG	20 J	17 HG					
		97									

this vector would have n subdivisions (Figure 11-6). The ith subdivision would hold codes for the countries that border country i. To reference a particular row of the table, say row i, one would only need to know the index in the MAP vector that corresponds to the first element (word) of the ith subdivision. The purpose of the access vector BCL (for *b*order *c*ountry *l*ist) is to hold n index values (actually, n+1, to be precise) such that the ith element of BCL holds the index of the ith subdivision within MAP. Moreover, the difference, $BCL_{i+1} - BCL_i$, gives the number of elements in the ith subdivision. This pointer scheme is illustrated in Figure 11-6 for the first five rows of the connection table.

To reference the jth element in the ith row of the table, that is, $table_{i,j}$, we would now use the expression

$$MAP_{BCL_i + j - 1}$$

As a quick check on the validity of this expression, let's compare the two ways of getting at the second element in the fourth row of the connection table.

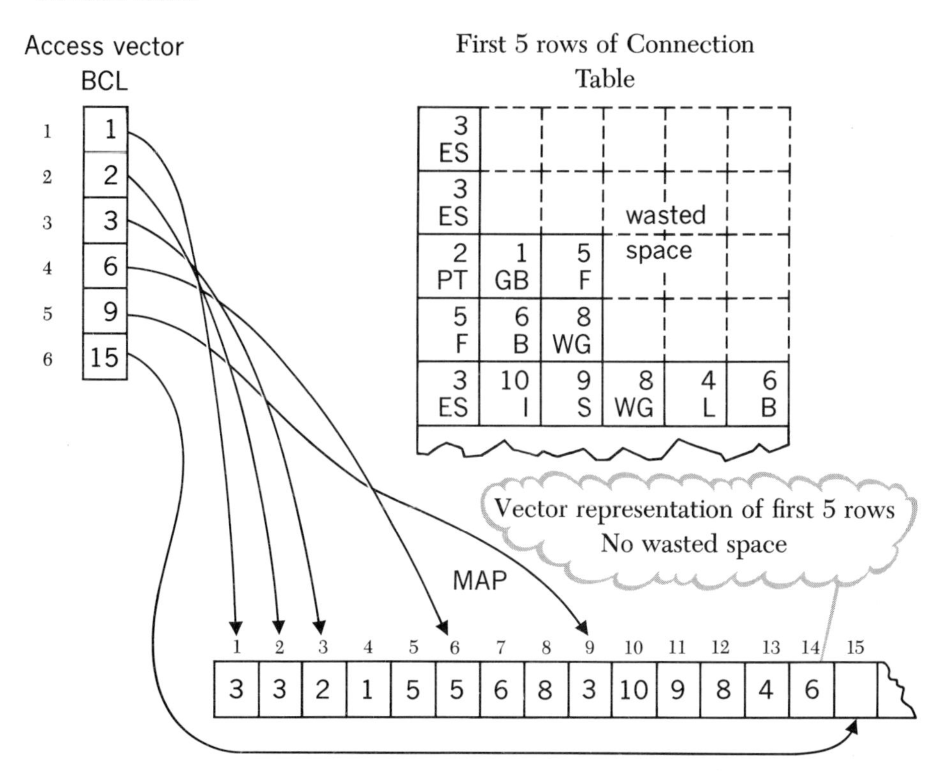

Figure 11-6 Use of an access vector for referencing elements of the connection table stored in the MAP vector.

$Table_{4,2}$ is seen to have the value $\boxed{\begin{array}{c}6\\B\end{array}}$. Correspondingly, for the access vector approach,

$$BCL_4 = 6$$
$$BCL_4+2-1 = 7$$

Hence,

$$MAP_7 = \boxed{6}$$

We get the same code value either way.

Representing the Tree in Memory

We must keep a record of the tree in memory at all times, you will recall, because when we have completed the tree through some level, k, on which one or more destination terminals have been found, we must print out all paths from the root node to the destination nodes at level k. The storage representation that we design for the tree should make these data retrieval operations easy.

In Figure 11-7 (top half) we illustrate a type of storage representation that will prove suitable. This is based on our earlier example of a path from Spain to Holland. The tree in this figure shows only the solid lines from the earlier illustration (Figure 11-3) and, moreover, uses integer codes in place of letter codes for the countries.

In trying to think how a "two-dimensional" tree can be stored in memory, you should try to invent an equivalent representation in which the tree's essential information can somehow be strung out in a line or sequence of memory positions. What comes to mind is the picture of the tree as a set of nodes, arranged as the elements of a vector. Of course, each vector element (node) would have to be properly related, somehow, to the vector element that represents its parent node. To do this we will have to store for each node two pieces of information.

(a) The country number ($CNTRY_i$) to identify the node.

(b) A pointer to (i.e., index of) the vector element that represents the parent node to this node.

Since the tree is to be constructed level by level, we will be developing information to be stored in the same order. Successive vector elements will then correspond to the nodes taken in level-by-level order.

Instead of using only one vector, we actually need two because each

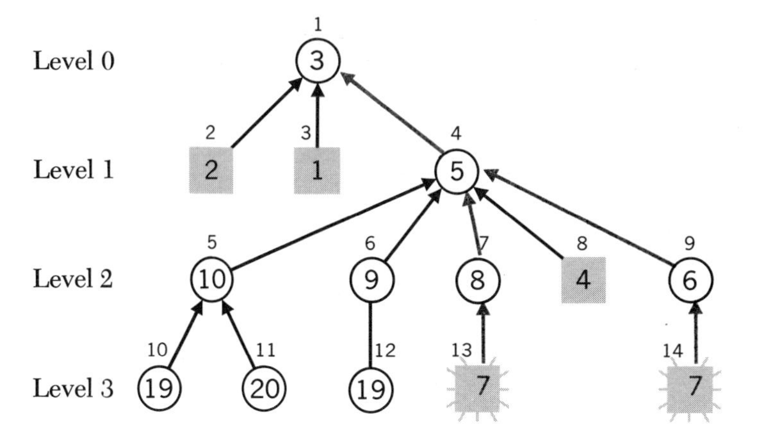

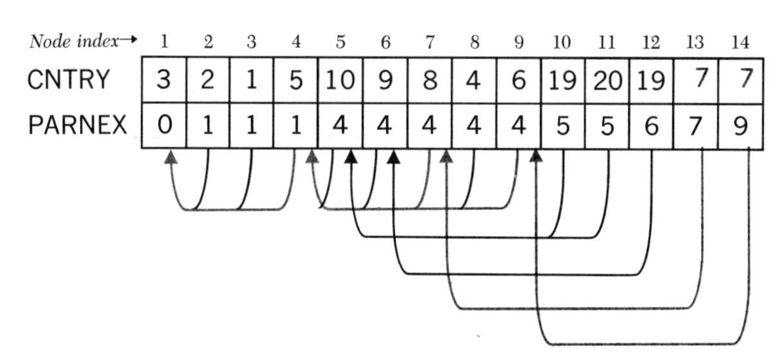

Node index→	1	2	3	4	5	6	7	8	9	10	11	12	13	14
CNTRY	3	2	1	5	10	9	8	4	6	19	20	19	7	7
PARNEX	0	1	1	1	4	4	4	4	4	5	5	6	7	9

Figure 11-7 Sample tree and its storage representation.

node is to be represented by two pieces of information. The lower part of Figure 11-7 shows this simple approach, suggesting the use of two vectors, one called CNTRY (each element of which will be a country code), and PARNEX (each element of which will be an ind*ex* for the element in CNTRY that represents the *par*ent *n*ode). The ith node encountered in the level-by-level search will be stored as the pair of values

$$\text{CNTRY}_i \quad \text{and} \quad \text{PARNEX}_i$$

Notice that since node number 1 (the root node) has no parent, PARNEX_1 has the value zero.

Once the elements of CNTRY and PARNEX are assigned values, as shown in Figure 11-7, the problem is essentially solved, since it is only necessary to output the codes for the list of countries encountered along each of the discovered tree paths from the destination nodes, the rust-

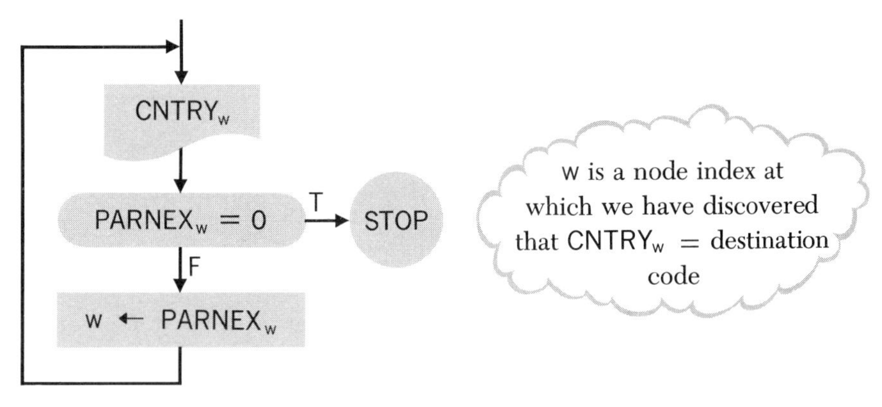

Figure 11-8 Printing out a best path by climbing to the root node from the destination and printing the country numbers that are encountered along the way.

colored 7's, to the root node. Starting from one of the easily recognized terminal elements in the CNTRY vector, we can *climb* back up the tree to the root rather easily. Figure 11-8 shows how. The terminals can, of course, be recognized by the fact that CNTRY_i = *the known destination code for this problem.*

The Computer Algorithm

We will leave it to you to develop a detailed flow-chart algorithm for the border-crossing problem. If you have studied the foregoing material, you should be well prepared to proceed. Be sure to consult the generalized level-by-level search algorithm in Figure 11-5.

We suggest the following guide. First, develop your algorithm on the assumption that the closing of a border will never occur. In this case, the overall flow chart would be something like what is shown in Figure 11-9.

If you are successful in producing the foregoing algorithm, it will be easy for you to add the necessary boxes that recognize the possibility of closed borders. The revised overall flow chart would appear as in Figure 11-10.

Here, the box labeled part b is inserted to take care of closed borders. The details of the box labeled part d would have to be revised slightly to recognize as inadmissible a segment that would lead to a neighbor country having a closed border.

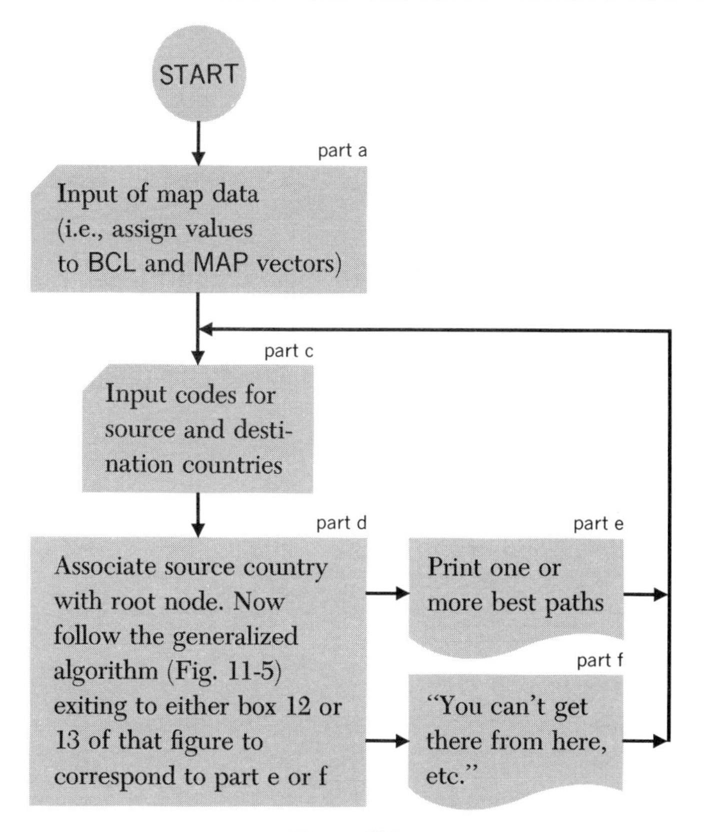

Figure 11-9

PROBLEMS 11-2

1. It was stated in the text that the storage structure we design for a tree should relate closely to the way we intend to *use* the tree. Consider the effect on part *e* of the border-crossing algorithm (Figure 11-9) resulting from a change in the storage representation of the tree (Figure 11-7) as follows. Instead of assigning to the vector elements $PARNEX_i$, the *index* to the parent node, we assign to $PARNOD_i$ the actual country code for the parent of node i. (Note the new name for this vector.)

(a) Redraw the lower half of Figure 11-7 under this change.
(b) Construct a new flow chart for part *e* of Figure 11-9 and compare it critically with the one you have already developed.

2. *Access vectors* are generally useful tools for improving the accessibility of array information. This problem will show you the striking improvements in sorting algorithms that are sometimes possible with the aid of access vectors.

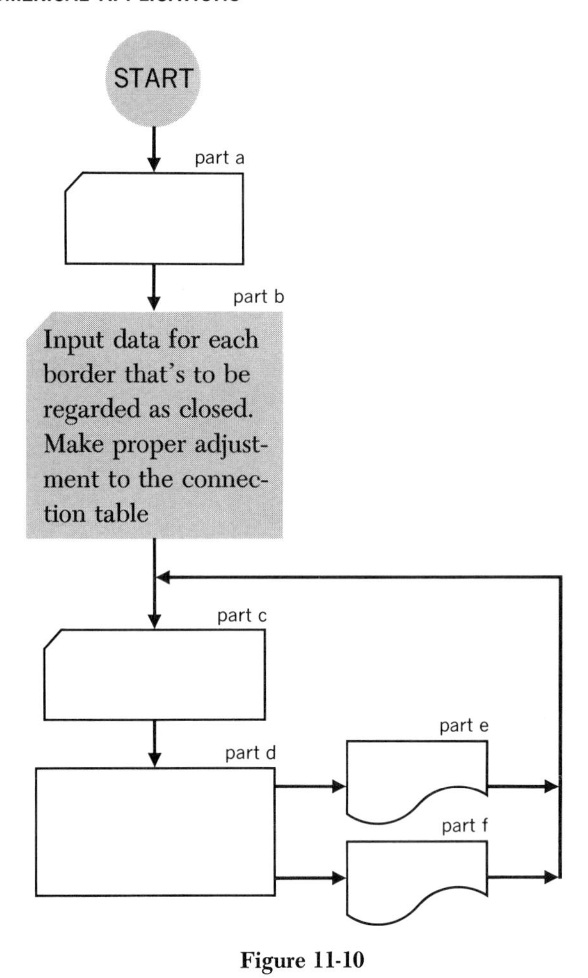

Figure 11-10

Recall the jagged array of data illustrated in Figure 11-6. Many data collections are conveniently displayed in this form. A very common one is a list of names and addresses (Table 11-2). Sometimes, as in the table, there are one or more identifying numbers associated with each row. These could include, for example, the Zip Code, the social security number, years of service, and the date of birth.

The identifying numbers in a table entry are often referred to as "keys" or "sorting keys" because it is often desired to see a copy of the list rearranged in, for instance, ascending order with respect to one of these sorting keys. Sometimes entries in such tables are referred to as *records.*

Now we wish to sort the rows of this table in ascending order of the first number in each row. We will regard social security numbers as the elements

TABLE 11-2 Names and Addresses

Entry		
1	329-21-8921	JOHN HENRY DOE, 4241 MERIWETHER, BOSTON, MASS.
2	196-26-8164	PETE R. INGLES, 96 HOPE, PARIS, TEXAS
3	162-19-1116	JOE FINK, WOODS HOLE, MASS.
4	316-81-8824	ALI ABEL, BOX 8, WINK, TEXAS
5	421-63-6622	JONATHAN PATRICK SNODGRASS III, 66211 SOUTH WAYMORE WAY, NEW CHAPEL HILL, N. CAROLINA
6	611-11-1892	JOHN HENRY DOE, 122 CHURCH ST., ANN ARBOR, MICH.

in column one of the array called TABLE. The heart of our earlier sorting algorithms (the one in Figure 4-49, for example) looked like Figure 11-11.

Applying this principle to the rearrangement of *rows*, we reword this rule to read as in Figure 11-12.

A more specific example is given in Figure 11-13.

The details of box 2 are simple only when you regard each row of TABLE as having the same length. In that case, box 2 has the form shown in Figure 11-14. Moreover, it's clear that when n is large, the cost of interchange can become prohibitive. Let's try a fresh approach.

Imagine the rows of TABLE stored as a single vector (such as MAP in Fig-

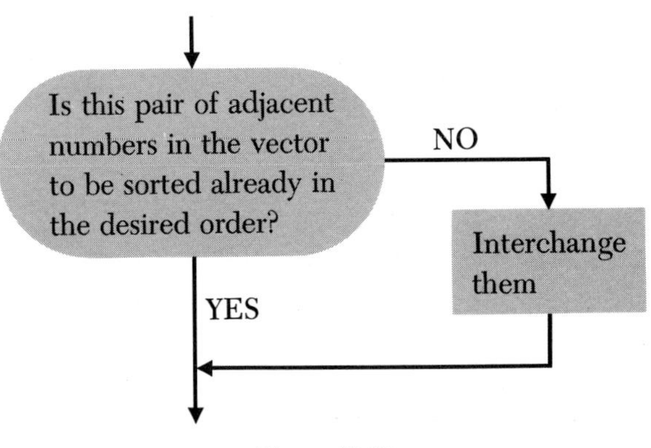

Figure 11-11

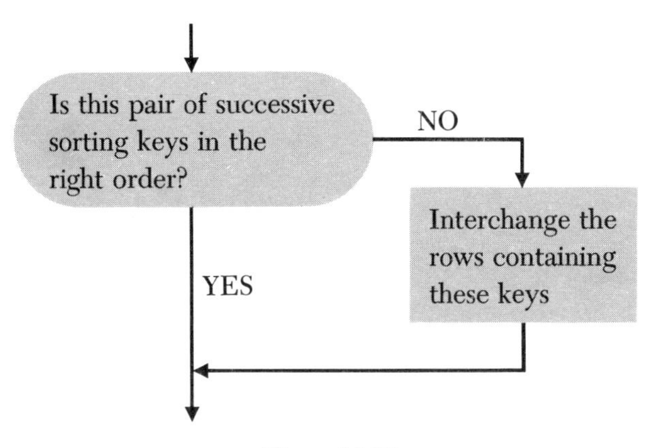

Figure 11-12

ure 11-6), and call this vector RECRDS. Define an access vector called AV (similar to BCL), with elements serving as *pointers* to the individual records now being thought of as subdivisions of RECRDS. Successive elements of AV can point to the sorting keys of successive subdivisions of RECRDS. Now, if an interchange is indicated, could we just interchange the elements of AV rather than interchanging the entire subdivisions to which they point? Think about it. Draw some pictures to help you visualize the process.

Would it help if we pictured adding one more data item to each record, namely, its length? If so, where should this item be placed, at the left end—next to the social security number, or at the right end—after the address? What good would it be to sort the list in the recommended way if we failed to keep a conveniently available indication of the length of each record?

Based on the above ideas, prepare a detailed flow chart for "sorting" the variable length records in RECRDS and printing them in sorted order. Assume that the sorting key is the first element of each record and that each of the m

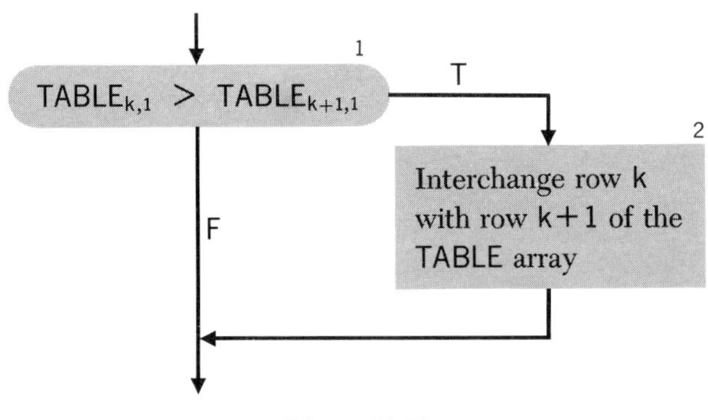

Figure 11-13

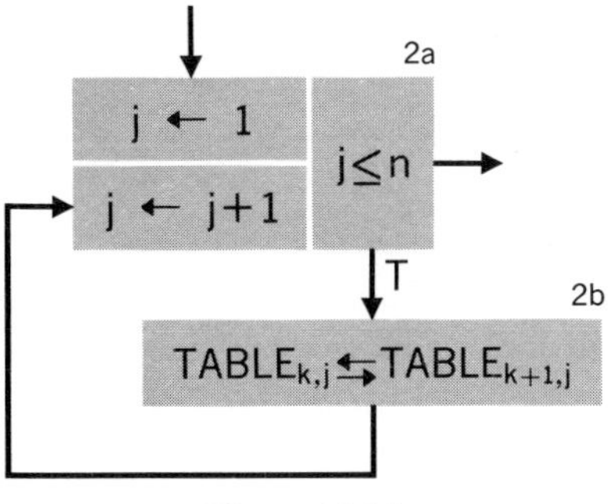

Figure 11-14

records is available for input as a vector of length n. (If you are thinking about a certain computer whose word size is too small to hold a 9-digit social security number, then feel free to picture that this number is stored in the first k words of a record. Here k is the smallest number of computer words that can contain a social security number.) Your algorithm is to generate the elements of the AV vector from the input information before sorting begins. An example of an overall structure is given in Figure 11-15.

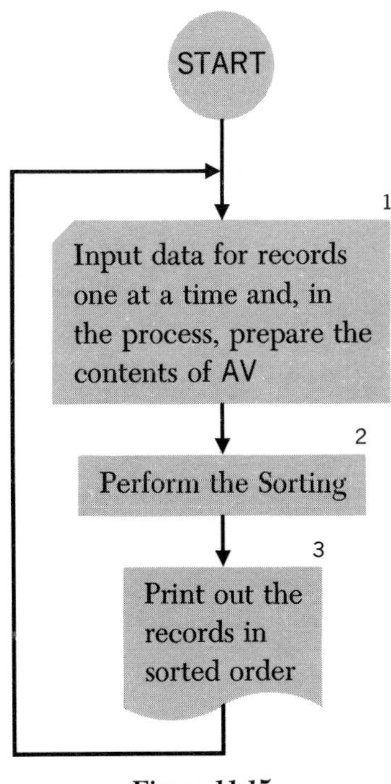

Figure 11-15

3. The *pruning* of a tree is the process of ruling out inadmissible segments during a tree search. Suppose that n segments emanate from a typical node but that $m \leq n$ of these are inadmissible. Depending on the design of the search algorithm, the inadmissibility of some of the m segments may not be immediately recognized and the search can proceed down unnecessary paths, resulting in a very costly, if not totally impractical algorithm.

Good pruning is usually a matter of having stored the right *kind* and *amount* of information on which to base the pruning decision.

In this problem an alternate approach to the solution of the border-crossing problem is suggested. Your job will be to compare the pruned trees developed during the tree search of the new method with those developed in the level-by-level technique worked out in the text.

The proposed method is what we will call the repeated *k-level natural order search*. This kind of tree search is like the one proposed for the four-color problem of Chapter 9, except that the search is never allowed to proceed down any one path beyond level k. Looking at the generalized algorithm of Figure 9-15, we see that it can be transformed to a k-level natural order search simply by inserting one box, box 6a, immediately after box 6, as shown in Figure 11-16. All unshaded boxes are identical with those of Figure 9-15.

The repeated k-level natural search idea tells us to start by carrying out a one-level natural search. If the destination node is not found at this level, we are to perform a two-level natural order search, then a three-level search, and so on. Eventually, when performing one of these searches, say, a j-level search, a destination node may be encountered. When a destination node is encountered at level j, data already stored identifies the countries from the root to the destination. This is a *best path*. All that needs to be done is to print out the vector of countries from root to destination. (If you have forgotten how the four-color algorithm was handled, you should review the fact that a COLOR vector was used with values representing the tree path being searched.) Presumably, we could keep an analogous CNTRY vector in this tree search.

The construction of an algorithm to perform a repeated k-level search is an interesting problem. That, however, is not what you are being asked to solve. Based on your present experience in constructing algorithms, visualizing the flow chart for a repeated k-level search should be no problem.

Your task will be to sketch and compare two trees similar in appearance to Figure 11-3 to be used in the search for best paths from *Spain to Poland:*

(a) Based on the level-by-level search technique.
(b) Based on the repeated k-level natural search described here.

When you are done, prepare a table of the number of nodes investigated at each level for each method.

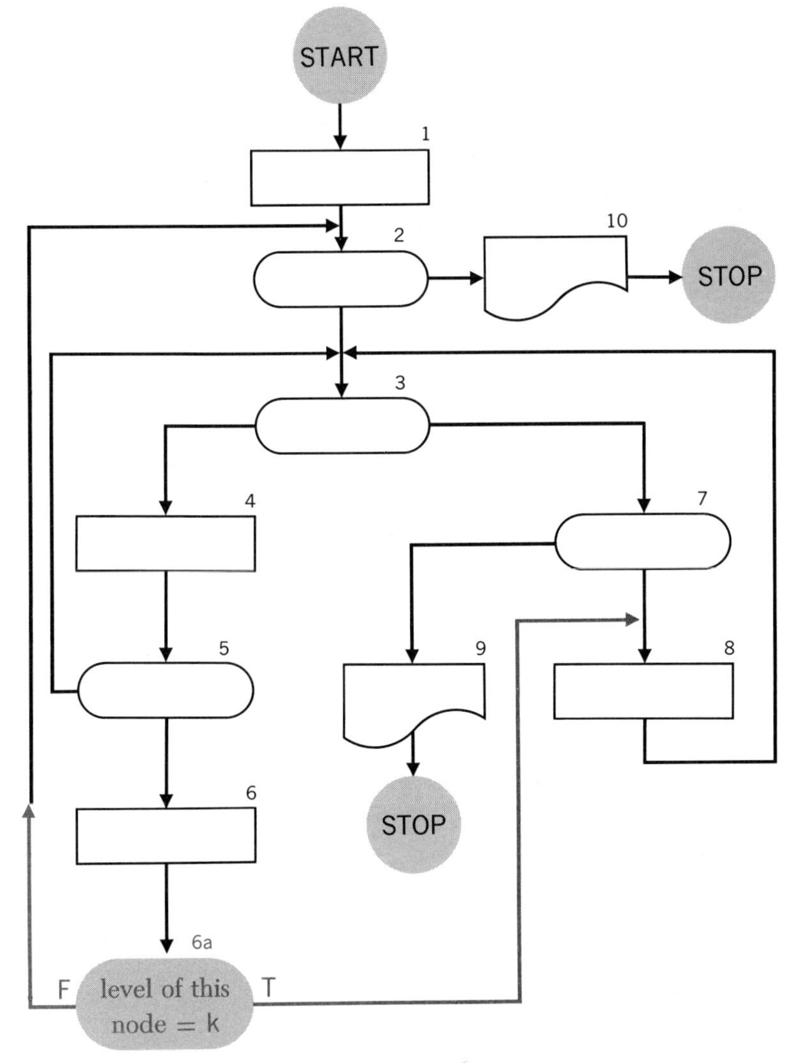

Figure 11-16

11-3 ANALYSIS OF TREE GAMES

As we suggested in Chapter 9, a great many two-player games are modeled by trees. We have called these "tree games." Among these are chess, checkers, go, nim, and tic-tac-toe, and each has a characteristic tree. In any of these trees, if we follow a path from the root node to a terminal, the segments we pass represent a set of legal moves constituting one completed game. The move made *from* the next-to-last node in the path represents a win for A, a win for B, or a draw (if a draw is allowed).

These games are finite in the sense that every path from the root node ends in a finite number of steps, and there can be only a finite number of paths.

There is a fascinating problem associated with every such finite tree game. It is known by the utterly drab and unrevealing name "analysis." For example, what we would really mean by *analysis of checkers,* if it were possible to do it in practice, is a study that would lead us to the following conclusion:

> Given that A is the first player and B the second player, and assuming that each player made each move in the best way possible, the game of checkers will inevitably end in a foreordained way as a ☐.

Unfortunately, we don't know how to end the last sentence because checkers has never been *analyzed.* But, because checkers is a finite game, we do know that one of the following three phrases completes the sentence.

win for A

win for B

draw

Our first challenge is to fully appreciate what we have just said, that is, to learn to understand that finite tree games are indeed *predetermined* in this way. Our second challenge is to learn how to go about developing an algorithm to analyze *any* such finite tree game.

Analyzing a Simple Game

The approach to game analysis can be best illustrated by a very simple game. We shall pick for study the game of Eight. Figure 11-17 is a reproduction of the game tree in Figure 9-4. To streamline its appearance,

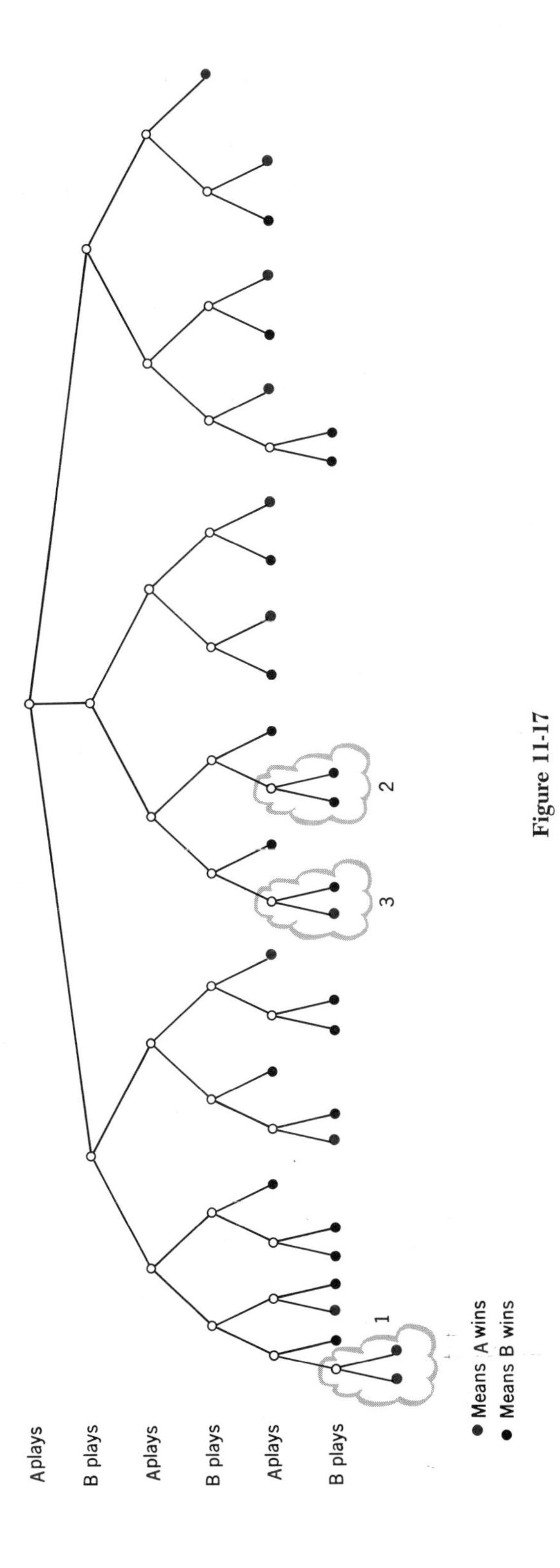
A plays
B plays
A plays
B plays
A plays
B plays
1
2
3
Means A wins
Means B wins

Figure 11-17

we've stripped off the segment labels and modified the appearance of the terminals.

Control of a game is a relatively simple but important concept in the analysis of any game. When, for example, during a game of Bridge, each player holds three cards, and you hold the Ace, King, and Queen of the trump suit, it is possible to lay down your cards face up and say, "I take the last three tricks." It is not necessary to *play out the hand,* because you *control* the remainder of the tricks, that is, you will win each remaining trick no matter what cards each of your opponents chooses to play on each of the last three tricks.

Branches of a game tree can be inspected for similar situations of control. Look, for example, at branch 1 in Figure 11-17:

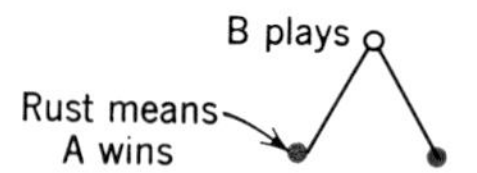

The unmarked node leading to the rust-colored terminals represents a point in a game of Eight where it is B's play and, no matter which of the two possible moves he makes, A wins. What can we infer about this unmarked node? If the play ever reaches this node, we know the game is won for A, so we can just as well color the node *rust,* as suggested in Figure 11-18.

By similar reasoning, if we have the situation that is shown in branch 2

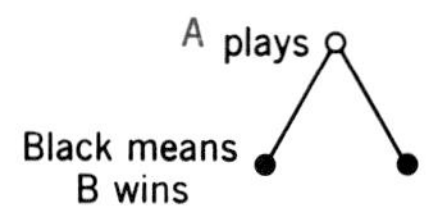

where it is clear that the unmarked node can now be considered a black node because, no matter what play A makes from this point, the game for A is lost.

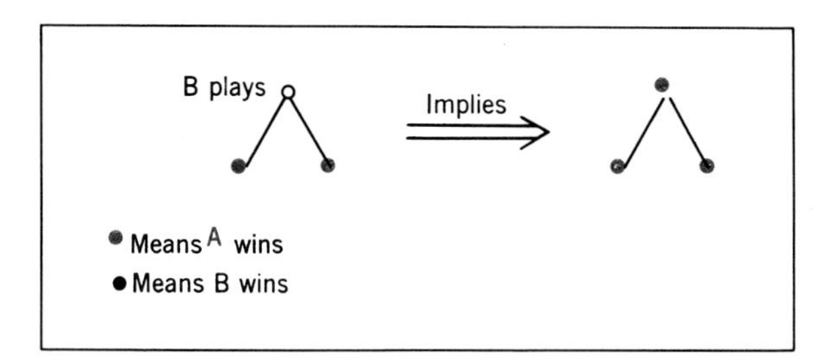

Figure 11-18

We take one more example before drawing an interesting generalization. Suppose we have this situation, as in branch 3;

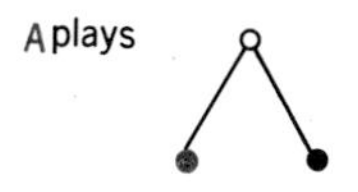

It's A's turn. He examines his alternatives and, if he's playing "heads up" Eight, he can be counted on always to select the move that leads to the *rust* terminal. In other words, in this situation, the unmarked node might as well be *rust.*

If you study Figure 11-19, which shows all possible control situations for the game, you cannot help but arrive at the following *node-marking rule:* (When you read the following sentence, substitute "A" or "B" for "*i*".)

> A node representing player *i*'s turn to move can be marked as a *win for i,* if at least one segment emanating from this node leads to a win for *i*; otherwise, it's marked as a win for *i*'s opponent.

It's possible by now that you already see how one can analyze a game tree like the one in Figure 11-17. In principle, it's an astonishingly simple process. Given a picture of the tree, all you do is repeatedly apply the node-marking rule until you are able to mark the root node by the same

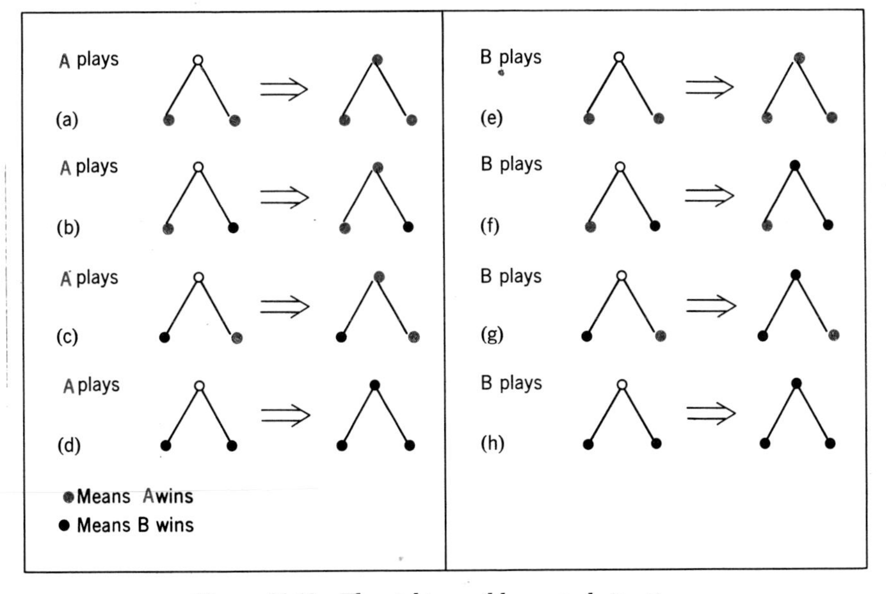

Figure 11-19 The eight possible control situations.

rule. *Remember:* Marking a node *rust,* for example, is equivalent to recognizing that A *controls* the game *from this node* down *all* paths of the branch defined by this node. That is, no matter what B chooses to do henceforth, A will win. Since the root node *controls* all the rest of the tree, marking it rust is equivalent to concluding that *A* controls the entire tree; making it black is equivalent to concluding that *B* controls the entire tree.

EXERCISE 11-3

Show that black is the right color for the root node of Eight (Figure 11-17), that is, that in the game of Eight, assuming best play on the part of both players, *the first player always loses.*

In a game tree as small as Eight's, it is but a five-minute exercise to determine the root node's color *if you are already given the full tree with all terminals properly colored.* Moreover, it makes very little difference how you go about it. One approach is to color nodes at each level, beginning with the level immediately above the terminals, then to color nodes at the next level, and so on, until you reach the root. This is certainly a systematic approach, and we couldn't quarrel with it. But keep in mind that in a typical game that is hard to analyze, *you are not given the tree at all.* For one thing, the tree is probably too big to be drawn without the aid of a computer.

Figure 11-20 suggests one very efficient method. In this method we follow what is basically a natural order tree-search algorithm (recall Figure 9-15) in the hunt for terminal nodes. After we find one, we retrace our steps to the preceding node and, at this point, attempt to color that node, *if sufficient information is available.* If not, we continue with the search for terminals. Eventually, we'll return to the same node with enough information to color it. Thus, in Figure 11-20, node 1 is colored rust after the two terminals emanating from it are determined. Retracing to node 2, there is sufficient information to color it immediately, on the basis of node 1's color alone, *by applying the node-marking rule.* Backing up to node 4 where it is B's play, we have this situation:

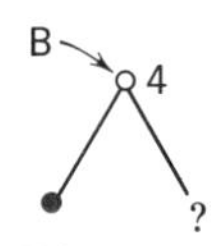

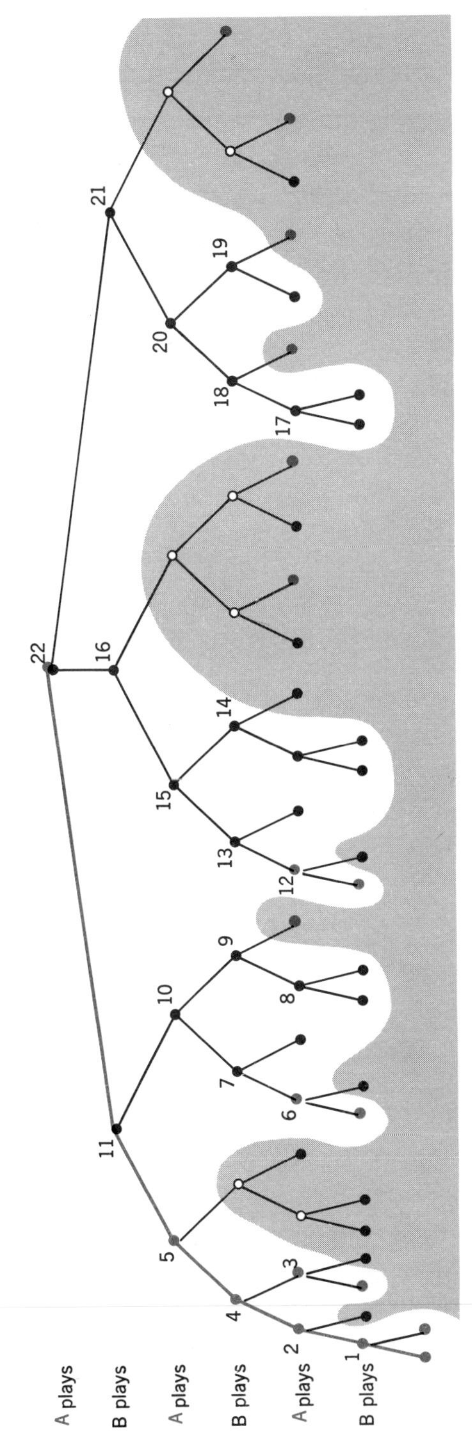
A plays
B plays
A plays
B plays
A plays
B plays
1
2
3
4
5
6
7
8
9
10
11
12
13
14
15
16
17
18
19
20
21
22

Figure 11-20

We can't decide if B controls this node until we determine the color of the nodes below node 3. After determining that the leftmost of these is a terminal and *rust,* and retracing to node 3, we can then color 3 rust, and then 4 rust, and so on, during the construction of the natural order search.

We see that as we proceed through the tree in this fashion, it is possible to reach a color decision on the root node even though we ignore several branches of the tree (the shaded areas). You can now see why we suspect that this method of modified natural order searching will prove to be very efficient for game tree analysis.

Analysis of "31"

Even though we are expert tree game analysts, we will still appreciate a look at a detailed algorithm which, if executed, would analyze a game, like "31," using the tree-search method just described. The algorithm is given in Figure 11-21 and discussion of it follows. First, however, we repeat the rules of "31" which were given in Problem 3, Exercises 9-1, Set B, (in Chapter 9).

Take a die and roll it. The side that turns up gives a running sum's initial value. Thereafter, each player moves by tilting the die over on its side (one of four possible sides, of course. Remember that opposite faces

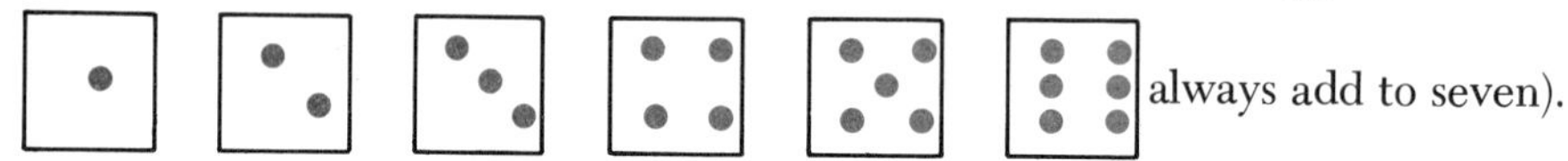

always add to seven).

The side that turns up after the tilt-over is then added to the running sum. The game proceeds tilt after tilt. A player whose tilt brings the total to exactly 31 wins the game; a player exceeding 31 loses. No draws.

Discussion of the Flow Chart in Figure 11-21

The initial roll of the die PLAY_0 is input at box 11. Box 12 initializes the variable SUM to PLAY_0. The variable i is always the index of the play under consideration. The variable PLAYER assumes the value 1 for odd-numbered moves and 0 for even-numbered moves. TALLY is a variable that counts the total number of forward and backward steps that are actually taken before the game analysis is complete and box 29 is reached. PLY is an auxiliary variable which holds the value of the play under consideration.

In box 13 the tally is set to 1 and we begin to move down the game tree. The first time we "drop through" box 16 and set PLY to 1 in box 17.

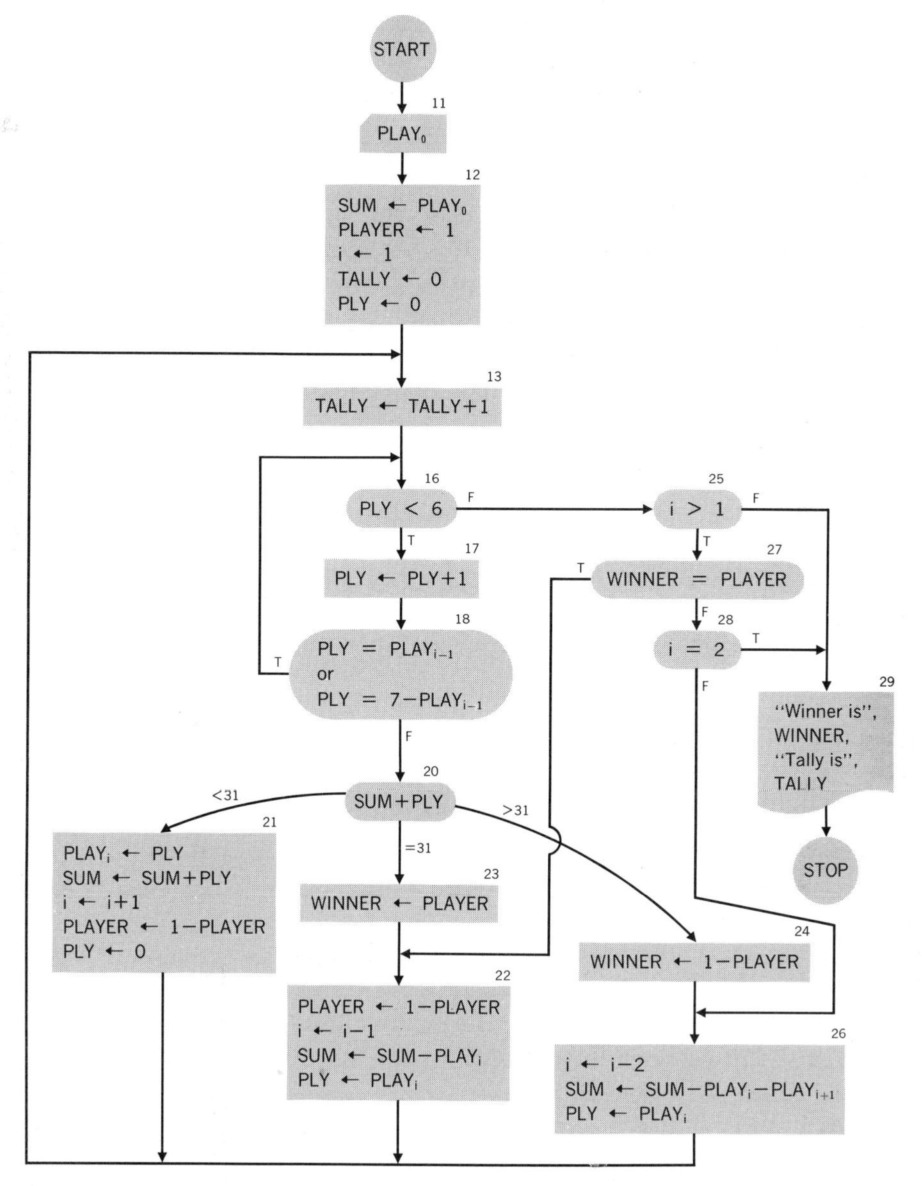

Figure 11-21 Analyzing the game of "31"

Box 18 tests the legality of this projected play. If PLY is equal to PLAY_0 or to $7 - \mathsf{PLAY}_0$, it does not constitute a legal move and we must therefore loop back and augment PLY by 1 until we find a legal value.

In box 20 we consider the value of SUM + PLY. If this sum is less than 31, then everything is satisfactory and we accept PLY as PLAY_i. In box 21 we make the proper assignments to PLAY_i and SUM. We update i, switch players, and set PLY to zero. Then we loop back to box 13.

If SUM + PLY = 31 then we know that our tentative move constitutes a win for the current player and we set WINNER to the current value of PLAYER in box 23. Now in box 22 we "back-up" or backtrack one play. This requires subtracting the last accepted play away from SUM, assigning it back to PLY and looping back to box 13.

If SUM + PLY > 31 then we know the tentative move constitutes a loss for the current player. This means a win for the other player (box 24). Now we must backstep or retract *two* plays in order to allow the current player to replay his previous play. In box 26 we make the proper adjustments to i and SUM.

Now consider box 16 again. Suppose the current value of PLY is 6. This means that we have considered all possible branches from the present node. If i > 1 then we need to backtrack. But do we backtrack one play and change players, or do we backtrack two plays and keep the same player? This depends on whether WINNER has the same value as PLAYER or not. If WINNER = PLAYER then we want to backtrack one play, whereas if WINNER ≠ PLAYER then we want to retract two plays. There is one exception: when i = 2 and WINNER ≠ PLAYER then we are finished because backtracking would take us to PLAY_0.

There are, of course, six possible values for PLAY_0, and the results of the game analysis will probably *not* be the same for all cases.

PROBLEM 11-3

After studying the algorithm for the analysis of "31" (hopefully you have now run this problem on the computer to find out the *outcome*), you should try your hand at writing an algorithm to analyze the game of Hex, whose rules are given in Problem 2, Exercises 9-1, Set B (Chapter 9).

You shouldn't need much help with this Problem but, just in case, here are a few suggestions to consider after you've had a go at it yourself.

Although the analysis of HEX is, in principle, similar to that of "31," there is more bookkeeping involved in the former. In "31," when play was at a level i, we saved, in the vector element PLAY_i, an integer that could later be used to tell what segments had not yet been tried for the node at level i, which lies along the current game's path. Saving this information amounts to saving the state of the game at every point in its history. In HEX we will also need to save the game's state at each play.

When we back up to a parent node for the purpose of trying another segment, we also have a problem in *reversing* the play to recover the earlier state of the HEX board. In "31" recovering the earlier state simply amounted, by careful design, to subtracting values of PLAY_i and PLAY_{i+1} from SUM (boxes 22 and 26 of Figure 11-21). In HEX, however, it may prove more convenient simply to save the full description of the HEX board, say, as a 3 by 3 array, or as a nine-element vector, for each state of the game. Then, to return to the condition of the board at an earlier level in the tree, it would merely be necessary to adjust the level index so that it corresponds to the desired array or vector. To be more specific, the condition of the HEX board could be coded thus.

Value assigned to array element	*Interpretation*
0	Presence of a black pawn
1	Presence of a rust pawn
9	An empty square

Now, for example, the HEX board on the left in Figure 11-22 could also be pictured by the grid shown to its right. Information in this grid could, in turn, be saved as a "row vector" of nine elements:

1,1	2,1	3,1	1,2	2,2	3,2	1,3	2,3	3,3
0	0	0	9	9	9	1	1	1
1	2	3	4	5	6	7	8	9

Imagine that this row vector belongs to an array of nine columns. We could then store the state of the game in each succeeding row after each move. We dub such an array the HEXH (for *HEX H*istory) and picture it below after *rust* makes his first move, say, by moving his rightmost piece forward, followed by a similar move by *black*.

	1,1	2,1	3,1	1,2	2,2	3,2	1,3	2,3	3,3
1	0	0	0	9	9	9	1	1	1
2	0	0	0	1	9	9	9	1	1
3	0	0	9	1	9	0	9	1	1

You might also consider ways to think about (and to code) the up-to-nine choices each player may have when he takes his turn. One way to picture these choices is as a 3 by 3 array, say, with rows corresponding to each of the

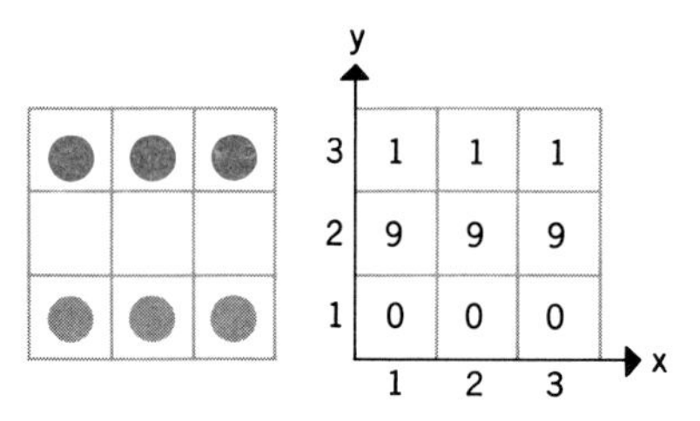

Figure 11-22

three *pawns* a player has to play with, and with columns corresponding to each of the three different *directions* each pawn might be allowed to move forward, (diagonal left, forward, and diagonal right). Row and column indexes could be updated appropriately as each new choice for a move is considered. Once a move is selected and we prepare to move along a chosen segment to the next node, we can save the associated row and column index values for later use whenever we have to backtrack to this node and scan the remaining choices.

Strictly speaking, we need to save only one number as the choice index. (An integer from one to nine will do.) This value could then be converted into the row and column indexes by these simple rules:

$$\text{row} \leftarrow \text{CHOP}\left(\frac{\text{choice}}{3}\right) + 1$$

and

$$\text{column} \leftarrow \text{choice} - 3 \times (\text{row} - 1)$$

There is clearly a tradeoff here between memory space and computer time. If you allocate space for pairs of indexes (row and column) in place of space for one index (choice), you avoid having to repeatedly compute the row, column pairs.

CHAPTER 12

LISTS AND STRINGS: THEIR STORAGE STRUCTURES AND USES

12-1 INTRODUCTION

There is a large class of everyday problems whose algorithmic solutions would be surprisingly awkward if they were expressed in our customary flow-chart language or in analogous programming languages like PL/I, FORTRAN, or ALGOL. One example of this is the editing of text. Typically, such a problem is now solved manually, but in a fast-increasing number of situations, computers are being employed.

A common use of computers in editing, for instance, is to create right-justified margins (squared off on the right) in the typeset columns of books, magazines, or newspapers. Computers are used to prepare and periodically revise large formatted tables and lists, such as railroad time tables, airline guides, and telephone directories.

In the field of literature, computers are used to analyze literary works for style and authorship. Some of this is done by carrying out statistical studies, looking for frequency in the use of certain words, phrases, or ideas. A *concordance* of a book, for instance, is a massive index giving an ordered list of each nontrivial word that occurs in the book and, along with each word, a complete set of citations, chapter, line number, and verse, in which that word occurred. The concordance of the Bible, for instance, is a necessary research document for the biblical scholar. In the past the preparation of a concordance has required a major manual effort—perhaps lasting many years. Today, concordances and other similar references for scholars are prepared routinely by computers.

Another example of this area of application is the editing of legal texts. The voluminous statements of some congressional bills are often revised many times from their original drafts, as a result of committee deliberations, before final enactment. Computer editing and automatic typesetting can speed the printing of each new draft of such bills.

12-2 EDITING

We are forced to admit that, while all these computer applications may have their merit, they do not appear to relate very closely to the everyday needs of a student. However, by analyzing the following problem (even though it may seem artificial), we will discover new ideas on the representation and management of data.

Suppose you are taking a laboratory course under Professor S. Legree, who insists that each lab report be neatly typed and at least twenty pages in length. Professor Legree once thought of himself as a journalist and is intollerant of errors such as misspelled words, split infinitives, and the like. Moreover, he has strong feelings about certain matters of technical content such as the arrangement of mathematical expressions, the proper use of technical abbreviations, and detailed description of the experimental situation.

You find that your first draft of a lab report is rarely acceptable to Prof. Legree; usually you are required to revise a report one or more times. For example, Table 12-1 shows the kinds of changes and corrections to be made on a draft of one of the lab reports. Some of the changes are to be made several times. Thus, one word has been misspelled *six* times and one phrase is to be replaced *seventeen* times. Your problem is to find a way to make these changes, produce a neatly typed version and, as part of the process, avoid having to completely retype the report.

It is reasonable for you to think that a computer would be helpful. Although most present-day students will not find a computer available for preparing lab reports, a number of research laboratories, printing and publishing houses, and a few model secretarial offices are already using computers to solve this very common problem. Perhaps it will not be long before some of you will also be using computers in this way.

How the Computer Plays its Role

A text to be edited can be read into a computer from paper tape, punched cards, or magnetic tape—or, in some cases, it can be entered through a keyboard, like a typewriter, attached directly to the computer. The computer, of course, can store the text in memory, print or type it out, or display it a line at a time or a page at a time on a TV screen. The editor can study the typed, printed, or displayed copy and prepare instructions expressed in a special editing language to show the changes he wants made. These instructions are then input to the computer and converted into a program which operates on the text as data.

After executing the editor's instructions, the new version of the text is printed or displayed and the editor can decide whether to make still more changes, as is often the case, by repeating the process. The editing cycle can be repeated as often as necessary until the editor is satisfied with the text. The text never needs to be entirely retyped by a person.

TABLE 12-1 Some Editing Changes

A. Spelling and typographical errors

As it appears now	Approximate number of occurrences	As it should appear
a. litle	6	little
b. stastistics	3	statistics
c. occurrance	4	occurrence
d. *()	1	890
e. intollerant	1	intolerant

caused by use of wrong case shift

B. Phrase changes

From		To
a. to safely run the experiment	2	to run the experiment safely
b. a terribly costly experiment	1	a costly experiment
c. in order to	17	to
d. cc/s	12	cc/sec
e. normal room temperature	4	normal room temperature, average humidity range and average barometric pressure
f. 4ac	6	4 × a × c
g. the sum a × b + a × c	4	the product a × (b + c)
h. LESS * MINUTES	3	LESS ⊛ SECONDS

*number represented by * is to be multiplied by 60 to get a number represented by ⊛.*

This chapter does not try to teach you how to use one of the editing languages we have just mentioned. Special editing language supplements or manuals may be available for this purpose and will be useful and easy to follow, especially after you have studied this chapter. Our purpose here is the more basic one of studying the algorithmic processes that are required to make editorial changes of the type suggested in Table 12-1. New ideas will emerge for the representation and manipulation of text data. These will, in turn, stimulate thoughts about ways to express editing operations, that is, new kinds of programming languages to make the construction of editing algorithms easier.

The first problem we will have to grapple with is how to visualize text data, such as a laboratory report, stored in memory. We could, for example, imagine the entire text of the report as one long string of characters. There are other ways of looking at the data structure. One that is particularly attractive for this discussion is to imagine the *report broken into a series of numbered lines.* Let each line be thought of as a string of, at most, 80 characters.[1]

12-3 INSERTING AND DELETING IN A STRING

Let's start by examining the fundamental problem of *replacement* in a string of characters. This is the task involved, for example, in replacing the misspelled "litle" with "little," which we mentioned in Table 12-1. Suppose we consider one of the lines that contains the misspelling:

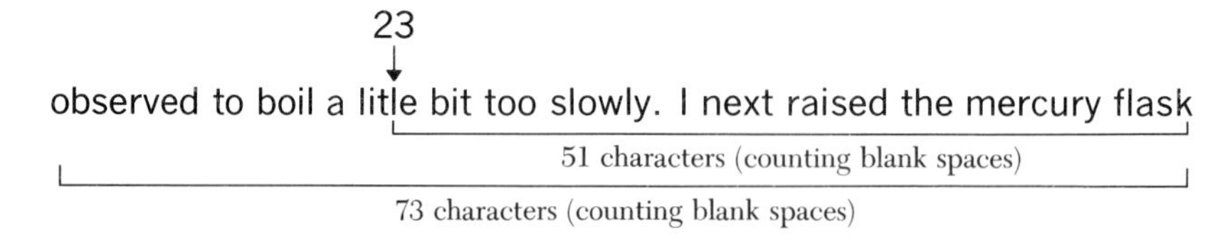

How might this string be stored in memory? Well, if this is line number 152, it *might* be stored as an 80-element vector named L152. That is, a vector of 80 window boxes, one character per box, with the leading character of the line assigned to $L152_1$. If all subsequent characters, including blanks, are stored in order, there will be seven unneeded boxes at the end which we can think of as holding blanks (□).

Inserting the letter "t" in the desired spot involves, in our computer model, shifting each of the last 51 characters one vector element to the *right* before we can assign "t" to $L152_{23}$, as flowcharted in Figure 12-1.

We think of *deletion* as the converse of insertion.

In removing a letter, such as the extra "s" in the misspelling of "stastistics," we have an example of *deletion.*

[1] We are assuming that we type on a sheet of $8\frac{1}{2}$ inch wide paper with a 1 inch left-hand margin using a typewriter whose horizontal spacing is 12 to the inch.

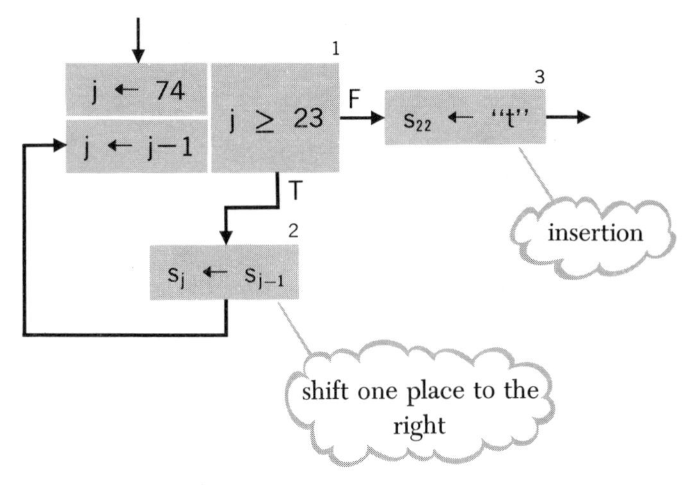

Figure 12-1 Inserting the letter "t".

Two Examples

1. Given the text line

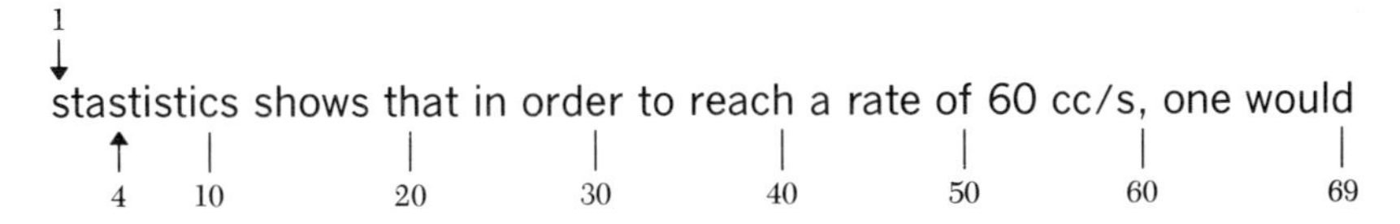

and assuming the vector model for storing text is one window box per character, write an algorithm that removes an offending character from the above line by the *left shift* process.

Answer

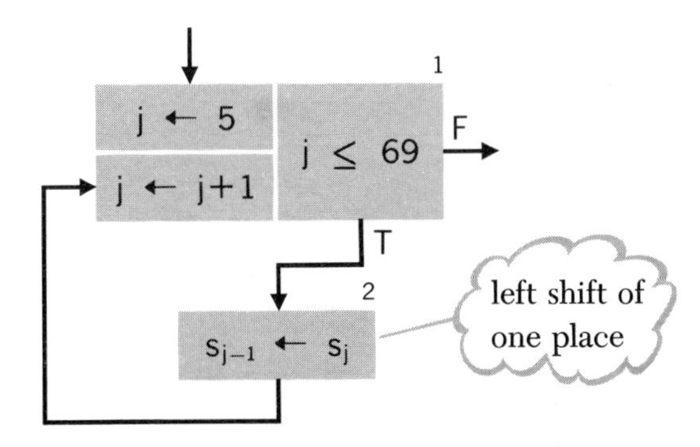

2. What can you say about the relative *efficiency* of the algorithm you just produced for deleting the s in sta̲stistics or for the replacement of one substring for another *of equal length,* such as occurrence for occurra̲nce and 890 for *().

Answer

For our model, the substitution of equal length strings is as efficient as possible but efficiency of insertion or deletion is a function of the number of shifts that needs to be done. Changes occurring near the right end of the left-justified string are more efficient than those at the left end.

There are some simple lessons to be learned here. The vector model for handling strings of characters seems efficient enough when substrings are to be replaced by others of *equal length*. However, for *general string substitution* [that is, where a substring of one length r (possibly null) is to be replaced by a substring of another length s (possibly null)], the vector storage model we initially proposed seems quite inappropriate.

Strings Stored as One-Way Lists

It's often true that a more judicious use of the storage already committed for the representation of data (or the expenditure of additional storage as it is required) can result in a significant increase in an algorithm's speed of execution. This will certainly prove true in developing the type of storage model we need for string substitution. Suppose we think of each window box as being large enough in capacity to hold, not only one character of the string, but also the *label* of the window box holding the *next* character of the string, as suggested in Figure 12-2.

It may help to think of each window box as being divided into two compartments, a *data* part and a *pointer* or label part. The pointer parts serve to effectively *link* each box to its successor. We call this a *one-way list.* "One-way" relates to the fact that the pointer parts can be used to scan the rest of the list in a *forward* but not in a *backward* direction.[2] The very last box does not have a successor, so instead of holding a pointer, the pointer part contains some mark which has the special significance meaning "The End." The mark we'll use in our drawings is "⊣".

The linkages given by the pointers from window box to window box provide a *thread* connecting the entire list together. By following this thread, one can find any element of the list. A list linked together in this way is often called a *threaded list.*

String Substitution in a One-Way List

Does this one-way list model appear to offer any advantages over the vector model in the operations of string substitutions?

[2] In a two-way list, each box would also hold the label of the box holding the *predecessor* element of the string.

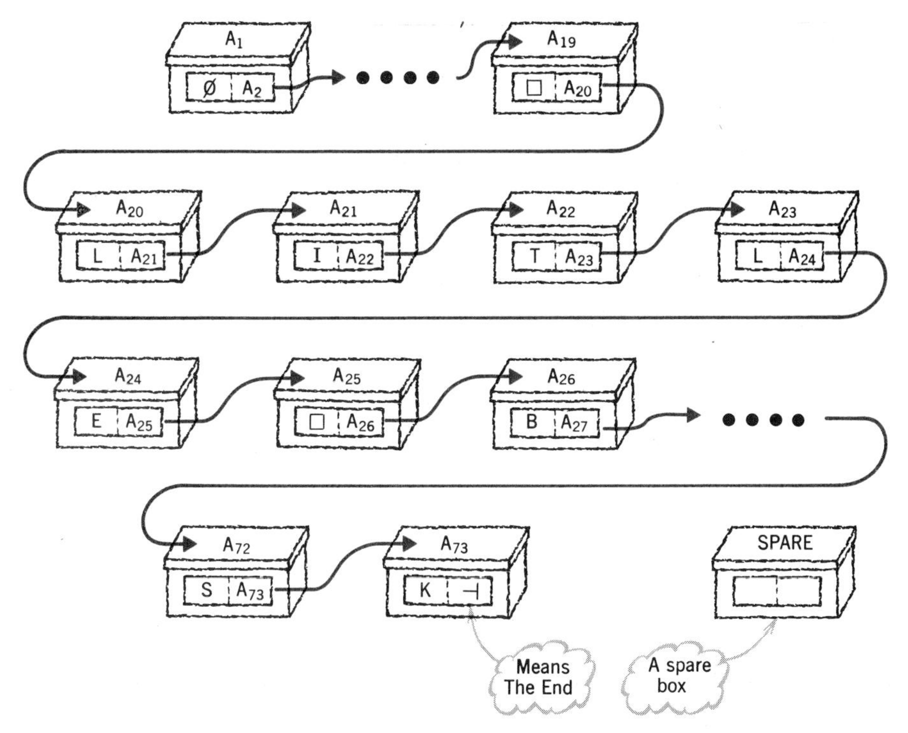

Figure 12-2 One-way list model of a string of 73 characters (before editing).

Suppose we want to insert the letter "t" between the 22nd and 23rd elements of the string shown in Figure 12-2. What we propose to do now is to locate a "spare" window box (for the moment, we'll assume it's labeled SPARE). Using it, we'll perform the following simple two-step operation.

1. Assign the value T | A_{23} to SPARE.

2. Assign the value T | SPARE to A_{22}

Figure 12-3 shows the appearance of the list after the operation. Study it a moment and see if you don't think that we're on the trail of a better storage structure model for use in string substitution!

Before we show any more examples, we need to develop a more compact method for picturing these lists.

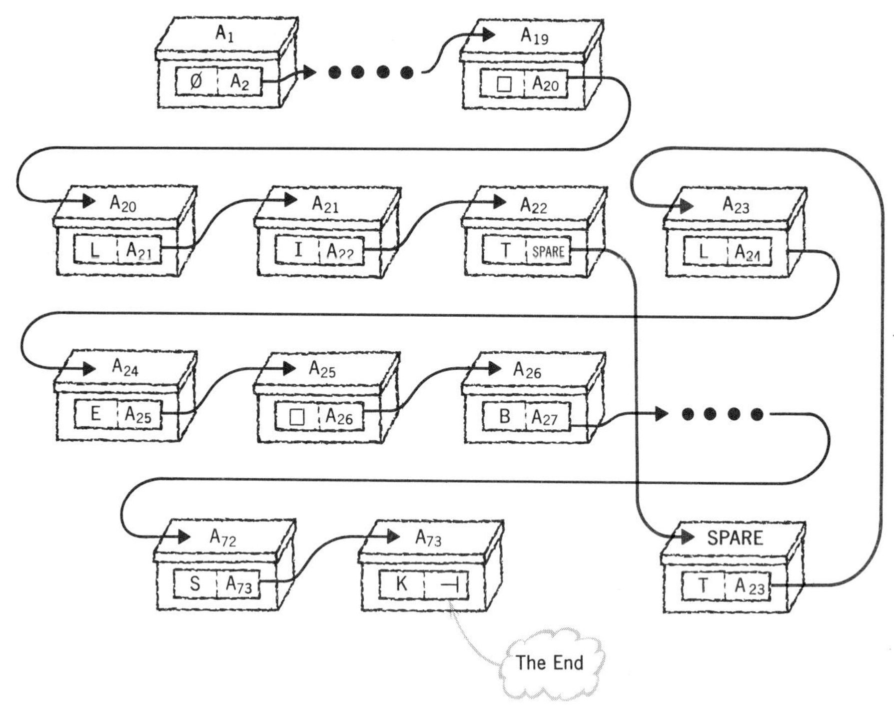

Figure 12-3 String after insertion of "T".

Our proposal is to abbreviate the picture of each window box so for example,

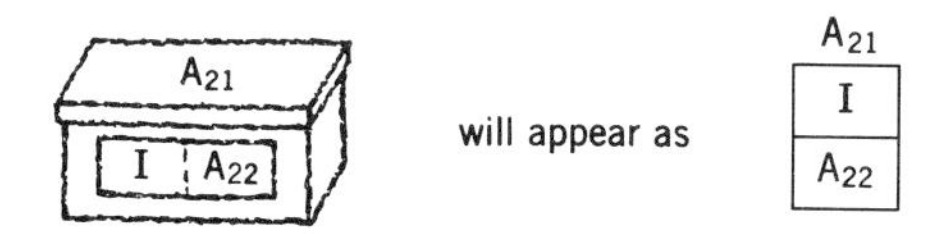

This type of representation will permit the one-way lists pictured in Figure 12-2 and 12-3 to look like those in Figure 12-4.

You may be wondering how other substitution operations might proceed in this scheme. Figure 12-5 shows three more such operations performed on a string, this time pictured as stored in a vector, B; the first two are deletions, and the third is an insertion.

EXERCISE 12-3, SET A

Using the techniques illustrated in Figures 12-4 and 12-5, show *before* and *after* appearance of one-way lists for the strings given below. In each

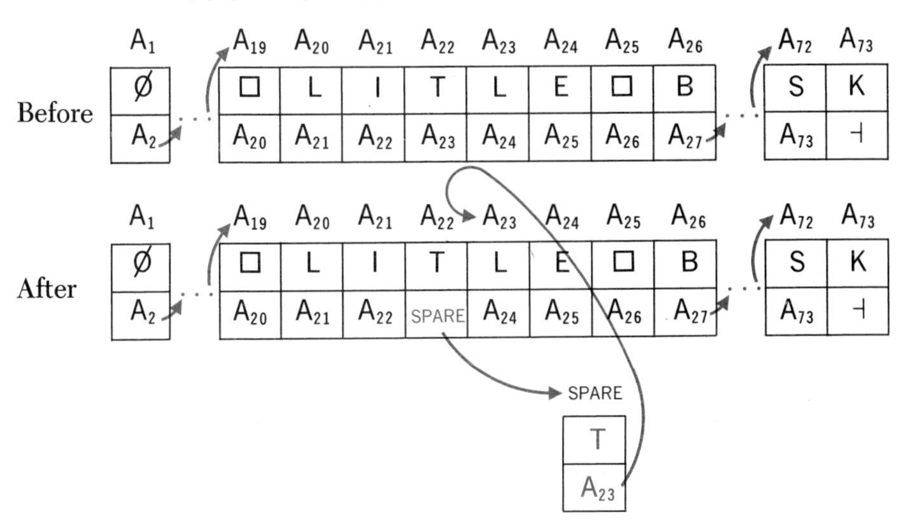

Figure 12-4 An abbreviated picture of one-way lists showing *insertion* of the character "T".

case, let the string initially be stored in the vector V (as a one-way list, of course) and obtain spares as needed from the vector Z, beginning at Z_{14}. Perform the applicable editing operations that are listed in Table 12-1.

(a) It was a terribly costly experiment in spite of good planning.

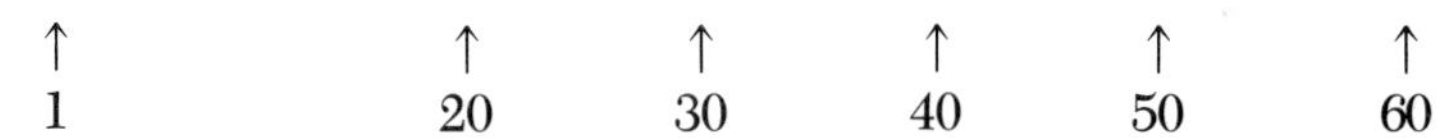

(b) equation. The expression in this case is B↑2 × (4AC).

(c) true in order to safely run the experiment at all.

↑ ↑ ↑ ↑ ↑ ↑ ↑
1 5 15 29 33 42 50

12-4 A STORAGE STRUCTURE FOR STRING MANIPULATION

If you are a shrewd observer, you may already have recognized several unanswered questions about the one-way list storage model presented thus far.

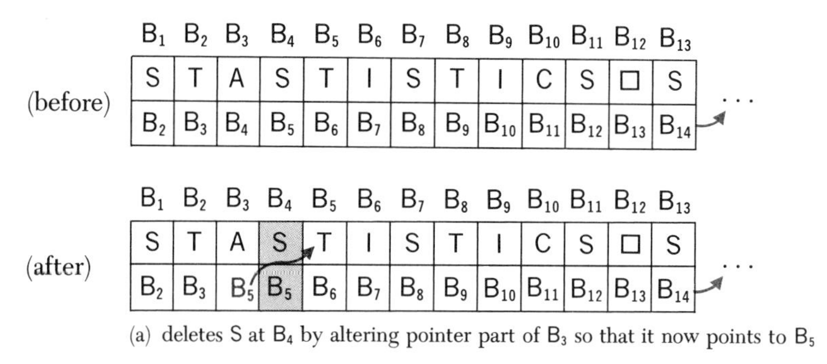

(a) deletes S at B_4 by altering pointer part of B_3 so that it now points to B_5

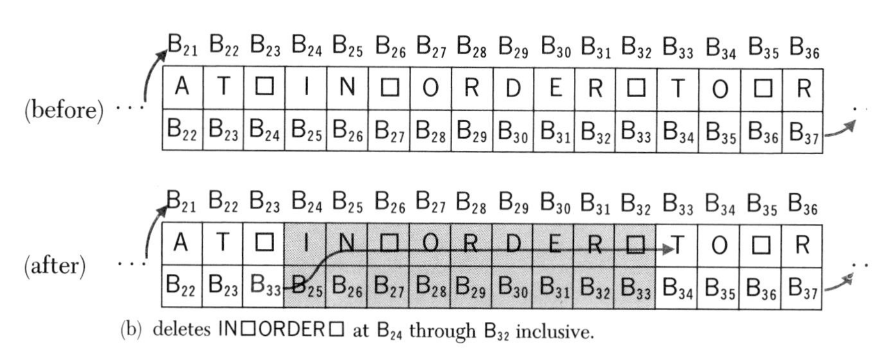

(b) deletes IN☐ORDER☐ at B_{24} through B_{32} inclusive.

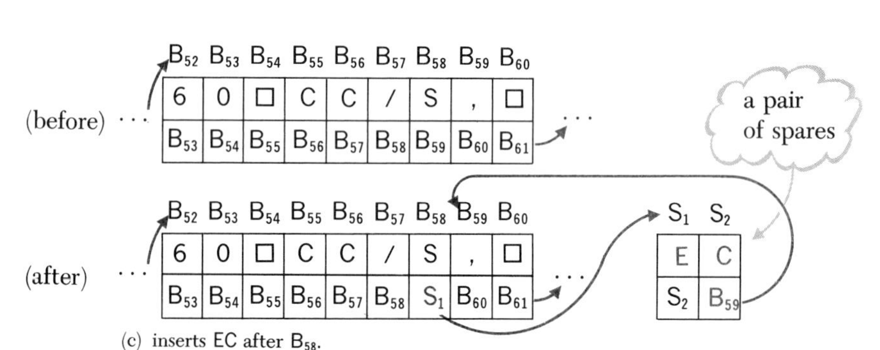

(c) inserts EC after B_{58}.

Figure 12-5 Three more examples of string substitution in a one-way list.

1. Where and how are the *spares* found when they are needed for in sertion? Is there some sort of a *pool* of available spares (a *free storage pool*)?

2. What happens to those substrings that are replaced or deleted, e.g., B_{24} through B_{32} in Figure 12-5? Once deleted, would we ever again want to use the contents of these boxes? Should these window boxes be recovered to be used again for some other purpose? What agent would accomplish this recovery and how would it be done?

3. When we start out to represent a text line, it seems sensible to employ a vector of up to 80 elements for the initial representation as a one-way list. After several deletions and insertions, however, the data parts of the list may no longer be limited to the original vector. Why then commit the use of a special vector for representing each text line in the first place? Any patchwork collection of window boxes properly *threaded* into a one-way list would do the job. If there is to be a pool of available spares, and this approach may be very attractive, why not simply draw from this *pool* as many window boxes as are needed to represent each text line and form the one-way lists from these?

We have raised some questions and in doing so have put forth a number of ideas that need to be thought out more carefully. It begins to appear that to do text editing, we must take a new look at the way we use the storage that is available to us in a computer memory. Here is a quick summary of our situation.

1. In a typical editing process we may need to make a large number of alterations (insertions and deletions). Moreover, the length of an altered character string may be substantially different from the length of an original string. Confining the storage of a string to a fixed amount of memory seems quite inappropriate. We need a structure that will allow a character string to be changed to any length as it resides in memory (up to a maximum length imposed by the finite amount of memory available).
2. Since there is a finite amount of memory available and we may wish to store a large amount of text, there is reason not to be wasteful of memory. We need a structure which can collect memory that has been released from use and reassign it to new use on demand.
3. It may be necessary to have several different character strings in memory at the same time. Of course, it will be necessary to identify each string by name and to locate it in memory regardless of how long it may be.

A structure satisfying these requirements can be achieved without serious conflict, provided we recognize that we are faced with a problem in the management of storage. This can be solved by employing certain *storage management* algorithms. We do not wish to do a detailed study of such algorithms here, but we do wish to sketch the general lines of one, which we will call the *memory allocator* (the *MA*).

You can think of the *MA* as a procedure that is automatically referenced by the main flow chart every time spares must be drawn from the *pool* or returned to the pool. The *memory allocator* is initially given full charge of a very long vector M (for memory). In reality, M represents the total space allocated for storing string data in the solution of a particular problem. Before any use is made of this vector, the memory allocator *threads* the elements of this vector into one long one-way list, as suggested in Figure 12-6. This list becomes the *free storage list* or *pool* to which we have alluded earlier. *Threading* in this case is merely the process of storing in the pointer part of each list element the name of its successor element.

In an effort to achieve further notational brevity, we will use only the subscript of the vector element in M as the label. That is, instead of the label M_{256}, we will just use "256". This means that the label of a window box becomes essentially synonymous with a memory address.

The element M_0 is used by the *memory allocator* algorithm for a very special purpose. The *pointer* part of M_0 points to the *head* element of the free storage list. The *data* part of M_0 also holds a pointer, and this one points to the *tail* element of the free storage list.

Initially, M_0's pointer part is M_1 or simply 1. Any time the memory allocator is requested to *disburse* some window boxes for use by other flow charts, the pointer part of M_0 will be reset so that it points to the leading element of what is left in the free storage list, that is, to the new *head*. When window boxes are to be released for return to the pool, the *MA* threads these boxes to the *tail* of the free storage list. At the same time, the data part of M_0 is reset so that it contains the label of the new tail of the list.

In short, boxes are disbursed from the head of the free storage list and are recovered by tacking them on the tail. (Some people refer to this as a *first in-first out* system.)

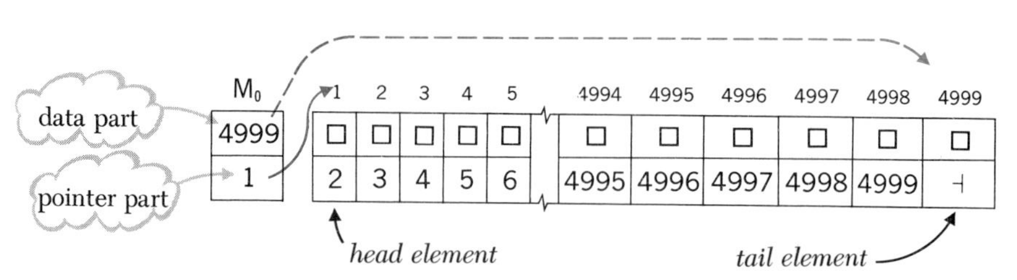

Figure 12-6 Free storage list ready for use.

Figure 12-7 pictures the changes in the M vector that take place during the operations of release to and disbursal from free storage (unshaded boxes). These changes would result from executing the editing steps described in Figure 12-5. Figure 12-7 is based on the assumption that the text line being edited is currently stored in a one-way list that uses consecutive addresses, 201 through 260, rather than B_1 through B_{60} as shown in Figure 12-5. After you have studied the step-by-step changes to the free storage list in Figure 12-7, you may correctly surmise that the free storage idea, although very simple, is a perfectly workable model for the allocation of memory in algorithms that deal with string-type variables.

Continuing to study Figure 12-7, shift your attention now to a study of the *shaded* boxes and to the changes that occur in these from line to line, i.e., from (a) to (b), (b) to (c), etc. You will recall that in Figure 12-5 these boxes were thought of as belonging to some other vector called "B". Now, of course, we see a more natural way to view this string. It is simply a part of the M vector that has been disbursed by the *MA* from the free storage list at some earlier time. In fact, every string (one-way list) can be thought of in this way; that is, as a series of one or more threaded-together "pieces" of the M vector.

If we think of strings in this way, of course, we need a new way to name or identify them. Otherwise, we'll have no way, in our algorithms, to refer conveniently to each string in a simple and unambiguous fashion. We are now ready to consider the last concept needed for the storage structure model for string data: the method of *naming* string variables.

String Variables (s-variables)

Suppose there is a table kept in memory that contains the name of every s-variable, that is, every string variable whose value is to be stored as a one-way list. We shall call this table the SVAT (*s*tring *v*ariable *a*ccess *t*able), and associate with every stored name a pointer part, as suggested in Figure 12-8. Conceivably, the SVAT could be constructed in advance, i.e., before we begin execution.[3] We can imagine that initially each s-variable is null. To reflect this fact, the pointer part for that variable in the SVAT table can have the tail mark (⊣) assigned to it.

Now, when we wish to assign a non-null string value to an s-variable, say, V, the action of assignment becomes a three-step process.

[3] This is true because in the usual situation every variable we intend to employ is already stated in the flow chart. String variables can be specially marked, of course, to distinguish them from the others.

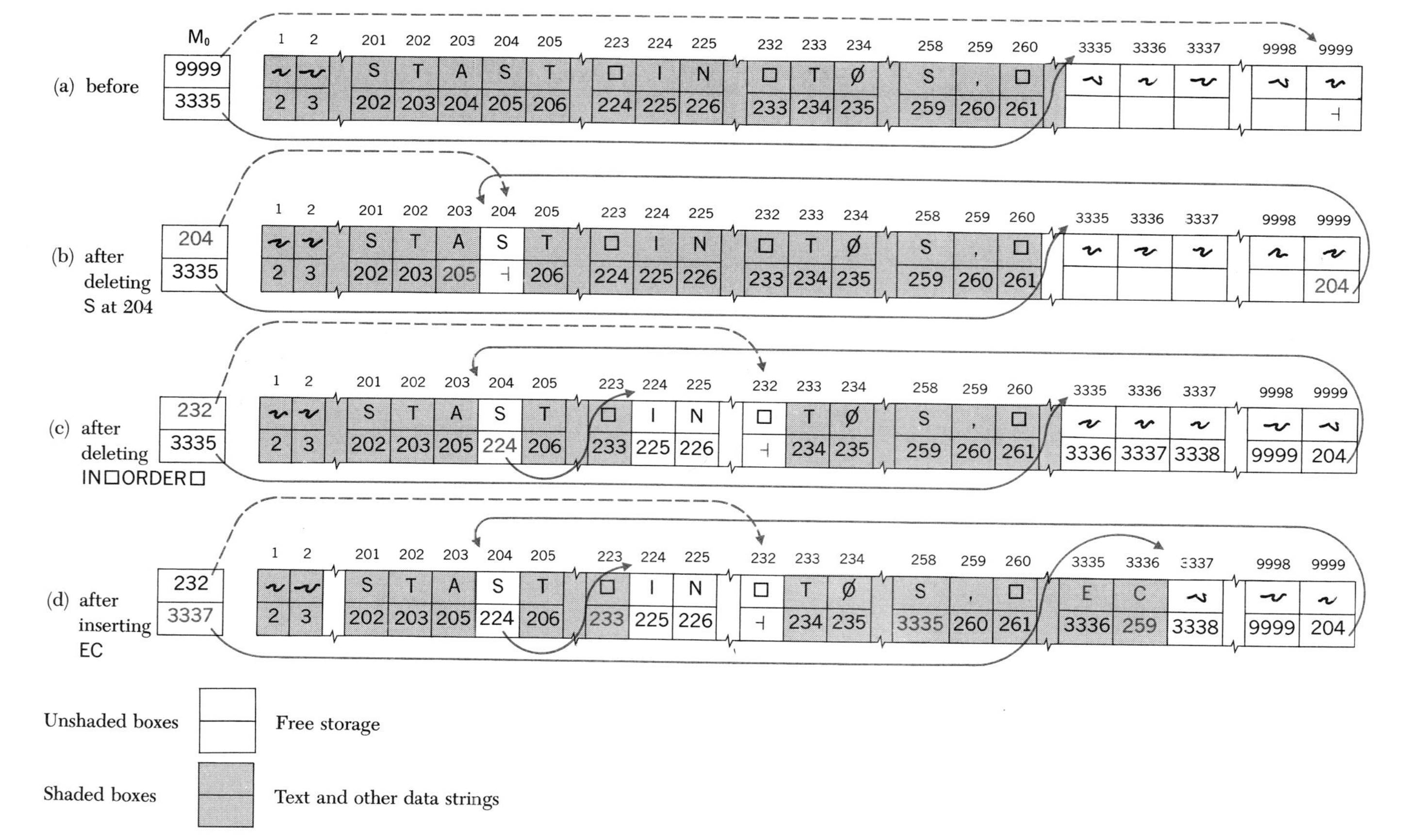

Figure 12-7 Picture of the memory space used for strings.

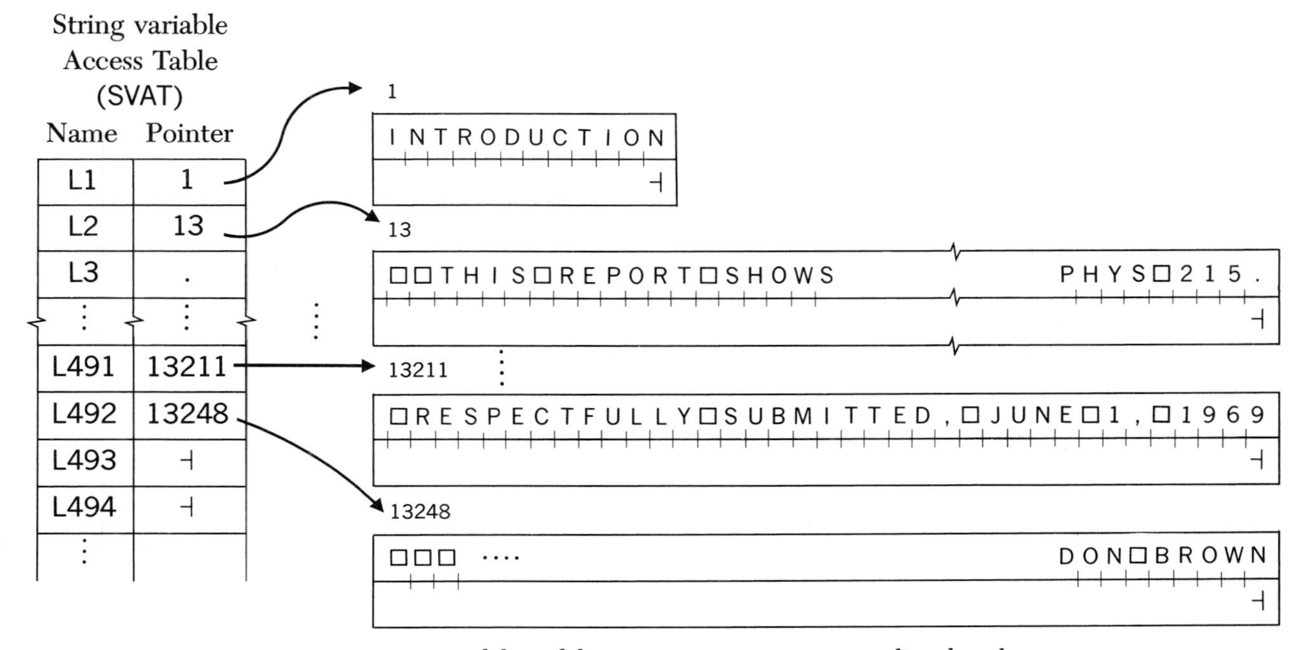

Figure 12-8 Picturing each line of the report as a separate one-way list whose boxes were drawn from the free storage pool. Pointers in the SVAT are set to each named list.

1. Ask the *memory allocator* for the required number of window boxes (one box for each character of the particular string you wish to form). The *MA* gives you these boxes in the form of a one-way list, tells you the address of its head, and has already marked its tail.

2. *Assign*, one-to-one, the characters of the string to (the data parts of) the boxes of the list.

3. *Link* this list to its *name* in the SVAT by assigning the *head* address to the pointer part associated with the name.

To help you remember these three steps, we offer this motto: *allocate, assign, and link.*

For purposes of comparison, we note the analogy with *ordinary assignment* that can be regarded as the *two-step* process

1. Find the right box (the one with the desired label on it).
2. Put the value into that box.

We see that:

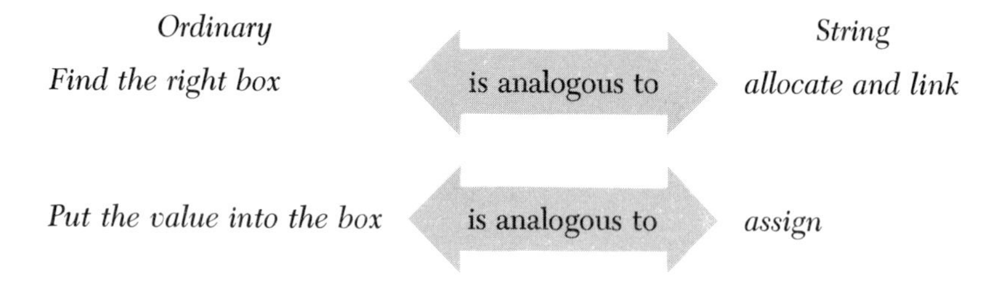
Ordinary
String
Find the right box
is analogous to
allocate and link
Put the value into the box
is analogous to
assign

EXERCISES 12-4

1. Given the string storage structure diagrammed below, answer the following:

(a) Write the unscrambled string P1, i.e., write out the characters of P1 in their *threaded order.*
(b) Write the unscrambled string P2.
(c) Change boxes 33 and 36 to read:

33	36
D	□
35	3

Now unscramble P2.

(d) Change box 18 to read:

18
□
22

Now unscramble P1.

Memory

M_0
4999
37

1	2	3	4	5	6	7	8	9	10	11	12	13	14	15	16	17	18
E	O	Y	O	U	□	I	D	E	A	H	A	V	V	Y	R	E	□
16	27	4	5	6	11	8	9	10	⊣	12	13	17	1	21	15	18	25

SVAT

P1	3
P2	14
P3	35
P4	28

19	20	21	22	23	24	25	26	27	28	29	30	31	32	33	34	35	36
E	□	□	N	G	O	T	H	□	E	O	O	T	A	D	K	,	□
20	7	23	2	24	30	26	19	7	29	31	33	32	34	⊣	⊣	36	⊣

2. Use the same string storage structure given for Problem 1 for each part below.

(a) Show the content of M_0 and SVAT if the first English word and its following space (□) is deleted from P1 and returned to free storage. Also show any *changes* in the string stored in memory.

(b) Show the content of M_0 and SVAT and the changes required in the string M if P2 is threaded on to the end of P1 and if P3 is then threaded on to the new end of P1. Assume that P2 and P3 are then made null.

(c) Show the changes of M_0 and SVAT and the changes required in the string M if P1 were to be assigned the value "GOOD". (Although we have not yet discussed reassignment to a string variable, you should be able to predict the result by holding fast to the motto: *allocate, assign, and link.*)

12-5 STRING OPERATIONS IN THE FLOW-CHART LANGUAGE

The string storage structure model we have constructed will form part of the necessary background for our next discussions. We are now in a position to introduce new string-handling capability to our flow-chart language and to suggest its use in various types of algorithms.

While we develop these concepts, the applications to be presented will be confined largely to algorithms for text editing. However, the same string-handling capability can increase our facility for developing a far wider variety of algorithms. In Chapter 13, for example, we will show an algorithm for the transformation of postfix strings (see Chapter 10 on compilers) into sequences of machine instructions.

Variables

For the flow charts in the remainder of this chapter, string variables will be distinguished from ordinary variables by a *bar*. Thus, the variable $\bar{S}$ will now refer to a string, while the variable T is an ordinary variable.

To be strictly correct about our terminology, we would have to say that $\bar{S}$ identifies a string of characters stored *in the data parts of a particular one-way list of boxes*. Moreover, $\bar{S}$ identifies this string by *pointing to its head* element, via a pointer kept in the SVAT. The tail element of the one-way list representation of the string is always specially marked. The variable T, on the other hand, is the familiar label on a window box.

String Assignment Steps

Here are several illustrations of assignment of value to a string variable $\bar{S}$. In each case we lean on our conceptual model to remind us of the three-step process.

(a) *Allocate* the required number of boxes as a one-way list.
(b) *Assign* the characters of the string to the respective data parts.
(c) *Link* the list to the name $\bar{S}$ via the SVAT.

First, we illustrate in Figure 12-9 what is meant by the flow-chart box

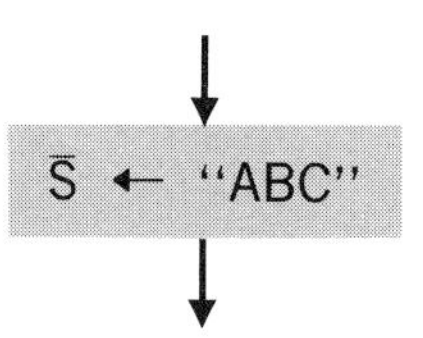

Strictly speaking, there is ordinarily a follow-up *fourth* step in string assignment. This is the *return* of no-longer-needed boxes to the *MA* which places them at the end of the free storage list.

When the alphabetic constant "ABC" is used in a string assignment step, it should be thought of as a particular, though unnamed, one-way list of three elements whose data parts have the values "A", "B", and "C", respectively. Used in this context, the constant "ABC" will be called a *string constant*. However, when the same alphabetic constant is used in an ordinary assignment step, for example,

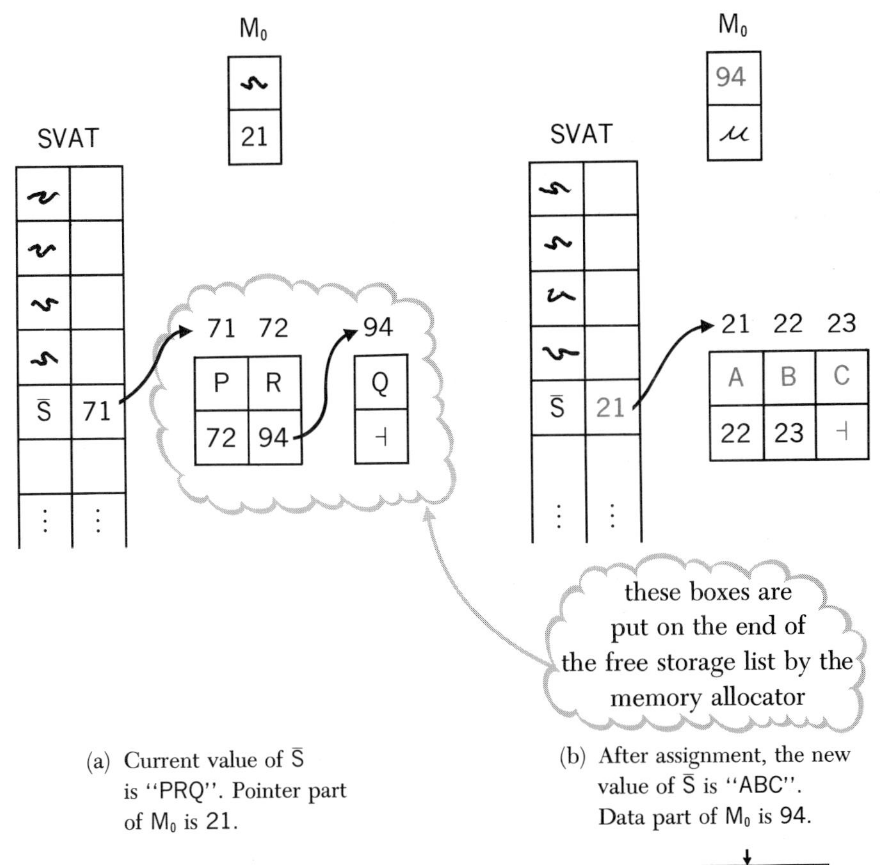

(a) Current value of $\bar{S}$ is "PRQ". Pointer part of M_0 is 21.

(b) After assignment, the new value of $\bar{S}$ is "ABC". Data part of M_0 is 94.

Figure 12-9 Showing what happens in the string assignment, $\bar{S}$ ← "ABC".

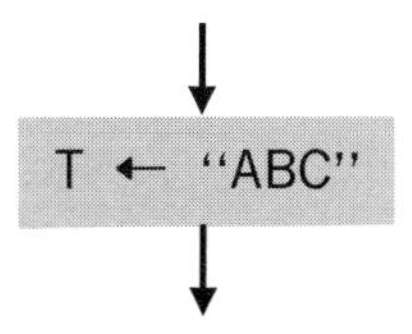

it will have the conventional meaning we gave it in the very beginning of this book.

We now extend our picture of string assignment with two more examples:

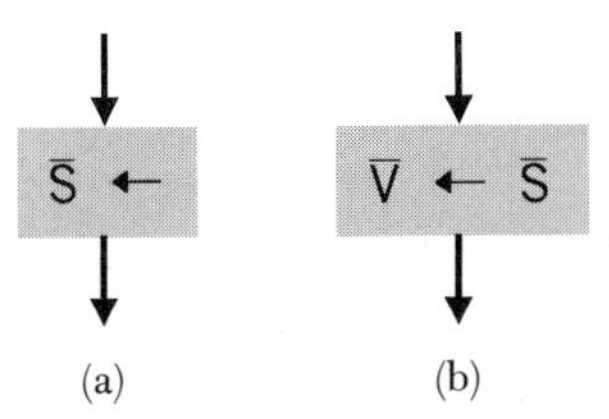

Let's see how to interpret them. The first assignment is to be read as: assign to $\bar{S}$ the *null* string, that is, the string with no elements. In the model (Figure 12-10) we show that $\bar{S}$ is null by replacing the SVAT pointer with the *tail* mark. The replaced string, being no longer needed, is returned to the memory allocator. The second assignment step is to be read as: assign to $\bar{V}$ a string whose data parts constitute *a copy of those in the string* currently assigned to $\bar{S}$. We picture this action in Figure 12-11 as follows.

(a) *Allocate* boxes from the *memory allocator* in sufficient number to make the desired duplicate.

(b) *Assign* copies of the data parts of the original string to the respective data parts of the duplicate.

(c) *Link* the newly created list to $\bar{V}$.

(d) *Return* to the *memory allocator* the list that was previously linked to $\bar{V}$.

String Expressions

We are accustomed to the idea of an arithmetic expression on the right side of the assignment arrow. An expression suggests a set of rules for developing a particular value. By analogy, what we put on the right of

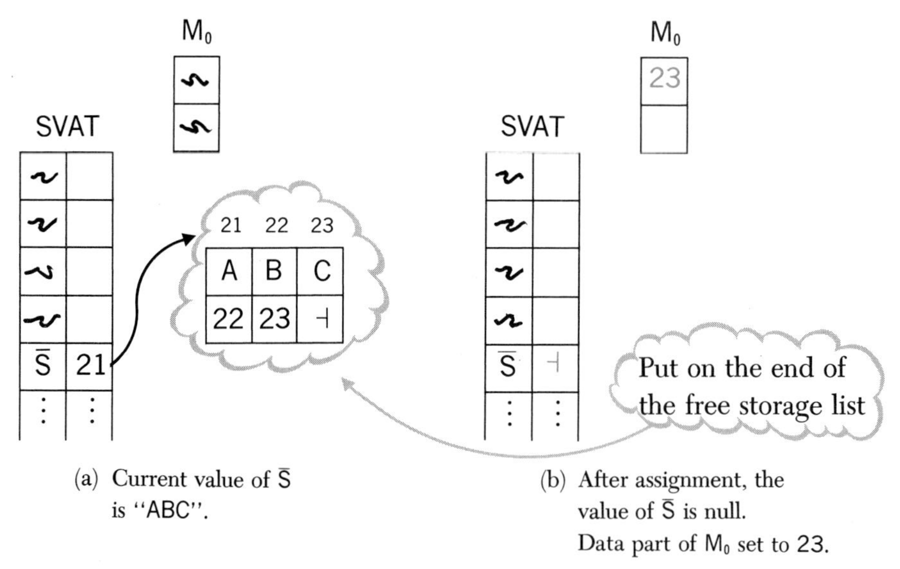

(a) Current value of $\bar{S}$ is "ABC".

(b) After assignment, the value of $\bar{S}$ is null. Data part of M_0 set to 23.

Figure 12-10 Showing what happens in the assignment $\bar{S} \leftarrow$.

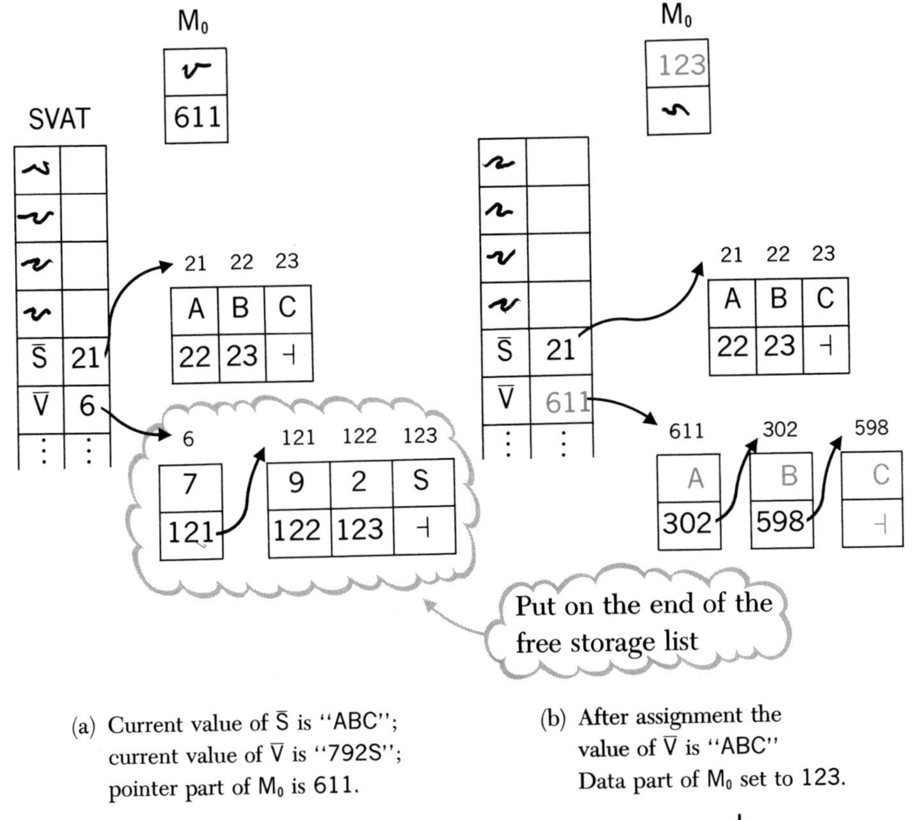

(a) Current value of $\overline{S}$ is "ABC"; current value of $\overline{V}$ is "792S"; pointer part of M_0 is 611.

(b) After assignment the value of $\overline{V}$ is "ABC" Data part of M_0 set to 123.

Figure 12-11 Showing what happens in the assignment $\boxed{\overline{V} \leftarrow \overline{S}}$.

the arrow of a string assignment step should also be regarded as an expression or, to be precise, a *string expression.* Every string expression implies a set of rules for developing a particular string (that is, a one-way list with the data parts filled with the characters of that string). So far, we have encountered three simple types:

string constant
string variable
null string

If it is possible to form more complex string expressions, it will be necessary to have *string operators.* Just as we were able to build the expression A + B or A × B, etc., using A and B with arithmetic operators, we will be able to designate rules with *string operators* for constructing new strings.

Concatenation. A good example of a string operator is the *concatena-*

tion operator whose symbol is || (a pair of vertical bars). For example, the string expression

$$\overline{A} \; || \; \overline{B}$$

means: form a new string consisting of a copy of $\overline{A}$, with a copy of $\overline{B}$ concatenated (i.e., linked) to the end. If, for instance, $\overline{A}$ had the value "MATH□" and $\overline{B}$ had the value "231A", then $\overline{A}$ || $\overline{B}$ is a string whose value is "MATH□231A".

Keep in mind that by a copy of $\overline{A}$ we mean a unique one-way list whose data parts (i.e., *values*) are identical with the corresponding data parts of $\overline{A}$.

Various types of string expressions can now be formed by employing the concatenation operator once, twice, or many times in one expression. We give several examples in Table 12-2.

We now explain three examples of string expressions used in assignment steps (Figure 12-12).

Recall that we have visualized string assignment as *allocate, assign, and link*. Evaluating the string expressions $\overline{A}$ || $\overline{B}$ or $\overline{B}$ || $\overline{A}$ on the right of the arrow includes the *allocate* and *assign* phases. It now also includes the extra step of *concatenation*. Thus, Figure 12-12(*a*) means:

> Make a copy of $\overline{A}$ and a copy of $\overline{B}$. Then form a string consisting of the copy of $\overline{B}$ joined to the end of the copy of $\overline{A}$. (*Allocate, assign, and concatenate.*) Then *link* the string thus formed to the symbol $\overline{T}$ in the SVAT, returning to the *MA* the string formerly linked to $\overline{T}$.

Examples *b* and *c* are special cases where one of the components of the string expression appears on the left-hand side. In these cases, if we

TABLE 12-2 Examples of String Formation Using the Concatenation Operator

Current values for strings used in the expression	Expression	Value after string formation[a]
$\overline{A}$="MATH"	$\overline{A}$||"231A"	"MATH231A"
$\overline{A}$="CHEM□" $\overline{B}$="191"	$\overline{A}$||$\overline{B}$||"□IS□A□HARD□COURSE."	"CHEM 191 IS A HARD COURSE."
$\overline{A}$="ENGLISH□" $\overline{B}$="16" $\overline{RATING}$="EASY"	$\overline{A}$||$\overline{B}$||"□IS□"||$\overline{RATING}$	"ENGLISH 16 IS EASY"
$\overline{M}$="66"	$\overline{M}$||$\overline{M}$||"5"	"66665"
$\overline{A}$="WILLINGLY" $\overline{B}$="REPRESENT"	"TO□"||$\overline{A}$||"□"||$\overline{B}$	"TO WILLINGLY REPRESENT"

[a] Blank symbols are omitted to make reading easier.

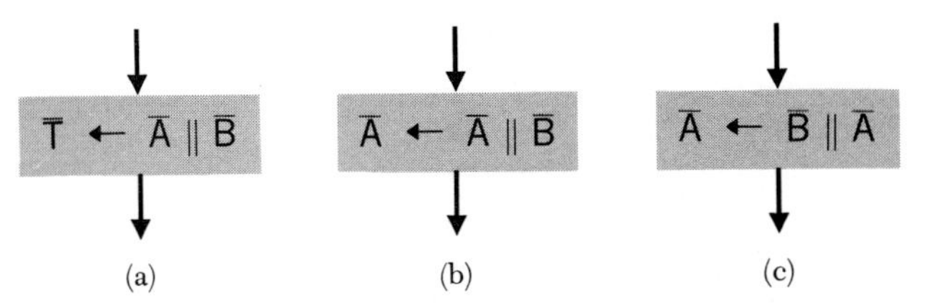

Figure 12-12 String formation and assignment.

follow the approach suggested in *a* faithfully, some inefficiency is inevitable. It is clear that the *allocate* and *assign* work done in making the copy of Ā is unnecessary when we have no further use for the original Ā. Conceivably, a computer that reads a statement equivalent to *b* or *c* could recognize that Ā appears on both sides and thus avoid generating the computer instructions to make the unnecessary copy of Ā.

EXERCISE 12-5, SET A

1. Consider the string assignment step: Ā ← B̄ ∥ Ā ∥ B̄ ∥ Ā . Now see if you can compose a general rule which, if followed, will perform string assignment without ever requiring that a copy of a string be made while at the same time discarding the original in the same operation.

2. The accompanying diagram displays the current state of M_0, SVAT and MEMORY

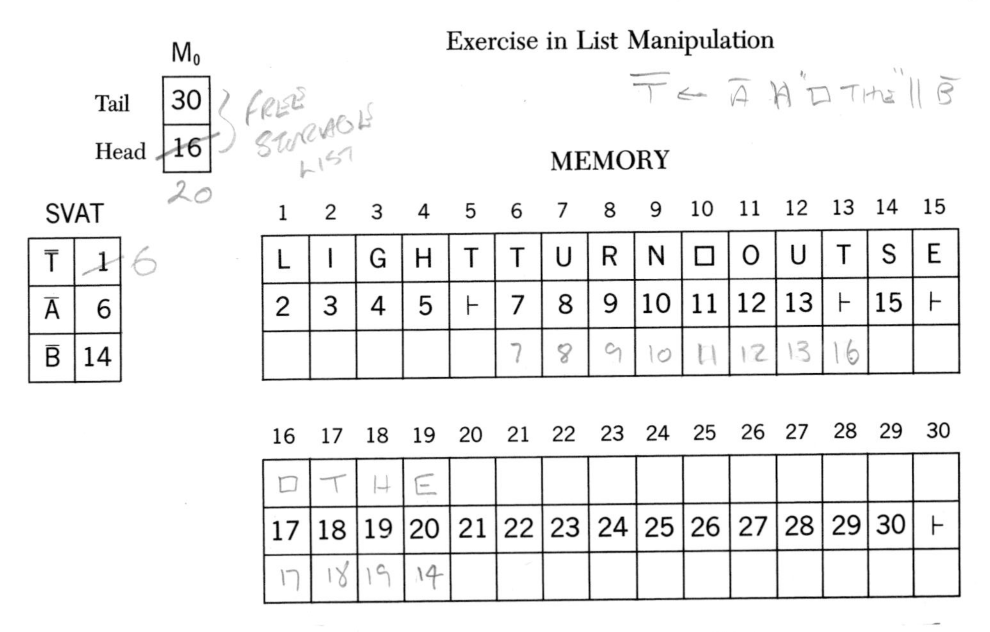

(a) Show the necessary changes to M_0, SVAT and MEMORY to execute the following assignment statement:

$$\overline{T} \leftarrow \overline{A} \,\|\, \text{"□THE"} \,\|\, \overline{B}$$

(b) Write the contents of $\overline{T}$ after execution.

3. The accompanying diagram displays the current state of M_0, SVAT and MEMORY

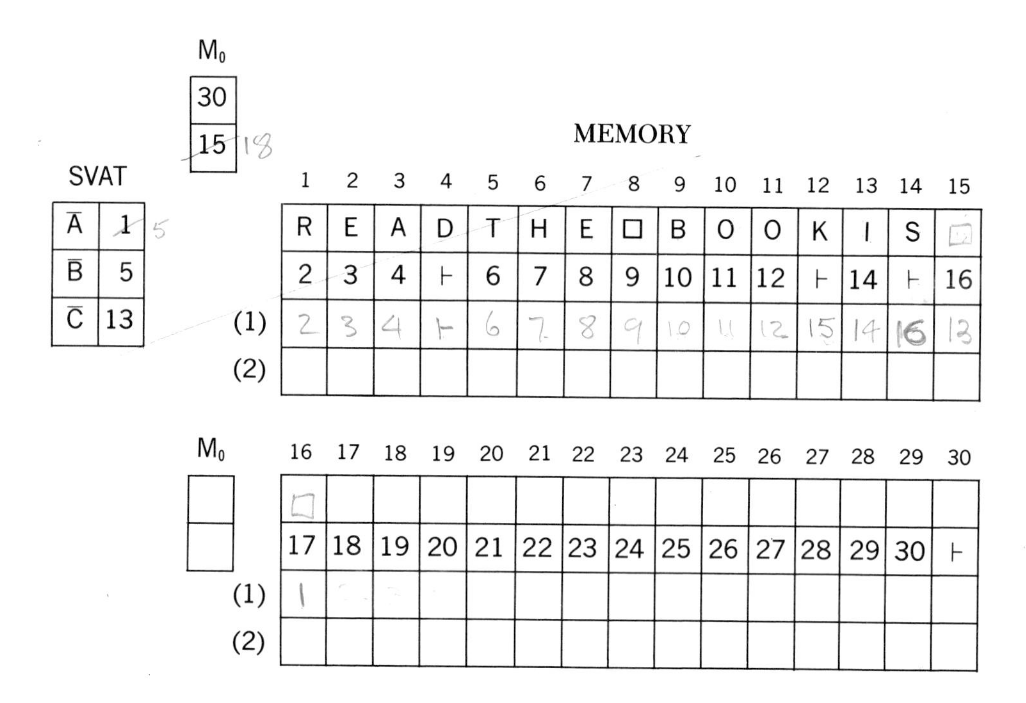

(a) Show the necessary changes to MEMORY, M_0 and SVAT to execute the following assignment statement:

$$\overline{A} \leftarrow \overline{B} \,\|\, \text{"□"} \,\|\, \overline{C} \,\|\, \text{"□"} \,\|\, \overline{A}$$

(b) Write the contents of $\overline{A}$ before and after execution.

Searching a String for a Particular String Pattern

Computer editing implies the ability to search and *find* particular words or phrases in a text line. If we can't find them, we certainly can't replace them with preferred versions. In Section 6-6 we examined in detail one algorithm that searches for a particular substring. Recall that this algorithm assumes the string being searched is represented as a vector, rather than as a one-way list. In Section 12-3 we learned that the essential difference between storing a string as a vector and storing it as a one-way list lies in the difficulty or ease with which we can replace one substring with another of a different length. Whether the string is stored as a vector or as a list, the flow-chart logic of the search will be essentially the same, differing only in the way we express the rules for stepping from one string element to the next. In subsequent study it will help if we ignore much of this type of detail and look at the overall search process as if it were a single operation.

When we think of search as an *operation*, we see that it falls into the category of a decision box, as suggested in Figure 12-13. That is, the only way to decide on the truth or falsity of the assertion in (*b*) is to search $\bar{S}$ and find out. In other words, there is always a search involved here.

As a more compact notation for the search implication, we shall use the operator symbol ⊂, which is ordinarily used in mathematics to mean *inclusion*. When we use the box

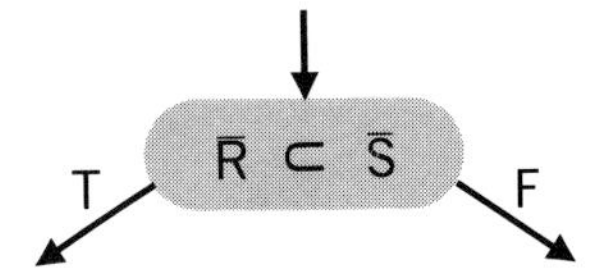

we mean it to be exactly equivalent to the box in (*b*) of Figure 12-13.

A more interesting example, perhaps, is

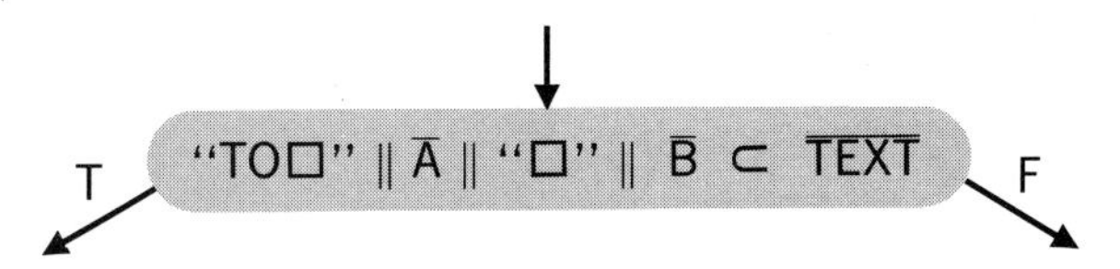

To see how we should interpret this kind of search, it is best to focus on a specific case first. Suppose the data parts of $\bar{A}$ currently consist of the characters, "UNWILLINGLY", and suppose the data parts of $\bar{B}$ are the

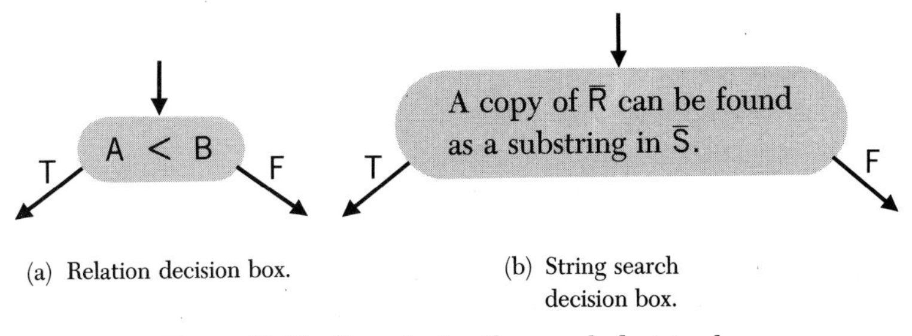

(a) Relation decision box.

(b) String search decision box.

Figure 12-13 Introducing the search decision box.

characters "REPRESENT". The assertion in box 1 is then tantamount to the assertion: A copy of the string of characters "TO□UNWILLINGLY □REPRESENT" can be found as a substring in the data parts of $\overline{\text{TEXT}}$. In more general terms, we can learn to read box 1 in the following way. Let the string of characters that represents the value of the string expression (on the left of the inclusion symbol) be called the *pattern*. The assertion in box 1 can now be read as: A substring of characters can be found in the data parts of $\overline{\text{TEXT}}$ that exactly matches the pattern represented by "TO□" || $\overline{\text{A}}$ || "□" || $\overline{\text{B}}$.

In our use of the inclusion symbol, ⊂, we see that it can be viewed as a relational operator. The right-hand operand is a string variable. The left-hand operand may be any string expression. We'll refer to it as the *string pattern*. The string search decision box is then seen to take this general form:

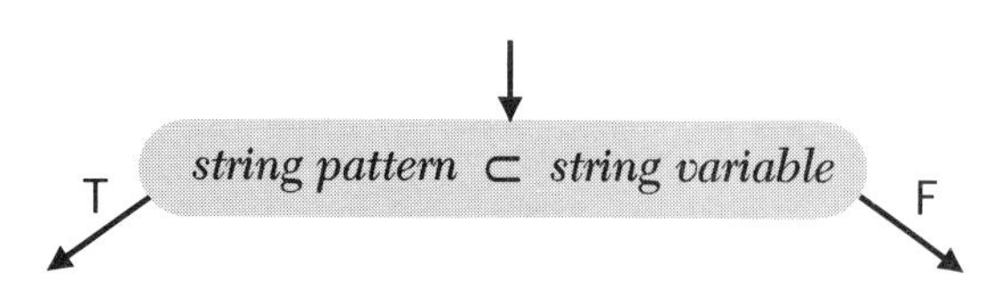

Alternatively, we'll refer to this box as a *pattern match*. You should especially remember that if the T exit is taken, there is *at least one occurrence* of the string pattern's value in the string variable. (We don't yet know how many.)

To summarize our study of string operations up to this point, we offer the algorithm in Figure 12-14. Here we illustrate a use of the pattern match (box 6), of string assignments (boxes 3, 5, and 11), and of output for the value of a string variable (box 8). The purpose of the algorithm is to determine if each of the following two phrases occurs in $\overline{\text{TEXT}}$.

(a) "to unwillingly represent"
(b) "to represent unwillingly"

Note that the algorithm is essentially independent of the *length* of $\overline{\text{TEXT}}$.

If box 11a

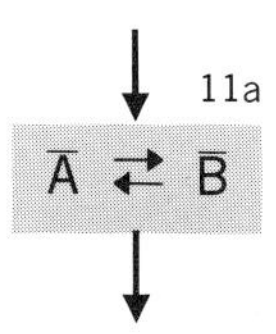

is used in place of box 11

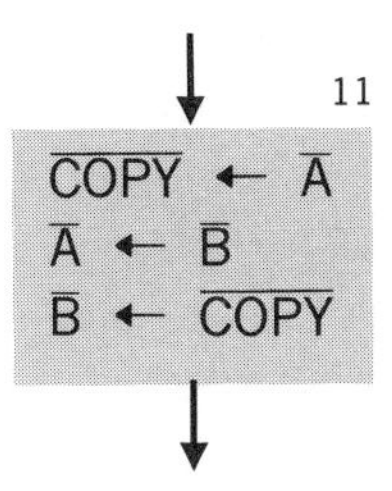

we can keep an open mind as to how string interchange should be performed. The use of $\overline{COPY}$ as an auxiliary string variable is a cumbersome business. Our storage structure model permits a far simpler solution, which is shown in Figure 12-15.

EXERCISE 12-5, SET B

You are to draw a flow chart to search $\overline{TEXT}$ to determine whether or not the pattern

$$\overline{A} \,\|\, \overline{B}$$

occurs, where $\overline{A}$ takes on four different values $\overline{A1}$, $\overline{A2}$, $\overline{A3}$, and $\overline{A4}$. Values of $\overline{A1}$, $\overline{A2}$, $\overline{A3}$, $\overline{A4}$, and $\overline{B}$ are to be read as input, and a message is to be printed concerning the occurrence of each pattern in $\overline{TEXT}$.

Substring Operations

The simple discovery that a string $\overline{S}$ does or does not contain a pattern $\overline{P}$ is fundamental to our ability to manipulate strings. However, we will often need to go one step further when $\overline{P} \subset \overline{S}$. A basic operation suggests itself: when $\overline{P} \subset \overline{S}$, replace the matched substring in $\overline{S}$ by a string $\overline{T}$ (possibly null).

This operation is a natural concomitant of the pattern-matching process. For an example, we can go back to Table 12-1. If we find the phrase "a terribly costly experiment" in $\overline{TEXT}$ we would like to replace it with the phrase "a costly experiment."

This substring replacement is so closely related to the pattern match that in our flow-chart notation we will want to include its specification as a second compartment within the pattern match box, as suggested in Figure 12-16. We interpret its meaning as follows.

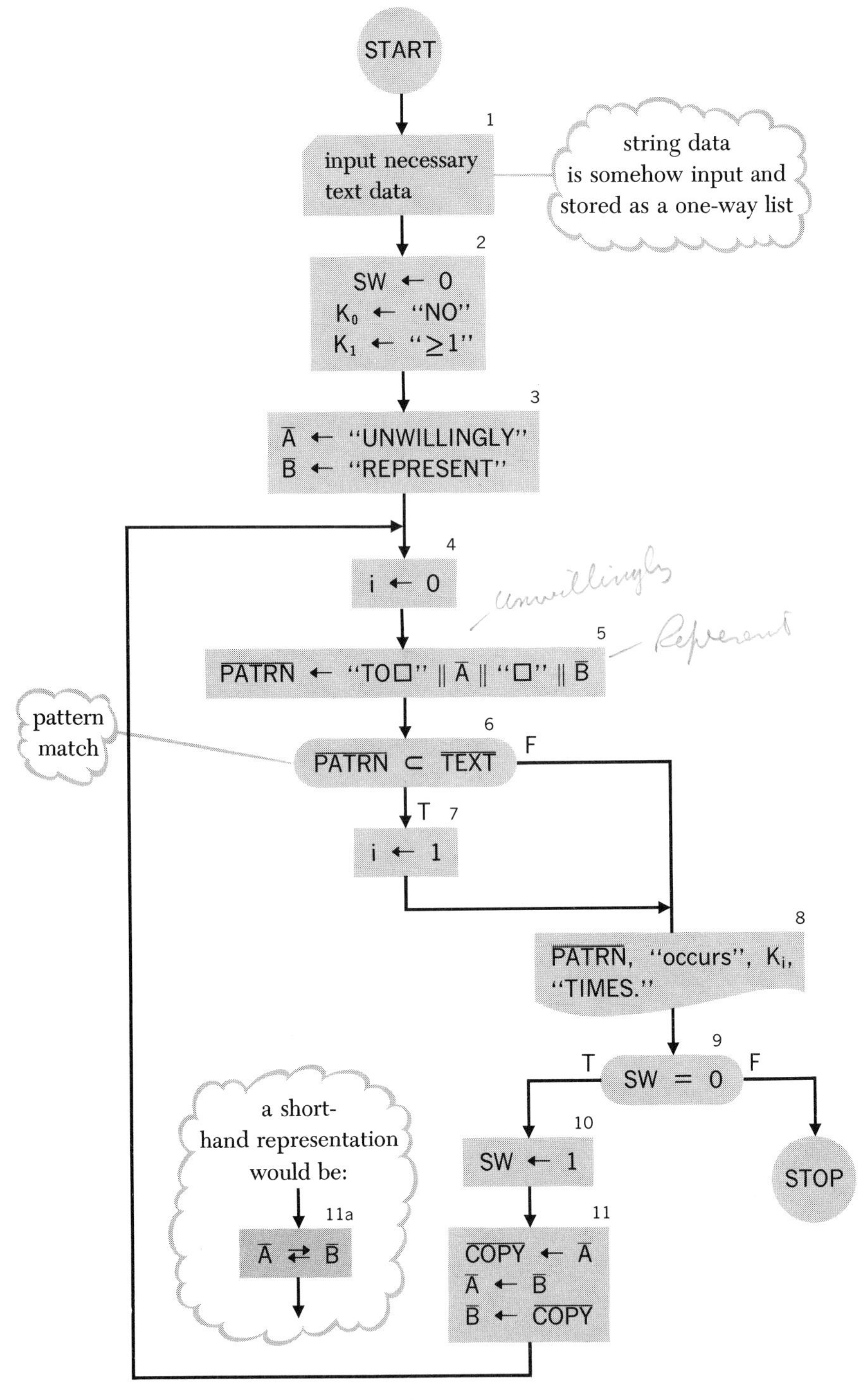

Figure 12-14 "OF INNOCENT MERRIMENT" (a phrase from Gilbert and Sullivan's *Mikado,* used without permission).

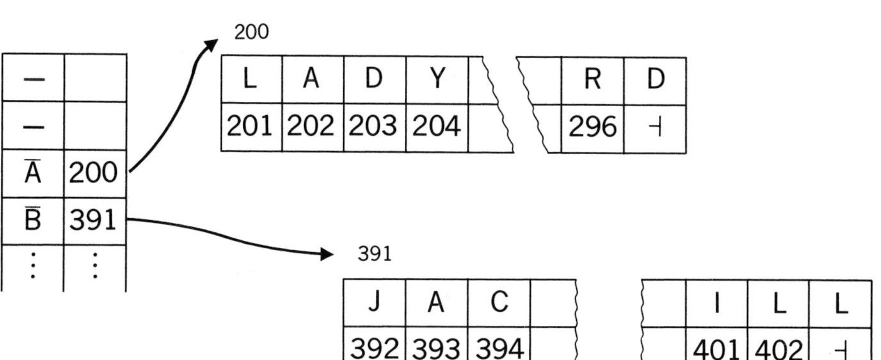

before

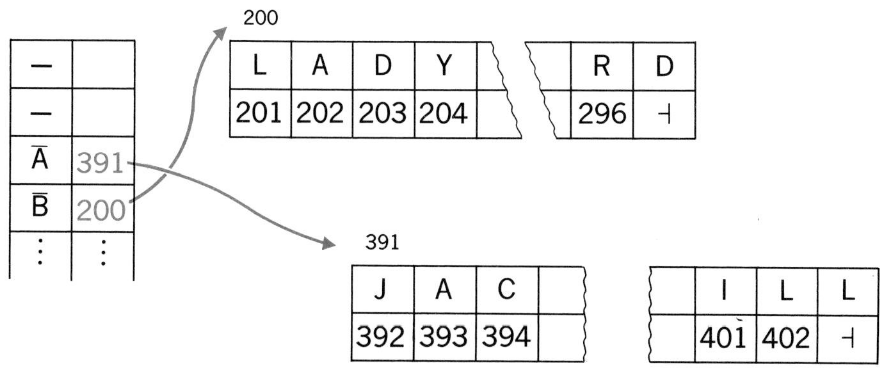

after interchange of $\bar{A}$ and $\bar{B}$

Figure 12-15 Simple way to accomplish string interchange.

If $\bar{P} \subset \bar{S}$ is *true*, then the first occurrence of the substring in $\bar{S}$ that matches the pattern $\bar{P}$ is replaced by the string $\bar{R}$ and the "true" exit is taken. If $\bar{P} \subset \bar{S}$ is *false*, then no replacement takes place and the "false" exit is taken. We use a new operator symbol, $\Leftarrow$, for substring replacement so that there will be no source of confusion with string assignment.

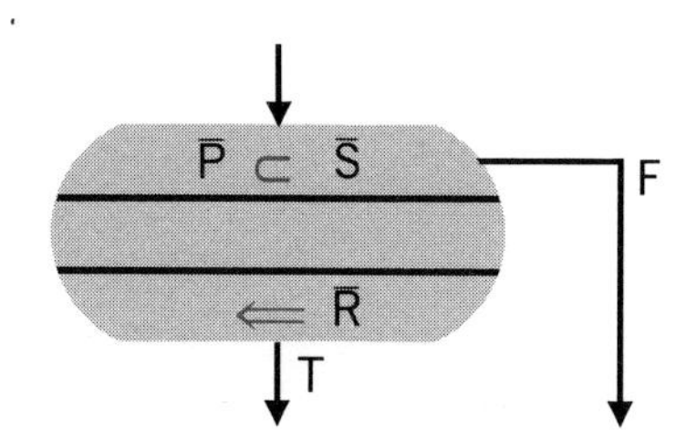

Figure 12-16 Pattern match with substring replacement. The *false* exit emerges from the *top* compartment. The *true* branch emerges from the *bottom* compartment.

When we use this form, the pattern match will always be expressed in the *top* compartment of the box and the *false* exit will always emanate from this part of the oval. The *true* exit will always emerge from the *bottom* compartment. This notation will make it evident that:

1. The pattern match is attempted first.
2. If the pattern match is not successful, the "false" exit is used.
3. If the pattern match is successful, the substring replacement is performed and the "true" exit is used.

An example. If $\bar{S}$ is the string

"THE RED RED ROSE IS A RED ROSE."
(positions 9 and 16 marked)

then

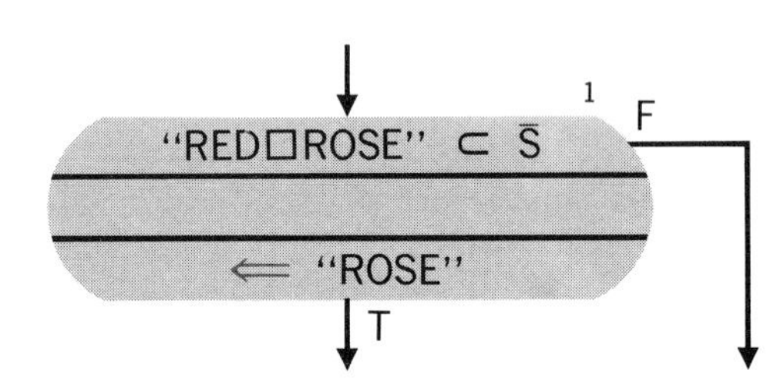

will find the first substring in $\bar{S}$ that matches "RED□ROSE" (string elements 9 to 16, inclusive) and replace that substring by "ROSE". In effect, the word "RED□" has been eliminated and the string $\bar{S}$ would now read

"THE RED ROSE IS A RED ROSE."

We know that a replacement has taken place, since we leave the pattern match box via the "true" exit.

Now, suppose we want to replace each occurrence of "RED ROSE" in $\bar{S}$ by "ROSE". This is accomplished very simply by looping back as shown in Figure 12-17. We see that $\bar{S}$ will be scanned repeatedly for the occurrence of "RED□ROSE". Each time this phrase is found, it is re-

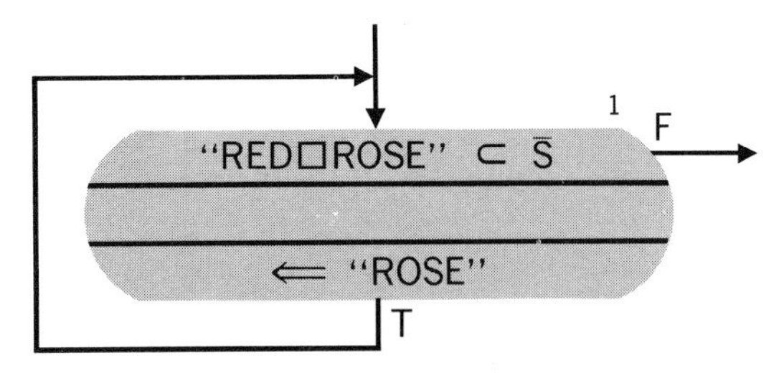

Figure 12-17 Replacing all red roses.

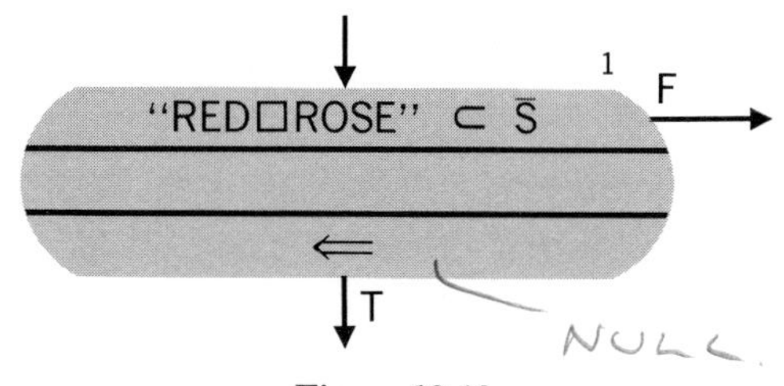

Figure 12-18

placed by "ROSE" until the phrase no longer occurs and the "false" exit is used.

Deletion of a matched substring will be considered a special case of string replacement. It is easily expressed in our new notation, as shown in Figure 12-18. This simply means replace the first occurrence of "RED□ROSE" in $\bar{S}$ by *the null string.*

Insertion of a string can also be treated in the framework of replacement. Suppose we wish to insert "□OF□SHARON" immediately after the first occurrence of "RED□ROSE" in $\bar{S}$. Then the pattern match box would be as shown in Figure 12-19.

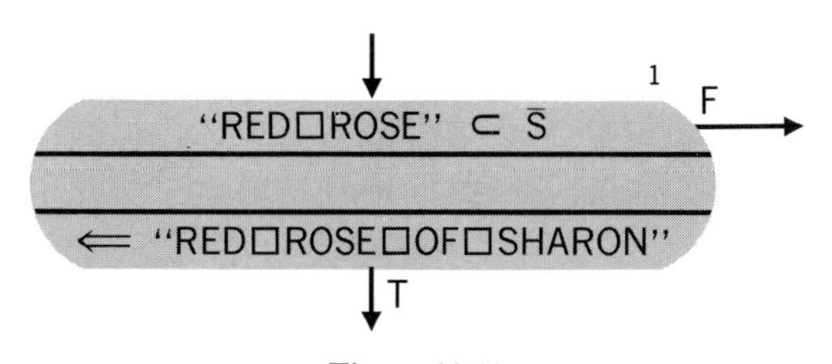

Figure 12-19

We remark in passing that the amount of writing can be considerably reduced by a deliberate use of string assignments as shown in Figure 12-20.

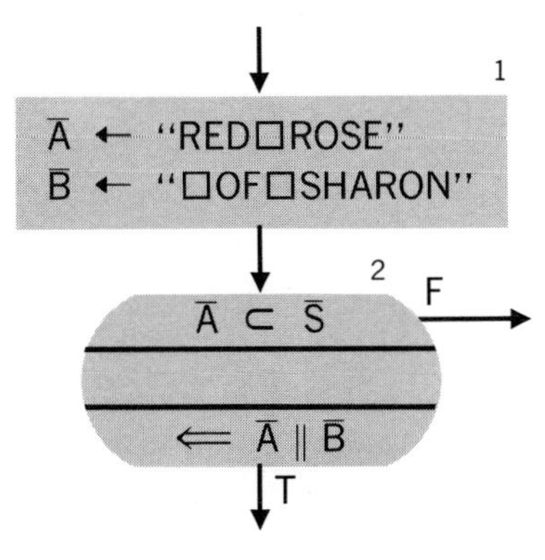

Figure 12-20

EXERCISE 12-5, SET C

1. What would happen to $\overline{\text{TEXT}}$ as a result of executing box 1, below, assuming the *true* exit is taken the first time the loop is executed? Is there a lesson to be learned here? If so, what is it?

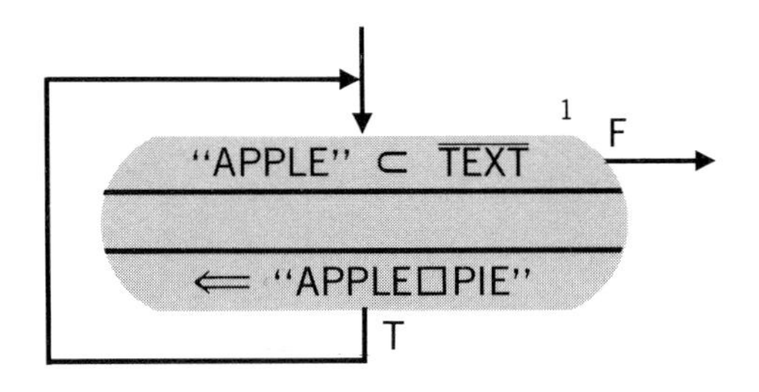

2. Suppose

$\bar{S}$ = "N\$W□*S□TH+□T*M+□T\$□−*D□Y\$/R□P−RTY."

after executing box 2 of the flow chart in Figure 12-21.

(a) What will be the output at box 8 with this input data?
(b) Note the necessity to draw five basically similar search loops. Problem 4, Set D at the end of the next subsection reexamines this question.

UNKNOWNS IN PATTERN MATCH OPERATIONS

Imagine you have a text from which you need to develop a list of words that immediately precede a given word. For example, if the given word were "TREE" you might expect to find:

MAPLE TREE, or SHADE TREE,
or BIRCH TREE, or FAMILY TREE,
or ORANGE TREE, or SHOE TREE, etc.

but you wouldn't know in advance what the preceding word was.

To express a search for such a pattern in the flow-chart language, we need a special notation for a pattern component which represents an *unknown*, that is, a string of unknown content and length. We choose the double asterisk ** for this purpose. Then the pattern match

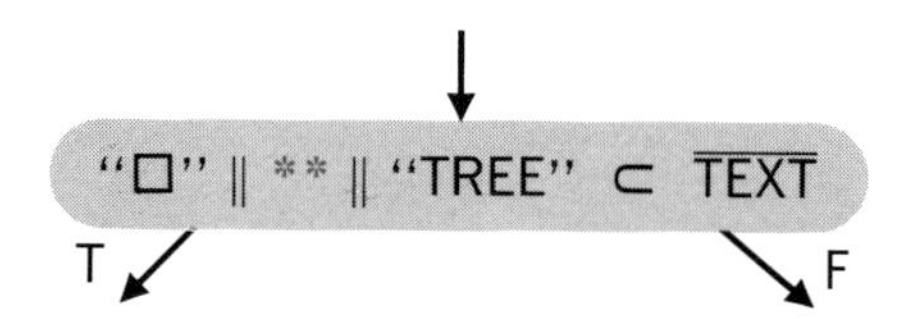

will succeed with all the examples listed above.

Since ** refers to an unknown of arbitrary length (including null length), the above pattern match will, in fact, match the substring in $\overline{\text{TEXT}}$ that begins with the *first* blank character and ends with the first occurrence of "TREE" following the first blank. To illustrate, if $\overline{\text{TEXT}}$ begins with

"□ONLY□GOD□CAN□MAKE□A□GREEN□TREE.□MORE . . ."

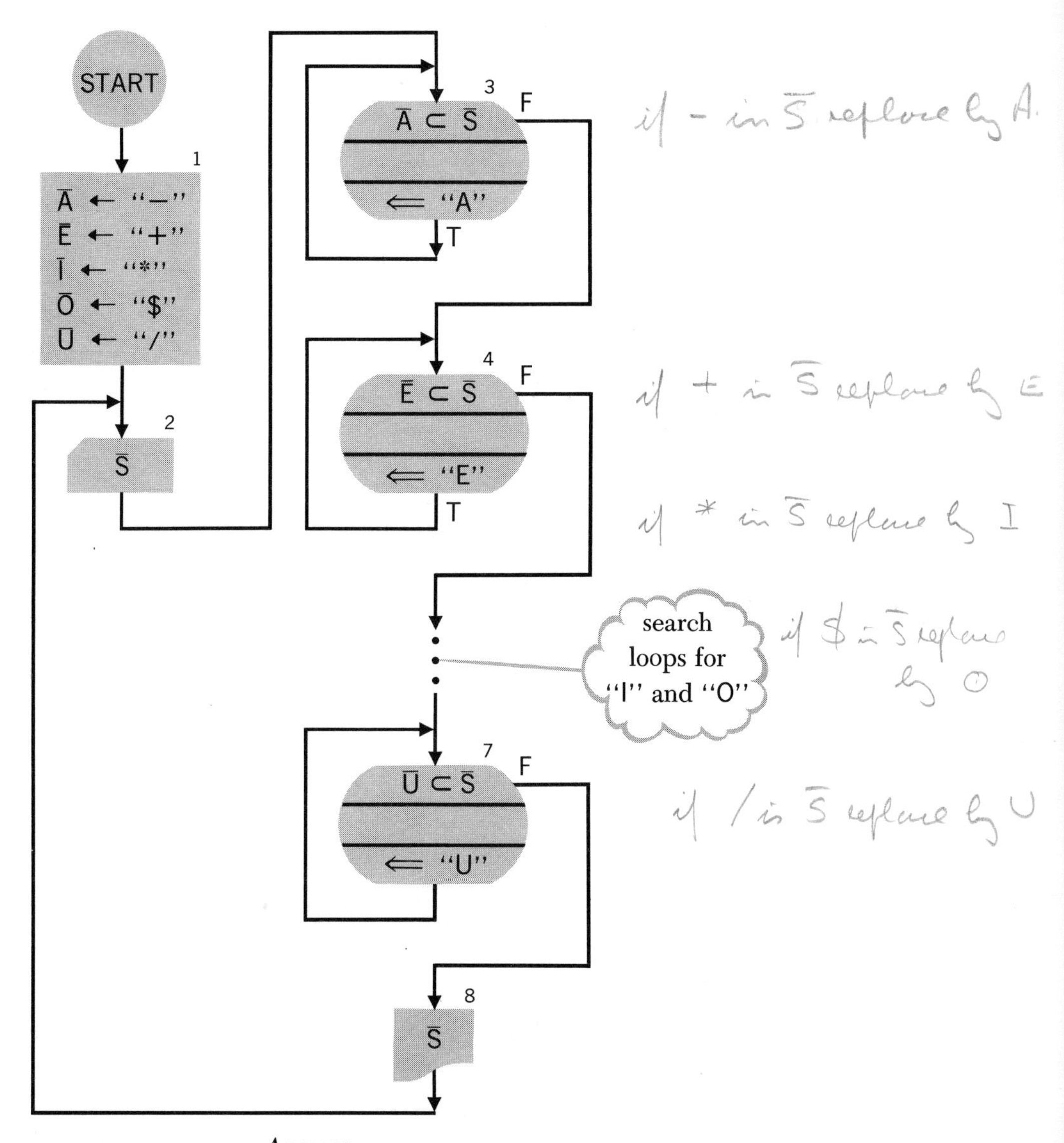

Answer
"NOW□IS□THE□TIME□TO□AID□YOUR□PARTY."

Figure 12-21

the underbracketed portion will be the substring that is matched by **, and not "GREEN□".

We could avoid being indiscriminate in what is matched if we were more specific about the nature of the unknown string. For instance, we might specify the length by writing the number of characters in the string between the two asterisks. To designate length of an unknown, we shall use forms such as:

4 meaning any string of four characters

and

n meaning any string of n characters.

In the sample list of trees at the beginning of this example,

"□" || *4* || "TREE" finds no match
"□" || *5* || "TREE" matches "SHOE TREE"

and

"□" || *6* || "TREE" matches "MAPLE TREE", "BIRCH TREE", and "SHADE TREE".

(Note that a blank space must be counted as a character.)

To develop a list of words in $\overline{\text{TEXT}}$ immediately preceding occurrences of the word "TREE", we might try the following pattern match:

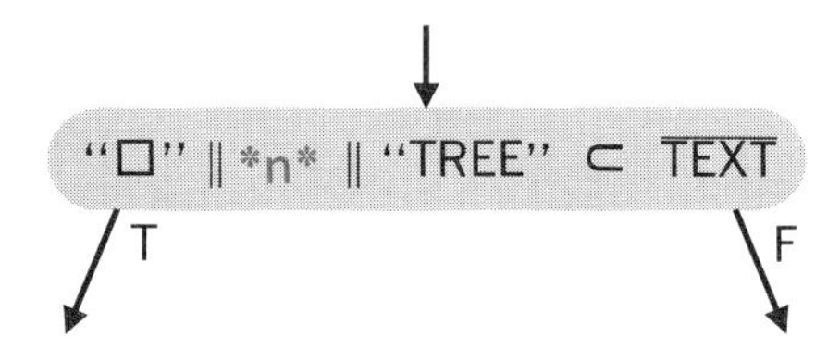

Depending on the exit from this pattern match, we would know that a blank space has or has not been found n spaces before "TREE" (the blank is assumed to delimit a word). However, we do not as yet have a way to know what the n intervening characters are. One solution would be to designate a string variable and assign the value of the unknown string to this variable after the unknown string has been determined in a successful pattern match. The notation to denote this special kind of assignment is shown in Figure 12-22. Notice that the special assignment will always be represented in the *middle* compartment of the oval. The operation and the notation used are somewhat similar (but in a reverse sense) to that of the pattern match with substring replacement displayed in Figure 12-16.

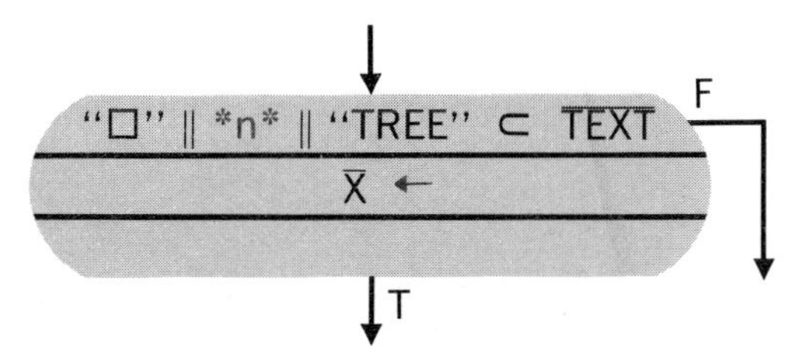

Figure 12-22 Assigning a determined unknown string to a designated string variable, $\overline{\text{X}}$.

Now that we are armed with suitable notation, let's go back to draw a flow chart for producing a list of all words containing from three to ten characters and occurring immediately before "TREE". This flow chart is shown in Figure 12-23.

The first three boxes of Figure 12-23 read the text to be searched, set the initial value of the string length, n, to 3, and set the initial content of the output string to be null. Box 4 tests to see that the string length, n, has not exceeded its maximum value. In box 5, $\overline{\text{TEXT}}$ is scanned for the first occurrence of "□TREE" preceded by a blank and n intervening characters. If this pattern is found, the string of n intervening characters is assigned to $\overline{\text{X}}$ and we go on to box 6. Having found the pattern once and knowing that we intend to search $\overline{\text{TEXT}}$ further for the same pattern, we need to change the string found in $\overline{\text{TEXT}}$. Box 6 does this by deleting the word "TREE" where it has been found in the text. This sequence of operations is quite common in string searches, but the notation used in Figure 12-23 is not efficient in that it implies that two scans of $\overline{\text{TEXT}}$ are to be made to find the same pattern. In such cases it makes sense to use the single, but more complex, pattern match box shown in Figure 12-24.

Figure 12-24 indicates that:

1. $\overline{\text{TEXT}}$ is scanned for the given pattern.
2. If a substring matching the pattern is found, a copy of the contents of the *unknown* substring is assigned to $\overline{\text{X}}$.
3. The substring matching the pattern is then replaced in $\overline{\text{TEXT}}$ by the new substring given on the right of the replacement symbol $\Leftarrow$.

Box 7 of Figure 12-23 is included to make sure that we will not have, in the output list, any string made up of two words preceding "TREE". Because of the fact that the search is conducted beginning with unknowns of short length and going on to longer unknown strings, the only phrase we can think of to be excluded by box 7 is "I A TREE". (It will also eliminate one- and two-letter words that might be included if more than one

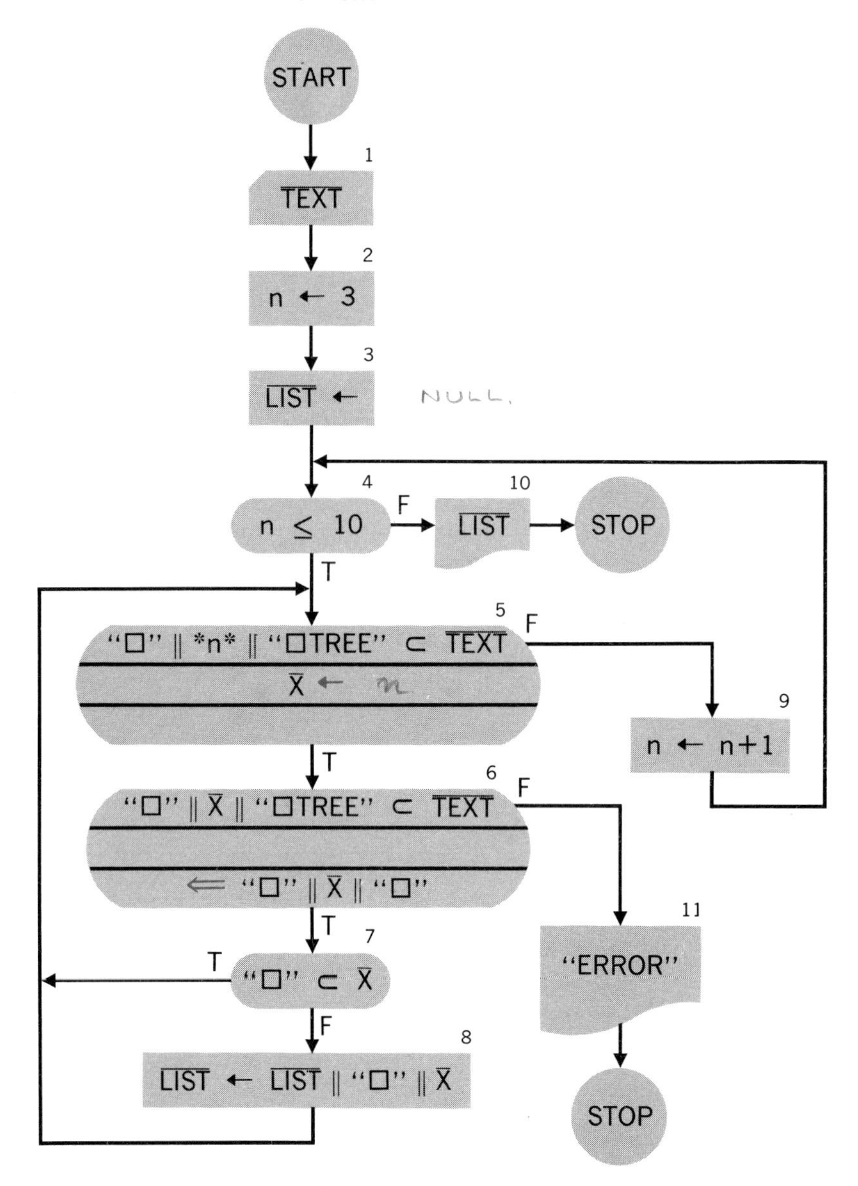

Figure 12-23 Making a list of the words preceding TREE.

blank occurred in succession.) Box 8 appends X̄, the word found, to the output string for later printing (box 10).

When a pattern match no longer occurs in box 5, it means that there are no more substrings of the desired length in the text so we increase n by one (box 9) and loop back to search further.

By now it has probably occurred to you that the repeated search of

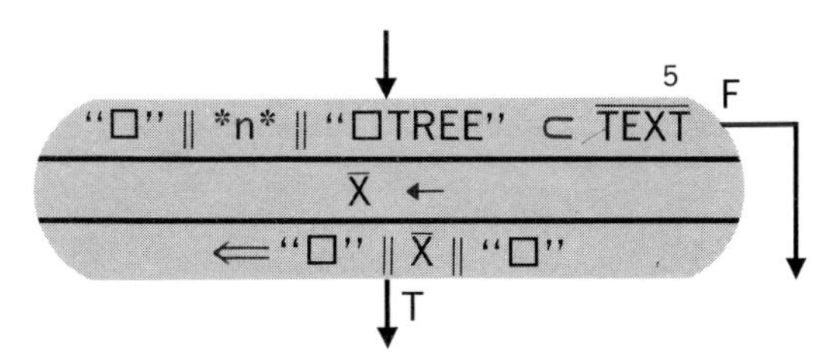

Figure 12-24 A fully grown pattern match, copy, and replacement. This box can be used to replace boxes 5 and 6 of the preceding figure.

$\overline{\text{TEXT}}$ in our improved algorithm (that is, using the new box 5 to replace the original boxes 5 and 6) is still a serious source of inefficiency. Once we search a text and find a particular n-character word, we should not have to repeat the scan of the left end of $\overline{\text{TEXT}}$. Instead, it makes sense to *resume* the search at the point immediately following the last discovered pattern. Unfortunately, a repeated execution of the same pattern match flow-chart box will force a re-search over "old territory", i.e., over a portion of $\overline{\text{TEXT}}$ that cannot possibly contain what we seek. We illustrate a way to avoid this inefficiency by considering the following related problem.

ILLUSTRATIVE PROBLEM 12-5

Draw a flow chart that counts the number of occurrences of the letter "T" in the string called $\overline{\text{TEXT}}$. Figure 12-25 contrasts two approaches, *good* and *unaesthetic*. The good way may look more complicated (more assignment steps), but scanning effort is greatly reduced when $\overline{\text{TEXT}}$ is a long string and has numerous occurrences of "T". In the "good" way, box 1 makes a copy of $\overline{\text{TEXT}}$. After each section of $\overline{\text{COPY}}$ is searched in the pattern match (box 2), the substring beginning with the left end of $\overline{\text{COPY}}$ and ending with the *next* occurrence of a "T" is deleted from $\overline{\text{COPY}}$. Each repeated execution of box 2 searches a shorter copy of $\overline{\text{COPY}}$. There is never any rescanning of what was previously examined.

EXERCISES 12-5, SET D

1. You are given a string $\overline{\text{TEXT}}$ and asked to prepare a list of each different word from three to ten characters (inclusive) in length that immediately precedes the word or phrase given in $\overline{\text{A}}$. With each word in your output list, you are to indicate the number of times it occurred in these circumstances. Draw the necessary flow chart.

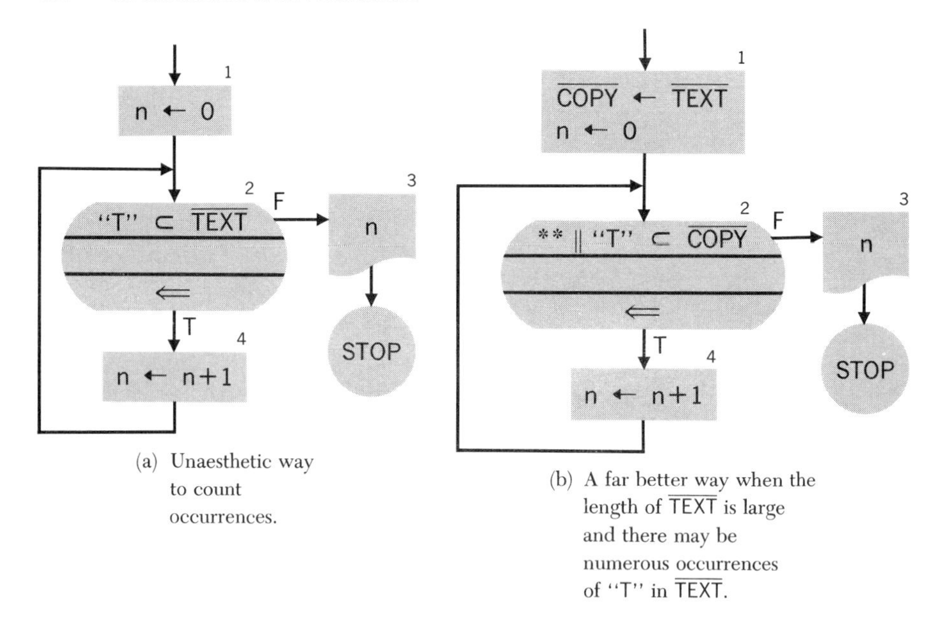

(a) Unaesthetic way to count occurrences.

(b) A far better way when the length of $\overline{\text{TEXT}}$ is large and there may be numerous occurrences of "T" in $\overline{\text{TEXT}}$.

Figure 12-25 One unaesthetic and one good way to make successive searches of the same string.

2. Scan a given text and prepare a table showing the number of words that occur for each word length in the range three to twenty letters per word (inclusive). For this exercise, you must assume that the text will contain punctuation and that several blanks may occur in sequence.

3. When executed, the flow chart in Figure 12-26 will decipher messages that have been written in a very simple code. The coded messages are input at box 1. Suppose the string input at box 1 is

"BATJNQMFADPEF"

(a) What would be the value of $\overline{\text{X}}$ immediately before the first execution of box 8?

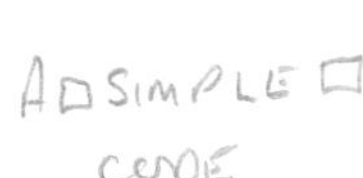

(b) What would be the value of $\overline{\text{X}}$ immediately after the first execution of box 8?

(c) What would be the value of $\overline{\text{TEXT}}$ that is printed when box 6 is executed?

4. Review exercise 2 in Set C of this section. By applying the various ideas and techniques for identifying unknowns, and using the unknown in conjunction with substring replacement and/or deletion, modify the flow chart given in the exercise so that the pattern match of $\bar{S}$ appears in only *one,* rather than in *five,* flow-chart boxes.

Hint. A study of the flow chart in Problem 3 of this set should prove helpful.

5. Many procedural programming languages (e.g., FORTRAN and MAD) permit the user to intersperse blanks freely anywhere within the body of the statement. The first step in compiling a statement in such a language is commonly the removal of all blanks within the statement body and the insertion of a special character not contained within the alphabet of that programming language (say, ";") immediately after the last nonblank character. Usually there is a label field of fixed width (or the equivalent) for each statement that must be handled differently. In the case of FORTRAN, the first six characters in a statement have special significance, for example. Moreover, the statement

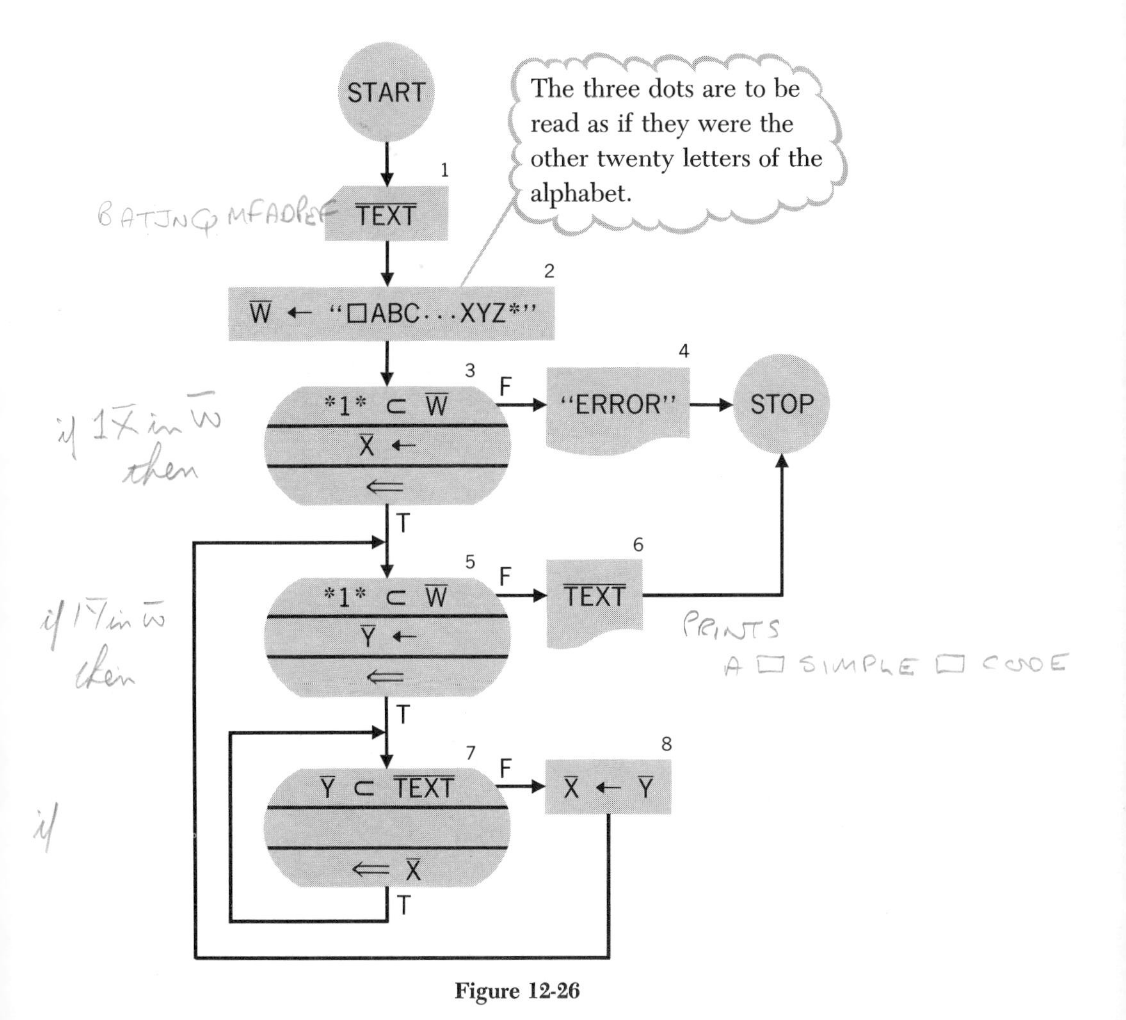

Figure 12-26

body is commonly required to lie within a fixed field (e.g., characters 7–72, inclusive, in FORTRAN).

Draw the flow chart for a string manipulation algorithm that will:

(a) Read in a text of 80 characters.
(b) Delete the last eight of them.
(c) Preserve unchanged the first six characters of the input statement.
(d) Remove all blanks from the next 61 characters (statement body).
(e) Insert the special character ";" after the last nonblank character of the statement body.
(f) Print out the modified text.

Hint. You will find it easiest if you separate the fixed length fields of the input text first.

More Elaborate Types of Patterns (Repeated Occurrence of the Same Unknown)

For further examples showing the use of unknowns in pattern matching, we will return to some of the editing requirements listed in Table 12-1. Consider the problem suggested on line B_g of that table. Any occurrence of "the sum a × b + a × c" can easily be recognized and transformed by a simple pattern search. One example is shown in Figure 12-27.

A somewhat more interesting problem, however, is one in which we are looking for expressions of the form

"a ×" something "+a ×" something else

where the *somethings* are each one letter in length. Figure 12-28 illustrates a solution. Now, two *different* unknowns, each one character in length, are needed in the pattern.

Two companion problems of still more interest suggest themselves and introduce certain complications in notation.

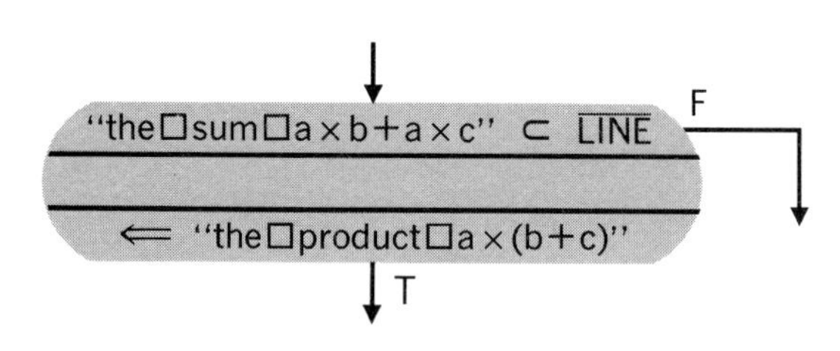

Figure 12-27

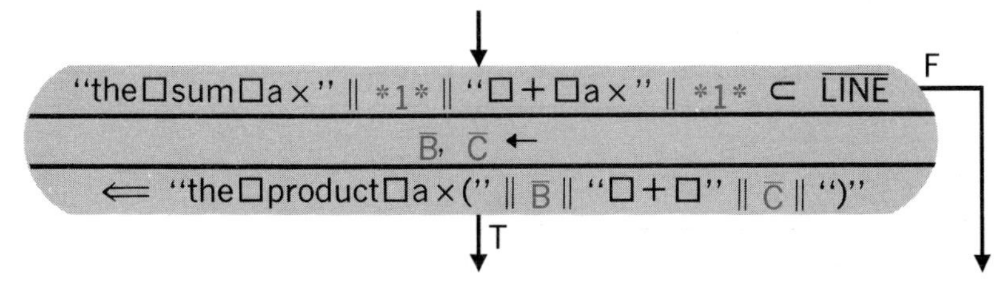

Figure 12-28 Two different unknowns in the same pattern.

1. Suppose we wish to search for expressions of the form

something " × b +" *same something* " × c"

which, if found, is to be transformed into the form

something " × (b + c)"

For example,

"y × b + y × c"

would be an instance of the above pattern but, of course,

"y × b + z × c"

would not.

What kind of pattern would be applicable for this kind of search? Obviously the same unknown must be identified twice at specified points in the substring. We can visualize such a search as one where the first occurrence of the unknown is regarded as *tentative.* The second occurrence of the same unknown (if found at the right place) will then be regarded as *confirming* the value that was tentatively determined during its first occurrence. Failure to find two occurrences, properly positioned, must be regarded as a failure.

So much for the idea of repeated occurrence of the same unknown. But how shall we represent such an unknown in a pattern expression? Obviously, there must be some way to recognize that two arbitrary unknowns, previously denoted by "*1*", refer to the *same* unknown quantity. We shall use the scheme of placing an identifying integer after the first "*" and following it with a "/" character. A suitable pattern match that can be expressed for this problem, is shown in Figure 12-29.

Here we see that if the match is successful, that is, after twice noting the same single character unknown at the right places in the matched

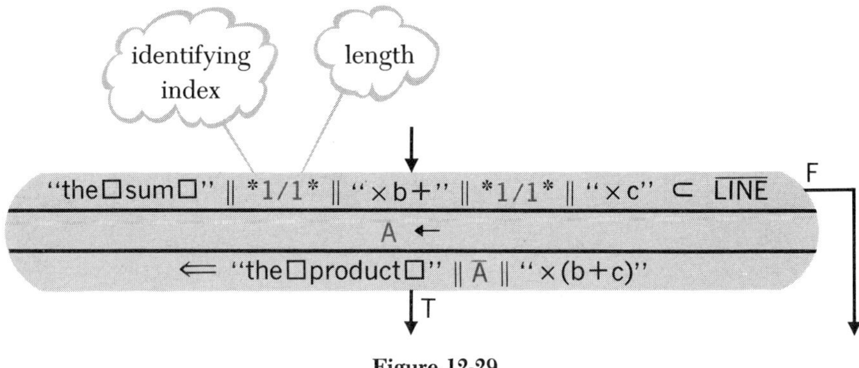

Figure 12-29

substring, the unknown is then assigned to Ā. The replacement compartment indicates the desired form of the altered substring.

2. We can generalize even further on this problem, and with fascinating results. Suppose, for example, we wish to search for *any* factorable arithmetic expression that has the form

$$a \times b + a \times c$$

where a, b, and c are each a single-letter unknown representing an arithmetic variable. A suitable pattern match to use for such a search is shown in Figure 12-30.

Converting Strings ⇄ Integers

Occasionally, it will be useful to interpret certain strings of digits as numbers rather than as characters. Line B_h of Table 12-1 is a case in point.

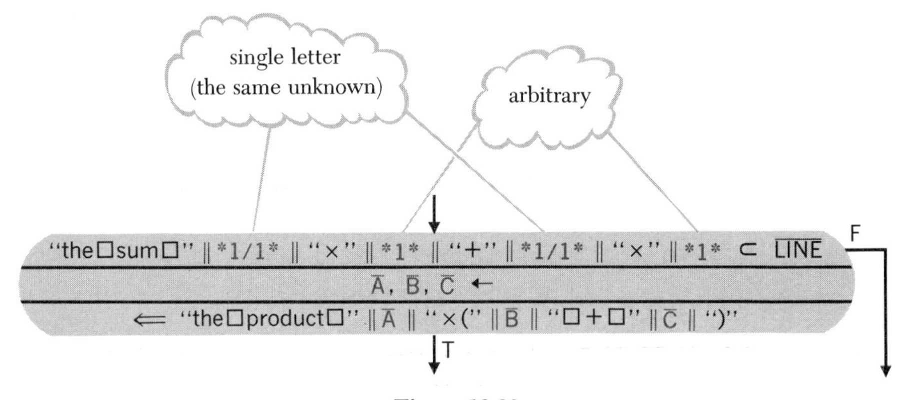

Figure 12-30

In this problem, we are essentially asked to search for an instance of the pattern

"LESS□" || *n* || "□MINUTES"

If we find a match with this pattern and if we are allowed to assume that the discovered value is a string of n characters, all of which are digits, then, after assigning the unknown to $\bar{X}$, our next steps are as follows.

Convert the digit string $\bar{X}$ to a new digit string, say, $\bar{Y}$. This new string, interpreted as an integer, is to be 60 times the integer interpretation of the string $\bar{X}$. The replacement phrase to be inserted in the text is of the form

"LESS□" || $\bar{Y}$ || "□SECONDS"

But how do we express the transformation from $\bar{X}$ to $\bar{Y}$? We hesitate to use the expression

$$60 \times \bar{X}$$

because it is not clear whether we are to think of the product as a string of characters or as an integer number. Suppose, instead, we imagine that two functional reference flow charts are available for *converting* from digit strings to integer representation and vice versa.

1. The function

stoi($\bar{X}$)

standing for *s*tring *to* *i*nteger, returns the *integer* value equivalent of the digit string argument $\bar{X}$.

2. The function

itos(i)

standing for *i*nteger *to* *s*tring, returns the digit *string* value (one-way list) equivalent of the integer argument i.

Using these functions, Figure 12-31 shows the steps necessary to accomplish this minutes-to-seconds "editing."

EXERCISES 12-5, SET E

The following two exercises involve construction of a function and a procedure involving string variables. To work these exercises, it is assumed you have studied Chapter 6.

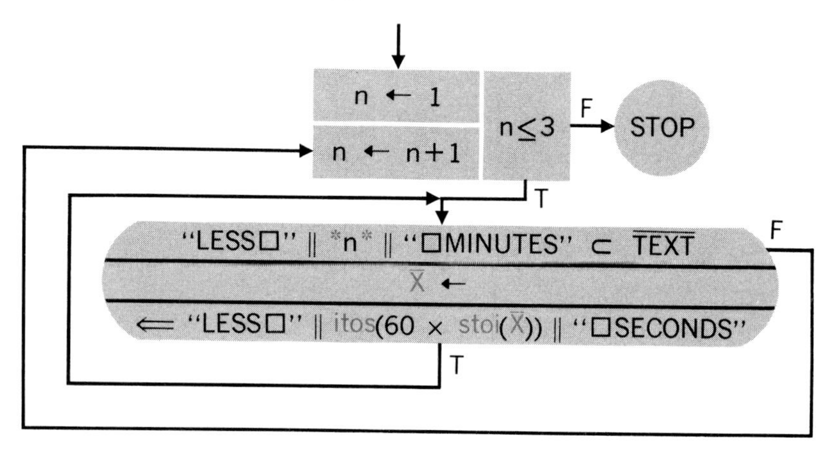

Figure 12-31 The minutes-to-seconds problem.

1. Construct a reference flow chart for a function to determine the size (number of characters) of a string. The name of this function will be SIZE and it will have one parameter—a string variable. The function should return an integer, which is the number of characters in the string whose name is supplied as an argument.

Example application:

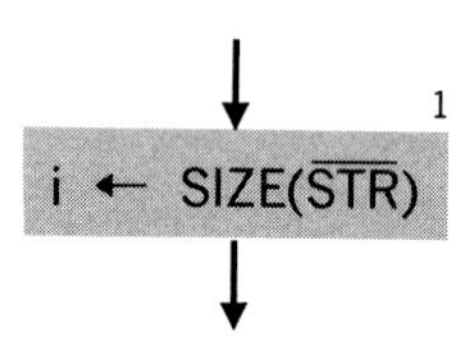

If the value of $\overline{\text{STR}}$, *prior* to execution of box 1, was "THE□NEW□MOON". then *after* execution of box 1, the value of i would be 12.

2. Construct a reference flow chart for a procedure called DELETE to delete *all* occurrences of *each* character contained in one given string from another given string. The two parameters of DELETE are as follows.

(a) $\overline{\text{STR}}$, the string from which the deletion(s) are to be made.

(b) $\overline{\text{LIST}}$, the string providing the characters whose occurrences in $\overline{\text{STR}}$ should be deleted. The matching argument for $\overline{\text{LIST}}$ may be either a string variable or a string constant.

Example application:

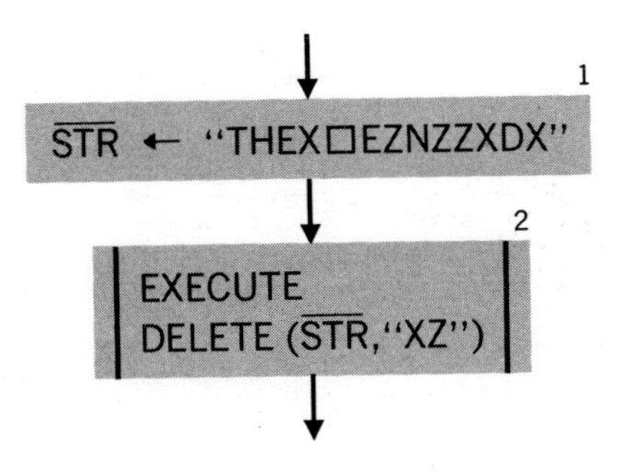

After execution of box 2,

$$\overline{\text{STR}} = \text{“THE END”}$$

CHAPTER 13

MORE ASPECTS OF COMPILING

13-1 INTRODUCTION

In the preceding chapter we were so busy learning about string operations and ways to represent them in flow charts that there was little chance to appreciate one broad implication, which is that "text editing" techniques are applicable to a wide range of important and challenging computer problems. For example, the new type of storage structure, together with the string operations and pattern match technique developed in Chapter 12, proves to be effective when we simulate industrial processes and business operations. The same (or similar) organization is also useful in attempts to translate languages mechanically.

To appreciate this broader view of text editing, we return in this chapter to the unfinished study of *compiling* (Chapter 10), that is, the translation of programs from a language like ALGOL or FORTRAN to SAMOS-like machine code. We will develop two algorithms useful in the compilation process.

(a) *Converting postfix strings* (produced by algorithms such as the one developed in Chapter 10) to a sequence of symbolic SAMOS instructions.

(b) *Converting the symbolic SAMOS instructions* into the final sequence of SAMOS (actual machine language) instructions.

Steps similar to these two "transformations" can be found in many of the most widely used compilers.

Transformation of Postfix Strings to SAMOS Machine Code

In Sections 10-3 and 10-4 you were introduced to an algorithm for converting expressions from infix to postfix form. We now want to see how we might carry out another step in the compilation process, that of converting a postfix string to a sequence of SAMOS-like instructions. We start our first example with the infix statement

$$Z \leftarrow C \times (A \times X + B)$$

Algorithms like those developed in Chapter 10 can be used to generate a postfix string, with exactly one blank character between each two elements or "atoms." The sample statement takes the form

$$Z\ \ C\ \ A\ \ X\ \ \times\ \ B\ \ +\ \ \times\ \ \leftarrow$$

We can view the task of transforming the postfix string into a sequence of SAMOS instructions as a two-step process.

1. Convert the postfix string into a sequence of *symbolic* SAMOS instructions. For example,

```
LDA A
MPY X
ADD B
MPY C
STO Z
```

2. Decide what storage addresses are to be assigned to the variables and then convert symbolic SAMOS to *actual* SAMOS. Thus, if A, B, C, X, and Z are associated with addresses 5000, 5001, 5002, 6000, and 6001, the actual instructions would have the form

```
□LDA0005000
□MPY0006000
□ADD0005001
□MPY0005002
□STØ0006001
```

The flow chart in Figure 13-1 is a first attempt at describing an algorithm to carry out step 1. Although we know the flow chart does not do the job completely or well, we will examine it in some detail to determine what is going on. After we understand this part of the algorithm, we will be able to add the refinements necessary to make it carry out step 1.

The first-attempt algorithm will convert a postfix string representing certain arithmetic expressions, but not entire assignment statements, into a list of symbolic instructions. The algorithm assumes that the atoms of the postfix string are separated by blank characters. The postfix string, called $\overline{\text{EXP}}$, is input at box 0, initialization steps are performed in box 1, and the symbolic list of instructions is printed in boxes 14, 15, and 17. The following two paragraphs give more details.

Each time the pattern match in box 2 proves successful, another element or atom is identified and assigned to $\overline{\text{ATOM}}$. Atoms identified in this way are *stripped* (i.e., removed) from $\overline{\text{EXP}}$, in left-to-right order. After an atom is separated from $\overline{\text{EXP}}$, it is inspected to decide whether it is a binary arithmetic operator (box 3, 5, 7, 9). If it is not an operator, the atom is assumed to be an operand and is placed at the end of a list called $\overline{\text{STACK}}$ (box 11); then, after looping from box 11 to box 2, the next atom is stripped from $\overline{\text{EXP}}$ for inspection. When an operator is identified, a corresponding string of characters is assigned to $\overline{\text{S}}$ (boxes 4, 6, 8,

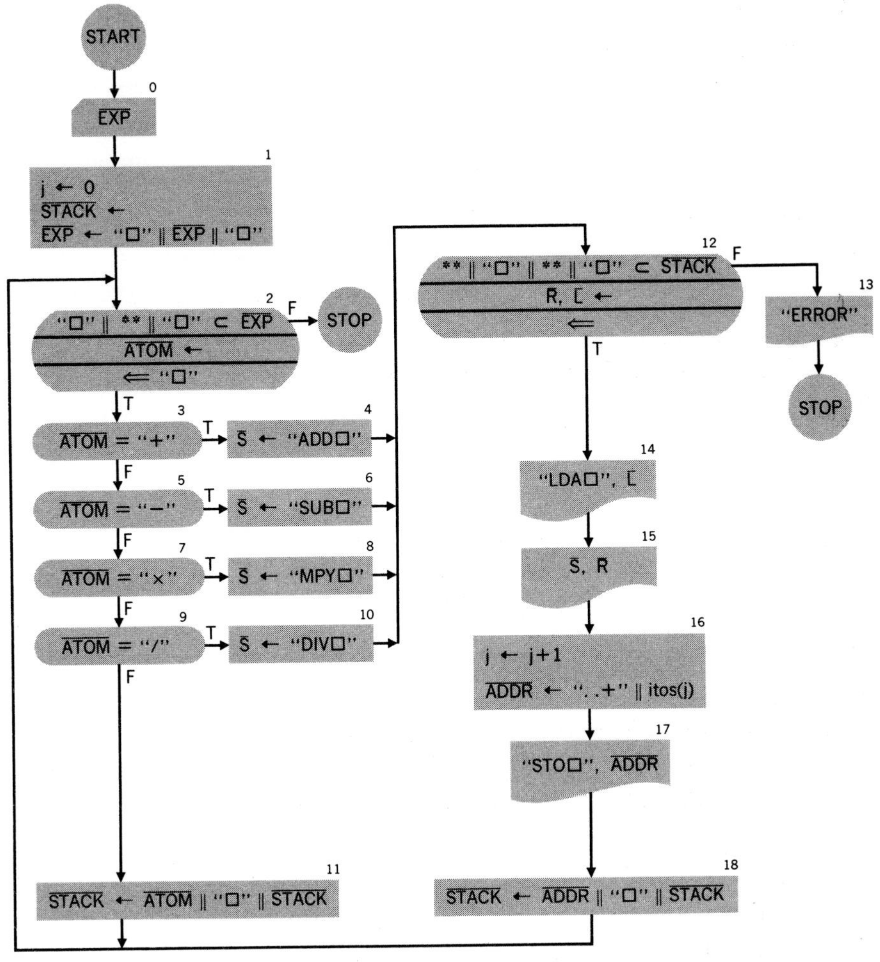

Figure 13-1 Translation of arithmetic expression from postfix to symbolic SAMOS. Results of each intermediate step are assigned to auxiliary variables beginning with ". . + 1".

10) and this string will become the operator part of the symbolic instructions to be generated. Next, two atoms are removed from the end of STACK in box 12. These will be the *right* and *left* operands of the binary operator that has been identified.

In this crude algorithm, three SAMOS instructions are generated (that is, printed for later use) for each operator in the postfix string. The first instruction generated will load the accumulator with the left operand (box 14). The second instruction will carry out the indicated arithmetic operation using the right operand (box 15). Finally, the third instruction will store the result of the operation in a "temporary location," that is, assign the result to an auxiliary variable. A symbol for this auxiliary variable is constructed and assigned to $\overline{\text{ADDR}}$ in box 16 and the third instruction is then printed in box 17. After this, the symbol for the auxiliary variable is placed at the end of $\overline{\text{STACK}}$ (at box 18) so that this *manufactured* symbol can subsequently be treated as any other operand.

Before looking more closely at box 16, where symbols for the auxiliary variables are manufactured, we will show the output generated by Figure 13-1 for the sample expression. Then we will review the major points learned from study of this figure.

The postfix string: "C□A□X□×□B□+□×"
is converted by this algorithm to:

```
                                Comments
LDA□A
MPY□X
STO□..+1          Assign intermediate result to ..+1
--------------
LDA□..+1
ADD□B
STO□..+2          Assign intermediate result to ..+2
--------------
LDA□C
MPY□..+2
STO□..+3          Assign intermediate result to ..+3
```

We have chosen an unusual form for the auxiliary variables to which we have assigned partial results. Our purpose is to make these symbols distinguishable from any that can be chosen by the programmer who originated the infix string. In many cases we will find that an auxiliary variable at the SAMOS level has only a temporary significance and is, in fact, used in a way distinct from that for ordinary variables. Therefore, we use a string of characters ". . +" followed by an integer so that we can count upward and downward to manufacture and later recognize these special variables.

Box 16 of the Figure 13-1 algorithm generates the addresses of the needed temporaries by appending to ". . +" the string equivalent of the integer j. Each time box 16 is encountered, another unique name (address) is generated by incrementing j.

Table 13-1 shows a trace of the algorithm as it processes our sample string. Study it carefully along with the flow chart until you are able to agree with results claimed for it.

TABLE 13-1 Trace of the Algorithm in Figure 13-1 for the Postfix String: C□A□X□×□B□+□×

$\overline{\text{ATOM}}$	$\overline{\text{STACK}}$	$\overline{\text{L}}$	$\overline{\text{R}}$	(printed output)
C	C□			
A	A□C□			
X	X□A□C□			
×	..+1□X□A□C□	A	X	LDA A MPY X STO ..+1
B	B□ ..+1□X□A□C□			
+	..+2□B□..+1□X□A□C□	..+1	B	LDA ..+1 ADD B STO ..+2
×	..+3□..+2□B□..+1□X□A□C□	C	..+2	LDA C MPY ..+2 STO ..+3

EXERCISE 13-1, SET A

By a tracing similar to Table 13-1, show the printed results for the postfix string equivalent to

$$E + F + (A + B) \times (C + D)$$

Now to review what we have learned. The key to the translation is the use of the string called $\overline{\text{STACK}}$ to save the operands until their corresponding operators have been encountered in $\overline{\text{EXP}}$. The operands are saved as they are encountered. When needed later, they are removed from (the left end of) $\overline{\text{STACK}}$ in reverse of the order in which they were saved. Corresponding to each binary operator, three symbolic instructions are generated. We recognize that this is not an efficient target code but postpone the attempt to generate a more efficient computer program until later. Auxiliary variables are needed, and we have found a way to generate names for them. In the interest of simplicity, we have made no effort to minimize the number of such names.

Improving the Algorithm

The present algorithm falls short in several respects. Two of the most obvious failings are as follows.

(a) It doesn't handle the assignment operator.
(b) It appears to generate more SAMOS instructions and use more temporary storage than necessary.

Figure 13-2 shows how simply we can add the capability for handling the assignment operator (boxes 101 through 105, shown in rust). Assignment differs from the arithmetic operations in that the right operand, rather than the left, must be associated with the load-the-accumulator instruction, and the left operand, rather than the right, is then coupled with the code for the particular action we want taken. For assignment we want to generate

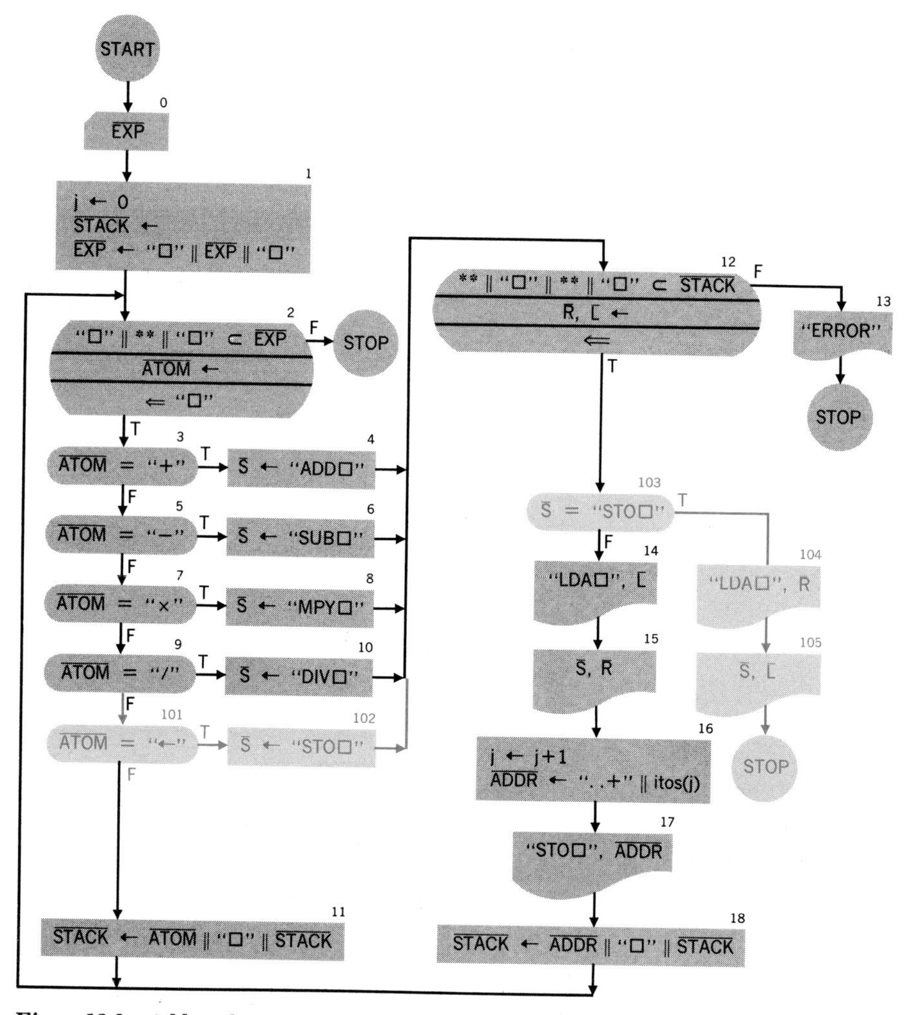

Figure 13-2 Adding the capability for handling the assignment arrow in translating postfix to SAMOS symbolic.

$$\text{"LDA}\square\text{"} \parallel \bar{R}$$
$$\bar{S} \parallel \bar{L}$$

whereas, for all the four arithmetic operations, the sequence we have used is

$$\text{"LDA}\square\text{"} \parallel \bar{L}$$
$$\bar{S} \parallel \bar{R}$$

Applying this modified algorithm to the postfix string corresponding to

$$Z \leftarrow C \times (A \times X + B)$$

will then cause two more instructions to be generated:

```
LDA ..+3
STO Z
```

to complete a workable but by no means efficient sequence of SAMOS instructions.

We see that three temporaries are employed. In general, our algorithm would use n temporaries in dealing with an arithmetic expression having n intermediate results, *whether or not they are all needed at one time* while executing the target instructions. It is possible to avoid employing new temporaries when old ones, no longer "in use," are available for re-employment. Thus, in our example, ..+ 1 could be used for three independent purposes. The surprisingly simple modifications necessary to husband temporaries are shown in Figure 13-3 (boxes 201 through 204, shown in rust). With these changes, the resulting SAMOS code is given in Figure 13-4.

EXERCISES 13-1, SET B

1. Prepare a trace of the algorithm in Figure 13-3, similar in format to Table 13-1, to verify the above output for the input postfix string corresponding to

$$Z \leftarrow C \times (A \times X + B)$$

2. What is the output generated by the Figure 13-3 algorithm for the postfix corresponding to

$$(C \times D - E) / (F - G \times H)$$

(A trace is recommended if you need more practice.)

Perhaps by working the problems in Set B, you have understood the basic idea behind boxes 201 through 204. If not, we will discuss it here. Each time the algorithm prepares to generate the three instructions associated with an arithmetic operation, a check is made if either the right operand and/or the left operand is a temporary. For each such operand, j is reduced by one to simulate the "release" of this temporary for use in storing other intermediate results. Suppose, for example, that

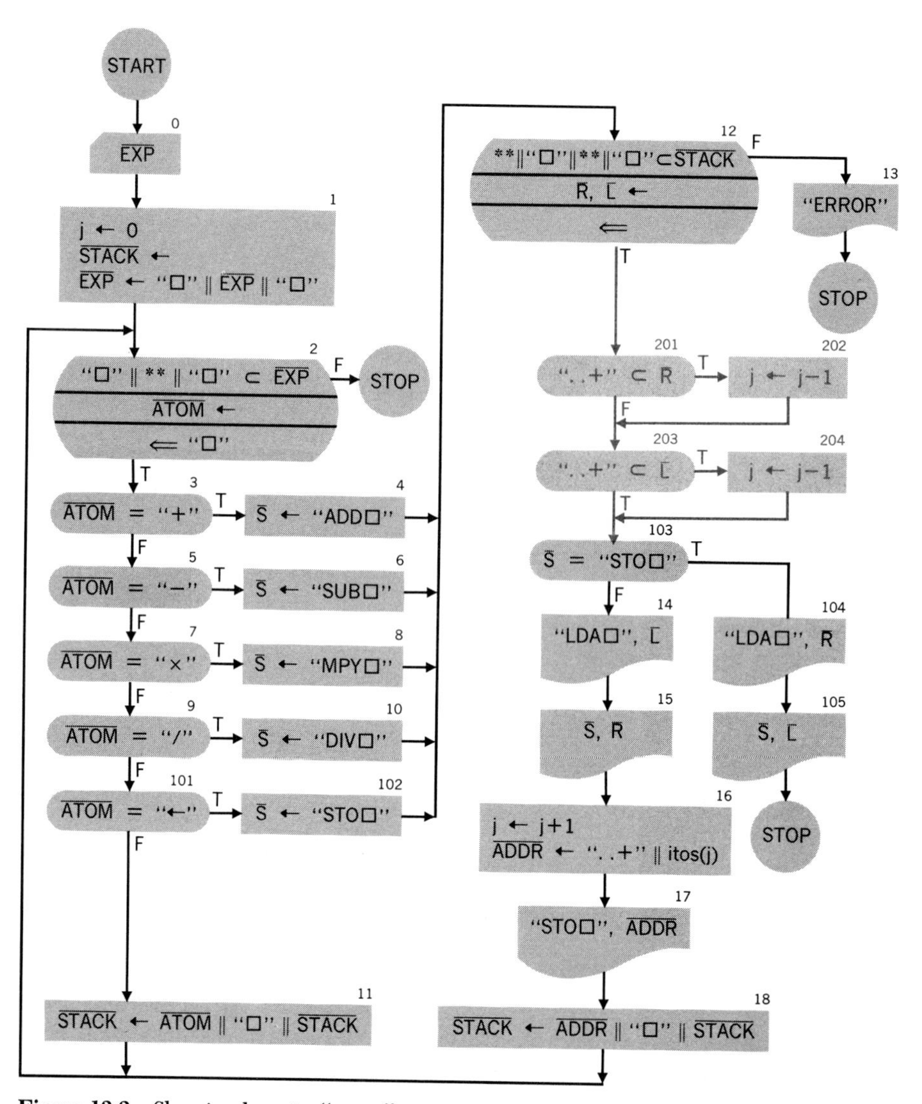

Figure 13-3 Showing how to "reuse" temporary storage. During subsequent execution of the generated SAMOS instructions, the temporaries hold values for all intermediate results that have not yet been employed in the evaluation. Once an intermediate result is used, its storage space is "released" (boxes 202 and 204).

```
LDA A
MPY X
STO ..+1  }
LDA ..+1  } Useless
ADD B
STO ..+1  }
LDA C     } This construction can also be shortened
MPY ..+1  }
STO ..+1  }
LDA ..+1  } Useless
STO Z
```

Figure 13-4 Output generated by the Figure 13-3 algorithm for the input corresponding to Z ← C × (A × X + B).

[is a temporary, say, . . + 1. When executing box 14, an instruction of the form "LDA . . + 1" will be generated. The consequence of *executing* this instruction later, as part of the compiled program, will be that the result saved in . . + 1 is retrieved from that temporary and loaded in the accumulator. Continuing to picture execution in the compiled program, we see that there is no further reason to hold on to the contents of . . + 1. Hence, the *compiler algorithm* should be free to reuse . . + 1 as a "receptacle" for another temporary. We do this in box 17.

A Minor Improvement (Table-Look-Up by Pattern Match)

The operations performed by boxes 3, 4, 5, 6, 7, 8, 9, 10, 101, and 102 in our Figure 13-3 algorithm amount to a table-look-up operation. A single pattern match could replace all of these boxes to perform this table-look-up (as suggested in Figure 13-5), provided one would *invest* in the creation of a special string that could serve as the table or *lexicon* that is being "looked up." In Figure 13-5 the variable called $\overline{\text{OPLEX}}$ (for *oper*ator *lex*icon) is assigned a string consisting of a sequence of pairs of values. The first value in each pair is the character that would be found in the postfix string, and the second value, i.e., the next four characters, is the SAMOS equivalent which we wish to assign to $\overline{\text{S}}$ for later use in the algorithm. A blank character separates each pair.

More Improvement

We should still be far from satisfied with this algorithm. The practice of generating a store instruction in connection with each operation in

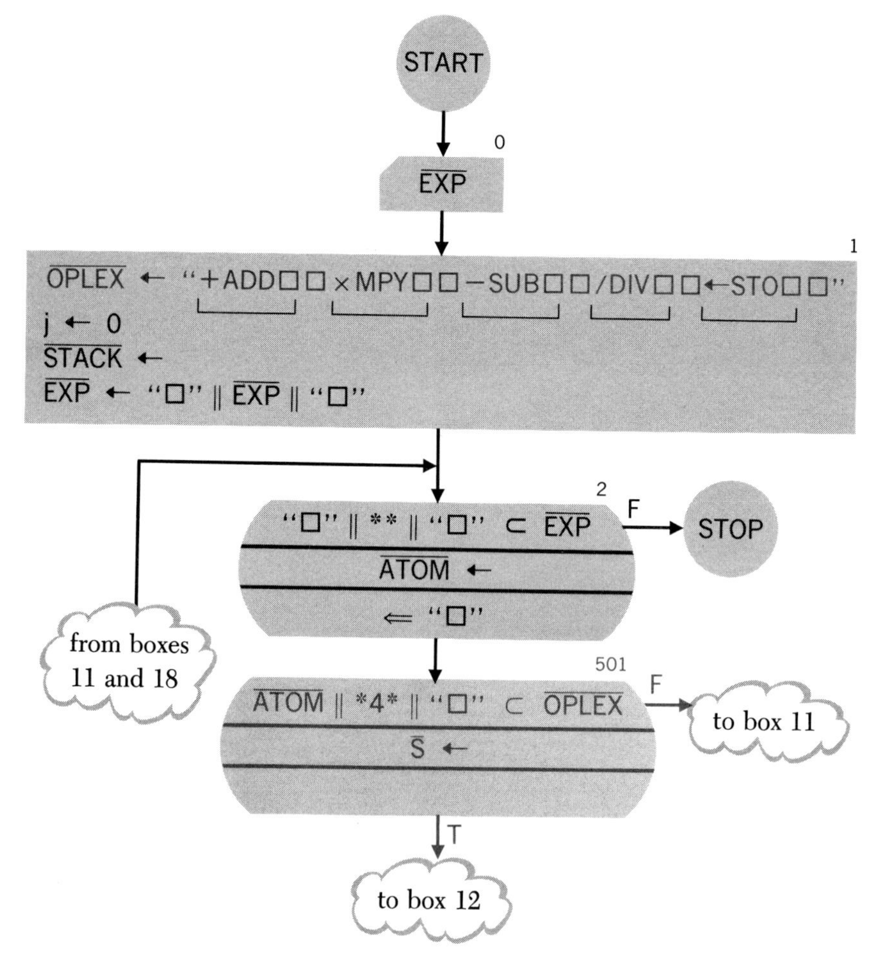

Figure 13-5 Table-look-up by pattern match using a lexicon, (Box 501, together with the assignment of a value to $\overline{\text{OPLEX}}$ in box 1, can be used to replace boxes 3, 4, 5, 6, 7, 8, 9, 10, 101, and 102 of Figure 13-3).

the postfix string leads to the generation of some obviously superfluous instructions. Typical is the utterly wasted pair

```
STO . . + 1
LDA . . + 1
```

which is generated each time the result of the previous operation becomes the left operand in the next operation. Also, there are constructions like

```
STO . . + 1
LDA C
MPY . . + 1
```

which are candidates for improvement. If we but remember that certain operations (among them, multiplication) are commutative, we see that it is perfectly permissible to replace the three instructions above simply by

MPY C

This particular simplification is feasible because, in the generated code, the result of the previous operation would already be in the accumulator and would serve as the multiplicand for the multiplier C.

Both types of improvements are illustrated in Figure 13-6 where boxes 301 through 304 are shown in rust to highlight the new strategy. For simplicity, this partial algorithm addresses itself to expressions involving only the commutative operations of add and multiply.

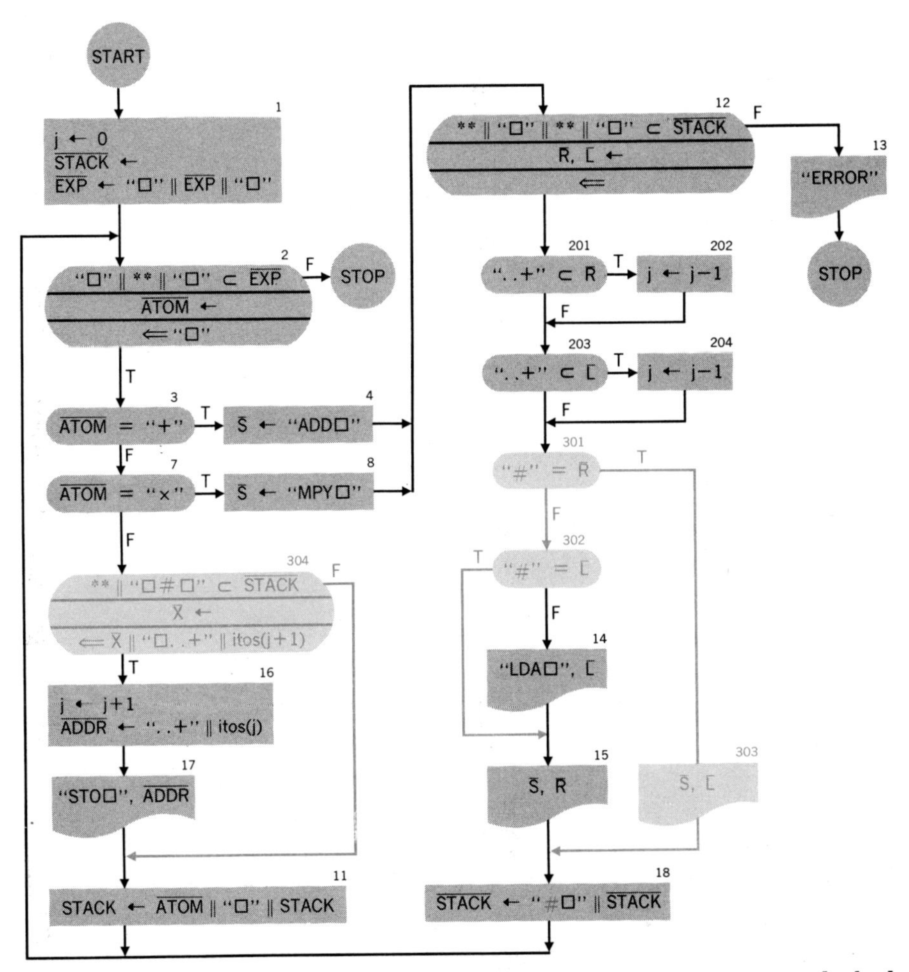

Figure 13-6 Showing how to avoid generating pairs of instructions that store and reload the accumulator in cases of commutative operations + and ×.

To gain the desired improvement, the following strategy is used. Previously, we generated the STO instruction (at box 17 of Figure 13-3) as soon as we had generated the instruction for the arithmetic operation (box 15 of the same figure).

Now the object of the game will be to *postpone* generating the store instruction until it can be determined whether it is really needed. The instructions that may be generated in boxes 14, 15, and 303 (of Figure 13-5) are such that, if executed, the result of the most recent operation would reside in the accumulator.

In Figure 13-3 we developed an address (ADDR) for a generated STO instruction, and we stacked this address (at box 18) before returning to box 2. Now, since we will not have generated such an address or STO instruction, we shall instead place a special mark on the stack (at box 18) and then return to box 2. The purpose of the mark is to signify that the accumulator would hold an operand at this point.

We use the number symbol (#) as the "accumulator mark." When in box 12 the accumulator mark is later found at the top of the stack it will signify that the value for the *right* operand would be in the accumulator. When in box 12 the number symbol is found in the next-to-the-top (nonblank) position of the stack, it will signify that the value for the *left* operand would be in the accumulator.

The accumulator mark can later be recognized (at boxes 301 and 302) when we are examining copies of the top two (nonblank) elements of the stack to decide what new LDA, ADD, or MPY instructions to generate—that is, at the time another operator has been encountered. The mark can also be recognized (at box 304) when we are trying to decide whether an STO instruction must be generated before stacking another atom.

Three different situations arise following the stacking of a number symbol, each necessitating somewhat different action. Each situation and the consequent action is discussed at some length.

(a) If the very next atom scanned in $\overline{\text{EXP}}$ is an operator, the accumulator mark will be found at the *top* of the stack and hence will be detected as the value of $\overline{\text{R}}$ at box 301. This detection is tantamount to the recognition that the *right* operand represents the accumulator.

Since the operator (ADD or MPY) that is dealt with in this hypothetical situation is commutative, it is perfectly satisfactory to treat the left operand *as though it were the right operand,* namely, generate as the next instruction one of the form, $\overline{\text{S}} \| \overline{\text{L}}$ (i.e., "ADD□" $\| \overline{\text{L}}$, or "MPY□" $\| \overline{\text{L}}$).

Notice that the store instruction, whose generation was previously postponed, is now found to be unnecessary. The improvement thus realized may be easily checked for a particular case, such as in the following expression:

A × (B + C)	infix
A B C + ×	postfix

You should verify by a trace of the flow chart (Figure 13-6) that the code generated would be

L D A □ B
A D D □ C
M P Y □ A
no intermediate instructions needed

(b) If the very next atom scanned in $\overline{\text{EXP}}$ is an operand, it will be placed on the stack when executing box 11, although, as you can see, the flow of control first reaches box 304. The chief purpose of box 304 will become clear when we consider case *c* below. For the moment, we will show that the pattern match attempted at box 304 will always fail in this situation, so control will reach box 11 via the false exit (and no STO instruction will have been generated.) Here is the reasoning behind this. At this juncture, just prior to stacking the next operand, the top character in the stack is the accumulator mark. The pattern match in box 304 can succeed only if the stack holds a "#" in the *next-to-the-top* position of the stack. Keep in mind, too, that there cannot be *two* such marks on the stack for the following reason. Only the discovery of an operator can cause the stacking of an accumulator mark, and then only after number symbols that are found in the two top nonblank positions have been removed from the stack (at box 12). Moreover, discovery of an operand causes a stacked accumulator mark, if found in the next-to-top nonblank position, to be removed (at box 304), thus preventing it from being pushed "deeper" into the stack.

Assuming control reached box 11 in this way, and the next operand is then put on the stack, control will then return to box 2, at which point the next character in the postfix string will be scanned. Suppose this character is an operator. After the operator is properly identified, control will pass through box 12, after which the "#", now at the next-to-the-top position in the stack, will be detected (at box 302) as the value of $\overline{\text{L}}$. This detection amounts to recognizing that the left operand represents the accumulator, so control is directed to box 15. Here, an instruction of the form

$$\bar{S} \parallel \bar{R}$$

is generated. Note two points.

(1) No assumption as to the commutativity of the operator represented by $\bar{S}$ is required in this case where the *left* operand is regarded as the accumulator.
(2) Again we find that the store instruction whose generation was previously postponed can now be disregarded altogether.

This improvement can be checked using a particular example, such as the following expression:

(A + B) × C   infix
A B + C ×   postfix

A trace of Figure 13-6 will show that the generated code would be

L D A □ A
A D D □ B
M P Y □ C
no intermediate
instructions needed

A similar case could be checked for the expression

(A + B) / C

If boxes 9 and 10 of Figure 13-3 are reinstated in Figure 13-6, you should be able to verify that the resulting code would be

L D A □ A
A D D □ B
D I V □ C
no intermediate
instructions needed

(c) In this case we picture that following the stacking of the accumulator mark, *two operands* are picked off the postfix string without any intervening operators. The first of these will have been stacked according to the explanation given under *b*. The discovery of the second operand enables us to recognize that generating the "postponed" store instruction cannot be avoided.

The reasoning goes like this. Sooner or later we will encounter another operator. At that time, the top two items in the stack will necessarily be operands, neither of which represents the accumulator. To carry out the indicated operation, it would be necessary to generate the pair

"LDA□" || [
$\overline{\text{S}}$ || $\overline{\text{R}}$

Before doing so, we would have to generate a store instruction so as to save the current contents of the accumulator.

We can detect this special situation by arranging for a special pattern match at box 304. This match will be attempted whenever we are getting ready to stack another operand that has been found in the postfix string. The test itself is simply to see if a "#" is found to be the next-to-the-top operand in the stack. If so, it means that the operand we are about to stack is then the second operand in sequence following the most recently scanned operator. We now initiate the action needed to generate the store instruction and to appropriately update the information in the stack. The first step taken (as part of box 304) is to replace the "#" in the stack with a manufactured symbol for a temporary. At box 16, this same symbol is then assigned to $\overline{\text{ADDR}}$. Finally (at last!), we generate the store instruction at box 17 for storing the accumulator in this temporary variable. The next operand is then stacked at box 11.

EXERCISES 13-1, SET C

1. Show, by a trace of the new algorithm in Figure 13-6, that the instructions generated for the postfix equivalent of

$$(A + B) \times (C + D)$$

would be

```
LDA A
ADD B
STO ..+1
LDA C
ADD D
MPY ..+1
```

2. Compare these results with the output that would be obtained using the algorithm in Figure 13-3.

3. Without looking ahead to the next discussions, see if you can now round out the algorithm in Figure 13-6 to handle the noncommutative operations of "−" and "/" and also the assignment operator.

Final Improvements

To develop our new strategy for eliminating the generation of unnecessary instructions to store and reload the accumulator, we temporarily confined our attention to the handling of "+" and "×" operations. Let's "reinstate" the other operators. First we show in Figure 13-7 how to handle the noncommutative operators "−" and "/". Boxes 5, 6, 9, and 10 are reinstated, and we add the new steps, boxes 401 through 404 (shown in rust). Also, we add in box 1 the assignment of a fixed string value, "SUB□DIV□", to the variable $\overline{\text{NONCOM}}$, which is employed in box 401.

The commutativity of the operator becomes an issue when the right operand is discovered to represent the accumulator (truth exit of box 301). Only then is a test made to determine the type of operator (box 401). If the operator is not "SUB" or "DIV", the false exit will be taken at box 401. We would then proceed to box 303 as before, generating the arithmetic instruction that lets the left operand be treated as if it had been a right operand. However, for the noncommutative operators, we must generate a sequence of instructions which, when executed, would store the right operand—that is, contents of the accumulator (box 402), load the accumulator with the left operand (box 403), and execute the arithmetic operation using the value originally held in the accumulator (box 404). The auxiliary variable chosen for this purpose is . . + 0. The memory space represented by this temporary can be used repeatedly for the same purpose. The space is free for reuse whenever the instruction sequence generated in boxes 402, 403, and 404 has been executed.

Figure 13-8 shows how we can complete the algorithm to handle the assignment operator by adding the test and print boxes 103 and 104, as shown in rust. Here, instead of reinstating boxes 101 and 102 as used in Figure 13-3, we employ the table-look-up features developed in Figure 13-5. We leave to you the study and verification of these latest changes as a useful exercise.

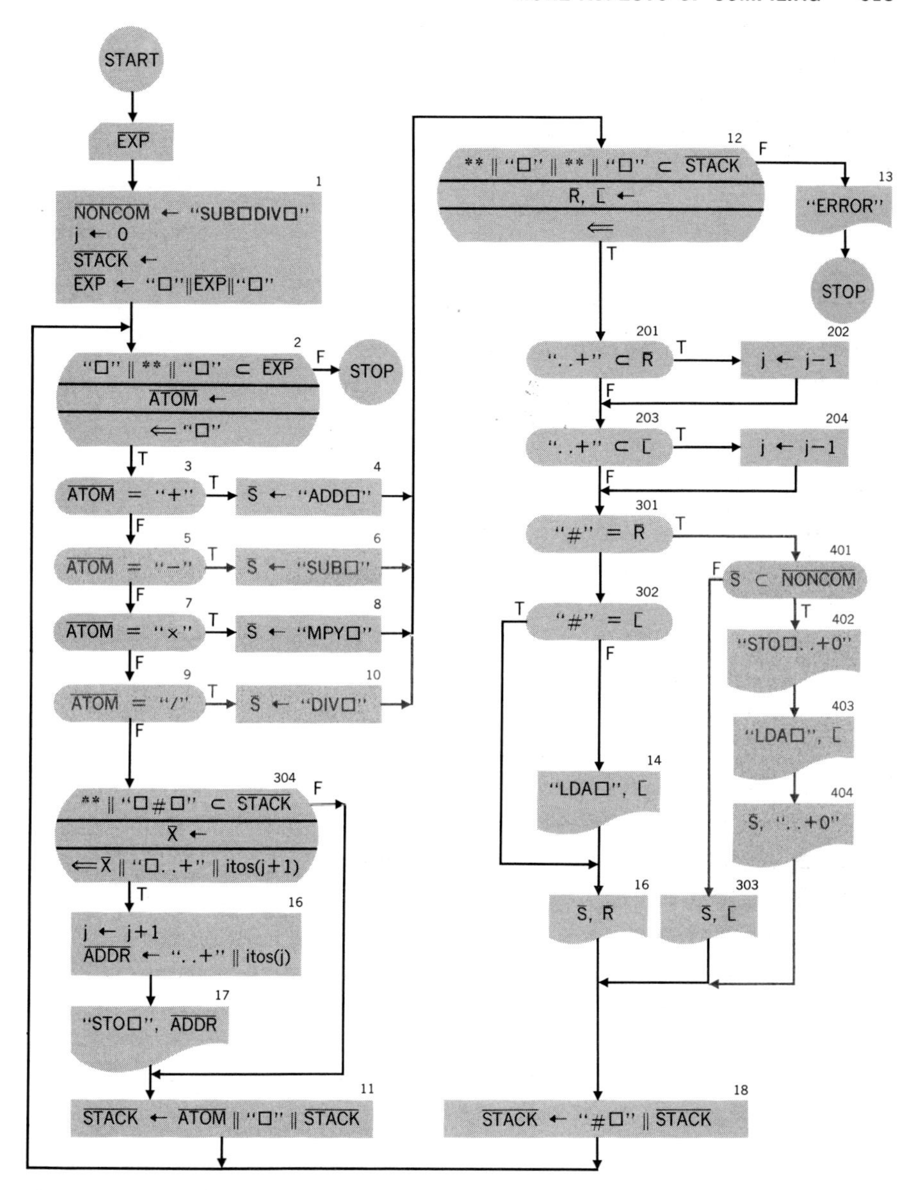

Figure 13-7 Handling the noncommutative operators when the right operand happens to represent the accumulator.

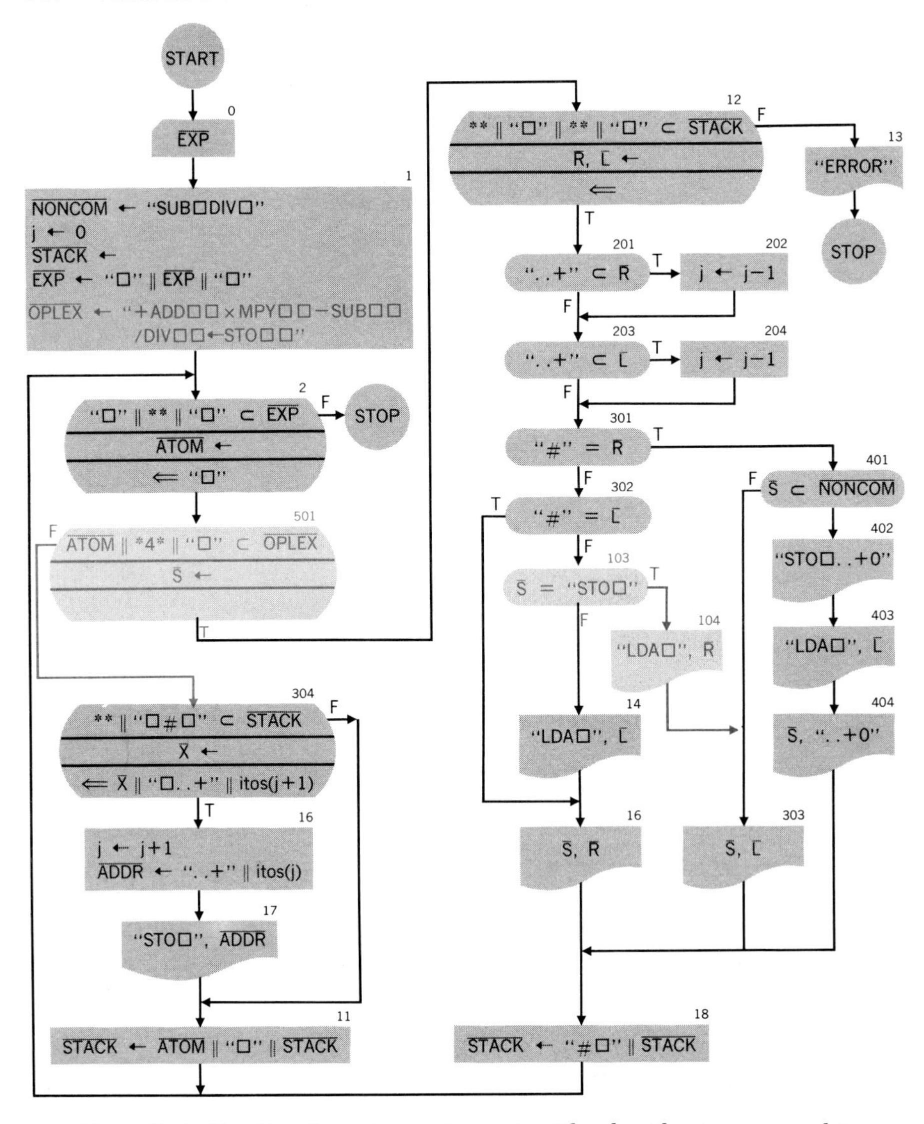

Figure 13-8 Handling the assignment operator. The algorithm is now complete.

EXERCISES 13-1, SET D

1. Without actually tracing through the Figure 13-8 algorithm, how many temporaries should be needed in processing the postfix string corresponding to this statement:

$$Z \leftarrow E + F + (A + B) \times (E + D)$$

2. Verify, by a trace of the Figure 13-8 algorithm, that the output for the preceding exercise is:

```
LDA E
ADD F
STO ..+1
LDA A
ADD B
STO ..+2
LDA E
ADD D
MPY ..+2
ADD ..+1
STO Z
```

3. What is the output for the Figure 13-8 algorithm when processing a postfix string corresponding to the expression:

$$(C \times D - E) / (F - G \times H)$$

We suggest you trace this one too.

13-2 CONVERSION FROM SYMBOLIC TO ACTUAL SAMOS

The last process we wish to consider, and only briefly at that, is the job of converting the symbolic SAMOS to actual 11-character SAMOS instructions. Figure 13-9 summarizes the problem for a specific case and Figure 13-10 gives an algorithm for this process.

Discussion of the Algorithm

Each symbolic instruction is input and assigned as a one-way list to $\overline{\text{INST}}$ (box 2). The leftmost four characters are stripped off, the first three being assigned to $\overline{\text{OP}}$ (box 3). We use the value of $\overline{\text{OP}}$ later (in box 10) for assembling the actual SAMOS instruction. The remaining characters in $\overline{\text{INST}}$ are then examined to see if they represent a "generated" symbol for a temporary location (box 5). If so, the distinguishing characters ". . +" are removed, leaving just the index of the temporary in $\overline{\text{INST}}$. In box 9 we form the address string $\overline{\text{ADDR}}$ by adding the integer equivalent of this index, stoi($\overline{\text{INST}}$), to 9000 and converting the integer address via the itos function to string form. Box 10 forms the 11-character string

Input statement: Z←E+F+(A+B)×(E+D)

Postfix: ZEF+AB+ED+×+←

Input	Output
Symbolic SAMOS	Desired actual (target) SAMOS
	1 2 3 4 5 6 7 8 9 10 11
LDA E	□LDA0001001
ADD F	□ADD0001002
STO ..+1	□STØ0009001
LDA A	□LDA0001003
ADD B	□ADD0001004
STO ..+2	□STØ0009002
LDA E	□LDA0001001
ADD D	□ADD0001005
MPY ..+2	□MPY0009002
ADD ..+1	□ADD0009001
STO Z	□STØ0001006

Figure 13-9 Showing conversion to actual SAMOS. *Assumptions.* (1) E, F, A, B, D, and Z are associated with locations beginning at 1001 in order of appearance, i.e., 1001, 1002, . . . , 1006, respectively. (2) The ". . +" temporaries begin at location 9000.

representation of the actual SAMOS instruction, $\overline{\text{ACTSAM}}$. We print its value (box 11) and return to box 2 for another symbolic instruction.

If the symbolic address has not been generated, control passes to box 6. Here we search an order-of-occurrence list of such symbols, called $\overline{\text{SYMLST}}$. This string, which is initially set to the value "□" in box 1, cannot at the outset contain an instance of the first symbol we search for, so we go to box 7, where the order-of-occurrence counter j is incremented. The symbol in question followed by the string value of j is concatenated with $\overline{\text{SYMLST}}$. At box 8 we form the actual address $\overline{\text{ADDR}}$ by adding 1000 to the occurrence number. String-to-integer (stoi) and integer-to-string (itos) functions are again employed in the process. Eventually, we will arrive at box 6 and find that a copy of the symbol does reside in $\overline{\text{SYMLST}}$. As a result of this same pattern match, we will have "looked up" the associated occurrence number stored as $\overline{\text{JAY}}$. This value is then used in box 8 to form $\overline{\text{ADDR}}$.

EXERCISE 13-2

After the 11 symbolic instructions shown in Figure 13-9 have been completely "processed" by the algorithm in Figure 13-10, what is the value of $\overline{\text{SYMLST}}$?

Answer. □E□1□F□2□A□3□B□4□D□5□Z□6□

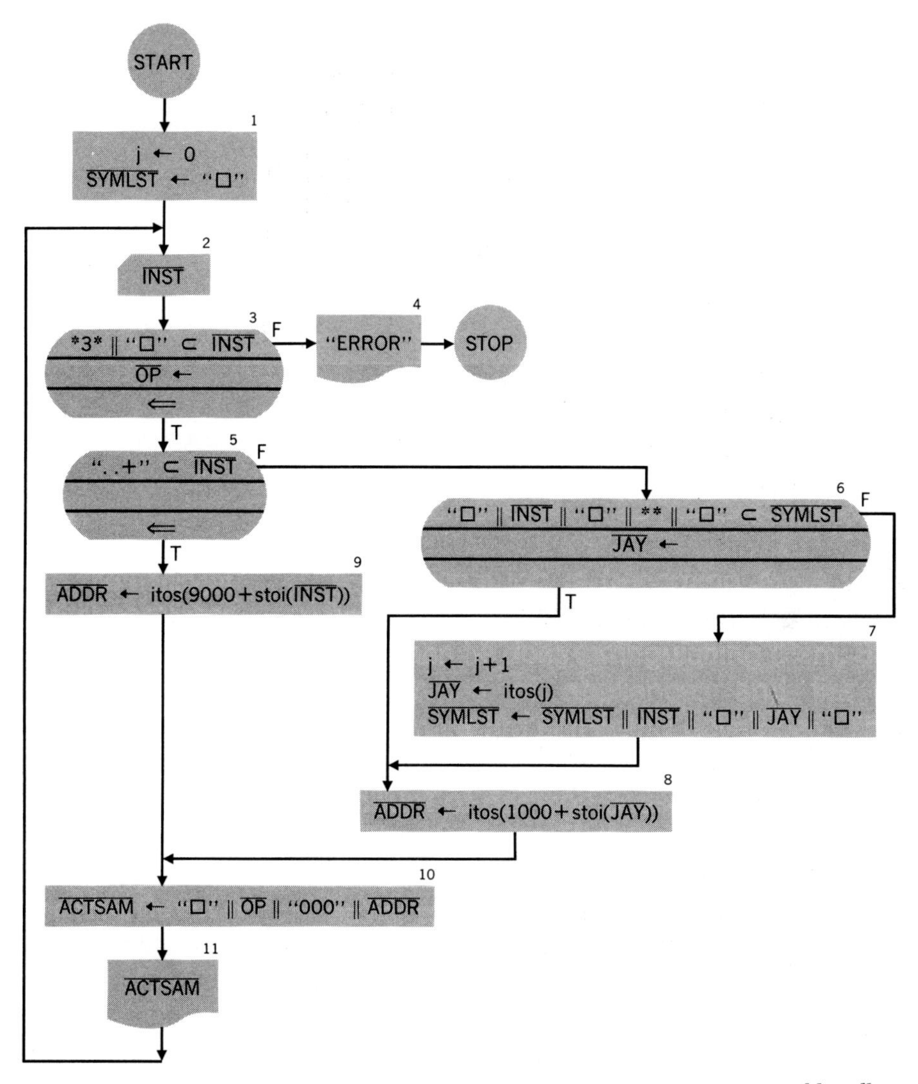

Figure 13-10 Algorithm for conversion to actual SAMOS instructions. Variables allocated addresses beginning at 1000. Temporary storage beginning at 9000.

PROBLEM 13-2

Near the beginning of Chapter 10, we suggested that statements of a program, say, in FORTRAN or ALGOL, could be preedited by a computer algorithm with the result that each distinct variable, constant (and operator) symbol could be converted to a unique, fixed length integer code. For convenience, we suggested that we think of these unique codes as single characters. This simplification made it possible to study the various phases of compiling without being troubled by difficult-to-read expressions resulting from the replacement of our meaningful problem variables by unfamiliar integer codes devoid of mnemonic value.

We are now prepared to return to the question of preediting that was postponed in Chapter 10. Your job is to develop a "preeditor" algorithm that takes FORTRAN or ALGOL assignment statements and converts them to a form suitable for conversion to postfix form.

Ground Rules

1. Consider that each infix (assignment statement) can be input as a single string and stored as a one-way list. You can also assume that at least one blank character separates each variable, constant, and operator in the statement.
2. Each distinct variable encountered is to be converted to a four-character string, the first character of which is "V" and the last three of which are digits whose integer value is assigned by order-of-occurrence in a fashion similar to the way symbols were handled in Figure 13-10.
3. Each distinct constant encountered is also to be converted to a four-character string of the form "Cxxx" where the x's represent an order-of-occurrence number generated in the same way as for variables.
4. Operator symbols are to be limited to

	:= ↑ / × + −	in ALGOL
and	= ** / * + −	in FORTRAN

These are to be converted to five-character strings in a standard form such as Ø0001 for ":=" or "=", Ø0002 for "↑" or "**".

After you have completed the preeditor algorithm for Problem 1, revise the infix to postfix algorithm given in Figure 10-1 so that it (a) accepts as input the output strings of your preeditor algorithm and (b) takes full advantage of the string-operation techniques we have developed in Chapters 12 and 13. The prior conversion of variables, constants, and operators to "standard" formats, as suggested in the ground rules for the preceding problem, should simplify the task.

APPENDIX

SAMOS

In Chapter 1 you were introduced to an imaginary computer called SAMOS. This appendix completes the description of the organization of such a computer and assumes you are familiar with Sections 1-5 through 1-8. This complete computer has sixteen different instruction codes, whereas real computers may have several hundred. Nevertheless, the SAMOS design is adequate for use in solving real problems. In fact, real computers have been programmed to behave like SAMOS (that is, SAMOS has been simulated). In this sense, SAMOS is no longer imaginary.

A-1 REVIEW

First, let us review briefly some of the features of SAMOS already discussed in Chapter 1. SAMOS is centered about a memory consisting of 10,000 separate cells, each identified by an integer address (from 0000 to 9999). Attached to this memory are an input device, an output device, and an arithmetic unit. These are shown schematically in Figure A-1, which is similar to Figure 1-28. Exercising control over all four components (dashed lines) is a control unit that receives its instructions (dotted line) from the memory in the following way. If the present instruction has come from memory address n, the next instruction will normally come from memory address n + 1. How this works can be seen by a quick glance inside the control unit where there are several specialized cells or *registers*. One register, the *operation register*, holds the three-character operation codes (e.g., LDA). One register, the *address register*, holds the four-digit address of the instruction being executed. Another register, the *instruction counter*, contains the four-digit address of the current instruction in memory.

These registers are shown in Figure A-2 where (for illustration) an instruction to load the accumulator with the contents of 1492 is to be executed; this instruction comes from memory address 0013. Of course, there are many other things in the control unit, including a device to increment the instruction counter by one when an instruction is completed.

The normal execution cycle of an instruction can be described in terms of these registers.

1. The instruction counter, IC, has some initial value that is sensed and used to establish a path from the specified memory cell to the control unit.
2. The contents of the specified memory cell is transmitted over the

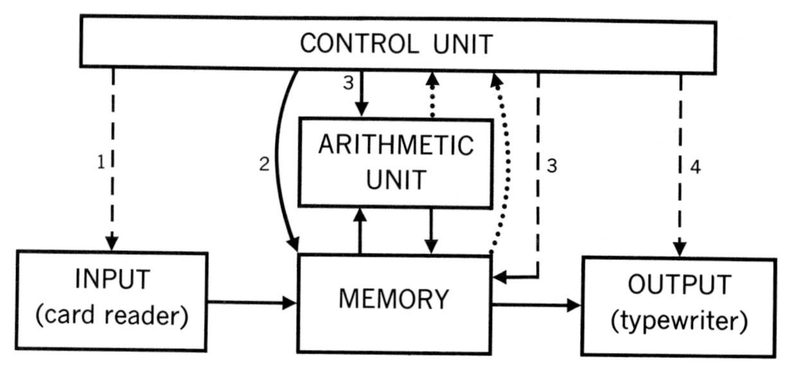

Figure A-1 Schematic Diagram of SAMOS.

established path, with the operation code entering the operation register, ØR, and the address part entering the address register, AR.

3. (a) The contents of the ØR register is sensed and its value used to connect circuits to perform the indicated operation.

(b) At the same time, the contents of the AR is sensed and used to establish a path between the specified memory cell and the arithmetic unit (or the input or output unit).

4. The instruction counter is incremented.

5. The instruction, for which the circuits and paths have been established, is now performed and the cycle repeated.

We shall presently see that some instructions require alterations to this "normal execution cycle."

You know from Chapter 1 that the arithmetic unit also contains a special

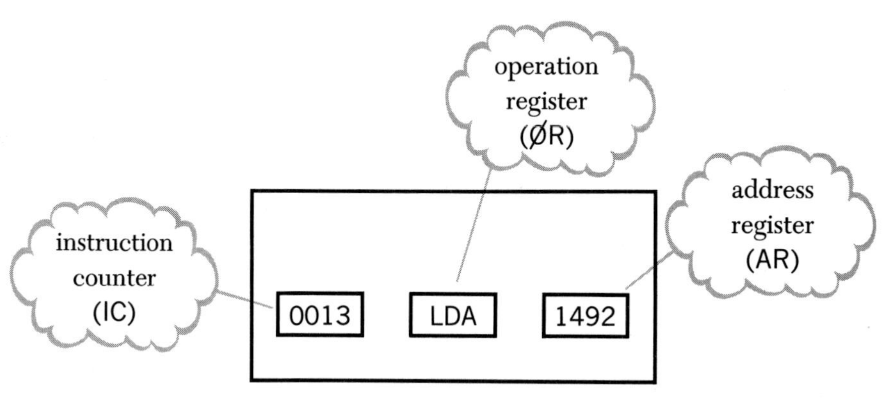

Figure A-2 Inside the control unit.

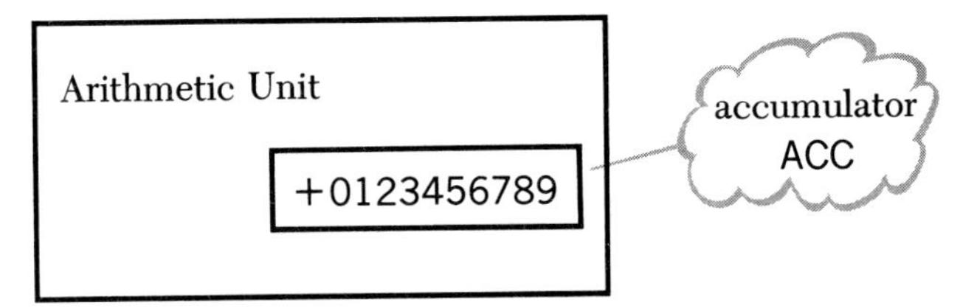

Figure A-3 Inside the arithmetic unit.

register called the accumulator, ACC. This register receives the result of each arithmetic operation (Figure A-3).

A-2 GETTING THINGS STARTED

As yet we have said nothing about how a program gets into the memory or how the instruction sequence gets started. Somewhere on the machine are buttons to allow external control. One pair of buttons turns the elec-

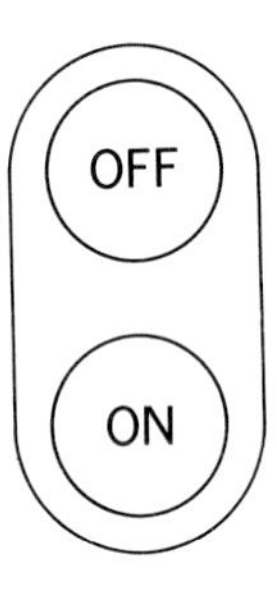

tric power off or on. Of course, many machines have buttons like this. Another pair is labeled "STOP" and "START." Pressing "stop" interrupts the instruction execution cycle, described above, just before step 1 (sensing the contents of the instruction counter). Nothing changes; the execution of instructions simply stops. Pressing the start button restarts the execution cycle again.

There is yet another button involved in the problem of getting started. It is called the "load" button and most machines have one of these, too. When you press "load," the computer reads a card and transfers what

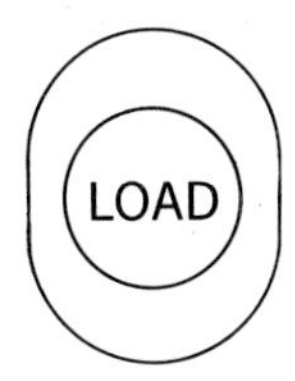

is punched in columns one to eleven to the memory cell with address 0000. It then reads another card and transfers the contents of columns one to eleven to address 0001. It continues to read cards, sending the contents of the first eleven columns to memory cells with successively higher addresses until it encounters a card on which the first eleven columns are blank. Upon finding such a card, the instruction counter, IC, is automatically set to value 0000 and the execution cycle begins.

Preparing and Loading a Program

The machine language instructions are punched, one to a card, in columns one to eleven. Any required constant values are considered to be part of the program. They are punched on cards in the same way. All cards are stacked in the card reader with the instructions first and a blank card placed at the very end.

Supplying Data

If data are to be read during the course of executing the program, cards punched with the data are placed in proper order *after* the blank card. When the LOAD button is pressed, the program's instructions and constants are loaded into memory and execution begins.

Note that the loading process assumes that for every program the first instruction to be executed is located in 0000. If the first instruction of your program is not in 0000, you must place an unconditional branch instruction (BRU) there so that a branch to the first instruction of your program will occur immediately.

A-3 A REVIEW OF THE ELEVEN BASIC INSTRUCTIONS

In Chapter 1 you studied ten of the basic instructions. These are sufficient to program many problems of interest and are reviewed in this section.

In explaining how a SAMOS instruction carries out its task, we will refer to a very particular memory cell (among the 10,000 available cells) or to a *special* register of the control unit or arithmetic unit. Memory cells are actually identified uniquely only by their numerical addresses, not by arbitrarily chosen pseudonyms. But let us adopt the convention that *one name for the number currently in a memory cell is its numerical address enclosed in parentheses.* Thus (0005) is a name for the number in the cell whose address is 0005. In a similar spirit we will give specific names to the contents of special registers and so avoid confusing these with "free" variables, as follows.

Special Register	*Name* (*for the number contained therein*)
Accumulator	(ACC)
Address register	(AR)
Instruction counter	(IC)
Operation register	(ØR)

Notice that the parentheses are *part* of the name.

The concept of reading a value from one of these cells and assigning it to another is similar to the one we used in Chapter 1. For example, reading the value contained in cell 0005 and assigning it to the accumulator can be expressed as an ordinary assignment:

$$\text{(ACC)} \leftarrow \text{(0005)}$$

Occasionally, we would like to be able to speak of the assignment of a constant value. For example,

$$\text{(ACC)} \leftarrow 0$$

means assign the constant value 0 (not the value contained in register 0) to the accumulator. Similarly,

$$\text{(ACC)} \leftarrow 1492$$

means assign the constant value 1492 to the accumulator.

Every instruction in SAMOS has the following form:

<table>
<tr><td>1</td><td>2</td><td>3</td><td>4</td><td>5</td><td>6</td><td>7</td><td>8</td><td>9</td><td>10</td><td>11</td></tr>
<tr><td>S
I
G
N</td><td colspan="3">Operation to be performed</td><td>0</td><td>0</td><td>0</td><td colspan="4">Storage Address</td></tr>
</table>

The instruction is composed of ten characters plus sign. If these characters are numbered from left to right, we have:

Position	
1	The sign has no meaning in the case of an instruction. We will either use + or leave it blank.
2, 3, 4	Characters in these positions indicate the operation to be performed. For example, ADD for addition, DIV for division, etc.
5, 6, 7	These positions are used for *indexing*, a concept to be explained later. For a while we will assume that they are zero.
8, 9, 10, 11	These characters form a four-digit number from 0000 to 9999, and they represent a memory address.

Now let us see how to move data to and from the accumulator.

Load the Accumulator

Example

+	L	D	A	0	0	0	1	4	9	2

Meaning (ACC) ← (1492)

The accumulator (thought of as a window box) is *assigned* (a copy of) the current value of storage address 1492. The contents of 1492 remain undisturbed.

The address 1492 is, of course, only one of 10,000 possible values that could be used in one of these instructions. Throughout the remaining discussions, we will select addresses for our examples essentially "at random." They are intended merely to be representative.

Store the Accumulator

Example

+	S	T	Ø	0	0	0	5	0	0	1

Meaning (5001) ← (ACC)

To the storage location 5001 is assigned (a copy of) the current value of the accumulator. The value of the accumulator remains the same.

Integer arithmetic is done with the following four instructions.

Add to the Accumulator

Example

+	A D D	0 0 0	7 2 2 2

Meaning (ACC) ← (ACC) + (7222)

A copy of the integer stored in location 7222 is added to the current value of the accumulator and the result is assigned to the accumulator.

Subtract from the Accumulator

Example

+	S U B	0 0 0	6 2 1 8

Meaning (ACC) ← (ACC) − (6218)

A copy of the integer stored in 6218 is subtracted from the current value of the accumulator. The result is assigned to the accumulator.

Multiply

Example

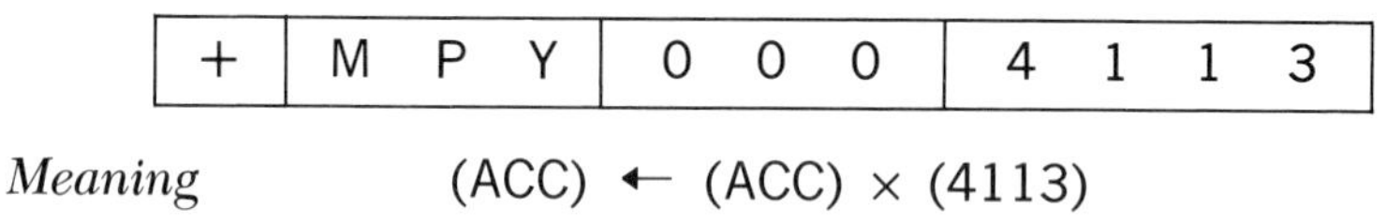

Meaning (ACC) ← (ACC) × (4113)

A copy of the integer stored in the accumulator is multiplied by the integer in 4113. The product is developed and assigned to the accumulator. Since the number of digits following the first nonzero digit in the product *can* equal the sum of such "nonzero" digits in the accumulator plus those in 4113, the programmer must be careful that the number of nonzero digits in that sum never exceeds ten. For example, if the accumulator contains a five-digit integer, the number in 4113 can have a maximum of five digits if the product is not to exceed the available ten digits in the accumulator. If SAMOS is instructed to produce a result of more than ten digits, it will stop as a result of what is called an "overflow."

Divide

Example

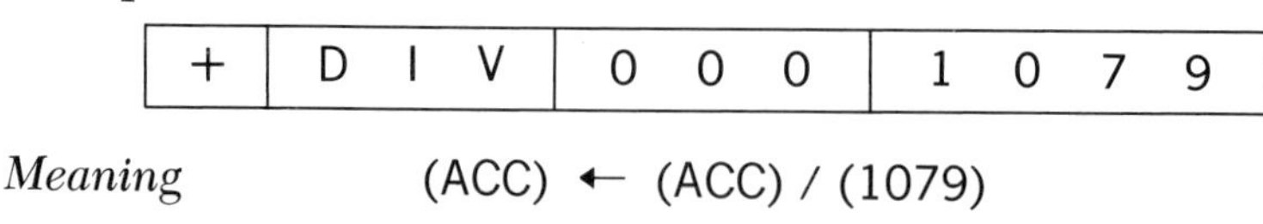

Meaning (ACC) ← (ACC) / (1079)

The integer value of the accumulator is divided by the integer value of (1079). The integer quotient is developed and assigned to the accumulator. *The remainder is lost.*

Halt

Example

+	H L T	0 0 0	2 0 2 2

The machine stops. The effect is exactly the same as pressing the STOP button. If the START button in the operator's console is then pressed, the next instruction will be taken from 2022. This is the first instruction we have studied that changes the normal execution cycle. First, it stops the cycle. Second, upon resuming the execution cycle, the instruction counter is set to the *value* 2022. That is,

$$(IC) \leftarrow 2022$$

A very important instruction is the next one, which automatically alters the sequence of instructions of a program. It is the "Branch Unconditionally" instruction.

Branch Unconditionally

Example

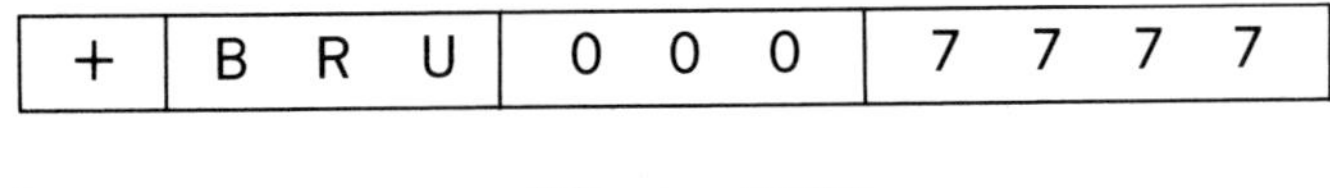

Meaning $(IC) \leftarrow 7777$

This instruction directs SAMOS to "pick up" the next instruction from 7777. No testing of the accumulator is required in this case.

Branch Conditionally

Some of the most important branching instructions are those which break the sequential nature of a program depending on the contents of the accumulator, for example, the "Branch on Minus" instruction.

Example

+	B M I	0 0 0	1 7 2 9

Meaning

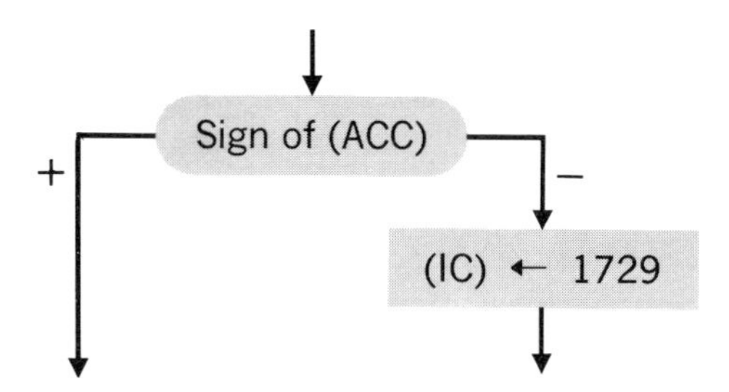

SAMOS is directed to "jump" to location 1729 for the next instruction if the sign of the accumulator is minus, that is, if the accumulator contains a negative number. If the sign of the accumulator is +, SAMOS will execute the next instruction in sequence. In SAMOS a zero will always be stored as +0000000000, never as −0000000000. Hence, the BMI instruction is logically equivalent to:

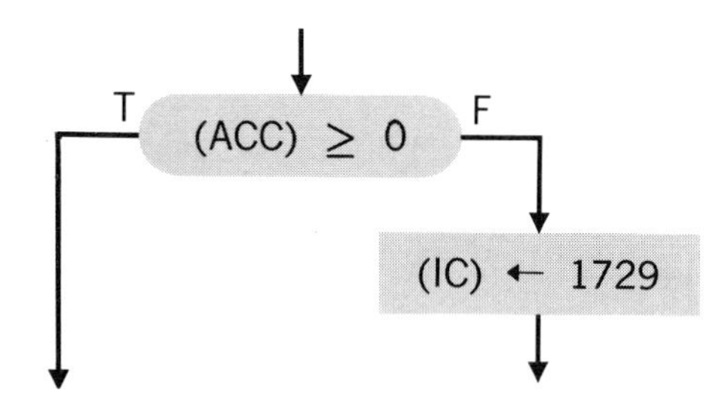

The following two basic instructions permit a program to input data and to output a result.

Read a Word

Example

+	R W D	0 0 0	3 3 4 6

Meaning (3346) ← (first eleven columns of next data card)

This instruction causes SAMOS to take a card into the card reader and to assign the data value found in the first eleven columns of the card (ten digits plus sign) to location 3346. Data that may be punched on the rest of the card is disregarded, and the card is itself discarded.

Results are printed in the typewriter by the "Write a Word" instruction.

Write a Word

Example

+	W W D	0 0 0	2 6 7 2

Meaning (output medium) ← (2672)

This instruction causes SAMOS to return the typewriter carriage, advance to the next line, and type the information stored in location 2672 in the first eleven columns of the typewriter.

A-4 SOME ILLUSTRATIVE PROBLEMS

Chapter 1 presented a SAMOS program for computing the terms in the Fibonacci sequence. Here, we consider several other programs in the language of SAMOS. The use of a printed coding form, as shown in Figure A-4, is a considerable convenience.

Suppose we want to type the information punched into the first eleven columns of a large number of cards. This usually referred to as "listing the cards." We can use the flow chart and program of Figure A-5.

The program occupies four words. Location 0003 is used to hold momentarily the information read from each card. The "Branch Unconditionally" instruction returns the machine to the beginning of the program. The machine will stop when it is unable to complete the execution of the RWD instruction, that is, when there are no more cards in the card reader.

Suppose we want to implement the flow chart of Figure A-6*a* which replaces A by its absolute value. Assuming that the numerical value of A

LOCATION	+ −	OPER.	INDEX REG.	ADDRESS	REMARKS
	1	2 3 4	5 6 7	8 9 10 11	← CARD COL.
0000		LDA	000	1001	(ACC) ← (1001)
0001		ADD	000	1002	(ACC) ← (ACC) + (1002)
0002		ADD	000	1003	(ACC) ← (ACC) + (1003)
0003		ADD	000	1004	(ACC) ← (ACC) + (1004)
0004		STØ	000	5000	(5000) ← (ACC)

Figure A-4 Coding form for SAMOS showing five instructions, where each is located, and remarks on each.

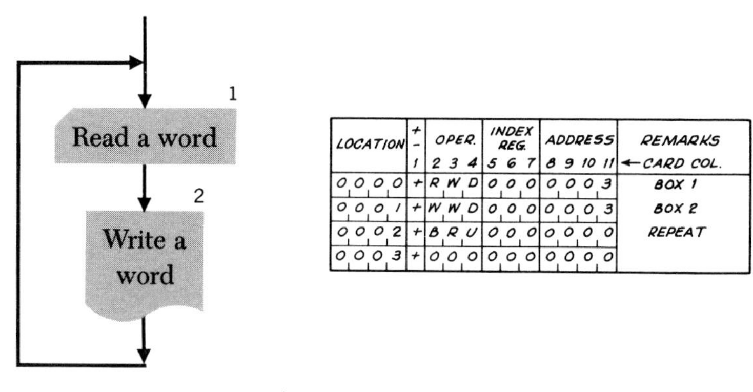

LOCATION	+ -	OPER.	INDEX REG.	ADDRESS	REMARKS
	1	2 3 4	5 6 7	8 9 10 11	← CARD COL.
0000	+	RWD	000	0003	BOX 1
0001	+	WWD	000	0003	BOX 2
0002	+	BRU	000	0000	REPEAT
0003	+	000	000	0000	

Figure A-5 Program to "list" the cards.

is stored in location 0500, the following program in Figure A-6*b* does the trick. Notice that A, here synonymous with (0500), is loaded into the accumulator. Then we say, "branch to location 0003 if the accumulator is minus, otherwise go to the next instruction in sequence, i.e., to 0002." The instructions located at 0003, 0004, and 0005 then generate −A by subtracting A from itself two times and storing the result in 0500. Eventually, the two branches merge at location 0006, since the instruction in 0005 is STØ, a nonbranching instruction. Executing this one sends SAMOS to location 0006 for the next sequential step.

We now see one way that SAMOS can be programmed to execute the unary minus operation. Simply load the value of the variable into the accumulator. Then subtract the same value two times. Figure A-7 shows the coding to achieve the assignment

$$(ACC) \leftarrow -(0552)$$

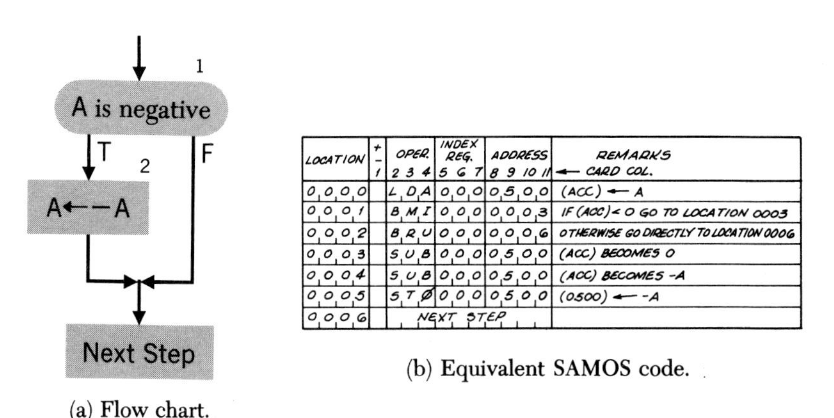

(a) Flow chart.

LOCATION	+ -	OPER.	INDEX REG.	ADDRESS	REMARKS
	1	2 3 4	5 6 7	8 9 10 11	← CARD COL.
0000		LDA	000	0500	(ACC) ← A
0001		BMI	000	0003	IF (ACC) < 0 GO TO LOCATION 0003
0002		BRU	000	0006	OTHERWISE GO DIRECTLY TO LOCATION 0006
0003		SUB	000	0500	(ACC) BECOMES 0
0004		SUB	000	0500	(ACC) BECOMES −A
0005		STØ	000	0500	(0500) ← −A
0006		NEXT STEP			

(b) Equivalent SAMOS code.

Figure A-6

LOCATION	+ - 1	OPER. 2 3 4	INDEX REG. 5 6 7	ADDRESS 8 9 10 11	REMARKS ←CARD COL.
0000		LDA	000	0552	(ACC) ← (0552) } MAKE (ACC) = 0
0001		SUB	000	0552	(ACC) ← (ACC) − (0552)
0002		SUB	000	0552	(ACC) ← (ACC) − (0552)

Figure A-7 A way to achieve unary minus.

A-5 PROBLEMS RELATED TO INDEXING

(Beginning with this section, we consider problems related to indexing. Do not try to read this material until after you have completed Section 3-5 of the text.)

Suppose we are asked to write a program for summing fifty numbers. There are several ways to do this. If the numbers are already stored in memory (say in addresses 1001 to 1050), and if the resulting sum is to be assigned to (5000), the flow chart and program of Figure A-8 will work. Does this remind you of repeatedly removing lugs when changing a tire (Chapter 1)? Can we include a loop? Certainly, one possible loop is to remove the assumption that the numbers are already in memory. Let the numbers be punched in 50 consecutive cards. Figure A-9 shows a flow chart and program to compute the sum. While this is a big improvement over the program in Figure A-8, there are still two reasons why we are not well pleased with the program of Figure A-9: (1) it provides no way of stopping (other than by running out of cards) and no way of storing or writing the sum; and (2) it limits us to summing numbers punched on cards. Nevertheless, Figure A-9 uses only one ADD instruction to sum 50 (or really any number of) numbers.

Let's return to the assumption that the 50 numbers are stored in memory and devise a way to use a single ADD instruction to apply to all 50 numbers. Evidently, the *address part* of the ADD instruction must be changed before each use. Since the storage addresses of consecutive ADD instructions in Figure A-8 differ by one, we first add

```
ADD 000 0000
      + 1000
------------
ADD 000 1000
```

to form what we may call the "base" ADD instruction. Then we can produce all the other needed ADD instructions by adding the numbers

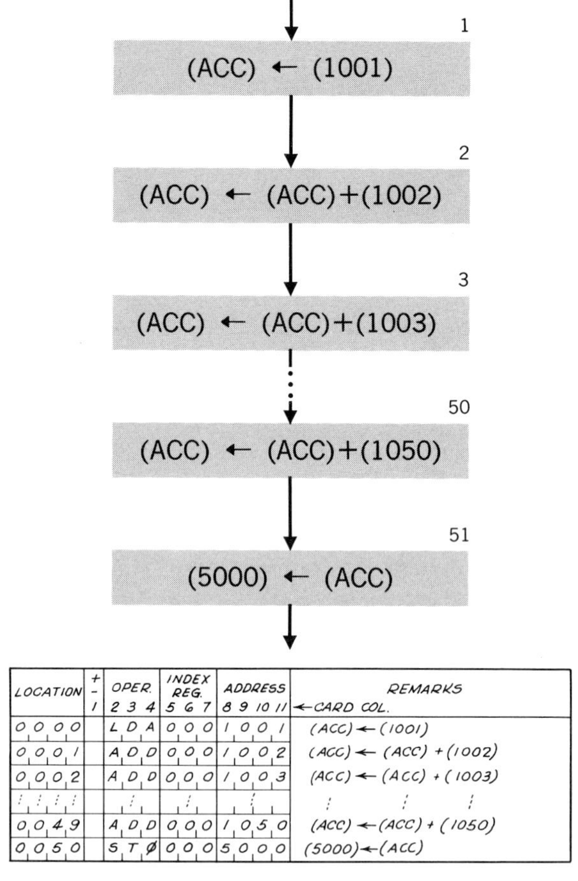

LOCATION	+ - 1	OPER. 2 3 4	INDEX REG. 5 6 7	ADDRESS 8 9 10 11	REMARKS ← CARD COL.
0000		LDA	000	1001	(ACC) ← (1001)
0001		ADD	000	1002	(ACC) ← (ACC) + (1002)
0002		ADD	000	1003	(ACC) ← (ACC) + (1003)
⋮		⋮	⋮	⋮	⋮ ⋮ ⋮
0049		ADD	000	1050	(ACC) ← (ACC) + (1050)
0050		STØ	000	5000	(5000) ← (ACC)

Figure A-8 One way to sum 50 numbers.

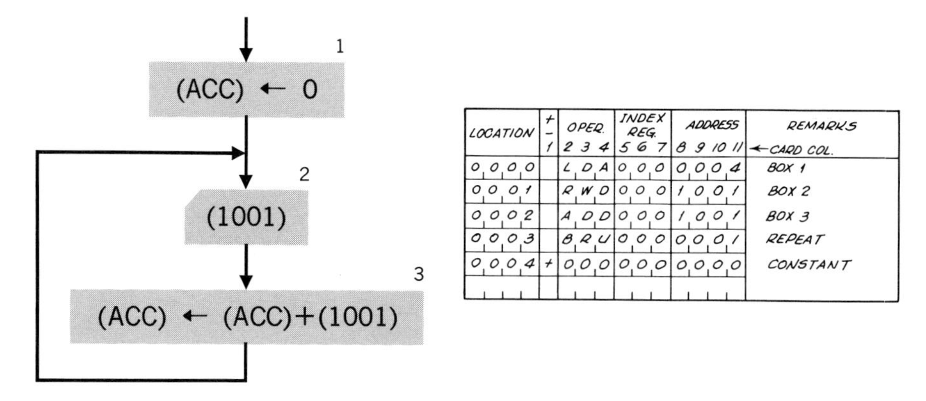

LOCATION	+ - 1	OPER. 2 3 4	INDEX REG. 5 6 7	ADDRESS 8 9 10 11	REMARKS ← CARD COL.
0000		LDA	000	0004	BOX 1
0001		RWD	000	1001	BOX 2
0002		ADD	000	1001	BOX 3
0003		BRU	000	0001	REPEAT
0004	+	000	000	0000	CONSTANT

Figure A-9 Another way to sum.

1, 2, 3, 4, . . . , 50 to the base instruction. For example, for the first instruction, we have

"base"	ADD 000 1000
	+ 1
first inst.	ADD 000 1001

In fact, we can generalize this process by saying that to obtain the ith ADD instruction, add i to the base instruction. Then, if i is called the "index," the 50 instructions are generated by repeating the process, the index taking the values i = 1, 2, . . . , 50. This process is shown in flow-chart form in Figure A-10. Here we are using the symbol i as an integer variable, not as the name of a memory cell. If, for example, the value of i is 4, the symbol (1000+i) is to be interpreted as a name for the contents of the cell whose address is 1000+4, i.e., (1004). The variable i (as we will see in the next section) will have its value stored in a special register of SAMOS we haven't yet talked about.

Another way to obtain the same results is shown in Figure A-11 where the index is started at 51 and decreased by 1 until it is zero.

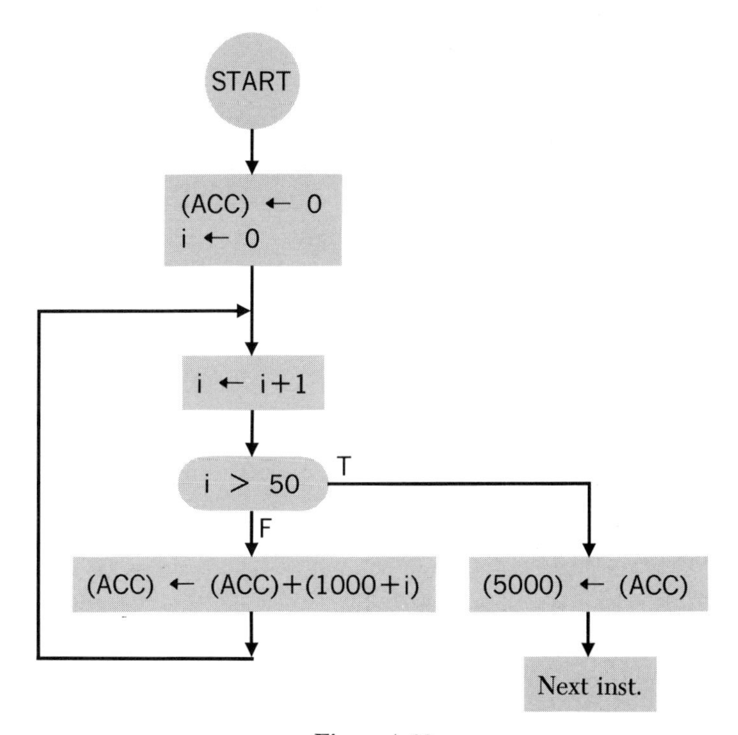

Figure A-10

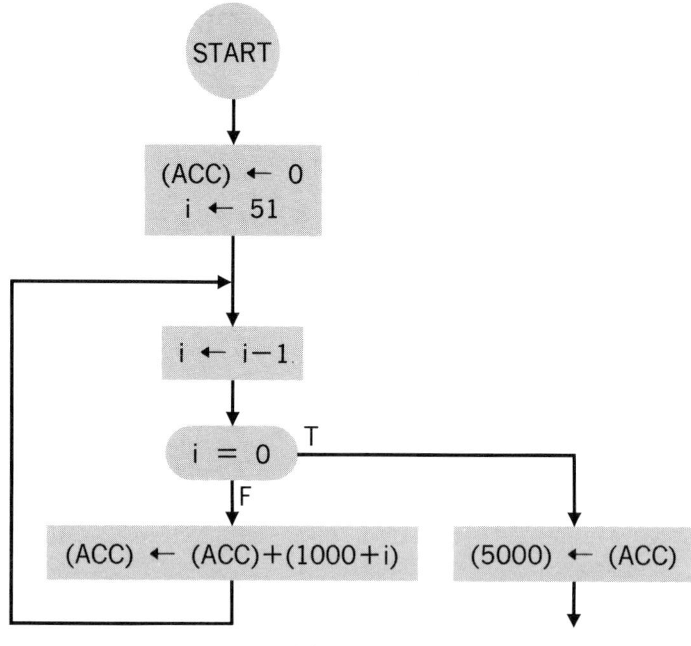

Figure A-11

After we introduce what are called *indexing instructions,* you will see how easy it is to write programs equivalent to these flow charts.

A-6 INDEXING INSTRUCTIONS AND THEIR USE IN LOOPS

SAMOS has three special index registers to be called X1, X2, and X3. Each is capable of holding a four-digit address. These registers can be

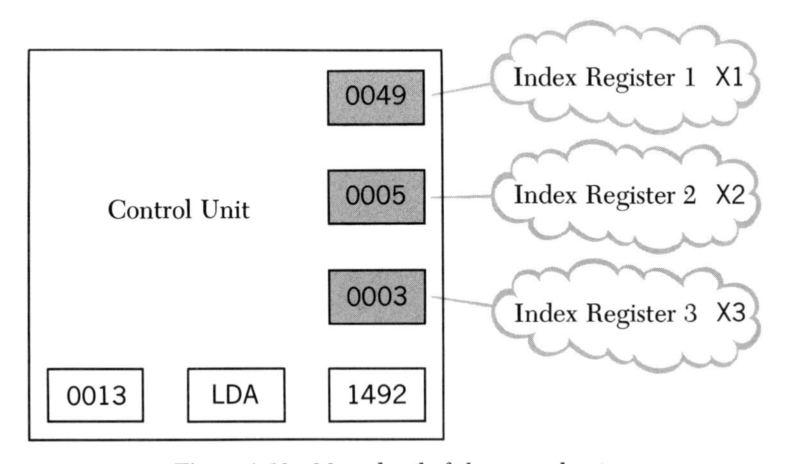

Figure A-12 More detail of the control unit.

thought of as part of the control unit shown schematically in Figure A-12. Notice that there is no place for a sign in an index register, so it cannot contain negative numbers.

How can index registers be used to alter instructions? Recall that positions 5, 6, and 7 in each instruction have not been used. They correspond to index registers 1, 2, and 3, respectively. If position 5, 6, or 7 in the instruction contains anything other than zero, the value of the corresponding index register will be *added* to the address register before the instruction is performed. For example, with the index registers as shown in Figure A-12:

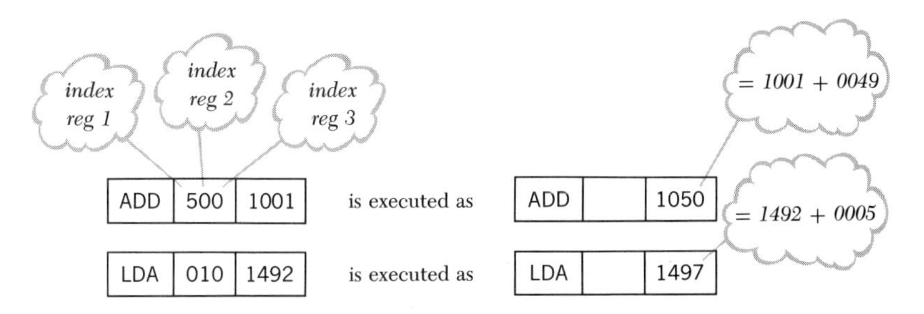

Thus, the index registers permit the address of an instruction to be altered before execution and *without changing the instruction as it appears in memory*.

The first type of indexing instruction we will show allows us to enter a four-digit number into one of the index registers.

Load Index

There are three of these: LI1, LI2, and LI3, one for each index register.

Example

+	L I 2	0 0 0	1 7 4 1

Meaning (X2) ← $(1741)_{8-11}$

This instruction assigns or "loads" (X2) with the address part, that is, positions 8, 9, 10, 11 of (1741).

The instructions complementary to the load index type are the *store index* type. Here the four-digit number currently held by an index register is assigned to the address part (positions 8, 9, 10, and 11) of a designated memory cell.

Store Index

There are three of these SI1, SI2, and SI3.

Example

+	S I 3	0 0 0	2 2 2 9

Meaning $(2229)_{8-11} \leftarrow (X3)$

This instruction assigns i.e., stores, the value of index register 3 to the address part (positions 8, 9, 10, and 11) of location 2229. This operation will leave sign and the next six positions of (2229) unchanged.

An index register can be decremented and tested by a *test index* type instruction.

Test Index

There are three of these: TI1, TI2, and TI3.

Example

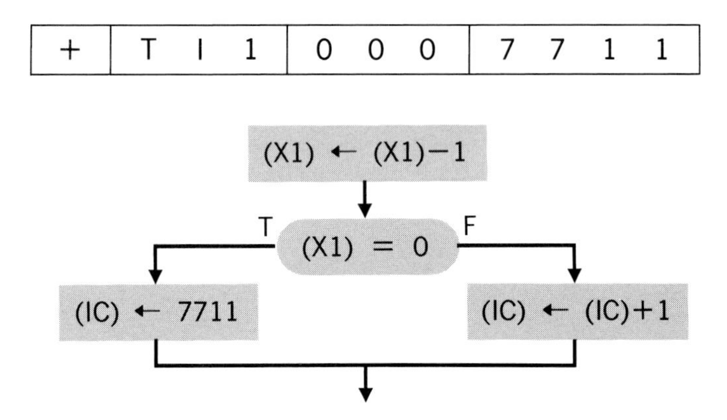

Meaning. Index register 1 is first decremented (reduced by 1). If the resulting value in the index register is zero, SAMOS then branches to location 7711 for the next instruction; otherwise, SAMOS continues in the normal instruction sequence.

Now we can return to the flow chart of Figure A-11 which sums fifty numbers to see how the index registers can help. In Figure A-13 we see that only nine locations are needed. Notice that the program starts in location 0000, with locations 0005 and 0006 being used to store the constants 0 and 51, respectively. The instruction at 0000 loads the ac-

LOCATION	+ −	OPER.	INDEX REG. (1 2 3)	ADDRESS	REMARKS
	1	2 3 4	5 6 7	8 9 10 11	← CARD COL.
0000		LDA	000	0005	(ACC) ← 0
0001		LI1	000	0006	(X1) ← $(0006)_{8-11}$
0002		TI1	000	0007	DECREMENT AND TEST X1
0003		ADD	100	1000	(ACC) ← (ACC) + (1000 + (X1))
0004		BRU	000	0002	GO TO 0002
0005	+	000	000	0000	THE CONSTANT 0
0006		000	000	0051	THE CONSTANT 51
0007		STØ	000	5000	(5000) ← (ACC)
0008		HLT	000	0000	STOP. IF START BUTTON IS PRESSED, GO TO 0000

Figure A-13 Summing with the use of an index register.

cumulator with a zero. At 0001 we "load index 1" with the address portion of (0006) as shown below.

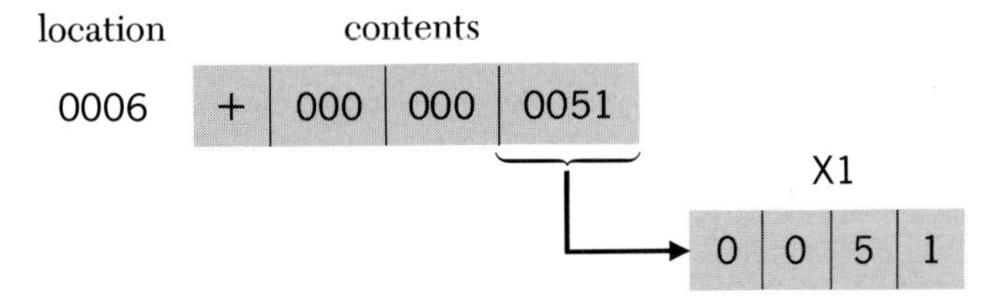

The instruction at 0002 does two things: first, it decreases (X1) by 1 (and makes it equal to 50 the first time around), then it performs a test of the value of (X1). If the value is zero (that is, if we have finished adding all the fifty numbers), SAMOS branches to location 0007 to store the sum in location 5000. Otherwise, SAMOS continues in sequence to 0003 where the base instruction is located. This instruction is executed as shown in Figure A-14.

Base Instruction: ADD 100 1000

Time the instruction is executed	Contents of X1	Instruction executed by SAMOS	Address of number added to the accumulator
first	0050	ADD 000 1050	1050
second	0049	ADD 000 1049	1049
third	0048	ADD 000 1048	1048
⋮	⋮	⋮	⋮
50th	0001	ADD 000 1001	1001

Figure A-14

After each ADD instruction, it is necessary to return to location 0002 by means of the "branch unconditionally" instruction. The TI1 instruction in location 0002 again decreases the value of (X1) by 1, tests whether or not (X1) is zero to choose between the ADD and the STØ instructions. Eventually, after "going through the loop" fifty times (X1) will be zero, the loop will be terminated, and the results will be stored in location 5000.

EXERCISE A6

Revise the program in Figure A-13 to *locate* the largest number among those being summed. The search for the largest can be conducted as part of the same loop in which the summing occurs. *Hint.* Since the *index* value of the largest number is what is wanted, it will be necessary to use the *store index* type of instruction to *save* the index value of the largest number.

A-7 SHIFTING INSTRUCTIONS AND THEIR USE IN REAL ARITHMETIC AND CHARACTER MANIPULATION

There is only one additional group of instructions in the design of SAMOS. Arithmetic is done on data as though all numbers were integers. Of course, all numbers are *not* integers. We want SAMOS to be able to perform a computation like

$$8.25 \times 3.5 - 17.5 = 11.375$$

But the integer numbers in SAMOS contain no decimal point, which means that the program must recognize where the decimal point should be. Let's treat each of the numbers in the computation above as an integer (i.e., 825, 35, and 175) and see how to insure a correct answer. First, we multiply 825 × 35 to get 28875. This we understand to mean 28.875 but SAMOS does not know that. From the product, 28875, we want to subtract 175 but that gives 28700, the wrong answer. What is the trouble?

You know that for addition or subtraction the units positions must be added (subtracted), the tens positions correspondingly, etc. In other words, the decimal points of the two numbers must be *aligned.* We didn't want to subtract 175 but rather 17500 to give 11375 (interpreted as 11.375).

This example points up the need to be able to move (shift) a number two positions to the left in a word. Obviously, other examples would require shifts of different distances. To accomplish these shifts, SAMOS provides the following *shift left* instruction.

Shift Left

Example

+	SHL	000	0006

Meaning (ACC) ← (ACC) × 10^6

This instruction shifts the contents of the accumulator six positions to the left. During the shifting process, the sign position remains unchanged, the left-most six digits (or characters) are *lost*, and the right-most six digits (or characters) are filled with zeros.

For example, suppose the accumulator contains the number

+0123456789.

ACC Before Execution of SHL Instruction

+	0	1	2	3	4	5	6	7	8	9

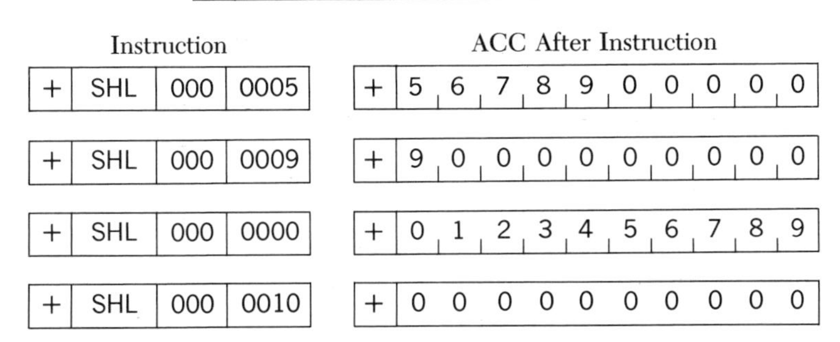

Instruction	ACC After Instruction
+ SHL 000 0005	+ 5 6 7 8 9 0 0 0 0 0
+ SHL 000 0009	+ 9 0 0 0 0 0 0 0 0 0
+ SHL 000 0000	+ 0 1 2 3 4 5 6 7 8 9
+ SHL 000 0010	+ 0 0 0 0 0 0 0 0 0 0

Similarly, suppose the accumulator contains the alphabetic characters "JOE SMITH".

ACC Before Instruction

+	J	O	E		S	M	I	T	H	

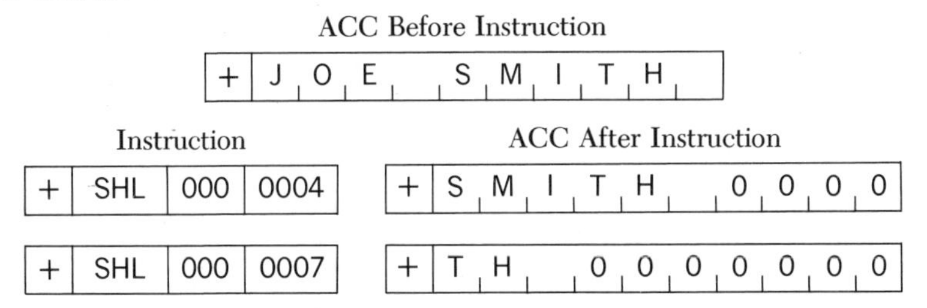

Instruction	ACC After Instruction
+ SHL 000 0004	+ S M I T H 0 0 0 0
+ SHL 000 0007	+ T H 0 0 0 0 0 0 0

It should be easy to convince yourself of the usefulness of the following complementary *shift right* instruction, which is also part of the SAMOS instruction set.

Shift Right

Example

+	SHR	000	0004

This is similar to the corresponding SHL, except that the contents of the accumulator are shifted four digits or characters to the *right.*

SHR Instruction

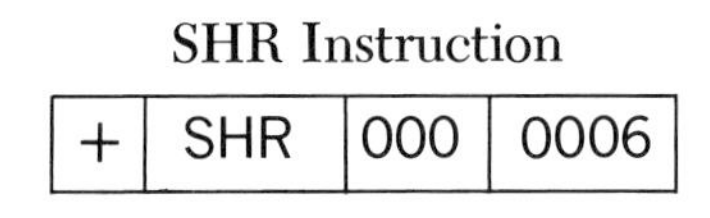

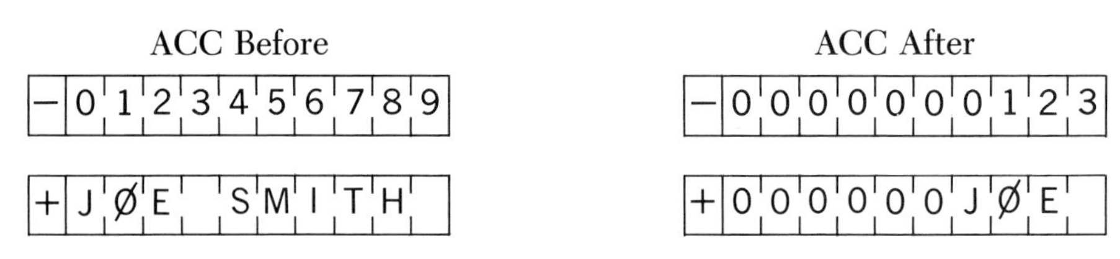

EXERCISE A7

Write SAMOS instructions to accomplish the calculation

$$8.25 \times 3.5 - 17.5$$

from integer inputs of 825, 35, and 175 assigned to (1001), (1002), and (1003), respectively.

A-8 FINDING VALUES IN A TABLE

Suppose we are given a table of integers between 0 and 1000 and their cube roots as shown in Figure A-15.

We want to write a program that will "look-up" values of the cube root in this table for any given integer n between 0 and 1000 and will

n	$\sqrt[3]{n}$
0	0.000 000
1	1.000 000
2	1.259 921
3	1.442 250
4	1.587 401
⋮	⋮
999	9.996 666
1000	10.000 000

Figure A-15

print this value on the typewriter. We will assume that the table of Figure A-15 has been punched in 1001 cards, each card containing the value of a cube root. The program should read the table into storage and then input from the card reader a value of n. SAMOS should print the value of n and its cube root, then read another value of n, and so on, until it runs out of data. Data sets should be separated with a blank line in the output.

A possible way to write the program is shown in Figure A-16. The instructions are given in locations 0000 through 0005. The instruction at location 0003 has been printed in rust to remind us that its address portion, 0008, is to be incremented by (X1).

Location 0006 is used to store the value of n temporarily. Location 0007 is filled with blanks for separating data sets in the output. The table is placed in locations 0008 to 1008. When instructions and data are read in from cards they are stored in locations 0000 through 1008, a final blank card will cause a transfer of control to location 0000.

The program works as follows. The instructions in 0000 and 0001 read an integer data value into location 0006 and print this value on the typewriter. The instruction in 0002 loads X1 with the integer found in the address part of 0006. The next instruction prints on the typewriter the value found in 0008 + (X1). The address 0008 + (X1) is the place in the table where the desired cube root is stored. For example, you should trace out the steps and see that when the given integer is 1, the cube root is

LOCATION	+ − 1	OPER. 2 3 4	INDEX REG. 5 6 7	ADDRESS 8 9 10 11	REMARKS ← CARD COL.
0000		RWD	000	0006	(0006) ← n
0001		WWD	000	0006	WRITE THE VALUE OF n ON TYPEWRITER
0002		LI1	000	0006	LOAD X1 WITH VALUE OF n
0003		WWD	100	0008	WRITE (0008 + (X1)), THE $\sqrt[3]{n}$
0004		WWD	000	0007	WRITE A BLANK LINE FOR SPACING
0005		BRU	000	0000	BRANCH TO 0000 FOR ANOTHER VALUE [OF n
0006	+	000	000	0000	n
0007	+				BLANK LINE FOR TYPEWRITER SPACING
0008	+	000	000	0000	$\sqrt[3]{0}$ (TABLE)
0009	+	010	000	0000	$\sqrt[3]{1}$
0010	+	012	599	2105	$\sqrt[3]{2}$
0011	+	014	422	4957	$\sqrt[3]{3}$
0012	+	015	874	0105	$\sqrt[3]{4}$
⋮		⋮	⋮	⋮	⋮
1007	+	099	966	6556	$\sqrt[3]{999}$
1008	+	100	000	0000	$\sqrt[3]{1000}$
					BLANK CARD TO TRANSFER TO 0000

Figure A-16

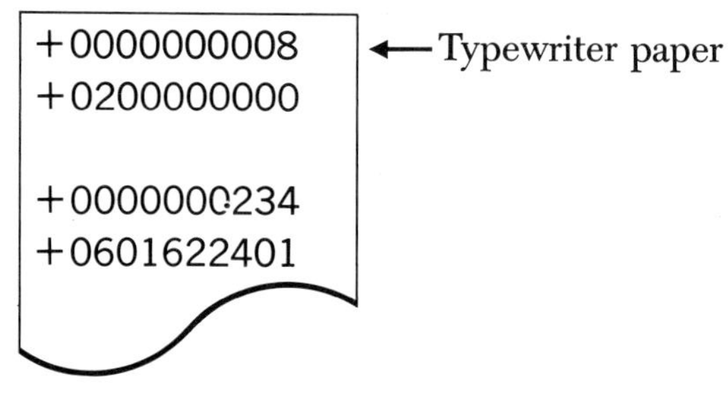

Figure A-17

found in location 0009; when the integer is 1000, its cube root is found in 1008, and so on.

Notice also that the decimal point which appears in the table of Figure A-15 has been eliminated in the table stored in SAMOS. What we have done is to store each cube root as an integer (actually $\sqrt[3]{n} \times 10^8$ as an integer), and we have kept in mind the fact that the decimal point is between the second and third digit from the left of the number. When the cube roots are printed as shown in Figure A-17, the programmer must recall the location of the decimal point and possibly mark it with pencil or pen on the output (such as $02_\wedge00000000$).

After the cube root of the number has been printed, the instruction in location 0004 causes a blank line to be printed. Then the instruction in 0005 causes a branch back for another value of n. Notice that the blank line has been supplied by location 0007, and that a + sign was attached to it. This sign is necessary because a completely blank card in the input deck would transfer SAMOS to location 0000 before the table was read into storage. This transfer is accomplished by the blank card following the cube root table.

The output of this program is shown in Figure A-17 for the values of $n = 8$ and $n = 234$, respectively.

The program of Figure A-16 may be easily modified so that the output shown in Figure A-17 will have the decimal points of n and $\sqrt[3]{n}$ aligned. The output would then be

+0008000000
+0002000000

+0234000000
+0006016224

A-9 THE USE OF SUBPROGRAMS

(You should not read this section until after you have studied Chapter 6.)

Functions and procedures can be programmed as independent sequences of instructions, often called subprograms or *subroutines* because they are used by other programs.

We will now show how the cube root program of the preceding section can be modified for use as a subroutine.

In this example we want to compute

$$x = 2 + 3a^{1/3} + b^{1/3}$$

where a and b are positive integers not greater than 1000. We assume that pairs a and b have been punched into consecutive cards, and that we want to compute x for m such pairs. The input deck is shown in Figure A-18. The output is shown in Figure A-19.

A Cube Root Subroutine

We first design a subroutine with the following specifications.

1. The subroutine will assume that the argument, an integer between 0 and 1000, inclusive, has been placed in the accumulator at the time control "passes" to it.

2. The *return address* is the address of the next instruction to be executed in the main program following the completion of the subroutine's task. This return address should be saved by storing it in some convenient

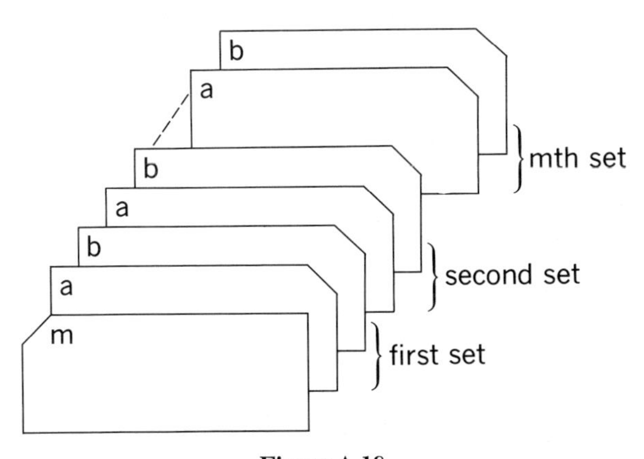

Figure A-18

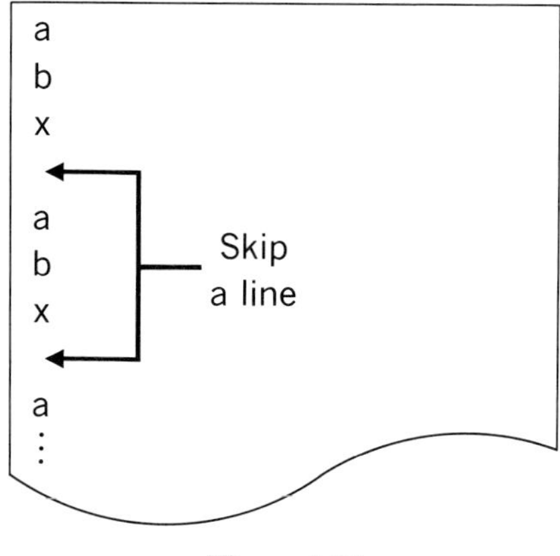

Figure A-19

register before entering the subroutine. We choose index register 2 for this purpose.

3. The subroutine should place the cube root in the accumulator before branching back, i.e., returning, to the main program.

The program of Figure A-20 follows these specifications. This is a slight modification of the program in Figure A-16. The table is stored in locations 0006 to 1006; location 0000 is reserved for branching to the main program. Whenever we want to use this subroutine, the following steps should be taken.

1. Place argument in the accumulator.
2. Load the address of the next instruction after the subroutine into index register 2.
3. Branch to location 0001.

LOCATION	+ − 1	OPER. 2 3 4	INDEX REG. 5 6 7	ADDRESS 8 9 10 11	REMARKS ← CARD COL.
0000					RESERVED FOR BRANCHING
0001		STØ	000	0005	(0005) ← (ACC)
0002		LI1	000	0005	LOAD X1 WITH THE VALUE OF n
0003		LDA	100	0006	(ACC) ← (0006 + (X1))
0004		BRU	010	0000	BRANCH TO ADDRESS IN (X2)
0005			n		ARGUMENT
0006	+	000	000	0000	$\sqrt[3]{0}$ (TABLE)
0007	+	010	000	0000	$\sqrt[3]{1}$
0008	+	012	599	2105	$\sqrt[3]{2}$
⋮		⋮	⋮	⋮	⋮
⋮		⋮	⋮	⋮	⋮
1005	+	099	966	6556	$\sqrt[3]{999}$
1006	+	100	000	0000	$\sqrt[3]{1000}$

Figure A-20 Cube root subroutine.

The cube root will be available in the accumulator upon exit from the subroutine. Since X1 and X2 are used by the subroutine, X3 is the only index register available for use in the main program.

The Main Program

The main program is shown in Figure A-22 and it occupies locations 1007–1042. A general flow chart is shown in Figure A-21. This diagram does not show all the steps required to enter the subroutine or other machine language details that are important when the actual coding is done. These details are explained in the remark section of the coding form of Figure A-22.

The program makes use of index register 3 to count the number of sets of data. Index registers 1 and 2 are reserved for the subroutine. You should follow the program, step by step, paying special attention to the contents of the accumulator and the index registers.

Notice that the constants located in 1033 and 1034 are used to load X2 with the addresses to which the subroutines should return. Other constants such as 1, 2, and 3 are available at locations 1035–1037. Locations 1038–1042 are used to store the values m + 1, m, a, b, and x.

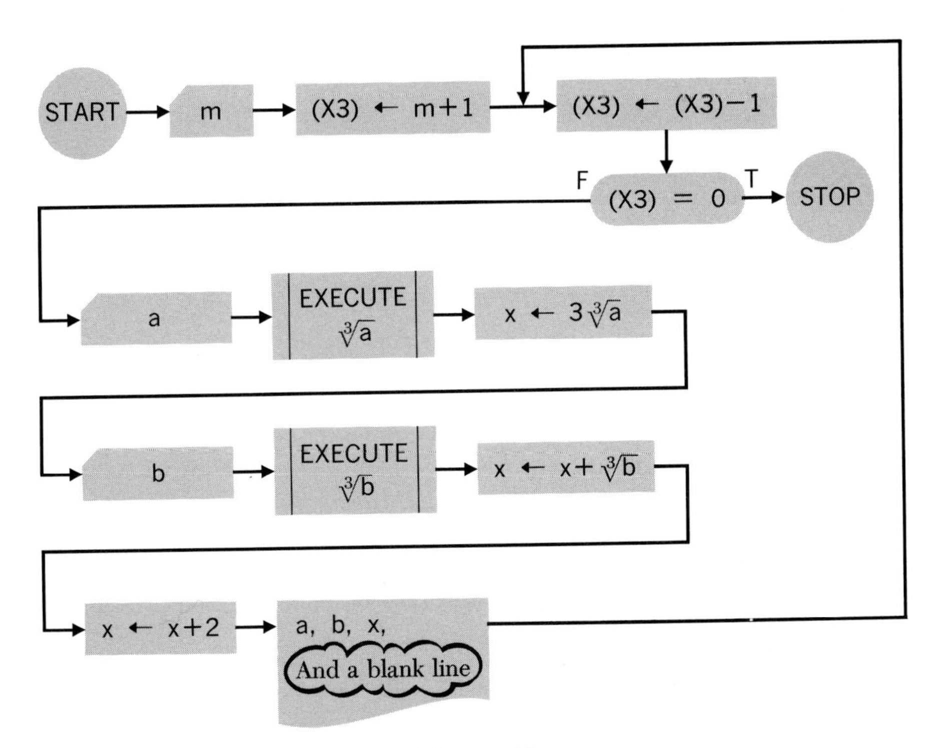

Figure A-21

LOCATION	±	OPER.	INDEX REG.	ADDRESS	REMARKS
	1	2 3 4	5 6 7	8 9 10 11	← CARD COL.
0000		BRU	000	1007	SUBROUTINE GOES IN PLACE OF HEAVY LINE
1007		RWD		1039	(1039) ← m
1008		LDA		1039	m ← m + 1
1009		ADD		1035	
1010		STØ		1038	
1011		LI3		1038	(X3) ← m + 1
1012		TI3		1031	DECREMENT AND TEST (X3)
1013		RWD		1040	(1040) ← a
1014		LDA		1040	(ACC) ← a
1015		LI2		1033	(X2) ← RETURN ADDRESS [1017]
1016		BRU		0001	BRANCH TO SUBROUTINE
1017		MPY		1037	(ACC) ← 3 X (ACC)
1018		STØ		1042	(1042) ← $3\sqrt[3]{a}$
1019		RWD		1041	(1041) ← b
1020		LDA		1041	(ACC) ← b
1021		LI2		1034	(X2) ← RETURN ADDRESS [1023]
1022		BRU		0001	BRANCH TO SUBROUTINE
1023		ADD		1042	(ACC) ← $\sqrt[3]{b} + 3\sqrt[3]{a}$
1024		ADD		1036	$x \leftarrow 2 + \sqrt[3]{b} + 3\sqrt[3]{a}$
1025		STØ		1042	
1026		WWD		1040	PRINT a
1027		WWD		1041	PRINT b
1028		WWD		1042	PRINT X
1029		WWD		1032	PRINT A BLANK LINE
1030		BRU		1012	BRANCH BACK FOR ANOTHER SET
1031		HLT	↓	1007	STOP.

CONSTANTS:

LOCATION	±	OPER.	INDEX REG.	ADDRESS	REMARKS
	1	2 3 4	5 6 7	8 9 10 11	← CARD COL.
1032	+				BLANKS FOR TYPEWRITER SKIPPING
1033	+	000	000	1017	FIRST SUBROUTINE RETURN ADDRESS
1034	+	000	000	1023	SECOND SUBROUTINE RETURN ADDRESS
1035	+	000	000	0001	+1
1036	+	020	000	0000	+ 2∧00000000
1037	+	000	000	0003	+3
1038	+	000	000	0000	VALUE OF m + 1
1039	+	000	000	0000	m
1040	+	000	000	0000	a
1041	+	000	000	0000	b
1042	+	000	000	0000	x
					BLANK TRANSFER CARD

Figure A-22

As before, the program will be executed by SAMOS if we place all the program cards in the card reader in ascending order of location, followed by a blank card and by the data, and press the START button. The instruction in 0000 branches to the start of the main program at location 1007 as soon as the blank card has been sensed.

INDEX*

* Regional network computer facilities at the Stanford University Computation Center have been used to aid in the preparation of this index (and to try out several of the algorithms in this text). The regional network is sponsored by the National Science Foundation's Office of Computing Activities' facilities program. This support is gratefully acknowledged.